INTRODUCTION TO
ORGANIC
CHEMISTRY

INTRODUCTION TO
ORGANIC
CHEMISTRY

CHARLES H. DePUY

Professor of Chemistry, University of Colorado

KENNETH L. RINEHART, Jr.

Professor of Chemistry, University of Illinois

JOHN WILEY & SONS, INC.

NEW YORK LONDON SYDNEY

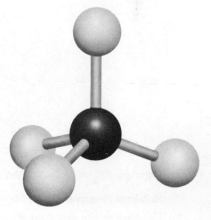

Library of Congress Catalog Card Number: 67-12561
Printed in the United States of America

PREFACE

We have written this textbook as a brief introduction to organic chemistry. In doing so, we have been guided by a number of firm prejudices which grew out of our own experiences in teaching the subject to nonmajors. Foremost among these prejudices is the conviction that modern organic chemistry should be taught to nonmajors as well as to majors, in quarter and semester courses as well as in year courses, and in general chemistry courses, both for majors and nonmajors. By "modern organic chemistry" we simply mean the subject as it is understood by research workers in the field.

We believe that the material in this book can be taught in one semester of three one-hour lectures per week. The first eleven chapters can easily be covered in two lectures per week for a semester or in three lectures per week for a quarter. Of course, a student will not know as much organic chemistry after one semester or quarter as he will after a year, but that which he does know should be accurate and current. If, after his semester or quarter of the subject, he should decide to take a second course in organic chemistry, he will not have to unlearn the material covered in this text, but can build upon it.

It is, of course, impossible to cover the whole of organic chemistry in any book. The facets of the subject which we have chosen to stress are the structures of organic compounds and their relation to biology. Within the framework of structure, we emphasize stereochemistry. Atomic and molecular orbitals are introduced in the first chapter and geometrical isomerism in the second. Rudimentary conformational analysis is first discussed in Chapter 1, and additional aspects of conformations are detailed in Chapter 2. Configurational isomerism is encountered relatively early, while dealing with the halides in Chapter 6.

Biological aspects of organic chemistry are stressed throughout. In the early chapters, examples of functional group types are drawn, where possible, from biologically important compounds. In later chapters, we discuss the building blocks of nature—lipids, carbohydrates, proteins, nucleic acids. In Chapter 14, on metabolism, we discuss how these compounds are converted to energy and to other compounds in biological systems. Other important natural products, the secondary metabolites like terpenes, steroids, alkaloids, and antibiotics, are used in illustrations of functional groups in early sections of the book, but are discussed from the standpoint of their biosynthesis in Chapter 15. We feel especially strongly that an introduction to biochemistry is important, both in a brief organic course and in general chemistry.

Of necessity, in stressing structure and biologically important compounds, we have given less attention to other areas of organic chemistry; we apologize to partisans of those areas. One area which is somewhat neglected is synthesis. We have done this by design: We feel that students at the beginning level need to know what organic compounds are and how they behave, but that they are less likely to need to know how to prepare complicated compounds in the laboratory.

This book contains a number of devices which we believe will be helpful in the learning process. Chief among these is the use of color in many of the figures. It is used to stress the point of the figure, the functional group, reaction, or particular aspect of stereochemistry under consideration, and is used only where we feel it will be of benefit. Many figures are included, which usually attempt to summarize the material under discussion. Thus, in reviewing a chapter, a student can remind himself of the main points by studying the figures and their legends. Most of the problems in the body of the chapters are designed to supplement the text. Those at the end of the chapters more often review the text.

We have included an appendix which is a selfstudy guide to nomenclature. It is tedious for the lecturer to discuss nomenclature when it is impossible for the student to learn the naming of compounds except by practice.

In preparing this text, we have had very much advice, often conflicting, always valued. We wish to express our particular appreciation to those teachers who read the manuscript—Professors George Hammond, John Holum, Maurice Shamma, and Gene Morris. Our families, our students, and our publisher were usually quite patient.

January 1967   Charles H. DePuy
                                                                 Kenneth L. Rinehart, Jr.

CONTENTS

CHAPTER 7 ■ CONFIGURATIONAL ISOMERISM AND ORGANIC HALIDES   117

CHAPTER 8 ■ AMINES AND THEIR DERIVATIVES   139

INTRODUCTION TO
ORGANIC CHEMISTRY

CHAPTER

STEREOCHEMISTRY, STRUCTURE, AND SATURATED HYDROCARBONS

In an age when atomic physics and interplanetary rocketry are preeminent, many persons contend that mathematics is the universal language of science. This is not entirely true. A vast area of science, containing the giant petroleum and plastics industries and pharmaceutical research, and stretching to the border of life itself, requires a second language: that of organic chemistry.

Organic chemistry is a complex science. In the hundred-year period since it became recognized as a distinct branch of chemistry, more than one million separate organic compounds have been prepared, and these are only a small portion of the possibilities. Fortunately, in spite of its complexity, organic chemistry is highly systematic and may be discussed in terms of classes of molecules and a few types of reactions. The existence of an infinity of numbers does not make arithmetic impossible, since the operations of addition, subtraction, multiplication, and division learned with small numbers may be applied without change to large ones; similarly, in organic chemistry an understanding of the reactions of simple molecules may be applied substantially without change to large ones. We shall therefore follow a pattern: We will introduce organic chemistry by discussing simple molecules; we will then often apply the principles learned to a discussion of complex molecules, in order to demonstrate the generality of the subject.

The application of the adjective "organic" to the chemistry of carbon compounds is in some ways misleading, since it implies a direct association between organic chemistry and living organisms. Indeed it was first thought that all organic compounds had to originate in living matter. Organic chemistry as a separate science is often said to date from 1828, when the German chemist Friedrich

Wöhler synthesized an organic molecule (urea) from an inorganic chemical (ammonium isocyanate). In the century following Wöhler's discovery, the complete separation of organic chemistry from biological systems became popular among many organic chemists, and the synthesis of complex molecules from "coal, air, and water" was often a goal in itself. More recently, enormous advances in our understanding of the chemistry of biological systems have completed the circle; today more and more time and effort in organic chemistry are being devoted to reactions and processes that bear directly upon organic systems arising from living matter. Consequently, at every opportunity we shall attempt to illustrate organic reactions and structure among naturally occurring molecules, and shall discuss the organic chemistry of biological systems. For our purposes, organic chemistry will be defined as the chemistry of carbon compounds wherever they occur, and an organic chemist as one who studies the structure and reactions of these carbon compounds.

Organic chemistry is a nonmathematical science. As such, it often appeals to students who enjoy the logic and rigorous thought of science, but who relish the concrete study of compounds or substances more than a more abstract study. Because organic chemistry deals with actual substances, it is three-dimensional. This three-dimensionality (called *stereochemistry*) has important practical consequences and so we will consider it at every opportunity. The interweaving of the three-dimensional aspects of the chemistry of carbon compounds with their simple reactions seems so vital that we shall begin our discussion of organic chemistry with the stereochemistry of the smallest organic molecule, *methane*.

METHANE AND ITS STEREOCHEMISTRY

Methane is a gas of the molecular formula CH_4, which occurs naturally in underground pockets in the petroleum-producing areas of the world. It is collected and piped over most of the United States as natural gas, for use in stoves and furnaces. Its molecular formula may be determined by analyzing the products of combustion, as is done for inorganic chemicals. (For an example of the method employed, see Prob. 1-1.)

Prob. 1-1. When a quantity of methane was burned with an excess of oxygen, 224 ml of carbon dioxide (measured at standard temperature and pressure) and 0.36 g of water were formed. Determine the ratio of carbon to hydrogen in methane.

However, we are concerned with the three-dimensional arrangement of the five atoms in methane, the stereochemistry of the methane molecule. The problem of the relative positions in space of the single carbon atom and the four hydrogen atoms in methane can now be solved precisely by the new tools of physics. However, the organic chemist had a rather accurate picture of the stereochemistry of methane long before modern instruments and tools became available. Explanation of a simple chlorination reaction will illustrate the reasoning used.

$$CH_4 \xrightarrow[\text{light}]{Cl_2} \underset{\substack{\text{methyl}\\\text{chloride}}}{CH_3Cl} + \underset{\substack{\text{methylene}\\\text{chloride}}}{CH_2Cl_2} + \underset{\text{chloroform}}{CHCl_3} + \underset{\substack{\text{carbon}\\\text{tetrachloride}}}{CCl_4} + HCl$$

Fig. 1-1. Methane reacts with chlorine in sunlight to form a mixture of chloro-, dichloro-, trichloro-, and tetrachloromethanes. Only one compound of each formula is known.

If a sample of methane is treated with chlorine gas in the presence of sunlight, a mixture of organic compounds results. Gaseous hydrogen chloride is also formed. The various products of the reaction all have different boiling points and may be readily separated from one another and identified. As their molecular formulas indicate, the products obviously correspond to compounds in which successively one, two, three, and four hydrogen atoms of methane are replaced by chlorine atoms. These compounds may be named *chloromethane* (or, alternatively, methyl chloride), *dichloromethane* (or methylene chloride), *trichloromethane* (chloroform), and *tetrachloromethane* (or carbon tetrachloride). Each of these molecules may be prepared in several ways by means of various other reactions. The important fact is that no matter how each of them is formed, *only one compound of each formula exists*. From this fact alone it is possible to deduce the correct stereochemistry of methane.

Consider first the observation that only one molecule of the formula CH_3Cl exists. This molecule is obtained from methane by the replacement of one hydrogen atom by a chlorine atom. One may reasonably deduce that all the hydrogen atoms in methane are equivalent, so that no matter which one is replaced, the same chloromethane results. This deduction immediately rules out an enormous number of possibilities for the structure of methane, but the existence of a single chloromethane may still be reconciled by a number of structures. Two of these structures, square and tetrahedral arrangements of the hydrogen atoms about carbon, are shown in Fig. 1-2, together with the corresponding structures of chloro-

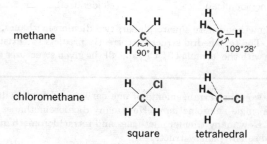

Fig. 1-2. Two possible structures for methane and chloromethane which correctly predict that only one compound of the formula CH_3Cl should exist. In the square model all four bonds from carbon are in the same plane (that of the page). In the tetrahedral model, the solid lines indicate bonds in the plane of the page, the dotted line, behind the page, and the heavy line, in front.

methane. Other structures may also be envisaged which satisfy the condition of hydrogen-atom equivalence (see Prob. 1-2).

Although both square and tetrahedral spatial formulas predict only one chloromethane, the square arrangement predicts that two dichloromethanes, CH_2Cl_2, should exist. In one of these molecules the two chlorine atoms would be adjacent to each other, and in the other they would be on opposite sides of the carbon atom. Note that the distance between the two chlorine atoms would differ for these two compounds. The tetrahedral model, on the other hand, correctly predicts the existence of only a single dichloromethane. Some practice may be required until this can be clearly recognized. *All aspects of the stereochemistry of organic molecules may be explained only if it is assumed that whenever a carbon atom is surrounded by four atoms, these atoms are tetrahedrally arranged.* This conclusion, first reached on strictly organic chemical grounds in 1874, has been fully confirmed by more recent physical methods.

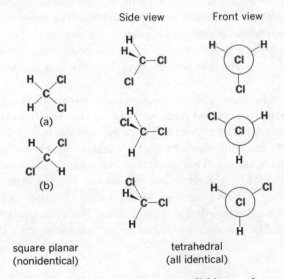

Fig. 1-3. If methane were square planar, two dichloromethanes, (a) and (b), should exist. The tetrahedral structure correctly predicts the existence of only one molecule with the formula CH_2Cl_2, and all the given structures are identical.

Prob. 1-2. Show two other arrangements of one carbon and four hydrogen atoms which would allow only a single chloromethane. How many dichloromethanes does each of these structures predict? How many trichloromethanes and tetrachloromethanes are predicted for the tetrahedral and square planar structures?

MOLECULAR MODELS

The term tetrahedral is used to describe the geometry of methane because a regular tetrahedron is formed when the centers of the hydrogen atoms of the mole-

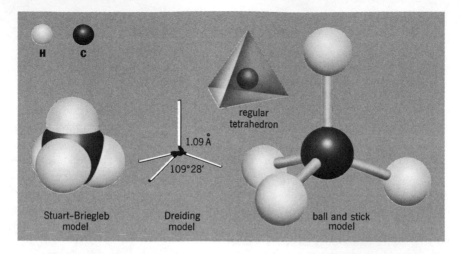

Fig. 1-4. Stuart-Briegleb models show the relative sizes of the atoms, while Dreiding models make bond-lengths and angles more obvious; both types are accurately constructed to scale. The cheaper ball and stick models are helpful in understanding stereochemistry.

cule are connected. If the carbon atom is regarded as being at the center of the tetrahedron, the lines linking it to the hydrogen atoms point to the corners of the tetrahedron. Organic chemists frequently rely on molecular models so that they can more easily visualize the stereochemistry of molecules (Fig. 1-4). For illustrations in this text we shall occasionally use two types of model: the type designed by Stuart and Briegleb, and that designed by Dreiding. The first type is the "space-filling" model. It represents to scale the space occupied by the electrons of the atoms involved. The other type, the Dreiding model, accurately represents only the positions of the atomic nuclei, yet clearly shows bond lengths and bond angles. For methane the C—H bond length is 1.09 Å (1 Å or Ångström unit = 10^{-8} cm) and the bond angle is 109°28'. Dreiding models provide a more open representation of the molecule and therefore permit a clearer view of the relationships among atoms. The Stuart-Briegleb models allow one to visualize the actual volume occupied by atoms.

BONDING IN METHANE

One may ask why the geometry of methane is tetrahedral. The answer lies in the nature of the forces that tie the carbon and hydrogen atoms into a molecule, namely, in chemical bonds. It seems appropriate at this point, therefore, to turn attention to the subject of *bonding* in organic molecules.

It will be recalled from a course in general chemistry that there are two extreme types of chemical bonding. One is the purely *ionic* bond, illustrated within the first row of the periodic table by lithium fluoride. This ionic bond results from the complete transfer of an electron from the lithium atom to the fluorine atom, as

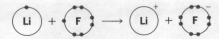

Fig. 1-5. Lithium fluoride contains an *ionic bond* formed by the transfer of an electron from a lithium atom to a fluorine atom.

in Fig. 1-5, so that the force holding the ions together is the electrostatic attraction between a positive and a negative charge. Ionic bonds are most common between atoms from opposite sides of the periodic table, because such atoms have large differences in their affinity for electrons. Elements at the right of the periodic table—the halogens, nitrogen, oxygen, etc.—have a tendency to acquire electrons, while those to the left in the periodic table—the alkali and alkaline earth metals like sodium, potassium, calcium, and magnesium—lose electrons easily. Molecules joined with ionic bonds commonly have high melting points, solubility in water, and the ability to conduct electrical currents.

The other extreme in chemical bonding is the purely covalent bond. Here two identical atoms are joined by a bond, as in the hydrogen molecule (Fig. 1-6), or a bond is formed between atoms like carbon and hydrogen, which neither acquire

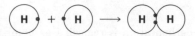

Fig. 1-6. The hydrogen molecule has a *covalent bond* formed by the sharing of a pair of electrons.

nor lose electrons easily; in both cases, the bonding electrons are shared. Compounds containing covalent bonds exclusively are usually characterized by relatively low boiling points, insolubility in water, and high electrical resistivity.

Many compounds are of an intermediate bonding type; they may be considered to have a bond that is partly ionic and partly covalent. Molecular hydrogen chloride, for example, is a low-boiling gas; however, it is soluble in water, in which it forms ions whose solutions conduct electricity. It is convenient to consider the bond in hydrogen chloride as "partially ionic." This indicates that it has both ionic and covalent characteristics; the bonding pair of electrons in hydrogen chloride is assumed to be unequally shared. More often they are in the vicinity of the chlorine atom, which is said to be more *electronegative* than the hydrogen atom. Conversely, the hydrogen atom is more *electropositive* than the chlorine. Through a study of bonding in many compounds, scales of electronegativity can be established. The halogens, oxygen, and nitrogen are more electronegative than carbon and hydrogen, which in turn are more electronegative than sodium, lithium, magnesium, and other elements (metals) on the left of the periodic table. Thus, in a carbon–carbon or carbon–hydrogen bond, the bonding electrons are about equally shared by the two atoms, whereas in a carbon–oxygen bond, the oxygen atom has a greater share than the carbon atom. In a carbon–lithium bond the carbon atom has a greater share than the lithium. We shall see how differences in electronegativity among the atoms in a molecule can profoundly influence the properties and reactions of the compound.

Since methane is low boiling ($-162°$)*, insoluble in water, and a complete electrical insulator, its bonding is obviously covalent. We can account for its tetrahedral structure most simply in the following way: Each carbon–hydrogen bond in methane involves two electrons; because electrons repel one another, each bonding pair of electrons will repel all other pairs. The four pairs of electrons constituting the bonds will wish to be as far apart as possible, and this results in tetrahedral geometry (Fig. 1-7).

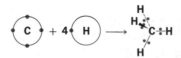

Fig. 1-7. The electrons of the C—H bonds will be at a maximum distance from one another in a tetrahedral arrangement, so that repulsion among the electrons of these bonds will be at a minimum.

Prob. 1-3. From what you know of their general physical properties, tell whether the bonding in each of the following molecules is mainly covalent, mainly ionic, or mainly intermediate.

  (a) sodium chloride   (c) water
  (b) tetrachloromethane   (d) chlorine

ELECTRONIC STRUCTURE OF ATOMS AND MOLECULES

Repulsions of the electrons of one bond by those of the others can account for the tetrahedral arrangement of four hydrogens around a central carbon. However, complex organic molecules require a more detailed description of their electronic structure. Let us, then, consider the relationship between atomic structure as developed in general chemistry, and organic molecular structure.

We begin with the simplest of all atoms, hydrogen. The hydrogen atom consists of a nucleus made up of a single proton, and a single electron outside the nucleus. This electron is confined to an orbital, which is defined simply as a region in space in which the electron may be found, and a mathematical formula can be written to describe this region, which for the electron of hydrogen resembles a sphere. It is incorrect, however, to think of the electron circling the nucleus as the earth circles the sun. Because it is impossible to devise an experiment that will determine the exact position of a particle as small as an electron, we can only refer to its average position over a relatively long (by electronic standards) period of time. One way to represent the type of data attainable is shown in Fig. 1-8. This is a graph indicating the relative probability of finding the electron of a hydrogen atom at various distances from the nucleus. The graph shows that a large number of measurements

---

* All temperatures given in this book will refer to the Centigrade (C) scale unless Fahrenheit (F) is specifically stated.

on a hydrogen atom to determine the electron's distance from the nucleus will yield a large number of answers. One measurement might produce an answer of 0.1 Å (1 Å or Ångstrom unit = 10^{-8} cm); another might be 10 Å. As the number of measurements increased, a larger number of values close to 1 Å would be noted. The most probable value is 0.53 Å, but there is a finite, though exceedingly remote, probability of finding the electron miles away from the nucleus. Thus, one cannot speak of the exact *position* of an electron, but only of the *probability* of finding it in any given volume of space.

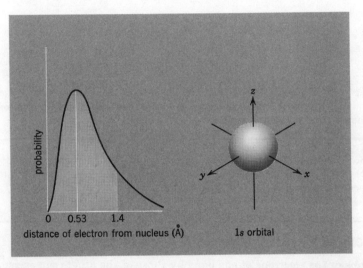

Fig. 1-8. The graph represents the relative probability of finding an electron at various distances from the nucleus of a hydrogen atom. The most probable distance is 0.53 Å (0.53 × 10^{-8} cm). The probability is 90% of finding it within the gray area (1.4 Å). A 1s orbital is defined as a region in space within which a 1s electron spends 90% of its time. This is a sphere with a radius of 1.4 Å.

Since neither a graph nor a discussion of probabilities provides the most useful representation of atomic orbitals, chemists have adopted the following modification: Although the electron has a certain probability of being at *any* distance from the hydrogen nucleus, it is fairly close most of the time; in fact, *it spends 90% of its time within a sphere with a radius of 1.4 Å from the nucleus*. In a graphic sense, then, let us regard an atomic orbital as *that region of space in which an electron spends 90% of its time*. This *atomic orbital* for hydrogen, known as the 1s orbital, is shown in Fig. 1-8.

An atomic orbital can hold only two electrons, which must have spins of opposite signs. Thus, the helium atom has a nucleus containing two protons, and its two electrons occupy its 1s orbital. Lithium, however, has a third electron which cannot enter the already-full 1s orbital and must go into the next orbital, called the 2s orbital. This 2s orbital is similar in shape to the 1s orbital but of higher energy, since the electron spends more of its time at a greater distance from the nucleus. As a consequence, the sphere that represents the $2s$ orbital has a larger diameter to enclose the 90% probability limits. Beryllium, which has four electrons, has two $2s$ and two $1s$ electrons.

The rest of the electrons that go into the atoms of the second row of the periodic table occupy p orbitals (Fig. 1-9). These orbitals are not spherical like the s orbitals. The probability of finding an electron in a p orbital is not the same in all directions from the nucleus, but is greater in some directions in space than in others; that is, p orbitals are directional. There are three p orbitals, each at right angles to the other two, and all of equal energy. These three are arbitrarily designated p_x, p_y, and p_z.

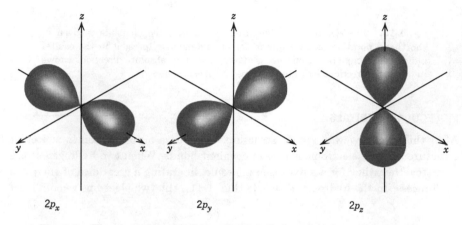

$2p_x$ $2p_y$ $2p_z$

Fig. 1-9. The three $2p$ orbitals are dumb-bell shaped and arranged at right angles to one another. Each can hold two electrons.

The boron atom, with five electrons in all, has two in the $1s$ orbital (designated $1s^2$), two in the $2s$ orbital ($2s^2$), and one in a $2p_x$ orbital ($2p_x{}^1$). Carbon, which is next in the periodic table, has six electrons. Since electrons repel one another, and since all three $2p$ orbitals are of equally low energy, the additional electron enters another p orbital. The electronic structure of a carbon atom in its lowest energy state may then be described by the shorthand notation $1s^2 2s^2 2p_x{}^1 2p_y{}^1$, indicating that the $1s$ orbital contains two electrons, the $2s$ orbital contains two electrons, and the $2p_x$ and $2p_y$ orbitals contain one electron each. In the nitrogen atom the next electron occupies the $2p_z$ orbital, and in the remaining three atoms of the row, the $2p$ orbitals are filled with a second electron each until the stable rare gas, neon, is formed. The electronic configurations of the first ten elements appear in Fig. 1-10.

Prob. 1-4. Patterning your answer after the example for carbon in the text ($1s^2 2s^2 2p_x{}^1 2p_y{}^1$), and using the chart of Fig. 1-10, write the correct notation of the electronic structures of atomic oxygen and atomic neon.

	$1s$	$2s$	$2p_x$	$2p_y$	$2p_z$	
	↿					H
	⇅					He
	⇅	↿				Li
	⇅	⇅				Be
	⇅	⇅	↿			B
	⇅	⇅	↿	↿		C
	⇅	⇅	↿	↿	↿	N
	⇅	⇅	⇅	↿	↿	O
	⇅	⇅	⇅	⇅	↿	F
	⇅	⇅	⇅	⇅	⇅	Ne

Fig. 1-10. The electronic configuration of the first ten elements is given in shorthand notation. Each arrow indicates one electron present in the orbital indicated. Though no significance is attached to their absolute direction, arrows in opposite directions indicate electrons of opposite spins.

MOLECULAR ORBITALS

After this brief review of atomic structure, let us turn our attention to molecular structure and the electronic nature of covalent bonds. When two hydrogen atoms come together, they form a hydrogen molecule, liberating a great deal of energy in the process. In the hydrogen molecule (Fig. 1-11), the two electrons remain most

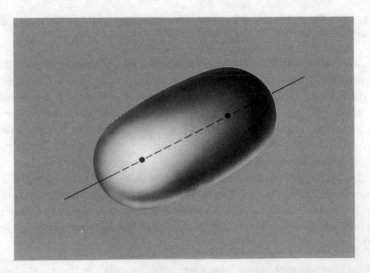

Fig. 1-11. The two electrons in the hydrogen molecule occupy a *sigma* (σ) molecular orbital, characterized by its complete symmetry around the axis of the bond.

of the time *between* the nuclei, holding the molecule together. As with the hydrogen atom, we can graphically represent the volume in space in which these two electrons of the hydrogen molecule spend 90% of their time. Such a volume is called a *molecular orbital* because it encompasses two or more atomic nuclei and not just a single atom. Continuing the analogy, we call this orbital a *sigma orbital* (from the Greek letter σ corresponding to the English s) because, although it is not a complete sphere like an s orbital, *it is completely symmetrical about the axis of the bond.* This means that if we look down the hydrogen–hydrogen bond, we have the same probability of finding an electron in all directions from the axis.

From experiment we know that the four hydrogen atoms in methane are arranged tetrahedrally about the central carbon. The molecular orbital picture of methane shows four orbitals, each of a σ type, joining the carbon and hydrogen nuclei together. Note that an isolated carbon atom with its four outer electrons already tetrahedrally arranged in orbitals, ready to join with four hydrogen atoms to form methane (Fig. 1-12), would look quite different from an isolated carbon atom in its most stable form. These tetrahedral atomic orbitals are neither pure *s* nor pure *p* orbitals; they have certain characteristics of each type and are known as *hybrid orbitals*. It can be shown mathematically that orbitals containing one part *s* and three parts *p* would have just such a tetrahedral shape. As a consequence, *tetrahedral atomic orbitals of carbon are called sp^3 orbitals.*

Because this concept of hybrid orbitals is so useful, we shall illustrate it further by the following extreme example. If a carbon rod is heated to a sufficiently high temperature, carbon atoms are vaporized. Such carbon atoms would have the

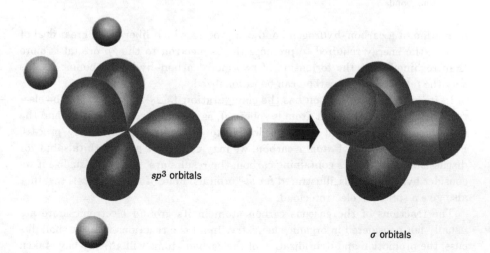

sp³ orbitals

σ orbitals

Fig. 1-12. In methane, the carbon and hydrogen atoms are held together in tetrahedral molecular orbitals, which are σ orbitals similar in shape to those of Fig. 1-11. Without the hydrogen atoms, the carbon atom would be left with its electrons in hybrid *sp³* atomic orbitals.

electronic configuration $1s^2 2s^2 2p_x{}^1 2p_y{}^1$, shown in Fig. 1-10. An atom in that configuration could form bonds with only two hydrogen atoms, because the $2s$ orbital already contains the maximum number of electrons it can hold. At first sight, it appears that CH_2 should be formed instead of CH_4.

If sufficient energy is available, however, one of the electrons of the $2s$ orbital may be moved (the technical word is promoted) to the $2p_z$ orbital, thus producing a carbon atom in an *excited state*. The process is illustrated schematically in Fig. 1-13. Such a carbon atom can combine with *four* hydrogen atoms instead of two, because it has four orbitals which are only half filled with electrons. Since the

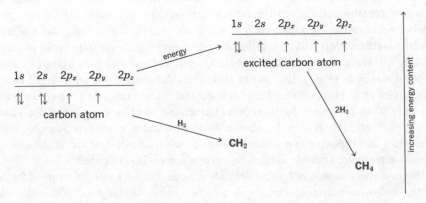

Fig. 1-13. A representation of the electronic transformations involved in accounting for the tetravalence of carbon. In stable molecules, carbon always forms four bonds.

formation of a carbon–hydrogen bond is a process which liberates a great deal of energy, the energy required to promote the $2s$ electron to the $2p$ orbital is more than regained from the formation of two more carbon–hydrogen bonds. In this way the *tetravalence* of carbon can be rationalized.

In its excited state, carbon has the configuration $1s^2 2s^1 2p_x{}^1 2p_y{}^1 2p_z{}^1$. The electron distribution in such an atom is spherical, as represented in Fig. 1-14, and the division of this spherical electron cloud into orbitals is an arbitrary process. For most discussions of *atomic* carbon, we may consider s and p orbitals, but for discussions of *molecules* containing carbon, the results are easier to visualize if we consider hybrid orbitals, illustrated for sp^3 orbitals. Four of these orbitals together also give a spherical electron cloud.

The reactions of the gaseous carbon atom in its ground electronic state are usually not considered in organic chemistry. In all the reactions that we shall discuss, the promotion and hybridization of the carbon atoms will already have taken place; this process probably occurred at the time the earth was formed, certainly by the time methane existed. Promotion is then not a common process in organic chemistry, but we must be aware of the concept in order to bridge the gap between atomic and molecular structures.

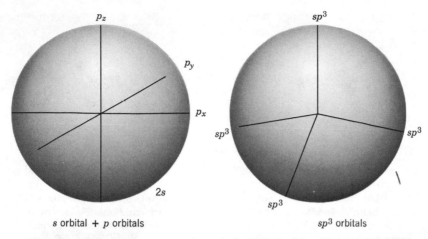

s orbital + p orbitals sp^3 orbitals

Fig. 1-14. The division of an electron cloud into orbitals is a useful, but some-what arbitrary, device. Both spheres contain the same electron density. For clarity orbital sizes are often reduced, as in Fig. 1-12.

Perhaps the most important single point for students of organic chemistry to remember is that carbon, in all its stable compounds, forms four bonds (and is thus tetravalent). Any formula showing carbon with more or fewer bonds either represents an unstable species or is incorrect. Carbon monoxide (CO) is an obvious exception. Even here its structure may be written $^-C\equiv O^+$, giving three covalent bonds and one electrovalent bond.

ETHANE

Organic chemistry exists as a separate science because of its complexity; one reason for this complexity is the ability of carbon atoms to form strong bonds with other carbon atoms. Two carbon atoms can form a σ bond with each other by making use of sp^3 orbitals, and at the same time form bonds with six hydrogen atoms. The resulting molecule, C_2H_6, is known as *ethane*. Notice that each carbon is attached tetrahedrally (with bond angles of 109°28′) to four other atoms (Fig. 1-15) just as in methane, although now one of the four is another carbon atom. Because carbon–carbon σ bonds are strong and difficult to break, ethane and methane are much alike in chemical properties. Indeed, when ethane is allowed to react with chlorine in the presence of sunlight, from one to six carbon–hydrogen bonds are replaced with carbon–chlorine bonds. It is instructive to see what our structural theory predicts for these compounds.

Prob. 1-5. Draw orbital pictures of the ethane molecule (as in Fig. 1-12).

No matter how it is formed, there is only *one* monochloroethane, C_2H_5Cl (Fig. 1-16). This is certainly consistent with the structure given for ethane, because

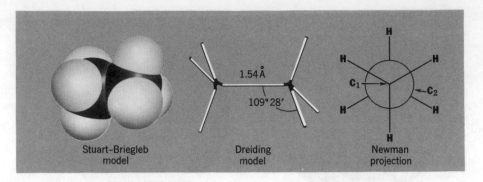

Stuart–Briegleb model

Dreiding model

Newman projection

Fig. 1-15. Two tetrahedral carbon atoms are joined with six hydrogen atoms in the ethane molecule. This figure gives three representations. Note that in the front view, which looks along the carbon–carbon axis and is called a *Newman projection,* the rear carbon atom is represented by a circle. The C—C bond length is 1.54 Å. As in methane, the C—H bond length is 1.09 Å, and the bond angles are 109°28′.

all six hydrogens in this molecule are equivalent. It is found, however, that there are *two* dichloroethanes, $C_2H_4Cl_2$, each having chemical and physical properties slightly different from the other. This is the first time we have encountered what will turn out to be a common situation: two molecules having the same formula but different structures. Such molecules are called *isomers* of each other. The existence of two isomers having the formula $C_2H_4Cl_2$ is readily explained. In one, the two chlorine atoms are attached to the same carbon atom; in the other, a chlorine is attached to each carbon. To give each of these compounds a distinctive name, we number the carbon atoms and speak of the first as 1,1-dichloroethane and the second as 1,2-dichloroethane.

Although organic chemistry is a three-dimensional science, convenience and the limitations of paper and blackboard require two-dimensional representations. Up to this point, we have used projection formulas to represent the third dimension. When formulas are condensed, stereochemistry is lost, but for our discussions of many reactions this loss is not important, and what is lost in precision is gained in convenience. Compare, for example, the two representations of the chlorination of ethane. In the upper line of Fig. 1-16 we see extended molecular formulas in which

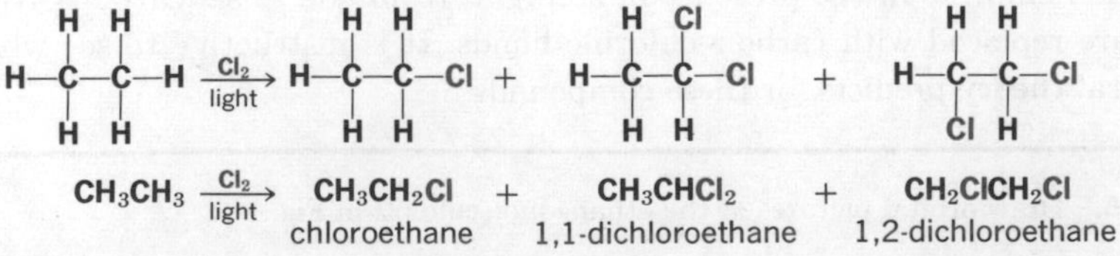

$$CH_3CH_3 \xrightarrow[\text{light}]{Cl_2} CH_3CH_2Cl + CH_3CHCl_2 + CH_2ClCH_2Cl$$

chloroethane   1,1-dichloroethane   1,2-dichloroethane

Fig. 1-16. Chlorination of ethane leads to a mixture of one monochloroethane, two dichloroethanes, and a number of more highly chlorinated ethanes. Here the reaction is written with both extended and contracted molecular formulas.

each bond is represented by a straight line. The lower line contains contracted molecular formulas, in which all atoms attached to each carbon atom are grouped together on a single line, usually following the carbon atom.

Prob. 1-6. What are the structures of the two trichloroethanes, two tetrachloroethanes, one pentachloroethane, and one hexachloroethane, formed in the chlorination of ethane? Name each.

The existence of a single 1,2-dichloroethane might seem surprising; considering the Newman projection of this molecule, one might expect three compounds to form. In fact, three forms do exist, but a carbon–carbon σ bond which is symmetrical about its axis allows the two ends of the molecule *freedom of rotation,* so that at room temperature the three forms may be interconverted extremely rapidly. Forms like these which are rapidly interconverted by rotation are called *conformers.* Obviously, an indefinitely large number of such conformers can exist, corresponding to different degrees of rotation. Generally, however, only two extreme types are considered—*staggered conformations,* in which the atoms attached to one carbon lie between those attached to the other carbon, and *eclipsed conformations,* in which the atoms attached to one carbon lie directly behind those attached to the other (Fig. 1-17). Staggered conformations are appreciably more stable than eclipsed conformations, and the molecules mostly exist with their groups staggered rather than eclipsed. This freedom of rotation simplifies many problems that may arise in relation to ethane, since for all practical purposes only one isomer of 1,2-dichloroethane needs to be considered.

Moreover, it is precisely this freedom of rotation about single bonds which allows us to use contracted structural formulas to represent organic compounds.

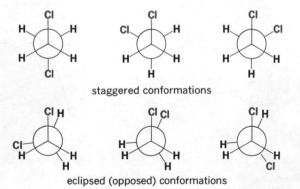

staggered conformations

eclipsed (opposed) conformations

Fig. 1-17. Six conformations of 1,2-dichloroethane. The three upper conformations are more stable than the three below, since the chlorine and hydrogen atoms are staggered between (instead of being opposed to) one another. These conformations are in rapid equilibrium with each other, because the two ends of the molecule are rotating with respect to each other about 10^9 times per second.

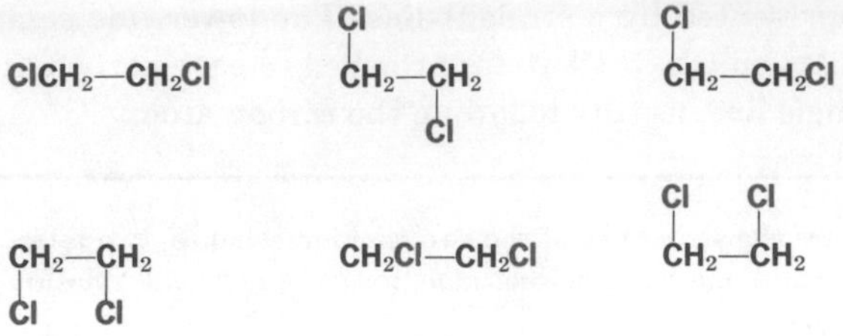

$$ClCH_2-CH_2Cl \qquad \overset{\displaystyle Cl}{\underset{\displaystyle Cl}{CH_2-CH_2}} \qquad \overset{\displaystyle Cl}{CH_2-CH_2Cl}$$

$$\underset{\displaystyle Cl \quad\ Cl}{CH_2-CH_2} \qquad CH_2Cl-CH_2Cl \qquad \overset{\displaystyle Cl\ \ \ Cl}{CH_2-CH_2}$$

Fig. 1-18. Six contracted formulas for 1,2-dichloroethane. All represent the same compound.

Nevertheless, care must be taken to draw contracted structural formulas correctly, and it takes practice to recognize identical compounds as identical when they are contracted in different ways (Fig. 1-18).

PROPANE

When three carbon atoms are joined with eight hydrogen atoms, the resulting product is propane, C_3H_8 (Fig. 1-19). Notice that in the series methane, CH_4, ethane, C_2H_6, and propane, C_3H_8, each molecule differs from the previous one by an additional unit of CH_2. The series can be extended indefinitely in steps of CH_2, so that each member fits the formula C_nH_{2n+2}. A group of molecules of this type, each differing from the next by the structural unit CH_2, is known as a *homologous series*. Methane, ethane, and propane constitute the first three members of the homologous series known as the *continuous-chain saturated hydrocarbons,* or *normal alkanes.* Since cell members of a homologous series have quite similar chemical and physical properties, one can predict with confidence that propane,

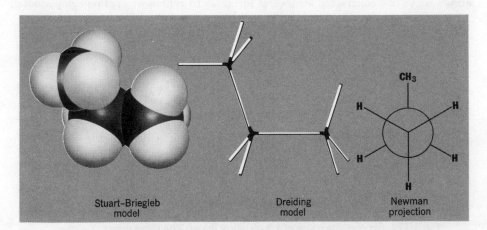

Stuart–Briegleb model   Dreiding model   Newman projection

Fig. 1-19. The structure of propane, C_3H_8, in a side view and in a Newman projection looking down the C-1, C-2 bond. Because there is free rotation about this and the other C—C bond in the molecule, several other conformations could be given.

for example, will react with chlorine in sunlight in a manner reminiscent of the reaction between either methane or ethane and chlorine.

Prob. 1-7. Since propane contains only single bonds, there is free rotation throughout all the bonds of the molecule. Chlorination of propane gives two different monochloropropanes and four different dichloropropanes. Draw the structure, and name each of these six compounds. When numbering the carbon atoms in propane, start from the end that will assign the smaller numbers to the chlorine atoms.

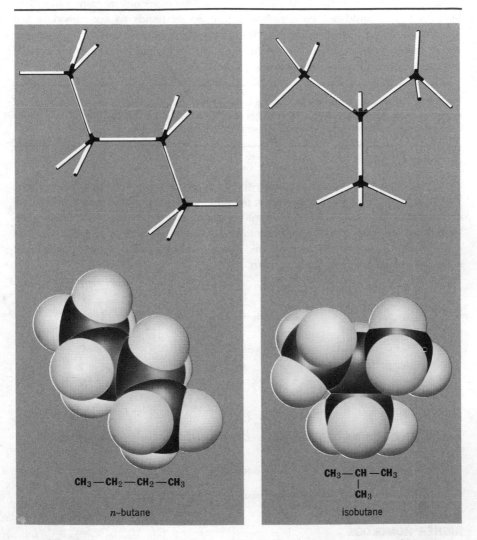

$$CH_3—CH_2—CH_2—CH_3$$

n-butane

$$CH_3—CH—CH_3$$
$$\mid$$
$$CH_3$$

isobutane

Fig. 1-20. Two isomeric butanes (C_4H_{10}) exist; *n*-butane has a continuous chain of carbon atoms, while isobutane has a branched chain. These isomers have somewhat different physical and chemical properties, *n*-butane boiling at $-0.5°$ and isobutane at $-12°$.

BUTANES

The next member of the homologous series of saturated hydrocarbons is butane, C_4H_{10}. There are two different hydrocarbons of this formula; this shows that the existence of isomers does not require the presence of any atoms other than carbon and hydrogen in an organic molecule. In butane, the four carbon atoms may be joined together either in a continuous chain, or with one carbon atom branched from the others, as in Fig. 1-20. (The carbon atoms must not be joined in a ring, because there would not be a sufficient number of bonds to accommodate ten hydrogen atoms.) To distinguish the two butanes by name, we call the first isomer, which has a continuous chain of carbons and no branches, *n*-butane (for *normal* butane) and the branched-chain isomer, isobutane.

Prob. 1-8. In a Newman projection of the C-2, C-3 bond of *n*-butane, there will be a methyl group on each carbon. Draw the three staggered forms. Although there is rapid rotation, one of these forms is more stable than the other two. Which?

PENTANES

As the number of carbon atoms increases, so does the number of possible isomers. The next member of the alkane series, pentane, C_5H_{12}, has three isomers. The five carbons may be arranged in a continuous chain to give *n*-pentane, with one branch to give isopentane, or with two branches to give neopentane (Fig. 1-21). Each of these pentanes is a well-known organic species, differing slightly in physical and chemical properties from the other two.

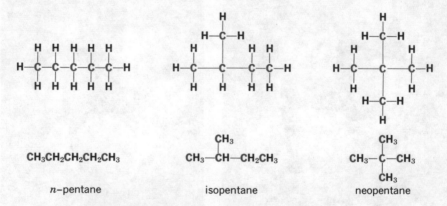

Fig. 1-21.   Three isomeric pentanes, C_5H_{12}, exist.

HIGHER HOMOLOGS

Table 1-1 contains the names and structures of the continuous-chain isomers of the first ten saturated hydrocarbons, and the number of possible isomers for each molecular formula. The names in the table should be memorized, because they

Table 1-1. Continuous-Chain Saturated Hydrocarbons and the Number of Their Possible Isomers

Compound	Structural formula	Boiling point	Melting point	Total number of hydrocarbons having the same molecular formula
methane	CH_4	$-162°C$	$-182°C$	1
ethane	CH_3CH_3	-89	-183	1
propane	$CH_3CH_2CH_3$	-45	-90	1
n-butane	$CH_3(CH_2)_2CH_3$	-0.5	-138	2
n-pentane	$CH_3(CH_2)_3CH_3$	36	-130	3
n-hexane	$CH_3(CH_2)_4CH_3$	68	-95	5
n-heptane	$CH_3(CH_2)_5CH_3$	98	-91	9
n-octane	$CH_3(CH_2)_6CH_3$	125	-57	18
n-nonane	$CH_3(CH_2)_7CH_3$	151	-51	35
n-decane	$CH_3(CH_2)_8CH_3$	174	-30	75

will be used frequently. Notice how quickly the number of isomers mounts, and how impossible it would be to memorize a different name for each. Obviously, a more systematic nomenclature is necessary; the standard one will be described in the next section.

The continuous-chain saturated hydrocarbons are often referred to as *straight-chain* hydrocarbons, because their formulas are frequently written in contracted form. Stretched out as far as possible, a molecule like heptane has a zigzag shape as shown in Fig. 1-22, and it is free to take up many other conformations. For this reason, we shall use the term *continuous-chain* rather than the term straight-chain, to indicate that there is no branching.

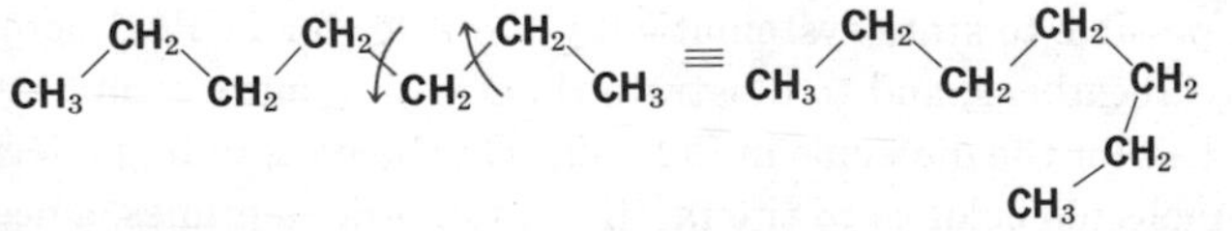

Fig. 1-22. Two conformations for *n*-heptane. The zigzag formula is the closest the molecule can come to a straight chain. Many other arrangements are possible because of the free rotation in the molecule. The U-shaped formula is obtained by rotation, as indicated.

Prob. 1-9. Draw condensed structural formulas for all five isomeric hexanes.

SYSTEMATIC NOMENCLATURE

If there are an infinite number of saturated hydrocarbons, there must be an infinite number of names to identify them. A simple unequivocal system of nomenclature is therefore a necessity. Such a system was devised by the International

Union of Chemistry at Geneva in 1892, and the task of keeping it up to date has fallen to its successor, the International Union of Pure and Applied Chemistry. The IUPAC system will be applied extensively throughout this book. Its basic rules can be easily illustrated for saturated hydrocarbons. Briefly, the longest *continuous chain* of carbon atoms in the molecule is considered to be the parent chain from which the molecule is derived through the replacement of hydrogen atoms. If we take isobutane as an example, its longest continuous chain of carbon atoms is three. In the IUPAC system, this compound would be considered to be a derivative of propane, in which one hydrogen atom has been replaced by a CH_3 group.

Table 1-2. Names of the First Four Alkyl Groups and of the Halogens Which Replace Hydrogen Atoms

Group	Name	Group	Name
CH_3^-	methyl	F^-	fluoro
$CH_3CH_2^-$	ethyl	Cl^-	chloro
$CH_3CH_2CH_2^-$	n-propyl	Br^-	bromo
CH_3CH^-	isopropyl	I^-	iodo
$\quad\mid$			
CH_3			

Names must be given to fragments like CH_3 and CH_3CH_2, which are not molecules but combining groups, which make up parts of molecules (Table 1-2). Because of its derivation from methane by the loss of one hydrogen atom CH_3 is called the *methyl group*. In the IUPAC system, isobutane becomes methylpropane. Similarly, CH_3CH_2, derived from ethane, is known as the *ethyl group,* and two different groups may be formed from propane, by loss of hydrogen from either the 1- or 2-carbon. As a class, these groups which result from loss of an hydrogen from an alkane are known as *alkyl groups*.

It is now possible to state systematically the rules for IUPAC nomenclature for saturated hydrocarbons, and to illustrate them with a more complicated molecule. We shall do this for the molecule in Fig. 1-23. On the basis of its molecular formula, C_7H_{16}, the molecule belongs to the family of isomeric heptanes, since it has seven carbon atoms. However, the IUPAC name is derived in a different manner. First, the longest continuous chain of carbon atoms is located and named. In this illus-

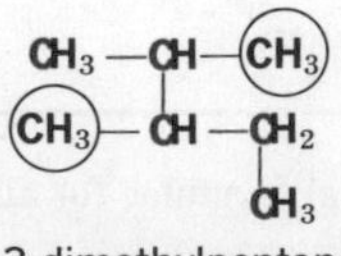

$$CH_3 - CH - CH_3$$
$$CH_3 - CH - CH_2$$
$$\qquad\qquad CH_3$$

2,3-dimethylpentane

Fig. 1-23. In the IUPAC nomenclature of an alkane, the longest continuous chain of carbon atoms in the molecule is located (even though it may not be written in a straight line), and named as the parent. The substituent groups (circled) are named, and the chain is numbered from the end that gives these groups the smallest numbers. The name is punctuated as shown.

tration the longest chain (shown in red) is five. Hence, the parent from which the name is to be derived is *pentane,* taken from the list of Table 1-1. Second, the substituent groups (circled) are named. In this case, two *methyl* groups are attached to the longest chain. Third, the parent chain is numbered from the end that gives the substituents their smallest numbers. Here, numbering from the left gives the full name *2,3-dimethylpentane.*

When the IUPAC system is to be used in naming saturated hydrocarbons these errors should be avoided:

(1) Failing to locate the longest continuous chain of carbon atoms, which may not be written in a straight line.

(2) Numbering from the wrong end.

(3) Failing to write the same number twice, when two identical substituents are on the same carbon atom.

(4) Confusing the *n*-propyl and isopropyl groups.

The IUPAC method of nomenclature is treated further in a set of graded examples in the Appendix. At this stage, the reader should turn to the Appendix and answer Questions 1 through 8. Upon completion of this assignment, one should be easily able to answer Probs. 1-10, 1-11, and 1-12, at the end of this chapter.

One further point of nomenclature needs to be introduced, not so much for the naming of the hydrocarbons as for naming the derivatives to be considered in future chapters. A fairly complicated molecule will ordinarily contain various types of carbon–hydrogen groups. At the ends of the molecule are CH_3 groups; along the chain are CH_2 and CH groups, and there may even be an occasional carbon atom that carries no hydrogen atoms at all and is attached to four other carbon atoms. A carbon atom attached to only one other carbon atom, like those of the methyl groups, is called a *primary carbon.* The carbon atom that is attached to two other carbon atoms, like those of the CH_2 groups, is said to be a *secondary carbon.* Carbon atoms attached to three and four other carbon atoms are called *tertiary* and *quaternary,* respectively (see Fig. 1-24).

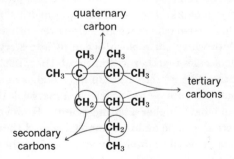

Fig. 1-24. It is convenient to designate carbon atoms as primary (1°), secondary (2°), tertiary (3°), or quaternary (4°), depending upon whether they are bonded to one, two, three, or four other carbons. All the methyl groups contain primary carbon atoms.

PROPERTIES OF ALKANES

The saturated hydrocarbons, or alkanes, are cheap readily available compounds found in enormous quantities in petroleum, which is discussed in Chapter 2. Sometimes the alkanes are called "paraffins," a word derived from the Latin *parum affinus,* meaning "of slight activity"; they are so named because they are among the least reactive of all classes of organic compounds. Their lack of reactivity accounts for one of their principal uses: as solvents. For example, naphtha, a familiar (and highly flammable) household solvent, is a mixture of saturated hydrocarbons.

The boiling points of the first ten *n*-alkanes are noted in Table 1-1, and one can see a fairly regular increase of about 25° per methylene group after the first few members of the series. Since the hydrocarbon molecules have relatively little attraction for one another, the boiling points of these compounds are determined mainly by their molecular weights. Branched-chain compounds generally boil somewhat lower than their normal isomers, but seldom boil as low as the next lower homolog (Table 1-3). This is illustrated by the boiling points of *n*-pentane (IUPAC name, pentane), isopentane (2-methylbutane), and neopentane (2,2-dimethylpropane). Methane, ethane, and the two butanes are gases at room temperature.

Table 1-3.   Effect of Branching on the Boiling and Melting Points of the Pentanes

Hydrocarbon	Boiling point	Melting point
n-pentane	36°C	−130°C
isopentane	28	−160
neopentane	9	−20
n-butane	−0.5	−138

The melting points of organic compounds are much less predictable. In a closely related series of compounds like the *n*-alkanes, the melting points are generally higher for those of higher molecular weight. However, other influences are also apparent—the ease with which the molecules can fit into a crystal lattice and the forces that hold the molecules together within that lattice. Usually the more nearly symmetrical molecules within a related group have higher melting points. Among the alkanes, the *n*-alkanes are more nearly symmetrical than the isoalkanes (2-methylalkanes), and have higher melting points. However, when branching is extensive, the molecules can be almost symmetrical and the melting points very high. An extreme example is the completely symmetrical compound neopentane, which resembles a sphere and packs nicely into a crystal; it melts at a much higher temperature than *n*-pentane, and its melting point is only 29° below its boiling point. Other completely symmetrical hydrocarbons have practically no spread at all between their melting and boiling points, and change directly from solid to gas.

REACTIONS OF ALKANES

Methane, as the simplest alkane, may be used to illustrate the reactions of this class of compounds. Methane is the principal constituent of natural gas, its proportion varying from 60 to 99%, depending upon the source. It is also the product of bacterial decay of vegetable matter when such decay takes place in the absence of oxygen. Decaying plants beneath the surface of the water in swamps give off *marsh gas,* chiefly methane; this gas occasionally catches fire, causing weird lights and tales of spirits, ghosts, and flying saucers. Although this example of spontaneous combustion is not important commercially, it does illustrate the greatest use of methane—in combustion (Fig. 1-25).

$$CH_4 + 2O_2 \xrightarrow[\text{temperature}]{\text{high}} CO_2 + 2H_2O + \text{energy}$$
methane

$$CH_3-\underset{\underset{CH_3}{|}}{\overset{\overset{CH_3}{|}}{C}}-CH_2-\underset{\underset{CH_3}{|}}{CH}-CH_3 + 12\tfrac{1}{2}O_2 \xrightarrow[\text{temperature}]{\text{high}} 8CO_2 + 9H_2O + \text{energy}$$ 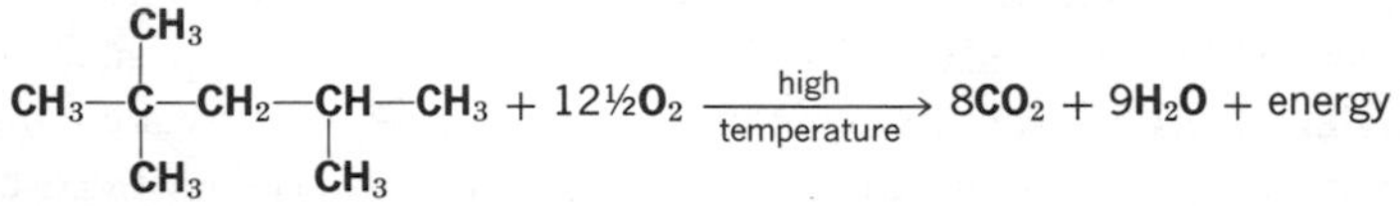
2,2,4-trimethylpentane

Fig. 1-25. The combustion of alkanes with oxygen, illustrated here with methane (found in natural gas) and 2,2,4-trimethylpentane (found in gasoline), is one of the greatest sources of energy in modern civilization.

Large amounts of methane are also used industrially in the production of many of the commonest chemicals. Thus, mono-, di-, tri-, and tetrachloromethanes (methyl chloride, methylene chloride, chloroform, and carbon tetrachloride, respectively) are all produced industrially by chlorination of methane (see Fig. 1-1); methyl alcohol, formaldehyde, acetylene, and a number of other compounds may also be synthesized directly from methane, although to do so requires high temperatures and other special conditions. Methane may be *nitrated* by treatment with nitric acid at high temperature (Fig. 1-26). The resultant *nitromethane* is a liquid used as a solvent, as a high-energy fuel for racing car engines, and as a chemical intermediate for conversion to other compounds.

$$CH_4 + HNO_3 \xrightarrow{420°} CH_3NO_2 + H_2O$$
methane   nitromethane

Fig. 1-26. Methane and other alkanes may be converted to nitroalkanes when treated with nitric acid.

Like methane, the other alkanes are used as fuels in internal combustion or jet engines and in candles or camp stoves. Most alkanes may also be converted by industrial processes employing high temperatures and special conditions, into other useful molecules, though the reactions are necessarily more complex. The most important point is that alkanes are chemically inert under normal conditions. Paraffin is used as an inert coating, and petroleum has lain for millennia beneath the ground.

REACTION MECHANISMS

The alkanes provide excellent examples of a general principle: More is required to make a chemical reaction proceed than favorable reaction energy. A mixture of methane and oxygen is indefinitely stable, despite the extremely *exothermic* (energy releasing) character of its reaction to give carbon dioxide and water. Similarly, a mixture of an alkane and chlorine can be kept indefinitely in the dark without reacting. However, if a spark is supplied to the former mixture or a burst of light to the latter, reactions rapidly ensue. To occur at an appreciable rate, a reaction must have a favorable pathway. The study of such reaction paths, called *reaction mechanisms,* has been very helpful in understanding how organic reactions take place and in correlating seemingly unrelated reactions.

It is difficult to bring about reactions of alkanes, because all their electrons (except the tightly bound $1s$ electrons of carbon) are involved in the formation of strong carbon–carbon and carbon–hydrogen bonds. The first step in the chlorination of an alkane has been shown to be the absorption of light by a chlorine molecule, which dissociates into chlorine atoms. A chlorine atom then attacks an alkane molecule, and, by removing a hydrogen atom, forms hydrogen chloride. This reaction occurs readily, because the energy of the hydrogen–chlorine bond formed in the process more than compensates for the energy lost in breaking the carbon–hydrogen bond. In this way, a highly reactive site is created in the alkane molecule: a carbon atom with only three of its four valences used, and with one additional electron not employed in bonding. Fragments of this type are known as *free radicals* and occur often as short-lived intermediates in chemical reactions.

$$Cl_2 \xrightarrow{\text{light}} 2Cl\cdot$$

$$\underset{\text{methane}}{Cl\cdot + CH_4} \longrightarrow HCl + \underset{\text{methyl radical}}{\cdot CH_3}$$

$$\cdot CH_3 + Cl_2 \longrightarrow CH_3Cl + Cl\cdot$$

Fig. 1-27. The *mechanism* of the chlorination of methane. A chlorine atom reacts in the second step while another one is generated in the third step, so that the sequence of reactions constitutes a *chain reaction.*

In the specific reaction for the chlorination of methane (Fig. 1-27), the *methyl free radical* ($\cdot CH_3$) is formed by the attack of a chlorine atom on methane. Under these conditions, the methyl free radical has a lifetime of approximately one-billionth of a second, before it reacts with a chlorine molecule to form methyl chloride and a new chlorine atom. After a comparably short time, the new atom in turn reacts with more methane, to form a new, equally short-lived, methyl free radical. These steps are repeated many times in what is known as a *chain reaction,* so that the dissociation of a single chlorine molecule can lead to the chlorination of many molecules of methane.

In summary, the alkanes as a class are characterized by their lack of reactivity toward most chemicals, and this inertness makes them useful as solvents and coatings. Under sufficiently vigorous conditions they may react, but they do so in a rather unselective manner, generally producing a mixture of products, or, as in combustion, being completely consumed. These characteristics are also generally imparted to the alkane portions of more complicated molecules; this means that, although a compound may contain several functional groups that react readily, an alkyl group in the compound normally remains unchanged through many transformations of the rest of the molecule.

Prob. 1-10. Draw the structures of the following compounds. In (c), label each carbon as 1°, 2°, 3°, or 4°.
    (a) 2,3-dimethylhexane
    (b) 4-isopropylheptane
    (c) 3,4-dimethyl-4-*n*-propyl-5-ethylheptane
    (d) isopropyl chloride
    (e) 3-bromo-5-iodooctane

Prob. 1-11. What is wrong with each of the following names? Give the structure and correct name for each compound.
    (a) 3,3-dimethylbutane
    (b) 2-*n*-propylhexane
    (c) 1,1-diethylpentane
    (d) 2,9-difluorononane

Prob. 1-12. Draw the structures of all nine isomers of heptane (C_7H_{16}). Name each according to the IUPAC system. (Hint: Draw the carbon skeletons first, starting with seven carbon atoms in a row, then with six, then with five, etc. Place carbon atoms at all possible positions, eliminate duplicates, then add hydrogen atoms.)

Prob. 1-13. Among the following condensed formulas are some for identical molecules written in different ways. Show which of these are identical.

(a)
$$CH_3-CH_2 \quad CH_2-CH(CH_3)-CH_2 \quad CH_3$$

$$CH_2-CH(CH_3)-CH_2 \quad CH_2 \quad CH_3 \quad CH_3$$

(b)
$$ClCH(CH_3)-CH-CH_2-CH(CH_3)-CH_3$$

$$CH_3-CH(Cl)-CH-CH_2(CHCl-CH_3)-CH_3$$

(c)
$$CH_3-CH_2 \quad CH_2 \quad CH_2-CH-CH(CH_3)-CH_3 \quad CH_3$$

$$CH(CH_3)-CH(CH_3)-CH_2-CH_3 \quad CH_2-CH_2-CH_3$$

Prob. 1-14. Write balanced equations for the combustion of hexane and for the complete chlorination of neopentane.

CHAPTER

CYCLIC SATURATED
HYDROCARBONS AND PETROLEUM

The molecules mentioned thus far all have been composed of carbon-atom chains, often having one or more branches. The ends of these chains can be joined together to form a ring or a cycle of carbon atoms. Molecules of this type are considered cyclic or, if all the atoms of the ring are carbon, *alicyclic*. Further, when all the carbon atoms are saturated, the molecules are said to be *cycloalkanes*. In most respects cycloalkanes resemble their noncyclic counterparts, both chemically and physically. However, certain of their chemical features merit special attention.

CYCLOPENTANE

The least complicated alicyclic hydrocarbon is cyclopentane. If the carbon atoms in this molecule lie in a plane, they form a nearly perfect pentagon (Fig. 2-1); in fact, the usual symbol for cyclopentane is a pentagon. The internal angles of a pentagon are $108°$, almost the normal tetrahedral angle ($109°28'$).

Cyclopentane and n-pentane are similar, except that the cyclic compound has two less hydrogen atoms. Although both are nearly inert chemically, they react with halogens in the presence of light through the substitution of one or more hydrogen atoms. Since the cyclic structure confers a high degree of symmetry on the molecule, only one monochlorocyclopentane is possible. Here cyclopentane differs from n-pentane in that three monochloro-n-pentanes may be formed.

Cyclic molecules give rise to a new type of isomerism. This is indicated by an examination of the possible isomers of dichlorocyclopentane. Both chlorine atoms may be attached to the same carbon atom to give 1,1-dichlorocyclopentane, or they may be on adjacent carbon atoms as in 1,2-dichlorocyclopentane, or they may

27

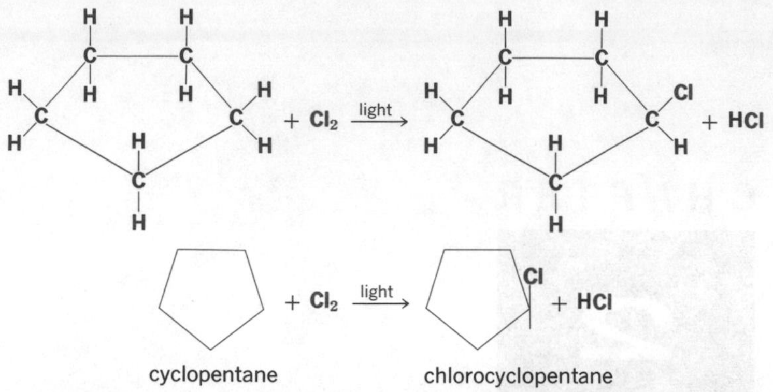

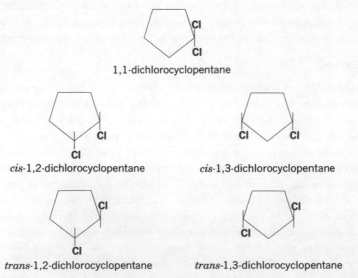

cyclopentane   chlorocyclopentane

Fig. 2-1. Cyclopentane hardly differs chemically from *n*-pentane, as is shown here by its reaction with chlorine and light. The symbol for a cyclic hydrocarbon is a regular polygon with as many corners as there are atoms in the ring. Unless otherwise specified, enough hydrogen atoms are understood to be attached to these carbon atoms so that each carbon has a valence of four.

be in the 1,3- position. *Two isomers of both 1,2- and 1,3-dichlorocyclopentanes exist.* In one of the isomeric 1,2-dichloro compounds, both chlorine atoms are attached to the same side of the ring to give *cis*-1,2-dichlorocyclopentane; in the other isomer, the two chlorine atoms are attached to opposite sides of the ring to give *trans*-1,2-dichlorocyclopentane. The prefix *cis* signifies that two substituents are on the same side of a ring, *trans,* that they are on opposite sides. Similarly, there are *cis*- and *trans*-1,3-dichlorocyclopentanes (see Fig. 2-2).

1,1-dichlorocyclopentane

cis-1,2-dichlorocyclopentane   *cis*-1,3-dichlorocyclopentane

trans-1,2-dichlorocyclopentane   *trans*-1,3-dichlorocyclopentane

Fig. 2-2. Five dichlorocyclopentanes. The two 1,2- and the two 1,3- isomers illustrate *geometrical isomerism.*

Notice the difference between the *cis* and *trans* isomers: Both have chlorines bonded to the same carbon atoms, but their arrangements in space differ. These isomers which differ in their three-dimensional structure are called *stereoisomers*. In the present example, in which the chlorine atoms are either on the same or on opposite sides of the ring, they are more precisely called *geometrical isomers*. This type of isomerism should be clearly distinguished from structural isomerism illustrated by *n*-butane and isobutane (Fig. 1-20), in which the isomers differ from one another in the order in which the atoms are joined together.

Figure 2-3 contains Newman projections of *cis*- and *trans*-1,2-dichlorocyclopentanes. Compare these structures carefully with those in Fig. 1-17 for 1,2-dichloro-

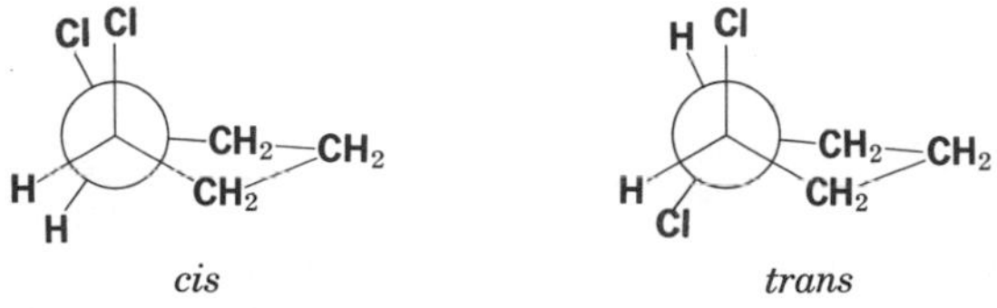

Fig. 2-3. Newman projections along the 1,2- bond of *cis*- and *trans*-1,2-dichlorocyclopentanes. In order to rotate around the 1,2- bond the ring would have to be broken; therefore, these isomers are distinct species.

ethane, and note the similarities. In dichloroethane, the isomers could not be separated because of rapid free rotation about the carbon–carbon bond. Forming the carbons into a ring prevents free rotation, so these *cis* and *trans* isomers have independent existence.

NOMENCLATURE

The IUPAC nomenclature of alicyclic molecules is not very different from that of noncyclic compounds; it does, however, incorporate extensions of the rules. The ring is generally considered to be the parent molecule, and the prefix "cyclo" is used. Since a ring has no end, the number 1 is assigned to the ring carbon atom that gives the smallest numbers to the substituents (Fig. 2-4). Group names may

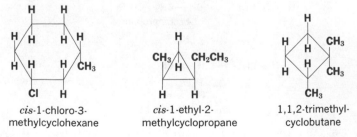

cis-1-chloro-3-
methylcyclohexane

cis-1-ethyl-2-
methylcyclopropane

1,1,2-trimethyl-
cyclobutane

Fig. 2-4. In the IUPAC nomenclature of alicyclic molecules, numbering is begun with the carbon atom that gives the smallest numbers for the location of substituents.

also be given to ring compounds; the cyclohexyl group, for example, is a cyclohexane ring less one hydrogen atom. The reader should turn to the Appendix and answer Questions 9 to 12.

STRAINED RINGS: CYCLOBUTANE AND CYCLOPROPANE

Cyclic hydrocarbons that contain rings of fewer than five carbon atoms must have internal bond angles that are much smaller than the normal 109°28′ of a tetrahedron. Simple geometry shows that these angles would be 90° in cyclobutane and 60° in cyclopropane; a square and an equilateral triangle are the usual symbols for these molecules (Fig. 2-5). Both of these hydrocarbons are reasonably stable to heat,

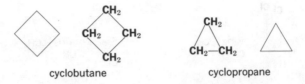

cyclobutane   cyclopropane

Fig. 2-5. Cyclobutane and cyclopropane are both stable molecules despite the fact that the carbon–carbon bonds must be highly strained to bend them from the normal tetrahedral angle of 109°28′ to 90° and 60°, respectively.

despite the fact that their bonds are bent greatly from normal. Bending does, however, impart an *angle strain,* so that both rings, especially the cyclopropane, have a tendency to open to noncyclic molecules in reactions that are quite different from those of saturated hydrocarbons. Cyclopropane, for example, behaves in a most unusual fashion for an alkane, by reacting with hydrogen bromide to form *n*-propyl bromide (Fig. 2-6). Cyclopropane is also reduced to propane with hydrogen. No noncyclic saturated hydrocarbon undergoes these types of reaction. On the other hand, cyclopropane is chlorinated in a typical hydrocarbon reaction by substituting chlorine for hydrogen. Cyclobutane reacts very slowly with hydrogen, and the other cycloalkanes are unreactive both to hydrogen and to hydrogen bromide.

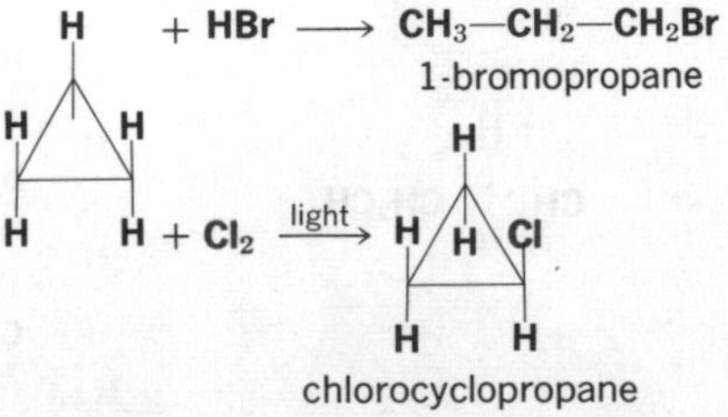

$$\text{H} \quad + \text{HBr} \longrightarrow \text{CH}_3\text{—CH}_2\text{—CH}_2\text{Br}$$

1-bromopropane

$$\text{H} \quad + \text{Cl}_2 \xrightarrow{\text{light}} \text{H} \quad \text{Cl}$$

chlorocyclopropane

Fig. 2-6. Although saturated hydrocarbons do not ordinarily react with hydrogen bromide, cyclopropane does, by opening the highly strained ring. It reacts more typically with chlorine, forming cyclopropyl chloride, as well as other more highly chlorinated products.

Prob. 2-1. Give equations for the reaction of cyclopropane with hydrogen, and of cyclo-butane with bromine in the presence of light. How many dibromocyclobutanes are possible? Draw their structures and name each.

NONPLANAR RINGS: CYCLOHEXANE

It might be predicted that rings larger than cyclopentane would also be strained by having angles larger than tetrahedral. For instance, the internal angles in a planar regular hexagon are 120°, in a heptagon, 129°, and in a decagon (a ten-sided polygon), 144°. Arguments of this kind led early chemists to predict that rings containing more than six carbons would be difficult to prepare and that they would be highly strained once they were formed. Later work has shown that, although some large-ring compounds containing six or more carbon atoms are hard to prepare, their rings do not have appreciable angle strain. The reason for the lack of angle strain appears obvious now: Cyclohexane and cyclic hydrocarbons with larger rings are not planar but puckered, so that their bond angles are all nearly normal. (In fact, modern physical methods have shown that even cyclo-pentane and cyclobutane are not quite planar.)

The shape of cyclohexane has been studied most carefully and will be considered in some detail. Molecular models show that a six-membered ring may take up three distinct nonplanar *conformations* while maintaining normal tetrahedral angles of 109°28′ (Fig. 2-7). Two of these are mirror images of each other, and

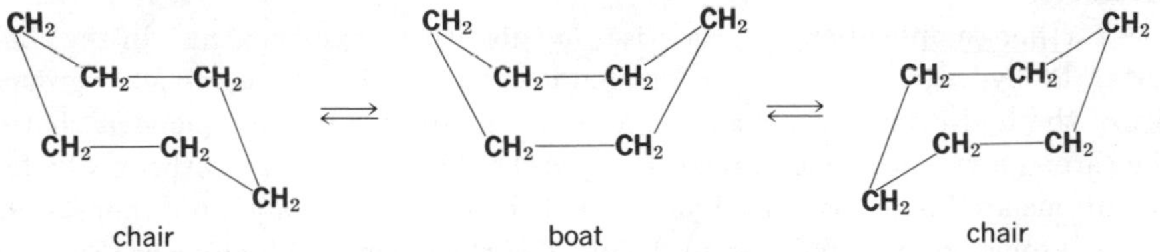

Fig. 2-7. Three nonplanar conformations for the carbon atoms in cyclohexane. Cyclohexane is predominantly a mixture of the two chair forms, which are in rapid equilibrium with each other.

because they look somewhat like chairs, are called *chair conformations* of cyclo-hexane. The third form is called a *boat conformation,* because of the obvious resemblance. All three conformations may be interconverted readily without breaking any of the bonds in the molecule; they cannot be separated from one another. The two chair forms, which are of the same energy, are more stable than the boat form; therefore, cyclohexane is essentially a *flexible nonplanar chair.* The boat form serves as an intermediate in the conversion of one chair form to the other.

Since cyclohexane rings form readily and are widely distributed throughout nature, it is of value to examine these conformations more carefully. It is evident from what we have already noted about conformations that the chair form of cyclohexane has greater stability than the boat form. Newman projections looking end-on at the ring (from the bow of the boat and the foot of the chair) may be seen in Fig. 2-8. Notice that in the boat form, the two CH_2 groups along the "gun-wales" are in the energetically unfavorable *eclipsed* conformation in which the hydrogen atoms are directly opposite one another. Sixty-degree rotation about the

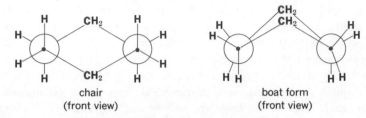

chair
(front view)

boat form
(front view)

Fig. 2-8. In the chair form of a cyclohexane ring, all C—C bonds are in the energetically favorable, staggered form; in the boat form there are opposed conformations, which are energetically unfavorable.

carbon–carbon bonds on the two sides converts this into either of the two more stable chair forms, in which the groups are *staggered* (compare with the discussion of Fig. 1-17). The chair form of cyclohexane is highly symmetrical, with each CH_2 group staggered in relation to its neighbors; as a consequence, this form is more favorable.

A further complication of form arises in substituted cyclohexanes. In the chair form, the hydrogen atoms can be divided into two distinct nonequivalent groups. Six of the hydrogen atoms make up a belt, roughly in the same plane as that of the carbon atoms; these are called the *equatorial* hydrogens. The other six hydrogen atoms are known as *axial* hydrogens, because the bonds joining them to the carbon atoms are perpendicular to the plane of the equatorial hydrogens (Fig. 2-9). When one chair form of cyclohexane converts into the other chair form, the equatorial hydrogen atoms become axial, and vice versa. Thus, in cyclohexane itself, each hydrogen atom is axial half of the time (while the molecule is in

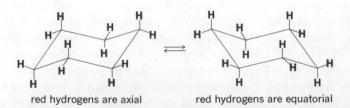

red hydrogens are axial

red hydrogens are equatorial

Fig. 2-9. The hydrogen atoms in the chair form of cyclohexane fall into two distinct groups, axial and equatorial. Those atoms that are axial in one chair form are equatorial in the other.

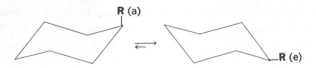

Fig. 2-10. A substituent attached to a cyclohexane will be more stable when it occupies an equatorial position.

one chair form) and equatorial the other half of the time (while the molecule is in the other chair form).

Suppose one of the hydrogen atoms in cyclohexane is replaced by a methyl group, or some other substituent. In one chair form this substituent will occupy one of the axial positions; in the other, it will occupy an equatorial position. This means *the two chair forms are no longer identical.* An axial substituent other than hydrogen obstructs other groups in the molecule, resulting in a relatively unfavorable conformation. When it occupies the equatorial position the substituent is as far away as possible from other groups, causing the chair form of the ring in which the substituent occupies the equatorial position to be favored at equilibrium. (Review Prob. 1-8 and its answer.) When the substituent is a methyl group, the equilibrium constant is about 10; that is, at any given time there are approximately ten times as many methylcyclohexane molecules in the conformation with the methyl group equatorial as in the conformation with the methyl group axial. As the size of the group increases, the preference for the equatorial position also increases.

Prob. 2-2. Despite the fact that the bond angles in a planar molecule of cyclopentane would be nearly normal, the molecule is slightly puckered, with one CH_2 bent out of the plane of the other four. Suggest an explanation for the fact that cyclopentane is not exactly planar.

LARGE RINGS

In theory at least, rings of any size may be prepared, and many compounds containing rings much larger than cyclohexane are known. Compounds with large rings occur naturally and some have considerable economic importance. An interesting example is muscone (Fig. 2-11), which contains a ring of fifteen carbon

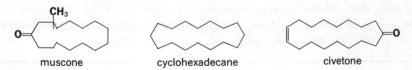

muscone   cyclohexadecane   civetone

Fig. 2-11. Examples of compounds containing large rings. The groups C=C and C=O will be discussed in Chapters 3 and 9, respectively. Civetone is from the civet cat and, like muscone, is also used in perfumes.

atoms. This compound is obtained from a small gland of the Himalayan male musk deer, and is an attractant for the female of the species. It is also the base of many expensive perfumes. In large amounts it has a powerful, disagreeable odor, but when sufficiently diluted it appears to elicit the same response from the human male toward the human female that it does from the female musk deer toward the male of her species. Stimulated by the economic advantage of obtaining an improved and less expensive substitute for muscone, many chemists have prepared a number of large-ring compounds and studied their properties.

UNUSUAL RING SYSTEMS

Rings both large and small have always fascinated organic chemists and inspired them to produce some of their most unusual synthetic efforts. When two rings share a single carbon atom, the resulting molecule is called a *spiro* compound. An extreme example is spiropentane; the angle strain is enormous, but the molecule is quite stable. Although organic chemists have dreamed for decades of preparing a compound with two interlocking rings, only recently have they synthesized the first examples. There seems little danger that chemists will run out of fascinating molecules to synthesize. Already they are giving thought to the preparation of rings with knots and to the synthesis of the compound resembling the Olympic symbol (Fig. 2-12).

spiropentane

catenane

Fig. 2-12. Two known and two unknown ring compounds. Spiropentane and an interlocking ring compound called a catenane have been prepared, but the knotted ring and the Olympic compound remain for the future.

FUSED-RING COMPOUNDS

If two adjacent carbon atoms are shared by two rings, the molecule is said to contain *fused rings*. The most important examples occur in the cyclohexane series. Decalin, for example, contains two fused six-membered rings and may exist in both *cis* and *trans* forms. These two molecules are isomers, and one cannot be converted to the other without breaking carbon–carbon or carbon–hydrogen bonds. In both molecules the cyclohexane rings remain predominantly in the chair form. Many hormones have the complex fused-ring system shown in Fig. 2-13. These molecules, called *steroids,* are discussed in more detail in Chapter 15.

Prob. 2-3.   Basing your answers on our discussion of axial and equatorial substituents, explain why *trans*-decalin is more stable than *cis*-decalin.

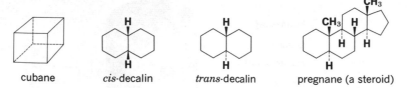

cubane   *cis*-decalin   *trans*-decalin   pregnane (a steroid)

Fig. 2-13. Rings joined along an edge are called *fused rings*. Cubane, which has six fused rings, was recently prepared. The compounds with two fused six-membered rings are *cis-* and *trans*-decalins. In a steroid, three six-membered rings and one five-membered ring are fused together consecutively.

Six-membered rings in their chair forms fuse together perfectly into a large number of strainless shapes. At a Congress of the International Union of Pure and Applied Chemistry in 1963, a prize was offered for the first synthesis of the cage-like molecule congressane; its preparation was announced recently, although in only 0.3% yield. If this molecule were elaborated by further fusions in all directions, progressively fewer and fewer hydrogen atoms would remain, and eventually pure carbon, in the form of *diamond,* would be left (Fig. 2-14). The great hardness and stability of diamond are accounted for by the fusing of carbon atoms into an infinite number of cyclohexane rings, all in stable chair form.

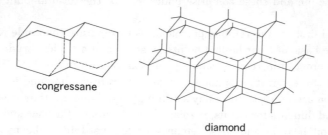

congressane

diamond

Fig. 2-14. Six-membered rings may be fused together in more than one dimension. Fourteen carbons are fitted together into a strainless cage in congressane. In diamond, fused six-membered rings continue in all directions.

Prob. 2-4. Adamantane ($C_{10}H_{16}$) is a very stable hydrocarbon first isolated from petroleum. In two dimensions its structure is ⬡⬡. Draw its three-dimensional structure and show its relationship to the diamond structure.

PETROLEUM

We have mentioned that the major source of alkanes, both acyclic and cyclic, is petroleum. Natural petroleum occurs beneath vast regions of the earth's surface and is generally believed to result from millions of years of decomposition of

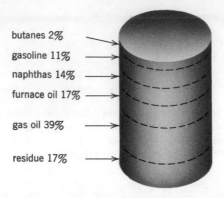

butanes 2%
gasoline 11%
naphthas 14%
furnace oil 17%
gas oil 39%
residue 17%

Fig. 2-15. The composition, in percentage of volume, of a West Texas crude oil.

marine plants and animals. Crude petroleum consists of a complex mixture of compounds, mainly hydrocarbons, but also of smaller amounts of organic molecules containing oxygen, sulfur, nitrogen, and even metals. The hydrocarbon content of petroleum may vary from as high as 97 to 98% in some Pennsylvania crude oil to as low as 50% for some Mexican and Southern oils. A recent compilation lists over 200 different hydrocarbons that have been isolated and characterized from a particular crude oil, and these comprise under 50% of the total amount of material present.

The usual first step in refining petroleum is to separate the crude oil into fractions on the basis of their boiling points. Fractions of a typical crude petroleum, arranged in order of increasing boiling point, can be seen in Fig. 2-15. The gasoline obtained in this separation is known as *straight-run* gasoline and is of too low a quality to be used directly in today's automobiles. The naphthas yield kerosene, solvents, and diluents for paints, varnishes, and lacquers. Furnace and gas oils are burned in oil heaters and diesel engines or are used to make more gasoline. The residues furnish a great variety of common products, ranging from waxes, mineral oils, and paraffin to asphalt for paving.

Straight-run gasoline contains a large number of different alkanes and other compounds, the exact mixture being dependent upon the source. Table 2-1 contains

Table 2-1. Per Cent (by Volume) of Various Hydrocarbon Types in a Fraction, Boiling from 40 to 102°, of Straight-Run Gasoline from Three Sources

Gasoline source	Branched alkanes	*n*-Alkanes	Cyclopentanes	Cyclohexanes
Oklahoma	36	21	23	20
Michigan	63	13	8	16
Texas	10	62	8	20

a comparison of the amounts of normal, branched, and cyclic alkanes in gasolines derived from some typical petroleum sources. The usual straight-run gasoline fraction encompasses hydrocarbons in the C_4 to C_{12} range. In this range there are 661 possible alkanes and 3,839 possible alkenes (a class of compounds discussed in Chapter 3), as well as a large number of aromatic compounds (Chapter 5). Because of this possible mixture, it is understandable that no single formulation for gasoline is achievable.

The quality of a gasoline is measured by its octane number. In an internal combustion engine like that in a modern automobile, a mixture of air and vaporized gasoline is drawn into the cylinder on the downstroke of the piston; this mixture is compressed by the piston on its upstroke and is then ignited by a spark from the spark plug. A high-octane gasoline will burn quickly and smoothly, giving a surge of power to the piston, forcing it down and into its next stroke. A low-octane gasoline, on the other hand, will explode, setting up a shock wave, which batters against the piston and cylinder walls and gives rise to the familiar "knocking" sound.

Alkanes vary greatly in their ability to burn in an engine without knocking. The *octane ratings* of a number of alkanes are presented in Table 2-2. These are relative values, determined under carefully defined engine conditions. It was discovered early that 2,2,4-trimethylpentane (called industrially "isooctane") caused little knocking, whereas *n*-heptane caused a great deal. A scale was therefore devised on which the octane rating of any gasoline or hydrocarbon was defined as being equal to the proportion of isooctane in an isooctane-*n*-heptane mixture that knocked under the same conditions. Methylcyclohexane, for example, knocks under the same conditions as a mixture of 75% isooctane and 25% *n*-heptane, and hence has an octane rating of 75.

Straight-run gasoline often contains a high percentage of *n*-alkanes, which makes its octane number low (typically around 70). In addition, the gasoline fraction amounts to only a relatively small percentage of the crude oil. Yet gasoline, along with fuel oil for heating, makes up the major market for petroleum. To solve the twin problems of low quality and low quantity, the petroleum industry began early in its development to study ways by which the higher-boiling components of petroleum could be converted to gasoline.

Table 2-2.   Octane Ratings of Some Hydrocarbons

Hydrocarbon	Octane number
n-heptane	0
2-methylhexane	42
methylcyclohexane	75
2,3-dimethylpentane	91
2,2,4-trimethylpentane (isooctane)	100

CRACKING PETROLEUM INTO GASOLINE

The industry found its solution in a process called "cracking." This process breaks large complex hydrocarbons into lighter ones through the application of heat and, generally, pressure. The first method used was *thermal cracking*. In this method the large alkane molecules are heated to temperatures near 700° until they split apart into smaller molecules. A great deal more gasoline thus becomes available, but, unfortunately, as thermal cracking leads primarily to *n*-alkanes, the octane number of gasoline from this source is not high. The low-octane problem was solved by the introduction of *catalytic cracking*. In this method, gas oils are mixed with a catalyst and heated to 400–550°, which cracks them to gasoline and at the same time causes the normal paraffins to rearrange to branched isomers. The octane rating of gasoline from this latter cracking is therefore higher than that of either straight-run gasoline or gasoline from thermal cracking (Table 2-3).

Table 2-3. The Composition of the Hexanes from Gasoline of Different Sources

Components	Catalytic gasoline	Thermal gasoline	Straight-run gasoline
n-hexanes	9%	63%	51%
branched hexanes	91	37	49
	100%	100%	100%

The process of catalytic cracking also produces hydrocarbons whose boiling points are too low for them to find much use in gasoline; these derivatives of butane, propane, and ethane are not wasted, however. Instead, some of them are *reformed* into higher molecular weight compounds (see Chapter 3) for inclusion in gasoline, while others are converted into a variety of commercial chemicals.

The octane number of a gasoline may be raised by increasing the quality of the hydrocarbons contained, or by including any one of a number of antiknock agents. Tetraethyllead (TEL) is the antiknock agent most commonly employed (Fig. 2-16).

$$4C_2H_5Cl + 4PbNa \longrightarrow Pb(C_2H_5)_4 + 4NaCl + 3Pb$$
ethyl chloride   tetraethyllead

Fig. 2-16. Tetraethyllead (TEL) is produced from ethyl chloride and a lead-sodium alloy.

The inclusion of as little as 3 ml of a TEL solution is sufficient to increase the octane rating of a gallon of typical straight-run gasoline from 70 to 84. The ethyl fluid used in modern gasoline contains about 61% tetraethyllead, 37% of a mixture of 1,2-dibromo- and 1,2-dichloroethanes, and 2% of a dye and impurities. The additive TEL moderates the combustion of the gasoline-air mixture and helps prevent knocking. In the process, the TEL burns and lead salts are formed. The chloro- and bromoethanes furnish halogen atoms for the formation of lead halides, which evaporate in the exhaust and pollute the air! In the absence of these additives, the cylinders of the engine would become coated with nonvolatile lead salts.

Gasoline is a carefully blended product. Although pure isooctane would make a 100-octane gasoline, it would be nearly useless in an automobile because the engine would never start without some very low-boiling components. The composition of gasoline must change with the season and with the altitude. Therefore, modern gasoline contains many additives—from "deicers" to dyes that improve the aesthetic appeal of the fluid.

OTHER PETROLEUM PRODUCTS

Kerosene is a petroleum fraction boiling approximately from 175 to 275° and is composed mainly of C_{10} to C_{14} hydrocarbons. The demand for kerosene to be used in lamps and heaters caused the original growth of the petroleum industry. However, the greatest demand for kerosene today is for use in jet fuel. Since a jet engine is quite different from an internal combustion engine, different hydrocarbon mixtures are required; curiously, *n*-alkanes give good burning properties.

Diesel oil is obtained from the petroleum fraction boiling slightly higher than kerosene. Like jet engines, diesel engines function best with *n*-alkanes. In diesel engines, *n*-hexadecane (cetane) is assigned a performance value of 100 and other compounds are given a cetane number.

Lube oil, or lubricating oil, is obtained from the vacuum distillation of petroleum. Like petroleum, it consists of a complex mixture of compounds, largely aromatic hydrocarbons such as those discussed in Chapter 5.

Mineral oil is a highly refined gas oil used as a solvent for certain drugs and occasionally as a mild laxative.

Petroleum waxes are obtained from the undistilled residue of fractionation. These are generally C_{22} to C_{32} hydrocarbons. When highly refined, they are referred to as *paraffin* and are used for candles, wax paper, and especially for milk carton coatings. Some crude oils give large amounts of *asphaltic* residue. Half or more of this asphalt is used for paving and the rest for roofing, paints and varnishes, brake linings, battery boxes, and similar purposes.

When certain petroleum oils are emulsified with water they form good insecticides. These insecticides are effectively used as fruit tree sprays against insects such as scale insects, red spiders, and aphids. They are also effective against mosquito larvae. The petroleum fraction that boils at about 300° at 40 mm pressure seems to have the maximum toxicity. Petroleum hydrocarbons also make good solvents for DDT, pyrethrum, and other insecticides.

Prob. 2-5. Draw structural formulas for the following compounds:
  (a) *trans*-1,2-dimethylcyclobutane
  (b) 1,1-dichlorocyclopropane
  (c) cyclodecane
  (d) cycloheptyl bromide
  (e) *cis*-1-ethyl-3-isopropylcyclohexane. (Approximate the cyclohexane ring as a planar hexagon.)

Prob. 2-6. Name each of the following compounds:

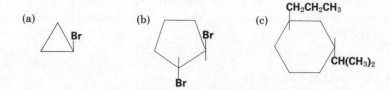

Prob. 2-7. Draw the two chair forms of *trans*-1,4-dimethylcyclohexane. Which form would you expect to be more stable? Now draw the two chair forms for the *cis* isomer. Is there any difference in stability between the two chair forms of this molecule?

CHAPTER

UNSATURATED HYDROCARBONS:
ALKENES, ALKYNES, DIENES

Hydrocarbons may be saturated or unsaturated. The saturated kinds, the alkanes and cycloalkanes, do not typify most organic molecules because they are relatively inert toward chemical reagents. Therefore, we will now discuss some of the unsaturated compounds and observe how the presence of functional groups influences the chemical properties of organic compounds.

Among the alkanes, as we noted, the tetravalence of carbon is demonstrated by the formation of a single bond to each of four different atoms. However, carbon is capable of forming more than just one bond to another atom. In some compounds, carbon forms a double bond with a second carbon atom, and the result is known as an *alkene*. In other instances, a carbon atom forms a triple bond with another carbon, producing a compound called an *alkyne*. Bonds of both kinds may also form between an atom of carbon and other atoms such as oxygen or nitrogen. The general idea of multiple bonding should be familiar to anyone who has studied general chemistry, who will recall that the nitrogen molecule, N_2, contains a triple bond.

Simple alkenes have common names, such as ethylene and propylene, but most of the group are named by the IUPAC system. Similarly, among the alkynes the simplest goes by the common name acetylene, yet other alkynes, like the alkenes, derive their names from the IUPAC system.

Concerning nomenclature, the rule establishing the root names must be revised for compounds that contain functional groups to: "The longest continuous chain of carbon atoms *containing the functional groups* is located and named, affixing the *characteristic endings* of the functional groups." The rule pertaining to the numbering of the chain must be revised to: "The parent chain is numbered from

Table 3-1.   Examples of Nomenclature of Alkenes and Alkynes.

Compound	Common name	IUPAC name
$H_2C\!\!=\!\!CH_2$	ethylene	ethene
$CH_3\!\!-\!\!CH\!\!=\!\!CH_2$	propylene	propene
$CH_3\!\!-\!\!CH_2\!\!-\!\!CH\!\!=\!\!CH_2$	(α-butylene)	1-butene
$CH_3\!\!-\!\!CH\!\!=\!\!CH\!\!-\!\!CH_3$	(β-butylene)	2-butene
$CH_3\!\!-\!\!\underset{\underset{\displaystyle CH_3}{\mid}}{C}\!\!=\!\!CH_2$	isobutylene	(2-methylpropene)
$CH_3\!\!-\!\!\underset{\underset{\displaystyle CH_3}{\mid}}{CH}\!\!-\!\!CH\!\!=\!\!CH_2$	isopropylethylene	3-methyl-1-butene
$HC\!\!\equiv\!\!CH$	acetylene	(ethyne)
$CH_3\!\!-\!\!CH_2\!\!-\!\!C\!\!\equiv\!\!C\!\!-\!\!CH_3$	(methylethylacetylene)	2-pentyne
$CH_2\!\!=\!\!CH\!\!-\!\!\underset{\underset{\displaystyle CH_2\!\!-\!\!CH_2\!\!-\!\!CH_3}{\mid}}{CH}\!\!-\!\!C\!\!\equiv\!\!CH$		3-n-propyl-1-penten-4-yne

that end which gives the carbon atom carrying the principal functional group its smallest number." Table 3-1 contains the names of a number of unsaturated hydrocarbons.

We have already seen that the ending for saturated hydrocarbons is *-ane,* whereas the endings for alkenes and alkynes are *-ene* and *-yne,* respectively. An example of the numbering convention is 1-butene. Note that for consecutive numbers, only the lower-numbered carbon need be indicated; also note that the name of this compound is *not* 3-butene. For a step-by-step introduction to the nomenclature of the alkenes and alkynes the reader should answer Questions 13 through 27 in the Appendix.

Prob. 3-1.   What is wrong with each of the following names? Write correct names for these molecules.

    (a) 2-*n*-propyl-1-butene
    (b) 6-methylcyclohexene
    (c) 3-methyl-2-butene

ETHYLENE AND ACETYLENE

Ethylene (C_2H_4), the simplest of the alkenes, is a gas with a lower boiling point than ethane. It is formed in large amounts during the cracking of petroleum and is such an important and common industrial chemical that in many parts of the United States a company desiring to use it as a raw material simply hooks up to an ethylene pipeline, much as a householder hooks up to a natural gas line.

Acetylene (C_2H_2) is a gas used widely in industry both as a fuel and as a chemical for conversion to other compounds. Acetylene is familiar to some as the fuel in a welder's torch and to others as the illuminating gas once widely used in miners' and campers' lanterns. Today it is principally used as an intermediate in the syn-

$$H-C\equiv C-H \xrightarrow[\text{Pd}]{H_2} \underset{H}{\overset{H}{C}}=\underset{H}{\overset{H}{C}} \xrightarrow[\text{Pd}]{H_2} H-\underset{\underset{H}{|}}{\overset{\overset{H}{|}}{C}}-\underset{\underset{H}{|}}{\overset{\overset{H}{|}}{C}}-H$$

acetylene	ethylene	ethane
(ethyne)	(ethene)	

Fig. 3-1. Alkynes (like acetylene) and alkenes (like ethylene) are both *unsaturated* toward hydrogen, while alkanes are saturated hydrocarbons. Note that each carbon atom maintains its tetravalence throughout these transformations.

theses of many industrially important compounds. A number of these are prepared by addition reactions, as we shall see later. Considering the reaction sequence in Fig. 3-1 will perhaps make interrelationship among alkynes, alkenes, and alkanes clearest. The reader can see that an alkyne may be converted to an alkene by adding one molecule of hydrogen in the presence of a catalyst; an alkene may be converted to an alkane by the addition of a second molecule of hydrogen. Alkanes are said to be saturated because they do not react with hydrogen; on the other hand, alkenes and alkynes both react with hydrogen and are often called unsaturated hydrocarbons.

SOURCES OF OLEFINS AND ACETYLENES

A number of compounds that contain double and triple bonds as their only functional groups occur naturally, especially among the compounds known as terpenes, which are found in many plants and trees (Fig. 3-2). Olefins are important indus-

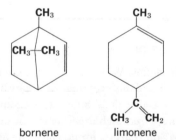

bornene	limonene

Fig. 3-2. Two examples of naturally occurring alkenes belonging to the class of chemicals known as *terpenes*. Limonene occurs in the skins of lemons and oranges.

trial chemicals; an enormous quantity of them is prepared each year, especially in the petroleum industry. They impart especially good burning properties to gasoline because they cause little knocking in an internal combustion engine. Some of them appear in crude petroleum; however, to increase the alkene content and the amount of gasoline, the petroleum industry employs the cracking process. This process, mentioned briefly in Chapter 2, is one of the principal sources of simple

$$C_{12}H_{26} \xrightarrow{700°} C_{10}H_{22} + H_2C{=}CH_2 + C_9H_{20} + CH_3CH{=}CH_2, \text{ etc.}$$
$$\text{ethylene} \qquad\qquad \text{propylene}$$

$$CaO + 3C \xrightarrow[\text{furnace}]{\text{electric}} CaC_2 + CO$$
$$\text{lime} \quad \text{coke} \qquad\qquad \text{calcium}$$
$$\text{carbide}$$

$$CaC_2 + 2H_2O \longrightarrow Ca(OH)_2 + HC{\equiv}CH$$
$$\text{acetylene}$$

Fig. 3-3. The chief industrial source of small olefins is cracking, employed in the petroleum industry. One of the main sources of acetylene is calcium carbide, produced by passing an electric current through a mixture of lime and coke.

olefins, which are included in the mixture of smaller molecules splitting apart from the large saturated hydrocarbons (Fig. 3-3).

Prob. 3-2. Draw a three-dimensional representation of the bornene molecule. What conformation will the cyclohexene ring in this compound have?

Although acetylene is the only commercially important alkyne, it is of enormous industrial significance. Acetylene may be generated from calcium carbide and water or may be formed at high temperatures and pressures from methane or ethane. The availability of these two processes has made acetylene one of the cheaper organic raw materials.

Prob. 3-3. Can you suggest a reason why acetylene is produced in large quantities near Buffalo, N.Y.?

GEOMETRICAL ISOMERS OF OLEFINS

Alkenes are also known as olefins. We are able to draw conclusions about the three-dimensional structure of the olefin ethylene (ethene) by using the same process which enabled us to draw conclusions about the alkane ethane: the number of dichloroethenes. There are *three* dichloroethenes. In one of these isomers, both chlorine atoms are on the same carbon atom, since the addition of hydrogen yields 1,1-dichloroethane; because the other two isomers are both reducible to 1,2-dichloroethane, their chlorine atoms must be on different carbon atoms. The existence of two different 1,2-dichloroethenes indicates rigidity in the C—C double bond; that is, free rotation about this bond cannot occur (Fig. 3-4).

The isomer whose two chlorine atoms lie on the same side of the double bond is known as a *cis* isomer; the isomer whose chlorine atoms are on opposite sides of the bond is known as a *trans* isomer. We encountered this type of isomerism, which depends only on the spatial arrangement of the atoms, in the cycloalkanes. It is called *stereoisomerism*, to distinguish it from *structural isomerism* in which the order of the bonding of the atoms differs. Thus, 1,1-dichloroethene is a

1-chloroethene
(vinyl chloride)

1,1-dichloroethene
(vinylidene chloride)

trans-1,2-
dichloroethene

cis-1,2-
dichloroethene

Fig. 3-4. The one mono- and three dichloroethenes. The existence of two 1,2-dichloroethenes indicates that there must be restricted rotation about a double bond.

structural isomer of both *cis*- and *trans*-1,2-dichloroethenes; the latter two are geometrical isomers of each other.

Prob. 3-4. Explain why a double bond in a six-membered ring must always have the *cis* geometry and never the *trans*.

Many compounds that contain double bonds can exhibit geometrical isomerism. For example, there are four butylenes: isobutylene (2-methylpropene), 1-butene, and *cis*- and *trans*-2-butenes (Fig. 3-5). The two latter compounds are geometrical

isobutylene
b.p. −7°C

1-butene
b.p. −6°C

cis-2-butene
b.p. +4°C

trans-2-butene
b.p. +1°C

Fig. 3-5. The four isomeric butylenes. Isobutylene and 1-butene are *structural isomers* of the *cis*- and *trans*-2-butenes, which are *geometrical isomers* of one another.

isomers of each other, and both are structural isomers of isobutylene and 1-butene. Like structural isomers, geometrical isomers have different physical and chemical properties.

Prob. 3-5. Draw all six structurally and geometrically isomeric alkenes having the molecular formula C_5H_{10}.

BONDING IN ALKENES AND ALKYNES

To understand more clearly the structure and reactivity of alkenes and acetylenes, it is helpful to have some conception of their bonding. The conception must be somewhat conjectural, but whether or not it corresponds to physical reality, it is valuable because it makes many otherwise isolated facts easier to remember.

In Chapter 1 we introduced the idea of a hybrid orbital (see Fig. 1-12) to account for the tetrahedal bonding among alkanes. This was an sp^3 orbital, a fourth of whose character was s and three-fourths of which was p. In the bonding of the alkenes and alkynes two other hybrid orbitals are believed to be involved:

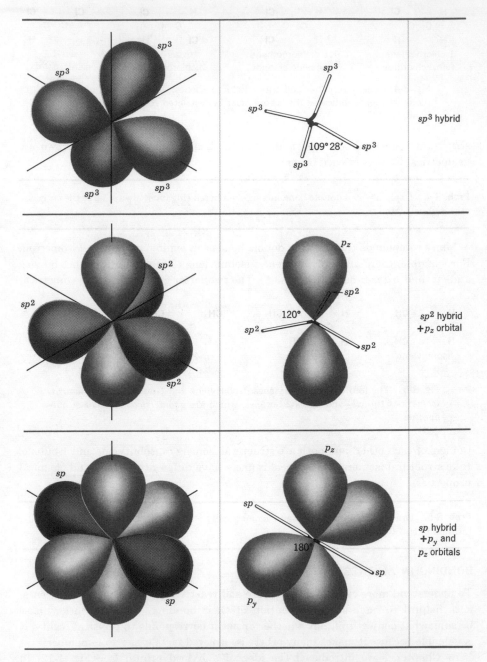

Fig. 3-6. The three important hybrids of 2s and 2p orbitals. Only the sp^3 hybrids are used in saturated molecules; the sp^2 hybrids are found in alkenes, and sp hybrids in alkynes.

the sp^2 in alkenes and the sp in alkynes. The sp^2 is comprised of one-third s and two-thirds p. Since a carbon atom has one $2s$ and three $2p$ orbitals available for bonding, three sp^2 orbitals can be formed by blending the $2s$ orbital with two of the $2p$ orbitals, say the $2p_x$ and $2p_y$ orbitals. All three sp^2 orbitals lie in a single plane and point to the corners of an equilateral triangle. The third $2p$ orbital (the $2p_z$) will remain. These orbitals, which constitute the bonding of alkenes, may be seen in Fig. 3-6.

The hybrid orbital involved in the bonding of alkynes, the sp hybrid, is composed of s and p orbitals in equal parts. Two such hybrids are available for two electrons of the carbon atom, and the resulting sp orbitals appear in linear configuration. The axes of the remaining p orbitals which are not hybridized lie at right angles both to the axis of the sp orbitals and to each other. Along with the sp^3 and sp^2 hybrids discussed earlier, the sp hybrid orbital is shown in Fig. 3-6.

In ethylene, two carbon atoms containing sp^2 orbitals are joined to form two bonds. One of them, the σ bond, results from an end-to-end overlap of two sp^2 orbitals; this bond, much like the bond found in ethane, is symmetrical about the carbon–carbon axis. The other bond, a π (pi) bond, is formed by side-to-side overlap of the two p_z orbitals. These π bond electrons lie above and below the plane containing the two carbon and four hydrogen atoms (Fig. 3-7).

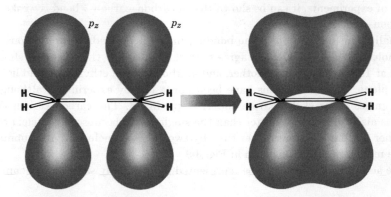

Fig. 3-7. In ethylene, the double bond consists of the end-on overlap of sp^2 hybrid orbitals (to form a σ bond) plus the edgewise overlap of the p_z orbitals to form a π bond.

This scheme has the advantage of making certain important properties of alkenes easily understood. First, the greater reactivity of alkenes as compared with alkanes can be ascribed to the pair of electrons in the π orbital. These electrons, which are relatively far from the nuclei, have no counterpart in the structure of alkanes. Second, the concept of a π bond also accounts for the existence of *cis* and *trans* isomers among alkenes. Notice in Fig. 3-8, that overlap of two p orbitals to form a π bond can occur only if the orbitals are parallel. Rotating one CH_2 group 90° completely destroys this overlap. Alkenes resist this rotation, and *cis*

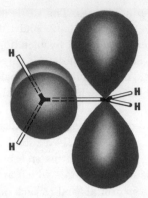

Fig. 3-8. The π bond is destroyed if the two double bonds are twisted about their axis. As a consequence, there is no freedom of rotation about double bonds.

and *trans* forms have separate existences. It is possible, by using sufficient energy (for instance, by heating) to convert a *cis* form to a *trans* form, or vice versa. A great deal of energy is required, but not so much as would be needed to break the whole molecule apart; only the π bond need be broken. From this and other types of experiments, it can be shown that a carbon–carbon π bond is weaker than a carbon–carbon σ bond.

Finally, this conception of the bonding in ethylene leads to predictions about the molecule's geometry which agree with the facts: The three orbitals should be found at 120° angles to one another, and all the atoms in ethylene should lie in the same plane. Both predictions have been borne out by experiment, although the bond angles differ slightly from the 120° predicted. The carbon–carbon double bond is also appreciably shorter than the single bond, because the nuclei are held together by four electrons rather than by two. These conclusions are summarized in the models of ethylene shown in Fig. 3-9.

The acetylene molecule can be represented in an equally satisfactory manner by

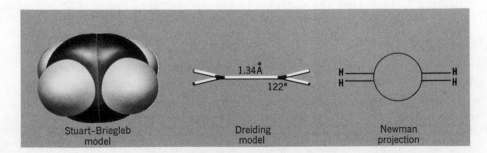

Fig. 3-9. Three views of ethylene, showing bond angles and geometry. Compare carefully with the models of ethane in Fig. 1-15.

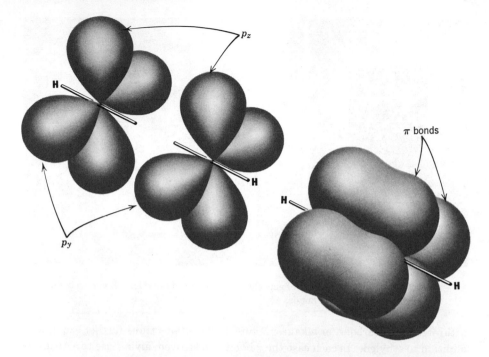

Fig. 3-10. In acetylene the triple bond consists of the end-on overlap of *sp* hybrid orbitals plus the edgewise overlap of both p_y and p_z orbitals to form two π bonds.

using *sp* hybrid orbitals of the carbon atom. Acetylene is known to be linear, and two π bonds form from the overlap of the two perpendicular unhybridized *p* orbitals (Fig. 3-10). These two π bonds are the source of reactivity in alkynes, just as the single π bond is the reactive center in alkenes.

Figure 3-11 shows scale models of acetylene. Note that a triple bond is shorter than a double bond, and that bond length decreases less from a double to a triple bond than from a single to a double bond. This is shown graphically in the figure where *bond order* (1 = single, 2 = double, 3 = triple bond) is plotted against bond length.

Prob. 3-6. Making use of the geometry of double and triple bonds given in Figs. 3-9 and 3-11, suggest an explanation for the fact that double bonds often occur within stable six-membered rings, but triple bonds never do.

ADDITION TO ALKENES AND ALKYNES

The most characteristic way in which alkenes and alkynes react is by addition to their multiple bonds. We have seen that adding hydrogen to these bonds yields

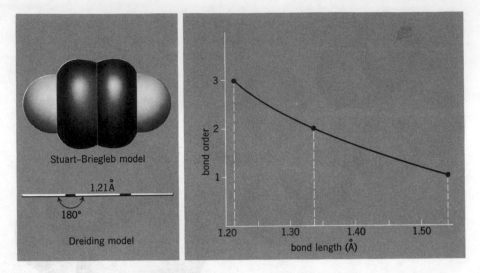

Stuart–Briegleb model

1.21Å

180°

Dreiding model

Fig. 3-11. Two scale models of acetylene, and a plot of bond length versus bond order for carbon–carbon bonds.

saturated hydrocarbons, or alkanes. Figure 3-12 contains three further examples of addition to ethylene. In each case the π bond is destroyed, giving rise to a saturated molecule. We see that π bonds react with acids, but ordinarily not with basic reagents. Through the orbital conceptualization of bonding which we have been developing, we can understand these reactions and account for the reactivity of double bonds with acids but not with bases.

As defined by Lewis, an acid is a reagent that seeks electrons; because of its electron-seeking character, it is considered *electrophilic*. A base, on the other hand, is a reagent that donates electrons; it thus seeks a nucleus or is *nucleophilic*. The simplest Lewis acid is the proton, which seeks to share a pair of electrons in order to complete its outer shell. Because a carbon–carbon double bond is rich in electrons, it is not surprising that an electron-seeking acid should react with it. However, there is little tendency for a base, which already has a surplus of electrons, to react with the electrons of a carbon–carbon double bond. A pictorial and

$$CH_2{=}CH_2 + HCl \longrightarrow H{-}CH_2{-}CH_2{-}Cl$$
chloroethane

$$CH_2{=}CH_2 + HOSO_3H \longrightarrow H{-}CH_2{-}CH_2{-}OSO_3H$$
(H_2SO_4)   ethyl sulfate

$$CH_2{=}CH_2 + Br{-}Br \longrightarrow Br{-}CH_2{-}CH_2{-}Br$$
1,2-dibromoethane

$$CH_2{=}CH_2 + NaOH \longrightarrow \text{No Reaction}$$

Fig. 3-12. Three addition reactions of ethylene. Basic reagents like sodium hydroxide do not usually react with double bonds.

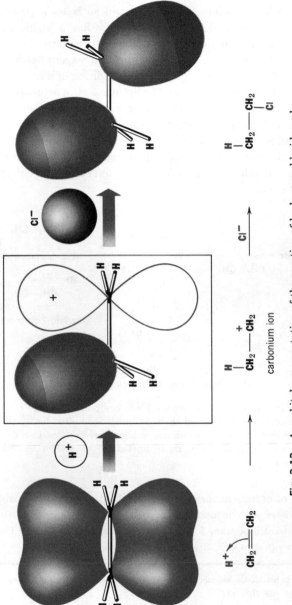

Fig. 3-13. An orbital representation of the reaction of hydrogen chloride and ethylene. Filled orbitals are shaded, empty orbitals are unshaded.

51

schematic diagram of the steps involved in adding hydrogen chloride to a double bond can be seen in Fig. 3-13. Notice that the reaction takes place in steps: In the first step the proton adds to the double bond and siphons off electrons to create a carbon atom which is deficient in electrons and so bears a positive charge—the *carbonium ion;* in the second step the carbonium ion, a highly reactive species, quickly combines with a chloride ion to complete the reaction.

Although step-by-step addition of a highly ionized reagent like hydrogen chloride may seem reasonable, we might doubt that the addition of a molecule like bromine to a double bond takes place in steps. Nevertheless, the evidence for this type of reaction is compelling. One argument stems from the observation that if bromine is added to a double bond in a solution containing sodium chloride, some chloro–bromo compound is formed along with dibromide. The experiment is summarized in Fig. 3-14. If addition occurs in steps, the intermediate carbonium ion can combine with either bromide ion or chloride ion (from the sodium chloride) or, indeed, with any added anion.

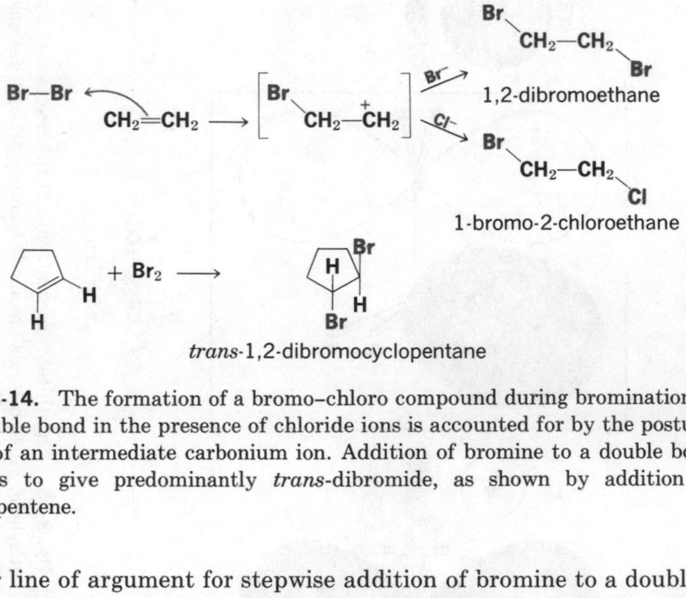

Fig. 3-14. The formation of a bromo–chloro compound during bromination of a double bond in the presence of chloride ions is accounted for by the postulation of an intermediate carbonium ion. Addition of bromine to a double bond occurs to give predominantly *trans*-dibromide, as shown by addition to cyclopentene.

Another line of argument for stepwise addition of bromine to a double bond is the stereochemistry of the addition. When bromine is added to cyclopentene, *trans*-1,2-dibromocyclopentane forms, and this can happen only if the two bromine atoms are not bonded to each other at the time of addition.

Prob. 3-7. Why is no 1,2-dichloroethane formed in the reaction of ethylene with bromine in the presence of sodium chloride?

If the two ends of a double bond are not the same, an unsymmetrical reagent like hydrogen chloride might combine with it in two different directions to produce

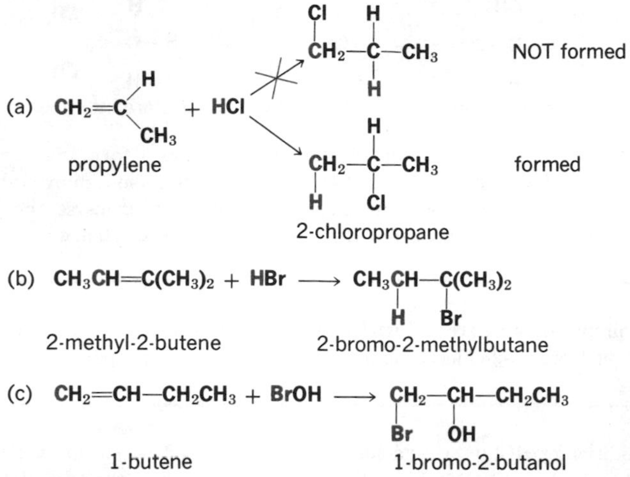

Fig. 3-15. In addition to a double bond, the positive part of the reagent (in red) adds to the carbon atom (in red) already bearing the greater number of hydrogen atoms.

two products. Actually, only one of the two possible products forms in almost all cases. This product is predicted by *Markownikoff's rule,* named after an eminent Russian organic chemist of the nineteenth century; the rule says that *the positive part of the reagent adds to that carbon atom of the double bond which has the greater number of hydrogen atoms* (Fig. 3-15). As applied to propylene, the positive part of the reagent (H$^+$) adds to the carbon atom of the double bond having two hydrogen atoms. Thus, 2-chloropropane forms.

Markownikoff's rule was developed long before scientists recognized that reagents added in steps to double bonds. Considering the rule in the light of present knowledge, we can see that the initial step determines the direction of addition. An example can be found in the addition of a proton to isobutylene. If the addition were to take place on C-2, a carbonium ion would form on C-1; this is called a *primary carbonium ion,* since it has only a single alkyl substituent. Addition of the proton to C-1, which is predicted by Markownikoff's rule, gives a *tertiary carbonium ion* bearing three alkyl groups. Tertiary carbonium ions are easier to form than primary carbonium ions, because the positive charge on the former can be stabilized by the electrons on the three surrounding carbon atoms, but the primary ion is surrounded by hydrogen atoms which have fewer electrons than alkyl groups. The alkyl groups are said to donate electrons to the electron-poor carbon atom, stabilizing its positive charge. *The ease of formation of carbonium ions is in this order: 3° easier than 2° easier than 1°* (Fig. 3-16). The carbonium ion intermediates play an important part in many organic reactions, and will be mentioned often in succeeding discussions.

$$
\underset{\text{1° carbonium ion}}{\overset{\displaystyle \underset{H}{\overset{CH_3}{\underset{|}{\overset{|}{{}^+C-C-CH_3}}}}}{}} \quad \overset{H^+}{\longleftarrow}\!\!\!\times\!\!\!\overset{}{} \quad \underset{\text{isobutylene}}{\overset{\displaystyle \overset{CH_3}{\underset{CH_3}{C=C}}}{}} \quad \overset{H^+}{\longrightarrow} \quad \underset{\text{3° carbonium ion}}{\overset{\displaystyle H-\overset{H}{\underset{H}{C}}-\overset{CH_3}{\underset{CH_3}{{}^+C}}}{}}
$$

Fig. 3-16. An acidic reagent adds to a double bond so as to form the more stable of the two possible carbonium ions. A tertiary carbonium ion is more stable than a primary one, because the attached alkyl groups help disperse the positive charge. The red "x" indicates that the reaction does not go that way.

Prob. 3-8. If propylene were treated with bromine in the presence of sodium chloride, would you expect to get 1-bromo-2-chloropropane or 1-chloro-2-bromopropane? Why?

Prob. 3-9. Addition of HCl or other acids to the salt shown proceeds in exactly the opposite direction to that predicted by Markownikoff's rule. Explain how the formulation of the rule in terms of intermediate carbonium ions allows one to account for this special case.

$$
HCl + CH_2=CH-\overset{+}{N}(CH_3)_3 \longrightarrow \underset{\underset{Cl\quad H}{|\quad\ |}}{CH_2-CH}-\overset{+}{N}(CH_3)_3
$$

In many respects alkynes react like alkenes. Acidic reagents like bromine and hydrogen bromide can be readily added to alkynes. In the first reaction an alkene forms, which then reacts further to yield a saturated product. Markownikoff's rule applies to alkynes as it does to alkenes (Fig. 3-17). The addition of acidic reagents to alkynes primarily gives a *trans* product, as happens with alkenes—although, surprisingly, this point has not been extensively investigated.

$$
R-C\equiv C-H \xrightarrow{\text{HBr}} \underset{Br}{\overset{R}{C}}=\underset{H}{\overset{H}{C}} \xrightarrow{\text{HBr}} R-\underset{\underset{Br}{|}}{\overset{\overset{Br}{|}}{C}}-\underset{\underset{H}{|}}{\overset{\overset{H}{|}}{C}}-H
$$

$$
R-C\equiv C-R' \xrightarrow{\text{Br}_2} \underset{Br}{\overset{R}{C}}=\underset{R'}{\overset{Br}{C}} \xrightarrow{\text{Br}_2} R-\underset{\underset{Br}{|}}{\overset{\overset{Br}{|}}{C}}-\underset{\underset{Br}{|}}{\overset{\overset{Br}{|}}{C}}-R'
$$

Fig. 3-17. Acidic reagents add to alkynes, obeying Markownikoff's rule.

Prob. 3-10. Alkenes usually undergo addition reactions more readily than acetylenes. In the manufacture of vinyl chloride by addition of hydrogen chloride to acetylene one worry is the further reaction of vinyl chloride with hydrogen chloride. In order to minimize this side reaction, should the reaction be carried out (a) with an excess of hydrogen chloride over acetylene, (b) with equal amounts of the two reagents, or (c) with an excess of acetylene?

CONJUGATED DOUBLE BONDS

Many molecules contain two or more double bonds, and are, accordingly, called *dienes, trienes,* etc. The IUPAC nomenclature of these compounds is presented in the Appendix, Questions 24 and 25. If the double bonds are separated by at least one saturated carbon atom, as in 1,4-pentadiene, the two have little effect on each other and react independently. Bonds of this type are said to be unconjugated, or isolated, double bonds (Fig. 3-18). When adjacent, as in 1,3-pentadiene, the

$$CH_2=CH-CH_2-CH=CH_2 \qquad CH_2=CH-CH=CH-CH_3$$
1,4-pentadiene   1,3-pentadiene
(*unconjugated*)   (*conjugated*)

Fig. 3-18. If double bonds are separated by one or more saturated carbon atoms, they are said to be *unconjugated*. If they are adjacent, in the sense that they are separated by only one single bond, they are said to be *conjugated*.

two double bonds are *conjugated* and interact, sometimes modifying the course of alkene reactions. As an example of this modification, addition reactions often occur at the *ends* of a conjugated system (Fig. 3-19). For instance, both 3-chloro-1-butene

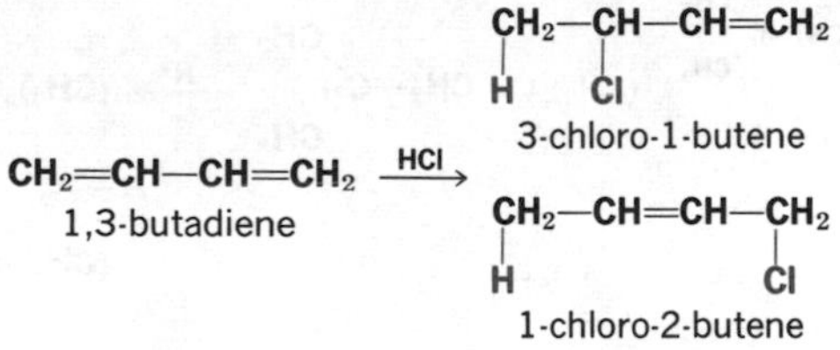

$$CH_2-CH-CH=CH_2$$
$$\quad\ \ | \quad\ |$$
$$\quad\ \ H \quad\ Cl$$
3-chloro-1-butene

$$CH_2=CH-CH=CH_2 \xrightarrow{\text{HCl}}$$
1,3-butadiene

$$CH_2-CH=CH-CH_2$$
$$\quad\ | \qquad\qquad\ |$$
$$\quad\ H \qquad\qquad Cl$$
1-chloro-2-butene

Fig. 3-19. Addition to conjugated double bonds may take place simultaneously in the normal manner and at the ends of the system.

and 1-chloro-2-butene form in the reaction of 1,3-butadiene with one molar equivalent of hydrogen chloride. The second product results from attack of the proton at C-1 and the chloride at C-4, while the double bond moves to the middle.

Prob. 3-11. What three products might you expect to obtain by the addition of one equivalent of hydrogen chloride to 1,3,5-hexatriene ($CH_2=CH-CH=CH-CH=CH_2$)?

SELF-ADDITION OF ISOBUTYLENE

Isobutylene (2-methylpropene) is an important product of the cracking process of petroleum. We have already seen that sulfuric acid adds to ethylene, and that this type of addition of acids to alkenes begins with the formation of a very reactive carbonium ion which then reacts with an anion. Similarly, the addition of an equi-molar quantity of sulfuric acid to isobutylene produces *tert*-butyl sulfate. The sulfate can be hydrolyzed to *tert*-butyl alcohol, a useful solvent (Fig. 3-20). Other useful products are obtained if only a small amount of sulfuric acid is present to serve as a catalyst.

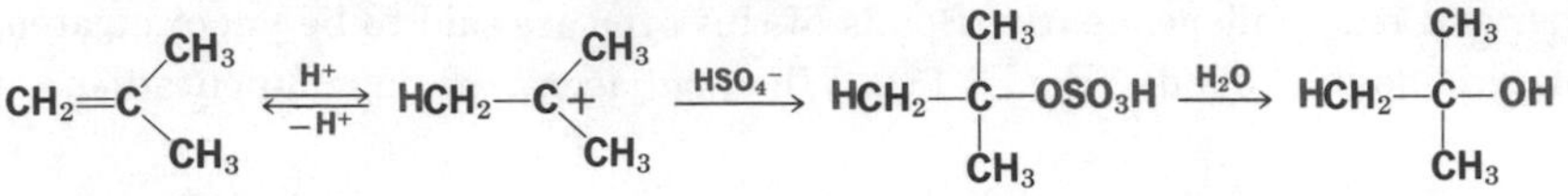

$$CH_2{=}C\overset{CH_3}{\underset{CH_3}{\Big|}} \underset{-H^+}{\overset{H^+}{\rightleftharpoons}} HCH_2{-}\overset{CH_3}{\underset{CH_3}{\overset{|}{\underset{|}{C}}}}{+} \overset{HSO_4{}^-}{\longrightarrow} HCH_2{-}\overset{CH_3}{\underset{CH_3}{\overset{|}{\underset{|}{C}}}}{-}OSO_3H \overset{H_2O}{\longrightarrow} HCH_2{-}\overset{CH_3}{\underset{CH_3}{\overset{|}{\underset{|}{C}}}}{-}OH$$

Fig. 3-20. Addition of sulfuric acid to a double bond followed by hydrolysis is a convenient method for the preparation of alcohols.

Under these conditions, the initially formed carbonium ion may not be able to find a sulfate anion with which to react. Instead, it is surrounded by molecules of isobutylene and reacts with the double bond of another isobutylene molecule. The *tert-butyl* carbonium ion initially formed thus functions as a Lewis acid, reacting with another molecule of alkene to give a new carbonium ion. In this addition Markownikoff's rule is obeyed, and the second carbonium ion formed is also tertiary (Fig. 3-21).

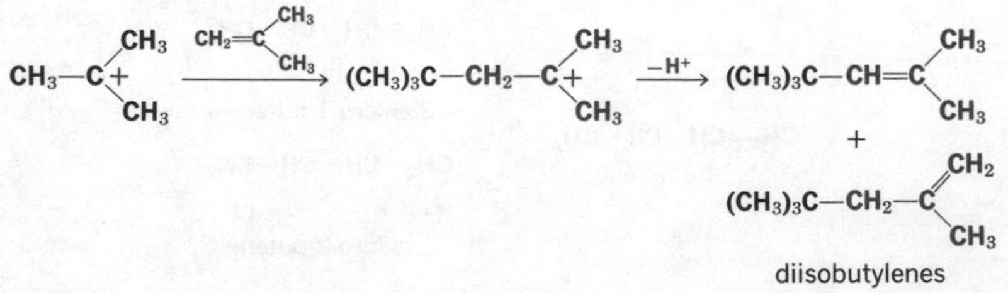

$$CH_3{-}\overset{CH_3}{\underset{CH_3}{\overset{|}{\underset{|}{C}}}}{+} \xrightarrow{CH_2{=}C\overset{CH_3}{\underset{CH_3}{}}} (CH_3)_3C{-}CH_2{-}\overset{CH_3}{\underset{CH_3}{\overset{|}{\underset{|}{C}}}}{+} \overset{-H^+}{\longrightarrow} (CH_3)_3C{-}CH{=}C\overset{CH_3}{\underset{CH_3}{}}$$

$$+$$

$$(CH_3)_3C{-}CH_2{-}C\overset{CH_2}{\underset{CH_3}{}}$$

diisobutylenes

Fig. 3-21. A carbonium ion, which is itself a Lewis acid, can add to a double bond, obeying Markownikoff's rule. Isobutylene can dimerize in the presence of a small amount of acid.

The new carbonium ion may do any of several things. It may react with a sul-fate anion or lose a proton to give a mixture of alkenes. In either event, eight-carbon compounds have been formed by the combination of two four-carbon com-pounds. The new ion may also react with a third molecule of isobutylene, to give a *third* carbonium ion which contains twelve carbon atoms. This latter ion can repeat the reactions of the second. In this way a whole series of compounds—principally alkenes and sulfates—can be prepared from isobutylene. In this reaction isobutylene is called a *monomer* (Greek *monos* = one, *meros* = part); diisobutylene, a mixture of two isomers, is called a dimer ($2 \times C_4H_8 = C_8H_{16}$), triisobutylene a trimer, etc. (Fig. 3-22). Similar monomers, dimers, trimers, tetramers, etc., are formed from propylene.

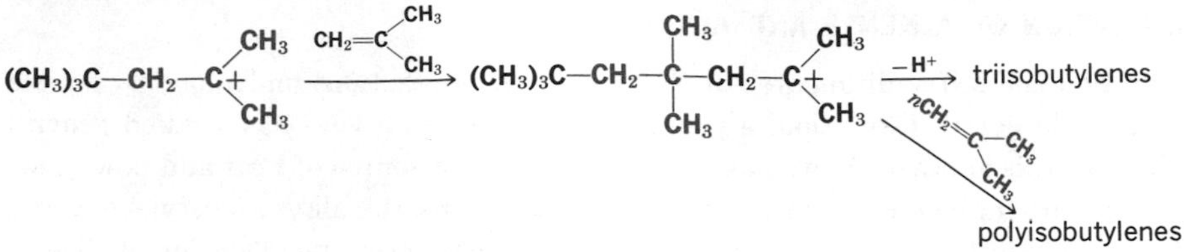

Fig. 3-22. Under the proper conditions the "self-addition" of isobutylene will continue, leading to trimers, tetramers, and eventually polymers.

Prob. 3-12. Give balanced equations for the conversion of triisobutylene (a mixture of two isomers) to tetraisobutylene (two isomers) in the presence of sulfuric acid catalyst. What are the IUPAC names of the two alkenes used as starting materials and the two products?

The products of the self-addition of isobutylene are valuable materials. Diisobutylene is used in gasoline and is also hydrogenated to 2,2,4-trimethylpentane, the standard hydrocarbon against which gasoline performance is rated (octane rating 100). Tetrapropylene is allowed to react with benzene, and the product is treated with sulfuric acid to give a synthetic detergent (Fig. 11-23).

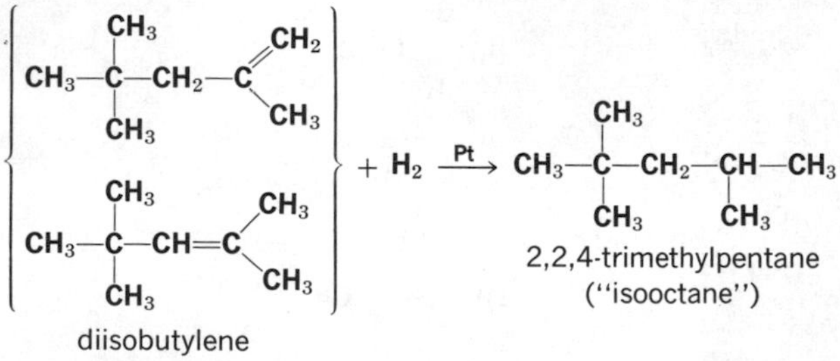

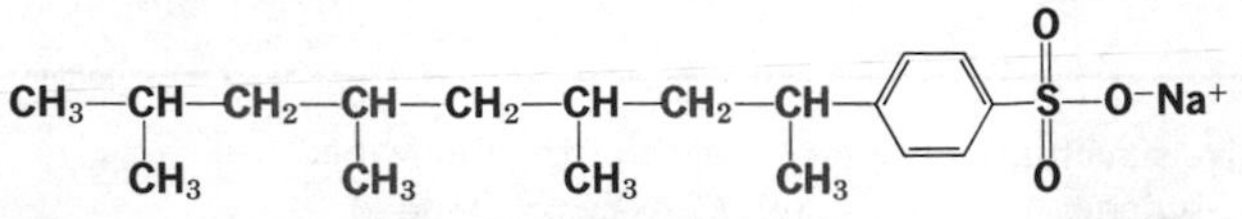

Fig. 3-23. Two important commercial products having their source in petroleum and made from isobutylene and propylene. "Isooctane" is an important constituent of gasoline, having an octane rating of 100. The other compound is a detergent.

The proliferation of monomers through self-addition leads to the vastly important process of polymerization which we shall discuss in detail in the next chapter. Polymerization can occur in many ways and gives rise to a great number of the most important products in the everyday life of people and nations.

OXIDATION OF ALKENES AND ALKYNES

Addition and self-addition are not the only types of reactions undergone by double and triple bonds. Oxidation, a process clear to anyone who has studied general chemistry, is another. As we have seen, oxidation is a source of heat and power, for alkenes are burned in internal combustion engines and the alkyne, acetylene, is the fuel for the welding torch and the miner's lamp. In a sense, the oxidation of alkenes is a type of addition reaction, and in alkynes it similarly begins with addition reactions. However, since the products of oxidation really belong to the classes of compounds containing oxygen, we shall defer discussion of the chemistry of oxidation reactions to the chapters in which aldehydes, ketones, and acids are discussed (see Chapters 9 and 11).

Prob. 3-13. Suggest visual chemical tests which would enable you to label bottles of 1-hexene and *n*-hexane which had lost their labels.

Prob. 3-14. Give the IUPAC name for each of the following, referring to the general rules of nomenclature in the Appendix where necessary.

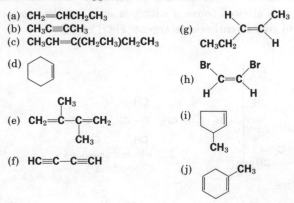

(a) $CH_2\!=\!CHCH_2CH_3$
(b) $CH_3C\!\equiv\!CCH_3$
(c) $CH_3CH\!=\!C(CH_2CH_3)CH_2CH_3$

(d)

(e) $CH_2\!=\!\overset{\displaystyle CH_3}{\underset{\displaystyle CH_3}{C}}\!-\!C\!=\!CH_2$

(f) $HC\!\equiv\!C\!-\!C\!\equiv\!CH$

(g)

(h)

(i)

(j)

Prob. 3-15. Give structural formulas for each of the following:

(a) *trans*-2-butene
(b) 1-heptyne
(c) 3-isopropyl-2-heptene
(d) cyclobutene
(e) 3,3-dimethylcyclohexene
(f) 1,5-hexadiene

(g) *trans*-cyclooctene
(the smallest cyclic *trans* olefin which has been isolated)
(h) 2,6-octadiyne

Prob. 3-16. Which of the following compounds are conjugated and which unconjugated dienes? Draw the structure of a 1,4-addition product of bromine with each of the conjugated dienes. Neglect *cis* and *trans* isomerism.

(a) 1,3-hexadiene
(b) 1,4-hexadiene
(c) 1,3-cyclohexadiene
(d) 1,4-cyclohexadiene

Prob. 3-17.   Cyclopropene has been prepared, but it is enormously reactive, and unstable at temperatures above $-70°$. Using bond angles, explain why cyclopropene should be so unstable.

Prob. 3-18.   Draw all three geometrical (*cis, trans*) isomers of 2,4-hexadiene.

Prob. 3-19.   Give the products of the following reactions:

(a) 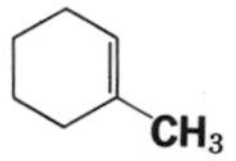 $+$ **HCl** $\longrightarrow$
CH$_3$

(b)   **CH$_3$C≡CCH$_3$ + Br$_2$** (excess) $\longrightarrow$

(c)  $+$ **H$_2$** (excess) $\xrightarrow{\text{Pt}}$

CHAPTER

FREE-RADICAL ADDITION
AND POLYMERIZATION

Like the river, some monomers go on and on, continuing to produce new compounds through the simple process of combination. Under the right conditions an unusually large number of units will combine to build up a product of massive molecular weight. This process is known as *polymerization*. The reverse of cracking, polymerization is the process of forming large molecules from small ones through repetition of the same structural units. For example, triggered by the acid catalyst boron trifluoride (BF_3), a product derived from isobutylene may contain 1400 isobutylene units and have a molecular weight of 80,000. This can be sold as butyl rubber.

From a commercial standpoint, polymerization is probably the most important reaction in organic chemistry. The resulting *polymers,* as the materials isolated in the process are called, account for a high proportion of the sales of organic chemical manufacturers. Butyl rubber, for instance, has many advantages over natural rubber or ordinary synthetic rubber, especially in the manufacture of inner tubes for tires. Polymers also turn up in nature. Many of the natural products considered indispensable to daily living are polymers. Proteins, like silk, hair, and meat, are sufficiently well-known. So are carbohydrates, which include cotton and the starches and sugars. In the course of this book, we shall encounter many further examples of natural and manmade polymers.

FREE RADICALS

Even more important than acids in the polymerization of alkenes and dienes are chemical species known as free radicals, already encountered in Chapter 1 (Fig. 1-27).

61

In principle, these valuable agents are formally derivable from the acids involved in the addition to double and triple bonds. Such acids all lack one pair of electrons to complete their outer shell. Figure 4-1 shows the structures of three of these acids. Notice that each acid is positively charged and shares an even number of electrons. Adding a single electron to each acid would give it an odd number of electrons and create a free radical.

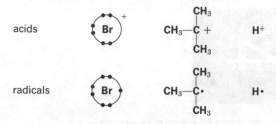

Fig. 4-1. The top three reagents are positively charged acids, each of which readily adds to a double bond. Note that each contains an even number of electrons. Below each is the corresponding free radical, a neutral species containing one more electron which is *unpaired*. Since free radicals are one electron short of having a complete shell, they too are reactive toward the electron-rich double bond.

Like the corresponding acids, free radicals are highly reactive. Ordinarily they occur as short-lived intermediates in chemical reactions. One principal reason for the short lifetime is their quick combination into stable neutral molecules (Fig. 4-2). Despite their usual neutrality, free radicals each lack one electron and therefore have incomplete outer shells. This makes them seek an electron and, like acids, add to carbon–carbon double bonds.

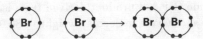

Fig. 4-2. Whenever two free radicals come together, they combine with the formation of a single bond. As a consequence it is seldom possible to have an appreciable concentration of free radicals, and they exist mainly as short-lived intermediates.

Because of their instability, free radicals are difficult to form. However, compounds of one class break down easily into free radicals and often serve to initiate organic free-radical reactions. These compounds, *peroxides,* contain oxygen–oxygen bonds. The bonds are so weak that when the peroxides are heated or irradiated with light, they split into two free radicals (Fig. 4-3).

$$\text{RO—OR} \xrightleftharpoons{\text{heat}} \text{R—O•} \quad \text{•O—R}$$

Fig. 4-3. Peroxides readily break down into free radicals, and are therefore convenient sources of small amounts of these species.

FREE-RADICAL ADDITION

When an unsaturated hydrocarbon like propene reacts with hydrogen bromide, ionic addition generally occurs. Markownikoff's rule holds, and 2-bromopropane is produced. In the presence of peroxide, a remarkable reversal of the direction of addition appears, however, and 1-bromopropane becomes the main product. The result is an anti-Markownikoff addition, involving free-radical rather than carbonium ion intermediates. The peroxides break down and yield a few free radicals; these radicals, which start the reaction, are called *initiator radicals* and the peroxide is called an *initiator*. The initiator radicals react with hydrogen bromide to form bromine free-radical atoms. Because of their low concentration, bromine atoms do not react with one another; instead they add to the double bond of propene, whose concentration is massive. The free bromine radical attacks the double bond at the carbon atom having the greater number of hydrogen atoms. This action produces a secondary free radical [step (c) in Fig. 4-4] that is more stable

(a) $RO\text{—}OR \longrightarrow 2RO\cdot$
peroxide

(b) $HBr + RO\cdot \longrightarrow ROH + Br\cdot$

(c) $Br\cdot + CH_2{=}CHCH_3 \longrightarrow Br\text{—}CH_2\overset{\cdot}{\text{—}}CHCH_3$

(d) $Br\text{—}CH_2\overset{\cdot}{C}HCH_3 + HBr \longrightarrow BrCH_2\underset{\underset{H}{|}}{C}HCH_3 + Br\cdot$

Fig. 4-4. Addition of hydrogen bromide to a double bond in the presence of peroxides or air and light leads to an anti-Markownikoff product. Free radicals are involved in the reaction, and steps (c) and (d) occur many, many times, so that the reaction is called a *chain reaction*. Compare to the chlorination of methane, Fig. 1-27.

than the primary radical, because the electrons of the two adjacent carbon atoms partially stabilize the electron-poor radical in much the same manner as a secondary carbonium ion is stabilized.

As the concentration of free radicals is so small, the secondary free radical is unable to find a kindred one with which to react. Instead, it reacts with hydrogen bromide to form 1-bromopropane and a new bromine free radical [see step (d) in Fig. 4-4]. Reacting with another molecule of propene, the new bromine free radical is able to undergo steps (c) and (d) (Fig. 4-4); this is repeated many thousands of times. One free radical formed in step (a) in Fig. 4-4 thus serves as the initiator for the addition of several thousand molecules of hydrogen bromide to propene, giving 1-bromopropane. This type of reaction is known as a *chain reaction*. Steps (c) and (d) are called *propagation steps*, inasmuch as they keep the reaction going.

Eventually the chain reaches its end through the chance contact of two free radicals. For instance, the secondary free radical formed in step (c) in Fig. 4-4 might unite with the bromine atom formed in step (b) or (d), to produce a molecule of 1,2-dibromopropane. Amid several thousand molecules of 1-bromopropane, the presence of this lone molecule of 1,2-dibromopropane would hardly be detectable. Thus, this reaction is a *termination reaction* that brings the chain to a stop.

Similarly, with alkynes, anti-Markownikoff addition of hydrogen bromide may occur in the presence of peroxides* (Fig. 4-5).

$$\text{R—C}\equiv\text{CH} + \text{HBr} \xrightarrow{\text{peroxides}} \text{RCH}\!\!=\!\!\text{CHBr} \xrightarrow[\text{peroxides}]{\text{HBr}} \text{RCH}_2\text{CHBr}_2$$

Fig. 4-5. The anti-Markownikoff addition of hydrogen bromide to alkynes takes place in the presence of peroxides. Neither hydrogen chloride nor hydrogen iodide undergoes this reaction with alkenes and alkynes.

The reader should carefully compare the free-radical *addition* of hydrogen bromide to alkenes and alkynes with the free-radical *substitution* of chlorine in alkanes that was described in Chapter 1 (see p. 24).

Prob. 4-1. Molecules other than hydrogen bromide may be added to alkenes by free-radical chain processes. An example is the addition of a mercaptan RSH. Complete the following equation, giving structures for A, B, and C based on analogy to HBr addition.

$$\text{ROOR} \longrightarrow 2\text{RO}\cdot$$
$$\text{RO}\cdot + \text{RSH} \longrightarrow \text{A} + \text{B}$$
$$\text{A} + \text{CH}_2\!\!=\!\!\text{CHCH}_3 \longrightarrow \text{C}$$
$$\text{C} + \text{RSH} \longrightarrow \text{RSCH}_2\text{CH}_2\text{CH}_3 + \text{A}$$

Suggest two possible termination steps for this chain reaction.

FREE-RADICAL POLYMERIZATIONS

One of the most significant industrial uses of free-radical reactions occurs in the formation of polymers. Polymerization induced by acids creates useful polymers from only a few alkenes. By using free radicals to touch off the reaction, the chemist may develop many useful products from substituted alkenes. The steps in the free-radical polymerization of an alkene closely resemble those in which an acid acts as catalyst, except that free radicals rather than carbonium ions serve as the agents. A few free radicals are first produced, usually through the breakdown of some peroxide molecules that have been added as an initiator; these free radicals then add to the alkene. If the object were to obtain a polymer like the one used in making vinyl tile, the chemist would employ *vinyl chloride* (IUPAC name: chloroethene) as the alkene. The two steps (a) and (b) in Fig. 4-6 which generate the polymerization are called the *initiation* reactions.

Next, the carbon free radical formed in the addition reacts with another molecule of vinyl chloride [step (c)]; this addition is repeated many times (*n* times in

---

* Only hydrogen bromide—neither hydrogen chloride nor hydrogen iodide—undergoes anti-Markownikoff free-radical addition to alkenes and alkynes.

$$\text{RO—OR} \xrightarrow[(a)]{} 2\text{RO}\cdot \xrightarrow[(b)]{\text{CH}_2\text{=CHCl}} \text{RO—CH}_2\overset{\bullet}{\text{CHCl}} \Bigg\}$$ initiation

$$\underset{\text{CH}_2\text{C}\cdot}{\overset{\text{H}}{\text{RO}}} + \underset{\substack{\text{vinyl} \\ \text{chloride}}}{\text{CH}_2\text{=CH}_2\text{Cl}} \xrightarrow[(c)]{} \text{ROCH}_2\overset{\text{H}}{\text{CH}}\text{—CH}_2\overset{\bullet}{\text{C}}$$

propagation

$$n\text{CH}_2\text{=CHCl}$$

$$\text{ROCH}_2\text{CH(CH}_2\text{CH)}_n\text{CH}_2\overset{\bullet}{\text{CHCl}} \Bigg\}$$

$$\underset{(d)\ \text{X}\cdot}{\downarrow}$$ termination

$$\text{ROCH}_2\text{CH(CH}_2\text{CH)}_n\text{CH}_2\text{CH—X}$$

Fig. 4-6. Steps in the free-radical polymerization of vinyl chloride; the same steps are followed in the polymerization of other substituted alkenes.

the example shown) until a long chain of atoms is produced. The repetitive steps in which the polymer is actually formed are said to be *propagation* reactions. In a typical polymerization sequence, more than 1,000 molecules of vinyl chloride will be incorporated into the chain. Sooner or later, the free radical in step (c) may collide with another free radical, (d), which may be either the end of another chain, a radical from peroxide, or even oxygen from the air, because oxygen contains two unpaired electrons. When this happens termination is said to occur: The chain ceases to grow. Thus, the steps in a polymerization reaction as in any other chain reaction are *initiation, propagation,* and *termination* (Fig. 4-6).

Simple alkenes are the source of many common plastics. Table 4-1 lists the names, structures, and products formed in some polymerization reactions. Certain well-known polymers like Nylon and Dacron are conspicuously missing from this list, however. These fibers are the products of an entirely different chemical process which we will discuss in later chapters.

Table 4-1 shows clearly that the properties of a polymer depend largely on the

Table 4-1. Some Common Monomers and the Polymers Formed from Them by Free-Radical Polymerization

Monomer	Polymer name	Trade name	Use
$CH_2\text{=}CH_2$	polyethylene	Polythene	squeeze bottles
$CF_2\text{=}CF_2$	polytetrafluoroethylene	Teflon	bearings
$CH_2\text{=}CHCl$	polyvinyl chloride	Koroseal	raincoats
$CH_2\text{=}CHCN$	polyacrylonitrile	Orlon	fibers
$CH_2\text{=}\overset{O}{\underset{CH_3}{C}}COCH_3$	polymethyl methacrylate	Lucite, Plexiglass	safety glasses

structure of the monomer selected. This is to be expected. A whole new spectrum of polymers is obtained if a mixture of two monomers is allowed to polymerize. The resulting polymer, called a *copolymer,* usually contains both monomers, more-or-less randomly distributed along the chain. The plastic Saran, familiar in kitchen wrapping and auto seat covers, is a copolymer formed by the polymerizing of vinyl

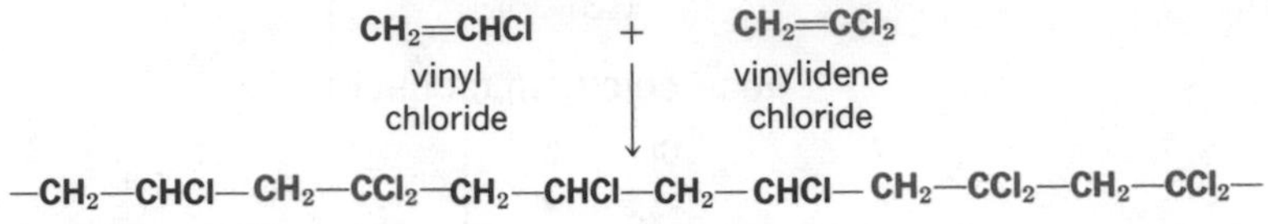

$$CH_2=CHCl \quad + \quad CH_2=CCl_2$$

vinyl   vinylidene
chloride   chloride

$$-CH_2-CHCl-CH_2-CCl_2-CH_2-CHCl-CH_2-CHCl-CH_2-CCl_2-CH_2-CCl_2-$$

Fig. 4-7. A portion of the chain of a one-to-one copolymer of vinyl chloride and vinylidene chloride. The distribution of the two monomers is approximately random throughout the chain.

chloride and vinylidene chloride (Fig. 4-7). The properties of a copolymer may be altered by changing the proportions of the two monomers employed in its production.

Prob. 4-2. Write equations for the copolymerization of vinyl chloride and vinylidene chloride using a peroxide ROOR as initiator and terminating by reaction with RO•.

Dienes also polymerize under radical conditions. Interest in their reactions was originally stimulated by the observation that natural rubber could be considered, at least on paper, to result from the polymerization of isoprene (Fig. 4-8). A great deal of research has been carried out on the polymerization of isoprene and other dienes, but unfortunately, normal radical polymerization of isoprene does not give natural rubber; the product is instead an isomer whose double bonds are mainly in the *trans* rather than the *cis* arrangement. A similar polymer, known as gutta percha, occurs naturally, but lacks elastic properties. Recently, several unusual catalyst systems (mentioned later in this chapter), some of which do not involve radicals, have been developed. These systems convert isoprene to a polymer indistinguishable from natural rubber.

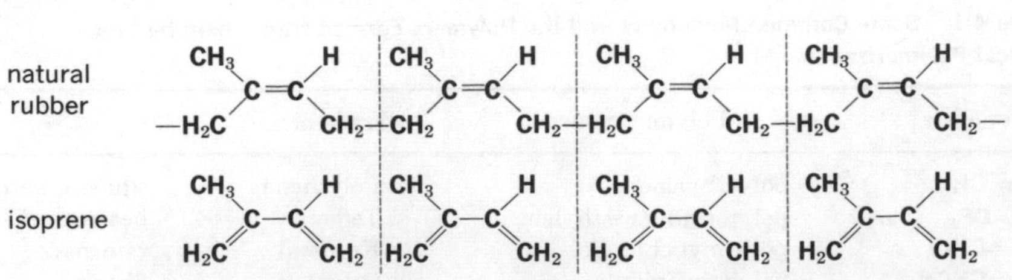

natural
rubber

isoprene

Fig. 4-8. Natural rubber is a highly unsaturated hydrocarbon which is obtained from the rubber tree. It might be considered to be obtainable from isoprene (2-methylbutadiene) by 1,4-polymerization. Note that all the double bonds are *cis* substituted in natural rubber.

It is amusing that, contrary to the original speculations about natural rubber, the rubber tree clearly does not use isoprene as such in its synthesis of rubber. Therefore, chemists have been led to duplicate a natural product by a process entirely different from that used by nature. The chemical and technological importance of industrial rubber syntheses is immense.

When the ordinary polymerization of isoprene failed to produce natural rubber, chemists turned to investigations of the polymerization of other dienes. Some of these polymerizations led to useful synthetic rubbers. One important example is Neoprene, formed from the polymerization of 2-chlorobutadiene (chloroprene, Fig. 4-9). This monomer, in which the methyl group of isoprene is replaced by a

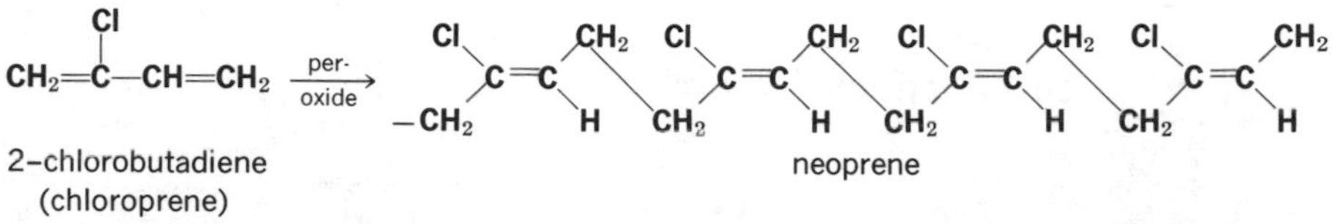

Fig. 4-9. Chloroprene upon polymerization is converted to Neoprene, an important synthetic rubber. Note the *trans* double bonds.

chlorine atom, is prepared by the addition of hydrogen chloride to vinyl acetylene. Neoprene is not affected by many organic solvents that cause natural rubber to swell, and is used in the hoses of gasoline pumps and many similar applications.

The most important synthetic rubber is, however, a copolymer of butadiene and styrene (Fig. 4-10). A large percentage of the tires in use today are made of this

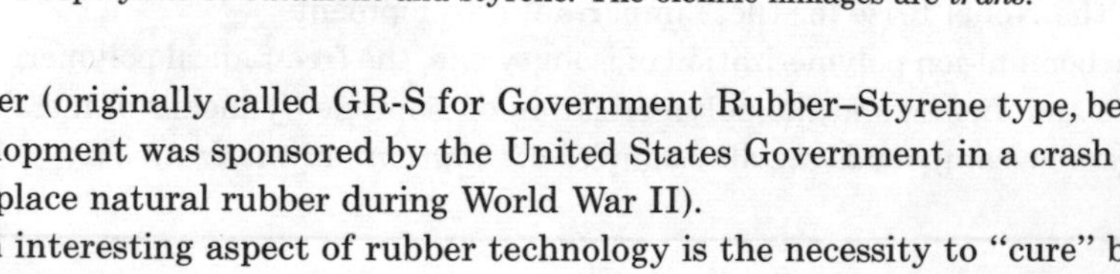

Fig. 4-10. The most widely used rubber, synthetic or natural, is GR-S rubber, a copolymer of butadiene and styrene. The olefinic linkages are *trans*.

rubber (originally called GR-S for Government Rubber–Styrene type, because its development was sponsored by the United States Government in a crash program to replace natural rubber during World War II).

An interesting aspect of rubber technology is the necessity to "cure" both synthetic and natural rubbers. This is often accomplished by heating them with sulfur. The sulfur reacts at the double bonds of two polymer chains, linking them together (cross-linking). The need to cure explains why a small amount of isoprene is required as an additive in butyl rubber, since pure polyisobutylene would not have any double bonds available for cross-linkage.

OTHER TYPES OF POLYMERIZATION

In recent years the chemical industry has worked to develop new polymerization catalysts that will produce polymeric materials with better properties. As we have seen, a synthetic material with all the properties of natural rubber has now been prepared from isoprene. Three different catalysts can be employed for this polymerization (Fig. 4-11): One is simply metallic lithium dispersed in paraffin oil; a

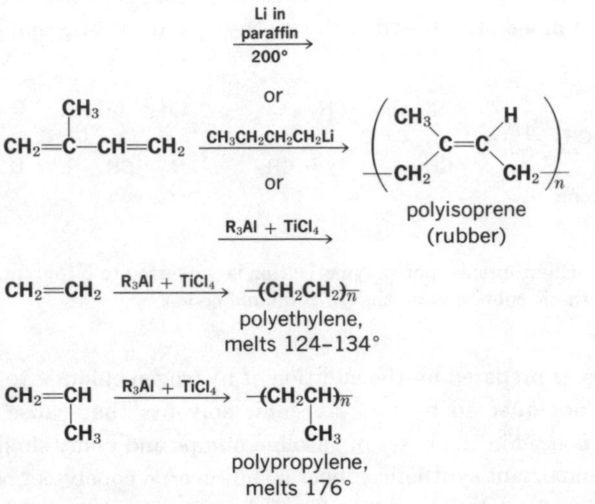

$$\text{CH}_2\text{=}\underset{\underset{\text{CH}_3}{|}}{\text{C}}\text{—CH=CH}_2 \quad \begin{array}{c} \xrightarrow[\text{200°}]{\substack{\text{Li in} \\ \text{paraffin}}} \\ or \\ \xrightarrow{\text{CH}_3\text{CH}_2\text{CH}_2\text{CH}_2\text{Li}} \\ or \\ \xrightarrow{\text{R}_3\text{Al + TiCl}_4} \end{array} \quad \left(\begin{array}{cc} \text{CH}_3 & \text{H} \\ | & | \\ \text{C=C} \\ | & | \\ \text{—CH}_2 & \text{CH}_2\text{—} \end{array} \right)_{\!\!n}$$

polyisoprene
(rubber)

$$\text{CH}_2\text{=CH}_2 \xrightarrow{\text{R}_3\text{Al + TiCl}_4} \text{—(CH}_2\text{CH}_2\text{)}_{\overline{n}}$$
polyethylene,
melts 124–134°

$$\text{CH}_2\text{=}\underset{\underset{\text{CH}_3}{|}}{\text{CH}} \xrightarrow{\text{R}_3\text{Al + TiCl}_4} \text{—(CH}_2\underset{\underset{\text{CH}_3}{|}}{\text{CH}}\text{)}_{\overline{n}}$$
polypropylene,
melts 176°

Fig. 4-11. New catalysts give all *cis*-1,4-polyisopropene, identical with natural rubber. They also allow the polymerization of ethylene and propylene under mild conditions to polymers of high melting points and crystallinity.

second is an organometallic reagent, *n*-butyllithium ($\text{CH}_3\text{CH}_2\text{CH}_2\text{CH}_2\text{Li}$); the third is a complex catalyst composed of another organometallic reagent, a trialkyl-aluminum, and titanium chloride. Butadiene itself and simple alkenes can be polymerized by the same catalysts. Ziegler (Germany) and Natta (Italy) were awarded the Nobel Prize for these important developments.

The carbonium-ion polymerization of isobutylene, the free-radical polymerization of alkenes and dienes, and the polymerization of isoprene by means of metals and organometallic compounds are all examples of *addition polymerization*.

Prob. 4-3. Give the product of the following reaction:

$$\text{CH}_3\text{CH}_2\text{CH=CH}_2 + \text{HBr} \xrightarrow{\text{peroxides}}$$

Prob. 4-4. The following table compares the electronic structure of various acids, bases, and free radicals. Complete the table, and add one or two examples of your own choosing.

acid	radical	base
Cl^+	$Cl\cdot$	Cl^-
	$H_3C\cdot$	
H^+		
		HO^-

Prob. 4-5. Certain substances are so effective in terminating free-radical chain reactions like hydrogen bromide addition and polymerizations that they are called *inhibitors* because they prevent any reaction at all. The gas nitric oxide (NO) is one of these. Draw its electronic formula and suggest a reason for its inhibitory action.

CHAPTER

AROMATIC HYDROCARBONS

The contrast in reactivity between the saturated and the unsaturated hydro-carbons is sharp. As we have seen, the single-bonded alkanes are inert to most reagents. When forced to react, they do so by substitution—with a halogen, for example, replacing a hydrogen atom. The unsaturated double- and triple-bonded alkenes and alkynes, on the other hand, react with acids and oxidizing agents, and undergo addition with halogens and other reagents.

A third class of hydrocarbons does not easily fit this complex of single-, double-, and triple-bonded compounds. This class comprises the *aromatic hydrocarbons.* They were originally given this name because many of them have spicy or other-wise pleasant fragrances and the name has persisted, although aromatic chemistry now embraces the chemistry of all compounds like benzene that behave in a special manner.

BENZENE

The mobile liquid benzene boils at 80°. Once considered atypical in behavior, ben-zene is now known to be truly representative of the aromatic compounds. Its formula, C_6H_6, suggests unsaturation—a saturated alkane would have the formula C_6H_{14} and a cycloalkane, C_6H_{12}; however, much of the behavior of benzene more closely resembles that of the saturated rather than of the unsaturated hydrocar-bons. For example, benzene will not react with either bromine or chlorine under conditions where alkenes and dienes like hexene and hexadiene rapidly add both. Benzene is also inert to hydrogen bromide, hydrogen chloride, and other reagents that readily add to double and triple bonds. When it does react, it usually does not undergo addition, but rather substitution, as it does in its reaction with bromine in the presence of ferric bromide (Fig. 5-1).

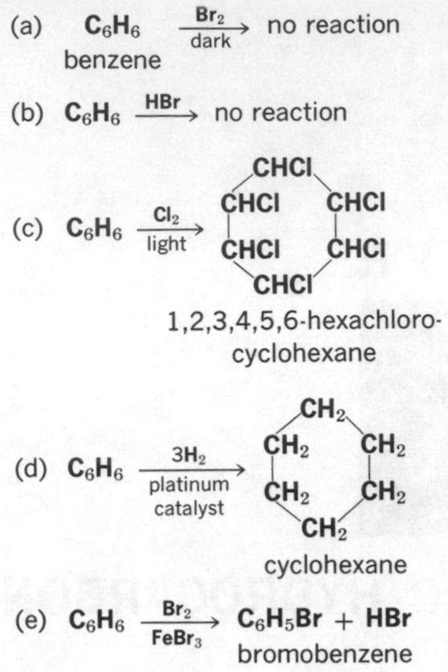

(a) C_6H_6 $\xrightarrow[\text{dark}]{Br_2}$ no reaction
      benzene

(b) C_6H_6 $\xrightarrow{HBr}$ no reaction

(c) C_6H_6 $\xrightarrow[\text{light}]{Cl_2}$

$$\begin{array}{c} \text{CHCl} \\ \text{CHCl} \quad \text{CHCl} \\ \text{CHCl} \quad \text{CHCl} \\ \text{CHCl} \end{array}$$

1,2,3,4,5,6-hexachloro-
cyclohexane

(d) C_6H_6 $\xrightarrow[\substack{\text{platinum} \\ \text{catalyst}}]{3H_2}$

$$\begin{array}{c} \text{CH}_2 \\ \text{CH}_2 \quad \text{CH}_2 \\ \text{CH}_2 \quad \text{CH}_2 \\ \text{CH}_2 \end{array}$$

cyclohexane

(e) C_6H_6 $\xrightarrow[\text{FeBr}_3]{Br_2}$ C_6H_5Br + HBr
      bromobenzene

Fig. 5-1. Benzene undergoes both addition and substitution reactions.

Benzene shows that it is actually unsaturated because it adds hydrogen or chlorine under certain conditions. When it is heated with hydrogen and a platinum catalyst, it adds three moles of hydrogen to produce cyclohexane. Further, when benzene and chlorine are irradiated with light, three moles of chlorine add to the benzene to yield 1,2,3,4,5,6-hexachlorocyclohexane, a potent insecticide named *Lindane* which will be discussed in more detail in Chapter 7. Both reactions demonstrate that benzene has six carbon atoms arranged in a ring, since cyclohexanes form in the process. They also suggest that benzene contains three double bonds, since the additions are of three moles of hydrogen or chlorine.

These reactions could be easily accounted for if benzene were 1,3,5-cyclohexatriene. However, by analogy with alkenes or dienes, a molecule with either of these structures should readily add acids and be oxidized by potassium permanganate under mild conditions. The trouble is that benzene does neither.

Although the peculiar nature of benzene has occupied the attention of organic chemists for a century, they have only acquired a general understanding of the compound's structure and its unusual chemical properties since the 1930's. The explanation now accepted has required the best modern physical evidence and mathematical theories.

Some of the evidence involves bond lengths. If the left-hand structure in Fig. 5-2 were the correct one for benzene, the bond between the two carbon atoms in red should be a double bond, with a bond length of 1.34 Å. However, if the correct structure were the one on the right, the bond between those atoms would be single and its length, 1.54 Å. Each of these structures should contain three carbon–carbon single bonds and three carbon-carbon double bonds. Physical measurements of benzene not only confirm that the six carbon atoms are arranged in a hexagon,

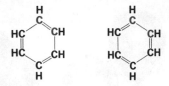

Fig. 5-2. Either of the cyclohexatriene structures shown would account for the addition reactions of benzene, but not for its substitution reactions, and not for its failure to react with hydrogen bromide or bromine.

but also show that *all* of the carbon–carbon bonds are of the same length, 1.39 Å, intermediate between the lengths of double and single bonds.

We discussed the variation of bond length with bond order in Chapter 3 and presented this variation in graphic form in Fig. 3-11. That graph is reproduced in Fig. 5-3. Notice that a bond length of 1.39 Å, as in benzene, corresponds almost exactly to a bond order of 1.5, namely, to one and one-half bonds. How can we account for half bonds?

ORBITAL PICTURE OF AROMATIC COMPOUNDS

The simplest pictorial presentation of the equivalence of all C—C bonds in benzene employs the orbital scheme that applies to unsaturated molecules. The internal bond angles in benzene are 120°, exactly the same as for carbon with sp^2 hybridized bonds (see Fig. 3-6). Six such carbon atoms can be joined to form a perfect hexagon. Owing to the symmetry of the molecule, the p orbital on each carbon can overlap equally well with the p orbitals of the two adjacent carbon atoms. This gives rise

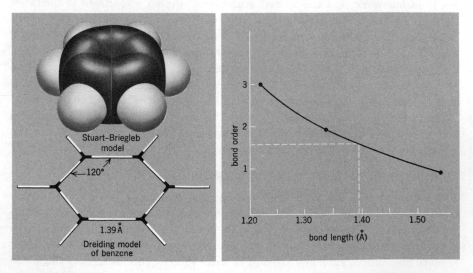

Fig. 5-3. Models of benzene. All the carbon–carbon bonds in benzene are the same length, 1.39 Å. This corresponds to a bond order of 1.5—a one-and-one-half bond.

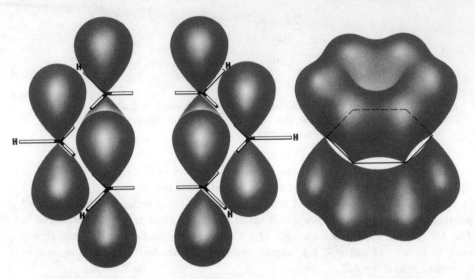

Fig. 5-4. The sigma bonds in benzene are formed by the overlap of sp^2 orbitals, while each carbon contributes to the π bond system by overlap of its p orbital with p orbitals of its two neighbors.

to a continuous cloud of p electrons on top of and below the six-carbon structure (Fig. 5-4). These p electrons are not localized between any pair of carbons, as in a double bond, but *delocalized* in π molecular orbitals over the entire ring. Each of the C—C bonds is identical, containing a pair of electrons in its σ bond, which unifies the framework, and also a one-sixth share of the six π electrons in the molecule. This makes a total of three electrons per bond, or one and one-half bonds.

Because the bonding in benzene is different from that in alkenes and alkynes, a new symbol is sometimes used to represent the compound. A common one is a hexagon with a circle inside to indicate the circular distribution of π electrons. Two or more hexagonal units of carbon atoms can fit together, thus forming molecules that contain more than one benzene ring. The simplest of these is naphthalene, $C_{10}H_8$, which has two six-membered rings "fused" together. Figure 5-5 indicates how the orbital picture of naphthalene accounts for the delocalization of the π electrons over the entire ten-carbon skeleton.

RESONANCE PICTURE OF AROMATIC COMPOUNDS

The orbital profile for bonding in unsaturated molecules is only a relatively recent concept. Long before it was developed however, chemists made an interesting observation: They noted that whenever an unsaturated molecule displayed the peculiar properties we have termed aromatic (resistance to oxidation, substitution in place of addition, etc.), any attempt to write its structure using only single and double bonds resulted in ambiguity. It is possible to place three double bonds in a

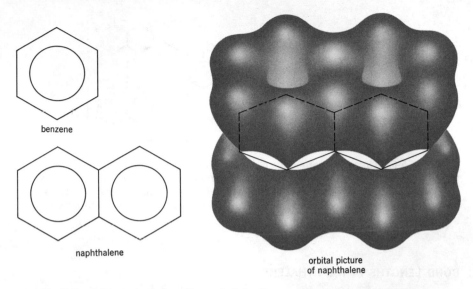

benzene

naphthalene

orbital picture
of naphthalene

Fig. 5-5. A hexagon surrounding a circle is often used as a symbol for a benzene ring. In the orbital picture for naphthalene, each of the carbons shared by both rings is involved in π bonding with three other carbons.

six-membered ring in two different ways without disturbing the position of any of the atoms of the molecule. Only the positions of the electrons of the double bond will differ in the two structures.

The reader should notice in Fig. 5-2 that each pair of carbon atoms is joined by a double bond in one structure and by a single bond in the other. Physical measurements have shown that the structure of this aromatic molecule is intermediate between the two normal structures. All the carbon–carbon bonds are the same length: half-way between the length of a double and a single bond. It is possible to represent the structures of an aromatic molecule by drawing all the possible normal structures for the molecule. Though rather cumbersome, this method of representing the molecule is quite useful.

This technique of accounting for aromatic properties was given theoretical justification and made quantitative by Linus Pauling (Nobel Prize in Chemistry in 1954). Pauling's method is now called the *resonance* picture of aromatic molecules (Fig. 5-6). It is important to remember that no single resonance structure or form adequately represents an aromatic molecule. Rather, a weighted average of all the forms is the true state. The molecule itself, called a *resonance hybrid,* partakes of some of the properties of each resonance form, much as a hybrid corn inherits some of the characteristics of each variety from which it springs. This is indicated by the special two-headed arrows in Fig. 5-6. They do not describe an equilibrium but an intermediate state (the resonance hybrid), in which the actual molecule resembles both forms.

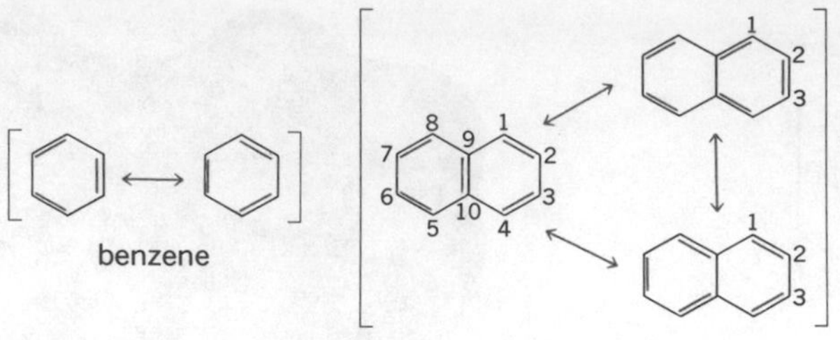

benzene

naphthalene

Fig. 5-6. The *resonance* picture of aromatic molecules starts from the observation that double bonds can be formally arranged in more than one way in standard formulas—two ways in benzene, and three in naphthalene. The actual molecule is considered to be a *hybrid* of these structures, that is, to have an intermediate structure.

BOND LENGTHS IN NAPHTHALENE

If we compare the compact pictures of benzene and naphthalene in the orbital representation of Fig. 5-5 with the cumbersome *resonance* representation of Fig. 5-6, we might wonder why the latter picture has survived. The answer is simple: The resonance picture contains a great deal of valuable information which is often obscured in the orbital picture. As an example, suppose we wished to estimate the bond lengths in naphthalene. If we used Fig. 5-5, we might guess that they were all the same length. If, however, we chose the resonance picture of Fig. 5-6 and assumed that all three structures made equal contributions to the hybrid we would see that the bond between C-1 and C-2 was double in two of the structures and single in the third. This bond is a 1⅔ bond (⅔ double and ⅓ single). By contrast the C-2, C-3 bond is a 1⅓ bond, ⅓ double and ⅔ single. If we refer to the graph of bond order *versus* bond length in Fig. 5-3, we observe that a 1⅔ bond is predicted to be 1.36 Å long and a 1⅓ bond 1.42 Å long. The precise values found for these bonds in naphthalene are 1.364 and 1.404 Å. Although agreement is not perfect, we thus arrive by a simple process at reasonable estimates of bond lengths. Other uses of the resonance picture will become obvious as we proceed, and we shall use both resonance and molecular orbital pictures interchangeably, depending upon which one appears to illustrate a point more clearly.

Prob. 5-1.   What is the bond order of the 9,10- bond in naphthalene? The 1,9- bond?

Benzene rings may be fused together indefinitely to form larger molecules called *polynuclear aromatic hydrocarbons* (Fig. 5-7). Three benzene rings are linked linearly in anthracene, angularly in phenanthrene.

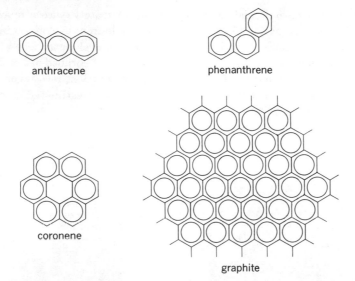

anthracene

phenanthrene

coronene

graphite

Fig. 5-7. Benzene rings may be fused together to form polynuclear hydrocarbons. Anthracene and phenanthrene are colorless and coronene is yellow; the color deepens as the number of rings increases, and graphite, which is essentially pure carbon, is black.

Prob. 5-2. Anthracene and phenanthrene both have enough π electrons (one from each of the 14 carbon atoms) to form seven double bonds. Show that the double bonds can be arranged in four different ways in anthracene and in five different ways in phenanthrene.

RESONANCE ENERGY OF BENZENE

Since either the orbital or resonance picture of benzene accounts reasonably well for the bond lengths in aromatic molecules, let us now see how to explain other typical aromatic characteristics, such as lowered reactivity relative to alkenes and substitution (rather than addition) with acid reagents. Suppose benzene were an ordinary cyclic triene with three normal double bonds. Such a compound, 1,3,5-cyclohexatriene, could not actually be prepared, since it would immediately transform itself into benzene. Nevertheless, we can make excellent forecasts of how such a molecule should react. By comparing an actual benzene molecule with this hypothetical model, we can estimate how much benzene will be stabilized by the delocalization of the π electrons. The amount of this stabilization is known as the *resonance energy of benzene*.

When an ordinary double bond is reduced with hydrogen, a large amount of energy is released, since an alkane is more stable than an alkene. For instance, hydrogenation of cyclohexene releases 28,600 calories of heat per mole of alkene. If a molecule contains two normal double bonds, approximately twice as much energy is released on hydrogenation (55,400 calories per mole from cyclohexadiene). One might expect that a molecule such as our hypothetical cyclohexatriene with three normal double bonds would release somewhere in the neighborhood of $3 \times 28,600 = 85,800$ calories. Hydrogenation of a mole of benzene, however, releases only 49,800 calories. The resonance energy of benzene may then be estimated as $85,800 - 49,800 = 36,000$ calories (36 kcal) of energy (Fig. 5-8).

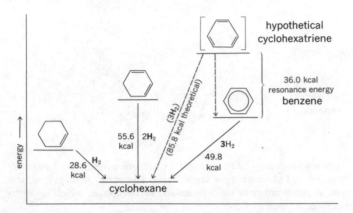

Fig. 5-8. The actual molecule of benzene is 36 kilocalories per mole more stable than the hypothetical cyclohexatriene. In order to observe normal alkene reactions of benzene, we would have to expend this additional amount of energy to localize the π electrons. Thus, more energy, usually in the form of higher reaction temperatures, is required for reactions of benzene than for similar reactions of nonaromatic alkenes.

Prob. 5-3. If 82.0 kcal of heat is released in the hydrogenation of naphthalene with 5 moles of hydrogen, calculate the resonance energy of naphthalene. Assume 28.6 kcal for the heat of hydrogenation of a normal double bond.

SUBSTITUTION IN BENZENE

The benzene model now accounts satisfactorily for the equality of its carbon–carbon bonds and its lack of reactivity toward addition, as compared with other unsaturated molecules. We must still deal with the problem of why benzene, in contrast to regular alkenes, undergoes substitution rather than addition with halogens and other reagents.

We have said that benzene does not react with hydrogen chloride or hydrogen bromide and can be recovered unchanged after prolonged boiling with these reagents. In fact, a reaction does occur, but does not lead to any observable change. It is of interest to compare this reaction with the similar reaction of hydrogen chloride with cyclohexene. As we saw in considering the addition of halogen acids to alkenes, the reaction starts with the addition of the electron-deficient proton to the electrons of the unsaturated system. With benzene, too, a proton may attack the ring, attaching itself to one of the carbon atoms (Fig. 5-9). In doing so, however, it at least partially localizes the π electrons, since the completely symmetrical system of overlapping p orbitals in benzene is disrupted in the carbonium-ion product. Proton addition will, therefore, be more difficult with benzene than with cyclohexene.

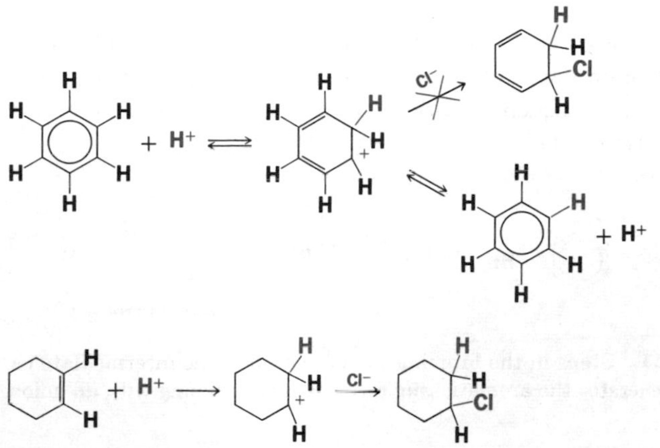

Fig. 5-9. Addition of a proton to benzene is more difficult than addition of one to cyclohexene, because additional energy must be supplied to localize the π electrons (that is, to overcome the resonance energy of benzene). No observable reaction takes place because the benzene ring is formed again by loss of the same or an equivalent proton.

In the addition to cyclohexene, when the carbonium ion is once formed, it rapidly combines with a chloride ion to produce the addition product, cyclohexyl chloride. Similar combination with the carbonium ion formed by addition of a proton to benzene *does not* occur because the resulting chloride would no longer have an aromatic system: The special stabilizing energy (resonance energy) of benzene would have been lost. Instead, a proton is ejected, and the benzene ring is regenerated. No net change has been accomplished, although one proton may have replaced another.

It is possible to demonstrate that the reaction actually takes place if, instead of hydrogen chloride, *deuterium chloride* is used (Fig. 5-10). Deuterium is an isotope of hydrogen, identical in chemical properties but distinguishable because it contains a neutron as well as a proton in its nucleus. If benzene is heated with a large excess of deuterium chloride, the recovered benzene has all of its hydrogen atoms replaced by deuterium (C_6D_6). Hexadeuteriobenzene is nearly identical to normal benzene, but has slightly different physical properties.

If any acidic reagent other than a proton reacts with benzene and the conditions

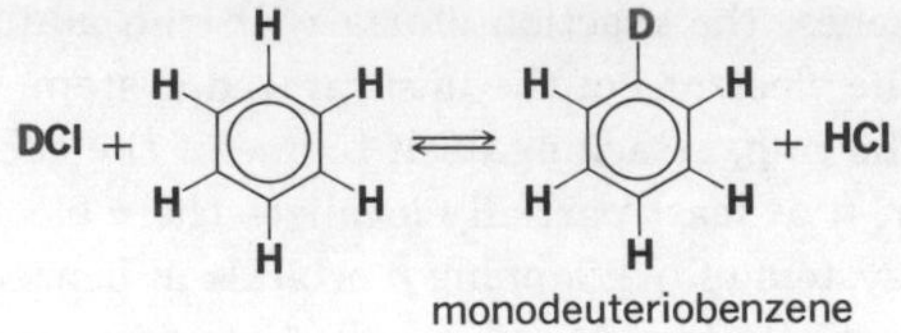

monodeuteriobenzene

Fig. 5-10. Any of the protons in benzene may be replaced with deuterium (an isotope of hydrogen) by heating with deuterium chloride.

used are vigorous enough to overcome the resonance energy of benzene, addition to form a carbonium ion may occur. As with hydrogen chloride, the reaction is not completed by a subsequent addition but by loss of a proton to reform a substituted benzene ring (Fig. 5-11).

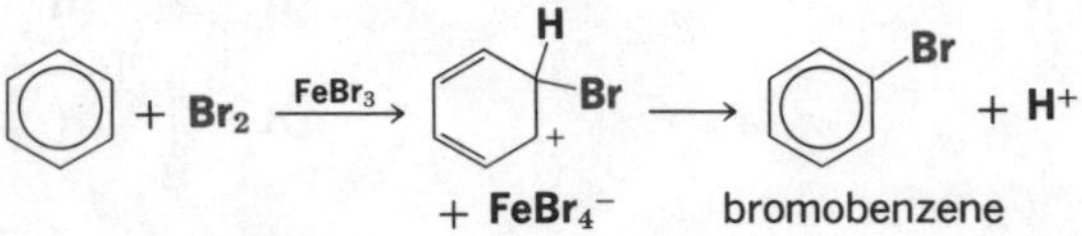

bromobenzene

Fig. 5-11. Steps in the bromination of benzene. The intermediate carbonium ion regenerates the aromatic ring rather than combining with an anion.

Benzene undergoes substitution reactions with nitric acid and with sulfuric acid to form nitrobenzene and benzenesulfonic acid, respectively. Analogous reactions with alkenes are not usually observed, because simple addition of the acids occurs first. In the case of nitration the reactive species is known to be the positively charged group formed by loss of hydroxide from the acid ($HONO_2 + H^+ \longrightarrow H_2O + {}^+NO_2$). By analogy a reasonable sulfonating species is ${}^+SO_3H$, formed from the reaction $HOSO_3H + H^+ \longrightarrow H_2O + {}^+SO_3H$ (Fig. 5-12).

Carbon–carbon bonds may be formed by an aromatic substitution reaction known as the Friedel-Crafts reaction. The attacking reagent is a carbonium ion which may be formed, as happens in the polymerization of isobutylene, by addition

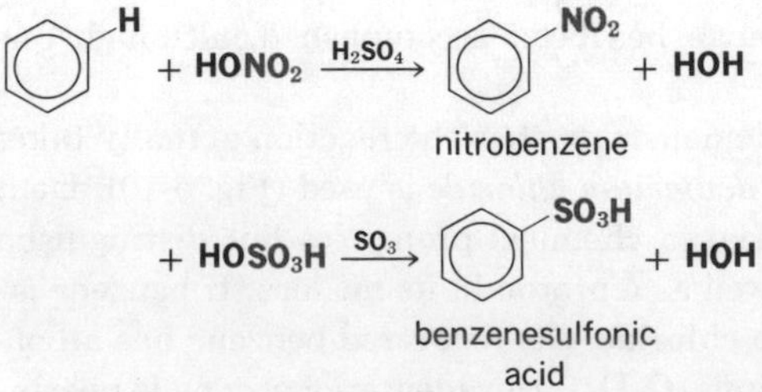

nitrobenzene

benzenesulfonic
acid

Fig. 5-12. Nitration and sulfonation of benzene are important synthetic reactions. The substituting agents are the Lewis acids ${}^+NO_2$ and probably ${}^+SO_3H$.

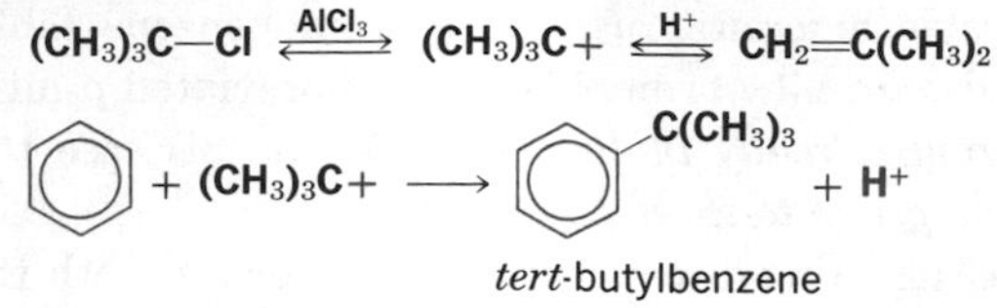

$$(CH_3)_3C—Cl \xrightleftharpoons{AlCl_3} (CH_3)_3C+ \xrightleftharpoons{H^+} CH_2{=}C(CH_3)_2$$

tert-butylbenzene

Fig. 5-13. Benzene undergoes substitution reactions with carbonium ions. The sequence is called Friedel-Crafts alkylation.

of a proton to a double bond, or by reaction of an alkyl halide with aluminum chloride (Fig. 5-13). By means of the Friedel-Crafts reaction, alkylated benzenes may be prepared which are useful in the production of synthetic detergents and many other commercial products.

Prob. 5-4. Draw the structure of the product formed when triisobutylene (the mixture of isomers) of Fig. 3-22 (and Prob. 3-12) undergoes a Friedel-Crafts reaction with benzene in the presence of acid.

Substituted benzenes may also undergo reaction. This results in di-, tri-, and polysubstituted benzenes. Suppose, for example, that bromobenzene reacts with nitric acid (using sulfuric acid as a catalyst) under nitrating conditions. From reactions at a position adjacent to the bromine atom, those at a position once removed from the bromine atom, and those at a position twice removed from the bromine atom, three isomeric products are possible. These are called the 2- or *ortho*, 3- or *meta,* and 4- or *para* positions, respectively, with reference to the bromine atom (Fig. 5-14). In fact, only two of the three possible products are

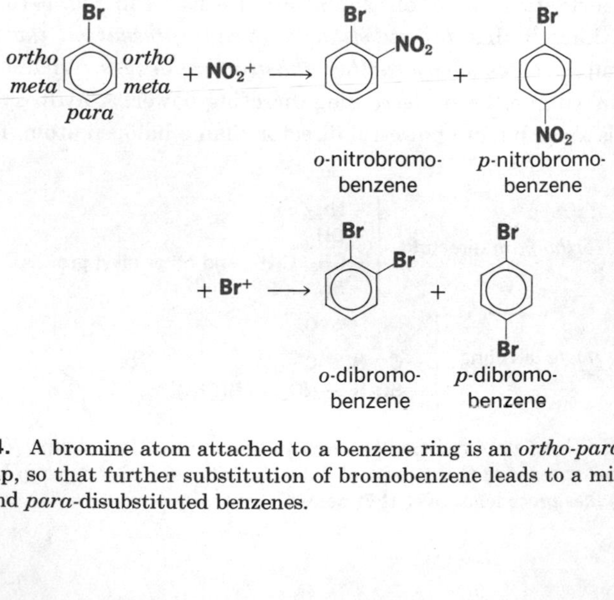

o-nitrobromo-benzene   p-nitrobromo-benzene

o-dibromo-benzene   p-dibromo-benzene

Fig. 5-14. A bromine atom attached to a benzene ring is an *ortho-para* directing group, so that further substitution of bromobenzene leads to a mixture of *ortho-* and *para*-disubstituted benzenes.

formed in appreciable amounts, *ortho*-nitrobromobenzene (abbreviated *o*-nitro-bromobenzene) and *para*-nitrobromobenzene (abbreviated *p*-nitrobromobenzene). *The substituent group already in the molecule,* in this case the bromine atom, *directs the incoming group to these positions.*

Bromine on a benzene ring directs substitution toward both the *ortho* and *para* positions and is therefore said to be an *ortho-para* directing group. Groups that favor *ortho* substitution also favor *para* substitution. The nitro group, on the other hand, is *meta* directing (Fig. 5-15). If nitrobenzene is brominated, the main

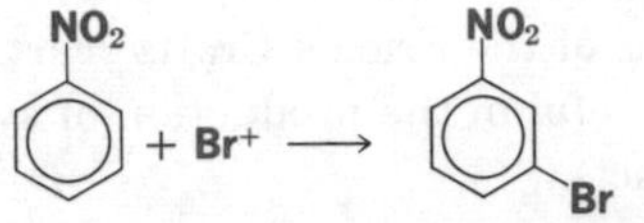

m-nitrobromobenzene
(or *m*-bromonitrobenzene)

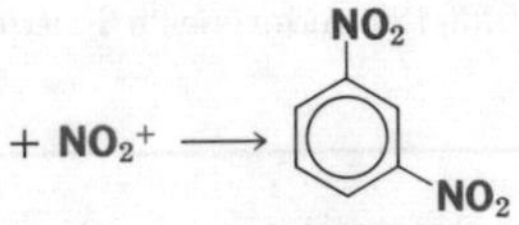

m-dinitrobenzene

Fig. 5-15. The nitro group is *meta* directing.

product is *meta*-nitrobromobenzene (abbreviated *m*-nitrobromobenzene). It is easy to see that in preparing disubstituted benzenes, the order in which the groups are introduced can be extremely important in determining the products formed.

Groups attached to a benzene ring may be classified either as *ortho-para* directing groups or as *meta* directing groups toward further substitution. Some of the more important members of each group are listed in Fig. 5-16. The student must remind himself that *the substituent already present on the ring,* not the incoming group, *decides where further substitution occurs.* Within the table the groups are ranked in order of decreasing directing power. A hydroxyl (OH) group, for example, is a much more powerful director than a halogen atom. If both groups

ortho-para directing
—NH$_2$
—OH
—CH$_3$, C$_2$H$_5$, and other alkyl groups
—Br, Cl, I

meta directing
—C≡N, —C—,
—SO$_3$H, —NO$_2$, —N(CH$_3$)$_3$

Fig. 5-16. Some important *ortho-para* and *meta* directing groups. When two groups are present in the same molecule, the influence of the group higher on the list takes precedence over that below.

were present in the same molecule, the hydroxyl group would control the position of further substitution.

Prob. 5-5. Predict what products would be formed in the mononitration of methylbenzene (toluene) and of cyanobenzene, and in the monobromination of toluene, chlorobenzene, and *p*-hydroxybromobenzene.

ORIGIN OF DIRECTIVE EFFECT

The action of *ortho-para* and *meta* directing groups may be explained by applying the same concepts used in the interpretation of Markownikoff's rule. Directive effects in aromatic substitution are really little more than an extension of that rule. Let us consider the nitration of toluene (methylbenzene) as an example.

A positively charged reagent like $^+NO_2$ attacking a toluene molecule can do so in any of three positions: *ortho, meta,* or *para.* We shall consider why it is easier to attack *para* than *meta,* leaving the case for *ortho* attack to be worked out in Prob. 5-6. Attack at the *para* position forms a carbonium ion (Fig. 5-17). This

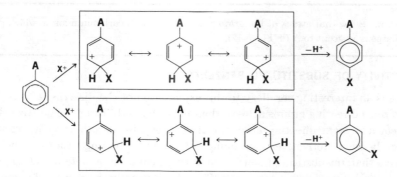

Fig. 5-17. Attack of a species X^+ at the *para* position leads to a carbonium ion in which the positive charge is shared by three carbons; on one of these the substituent A is attached. In an attack on the *meta* position, the carbons sharing the positive charge do not include the one bearing A. If A repels the adjacent charge, A is *meta* directing; if it stabilizes the charge, A is an *ortho-para* directing group.

ion is a resonance hybrid, since three formally different structures can be written for it which involve only delocalization of π electrons. In one of these structures the charge is adjacent to the methyl group, and we have seen in discussion of Markownikoff's rule that a methyl group stabilizes an adjacent positive charge.

For attack at the *meta* position, three resonance structures can also be drawn. The positive charge is not adjacent to the methyl group in any of them. Reaction at the *para* position is, therefore, easier than at the *meta,* because the methyl group helps stabilize the carbonium ion. All other *ortho-para* directing groups are like methyl because they are electron-donating groups and help to stabilize the positive charge.

Meta directing groups are electron attracting; therefore, they destabilize positive charges. Attack at the *meta* position is favored, since in that way the charge never needs to be on the carbon next to the electron-attracting group. The comparison with Markownikoff's rule can be made particularly clear if we consider A to be the *meta* directing $-\overset{+}{N}(CH_3)_3$ group and if we review Prob. 3-9 and its answer. We saw that this group induces non-Markownikoff addition, because it opposes the introduction of a second positive charge adjacent to the one already in the molecule. So it is with all the other *meta* directors—they have either a permanent positive charge, like the nitro group ($-\overset{+}{N}\overset{\overline{O}}{\underset{O}{\Big\langle}}$), or a partial positive charge resulting from charge separation ($-\overset{O}{\underset{}{\overset{\parallel}{C}}}- \longleftrightarrow -\overset{O^-}{\underset{+}{\overset{\mid}{C}}}-$). All of these groups oppose introduction of a second positive charge on an adjacent carbon atom and direct incoming groups to the *meta* position.

Prob. 5-6. Show that attack at the *ortho* position leads to a carbonium ion in which part of the charge is adjacent to A (in Fig. 5-17).

REACTIVITY OF SUBSTITUTED BENZENES

There is an interesting corollary to this explanation of the directing effects. Since *ortho-para* directing groups achieve their effect by stabilizing the positive charge formed, and *meta* directing groups achieve theirs by destabilizing it, we might expect benzene derivatives containing *ortho-para* directing groups to be more reactive than unsubstituted benzene, and those containing *meta* directing groups to be less reactive than benzene itself. That this is usually the case can be seen from Fig. 5-18, where conditions required to nitrate a variety of substituted benzenes are compared with the conditions required for benzene itself. Further substitution on nitrobenzene is quite difficult, and it is nearly impossible to nitrate dinitrobenzene further to trinitrobenzene. Toluene, on the other hand, can be trinitrated yielding trinitrotoluene, the explosive TNT, because the methyl group activates the ring. The halogens are the main exception. These *ortho-para* directing atoms also make the ring less reactive.

NOMENCLATURE

We have already seen a number of examples of the naming of aromatic compounds. Common names are largely employed for the unsubstituted hydrocarbons, such as benzene, naphthalene, and anthracene, and sometimes for simple substituted compounds, like toluene, xylene (dimethylbenzene), and phenol. More complex compounds and those lacking common names are identified by locating each sub-

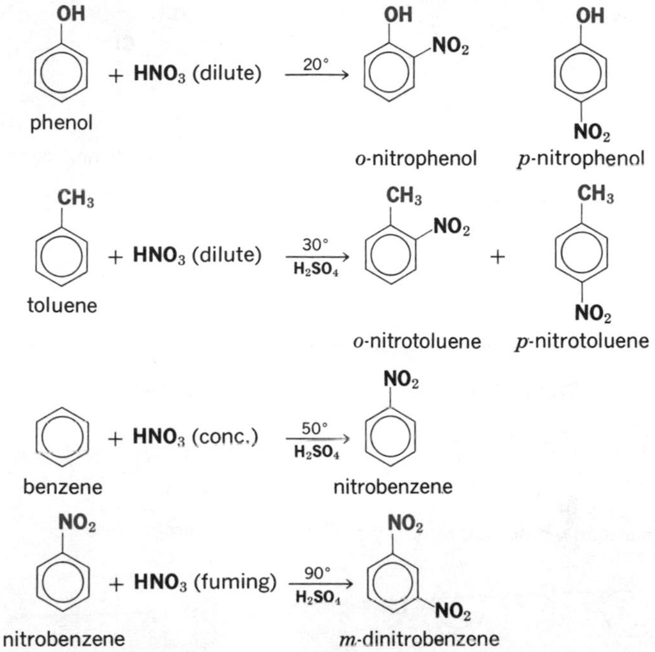

Fig. 5-18. Further substitution of a benzene ring already containing an *ortho-para* directing group (OH, CH_3) is usually easier than substitution of benzene itself. Further substitution of a benzene ring containing a *meta* directing group (NO_2) is more difficult.

stituent on the parent aromatic nucleus and giving it a designation. Figure 5-19 contains examples. Note that substituents on benzene can be located by the *ortho-meta-para* scheme as long as there are only two. When three or more substituents are present, numbers are required. The smallest number should be given to the most important substituent, or, in the case of common names like toluene, to the substituent included in the name. Aromatic hydrocarbons other than benzene are nearly always numbered; each has its own system.

Alkyl benzenes can be named in two ways, as derivatives of the aromatic or of the aliphatic hydrocarbon; although the former is more common, the latter is according to the IUPAC system. Which method is used depends on where other substituents may be located, as illustrated in Fig. 5-19. Two new common group names are encountered here for the first time—phenyl (benzene minus one hydrogen atom) and benzyl (toluene minus a methyl hydrogen atom). Additional practice in the naming of aromatic compounds will be provided by Questions 28 and 29 in the Appendix.

SOURCES OF AROMATIC HYDROCARBONS

Aromatic hydrocarbons were originally obtained mainly from coal, and aliphatic hydrocarbons mainly from petroleum. Heating coal in the absence of air leads to

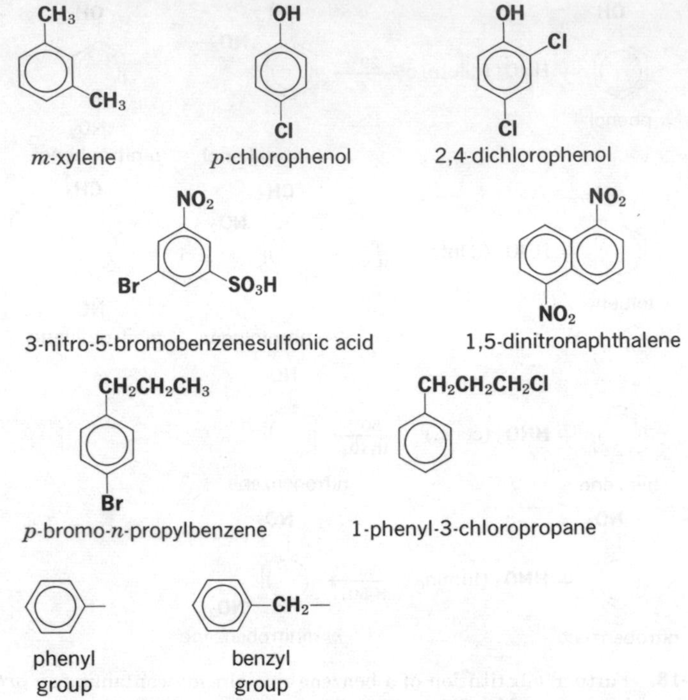

Fig. 5-19. Examples of aromatic nomenclature.

the distillation of *coal tar,* a complex mixture of compounds from which benzene, alkyl benzenes, naphthalene, anthracene, and more complex aromatic compounds may be isolated. The residue from this distillation is *coke,* which is mainly graphite. *Coal gas,* a mixture consisting mostly of hydrogen and methane, is also produced. A variety of compounds containing oxygen and nitrogen is also obtained from coal tar.

These aromatic compounds do not all exist in coal itself, but form during the strong heating involved in the distillation process. A number of the polycyclic hydrocarbons found in coal tar have the ability to cause cancer when applied to the skin. They are called *carcinogens.* 3,4-Benzpyrene, for example, is quite carcinogenic (Fig. 5-20) and occurs to the extent of 1.5% in coal tar. Before this was recognized, skin cancer was a common occupational hazard among people like chimney sweeps who came into frequent contact with coal tar. Polynuclear hydrocarbons are almost always formed to some extent whenever organic molecules are heated to high temperatures, and it is presumed that carcinogenic hydrocarbons formed in the burning of cigarettes are a main cause of lung cancer.

Coal tar has not proved, however, to be an adequate source for aromatic hydrocarbons; therefore, methods for converting aliphatic hydrocarbons from petroleum into aromatics have been developed. Passing *n*-heptane over a catalyst at 500°

coal $\xrightarrow[\text{(no } O_2)]{\text{heat}}$ coal gas + coal tar + coke

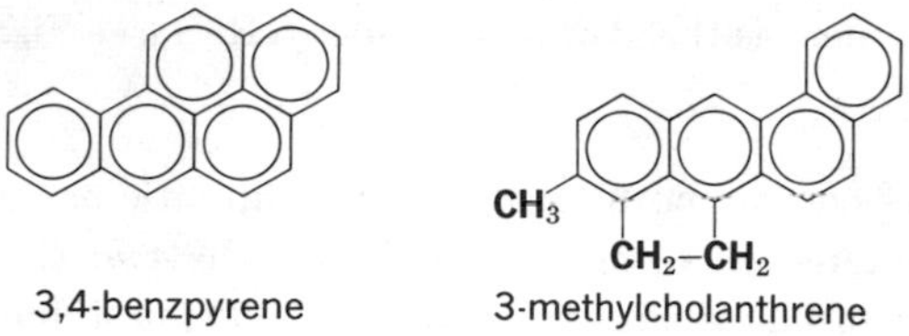

3,4-benzpyrene

3-methylcholanthrene

Fig. 5-20. Distillation of coal is an important source of many aromatic hydrocarbons, including benzene and naphthalene. The two polynuclear hydrocarbons shown are *carcinogens*. The process by which they cause cancer is not known.

converts it in high yield into toluene (Fig. 5-21); similarly, acetylene can be converted into benzene.

A number of alkyl benzenes are prepared industrially by the Friedel-Crafts reaction mentioned previously. An important example is the reaction of benzene with

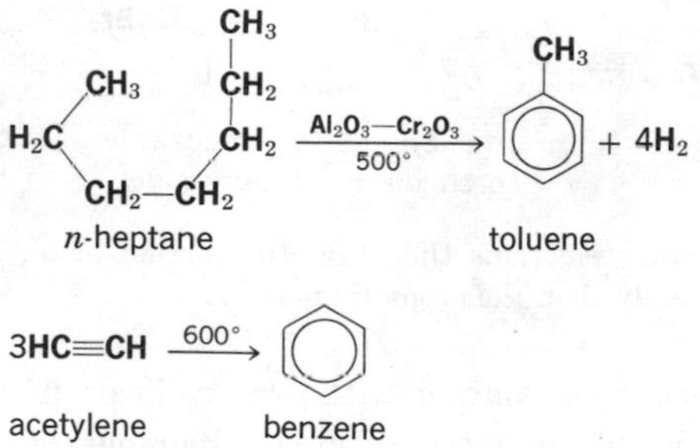

n-heptane $\xrightarrow[500°]{Al_2O_3\text{—}Cr_2O_3}$ toluene $+ 4H_2$

$3HC\equiv CH \xrightarrow{600°}$ benzene

Fig. 5-21. Toluene and other aromatic hydrocarbons may be formed by *dehydrogenation* of aliphatic hydrocarbons, and benzene by the trimerization of acetylene.

tetrapropylene, whose product is then sulfonated to furnish a synthetic detergent (Fig. 3-23). A simpler example is the formation of ethylbenzene from benzene and ethylene (Fig. 5-22). Dehydrogenation gives the extremely important molecule

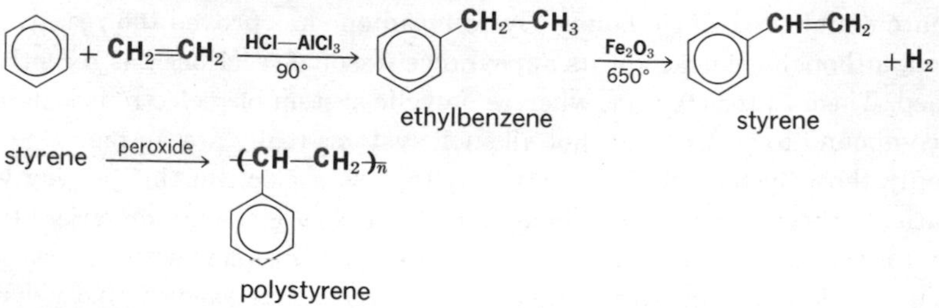

$+ CH_2=CH_2 \xrightarrow[90°]{HCl\text{—}AlCl_3}$ ethylbenzene $\xrightarrow[650°]{Fe_2O_3}$ styrene $+ H_2$

styrene $\xrightarrow{\text{peroxide}}$ polystyrene

Fig. 5-22. Many alkyl benzenes can be prepared from benzene by reaction with an alkene and an acid. Styrene is widely used in making polymers.

styrene, a useful monomer for the formation of a variety of plastics. Polystyrene is widely used in such items as toothbrush handles and plastic toys, and a copolymer of styrene and butadiene is the synthetic rubber GR–S (see Fig. 4-10).

ARYL ALKANES

The alkyl benzenes contain both aromatic and aliphatic parts; in their reactions they provide an interesting comparison between the two classes of compounds. Such molecules are often called *aryl alkanes.* The great stability of the aromatic ring system is shown in the oxidation of these compounds. The aliphatic portion of the molecule is attacked and the side chain, no matter how long, is removed (Fig. 5-23). Again, while ionic halogenation with acids as catalysts causes the

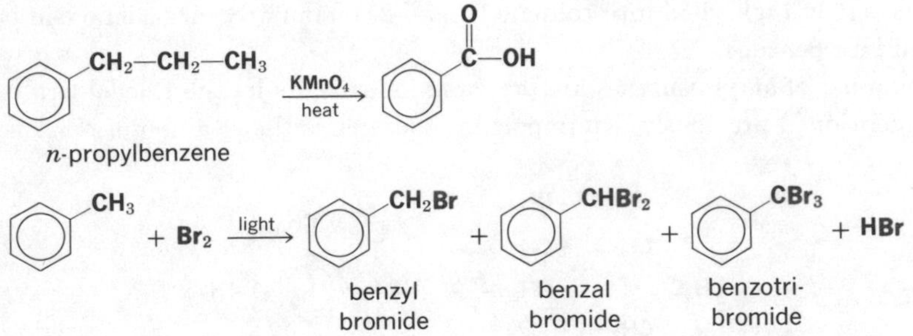
CH₂—CH₂—CH₃
KMnO₄
heat
C—OH
O
n-propylbenzene
CH₃
+ Br₂
light
CH₂Br
CHBr₂
CBr₃
+ HBr
benzyl bromide
benzal bromide
benzotri-bromide

Fig. 5-23. In many reactions the aliphatic portion of an alkyl benzene is attacked more readily than the aromatic portion.

benzene ring to react, halogenation with free radicals in the presence of light induces substitution in the aliphatic portion of the molecule.

NONBENZENOID AROMATIC HYDROCARBONS

One might well inquire whether it is possible to have an aromatic compound that does not contain a benzene ring. A four-membered ring containing two double bonds (cyclobutadiene) or an eight-membered ring with four double bonds (cyclooctatetraene) might be expected to display delocalization of electrons and other aromatic properties. Yet these two compounds do not. Cyclooctatetraene is a well-known chemical whose double bonds are normally reactive; the molecule contains alternate double and single bonds. Cyclobutadiene has proved too reactive to be isolated, although evidence for its appearance in some reactions has recently been obtained. Theory predicts that, whereas a cyclic system of π electrons is necessary for a compound to be aromatic, not all such systems really are. In fact, we predict that only those systems with 2, 6, 10, 14, 18, . . . π electrons in the ring will be aromatic. In these systems the number of π electrons is given by the series $(4n + 2)$ where n is zero or an integer 1, 2, 3, etc. Those cyclic systems with only $4n$ π electrons, like cyclobutadiene with 4 π electrons or cyclooctatetraene with 8 π electrons, will not be aromatic (Fig. 5-24). In this respect, there are closed shells of aromatic stability analogous to the closed shells of 2, 8, 18, . . . electrons observed in atomic structure.

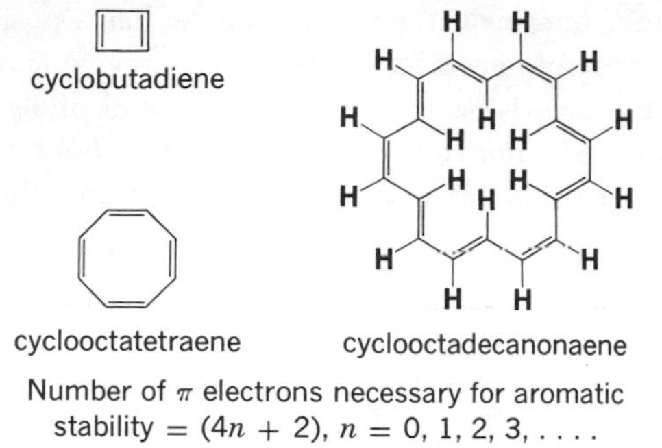

cyclobutadiene

cyclooctatetraene   cyclooctadecanonaene

Number of π electrons necessary for aromatic
stability $= (4n + 2)$, $n = 0, 1, 2, 3, \ldots$.

Fig. 5-24. Cyclobutadiene and cyclooctatetraene, with 4 and 8 π electrons respectively, do not meet the $4n + 2$ requirement for aromatic stability. Cyclooctadecanonaene, with 18 π electrons, fits the rule ($n = 4$) and has some aromatic characteristics.

One would predict, then, that a ten-membered ring with five double bonds (a total of 10 π electrons) would be an aromatic system. A derivative of such a system has recently been prepared and does indeed display aromatic characteristics, despite the inability of ten atoms with 120° bond angles to fit comfortably into a ring. An 18-membered ring containing nine double bonds has also been prepared and shows definite aromatic properties.

Prob. 5-7. Which of the following systems would you expect to be aromatic and which non-aromatic, according to the $4n + 2$ rule, assuming they could be made without undue bond strain: (a) a 20-membered ring with 10 double bonds, (b) a 30-membered ring with 15 double bonds?

The aromatic character shows up in an even more striking way in certain organic ions. The carbonium ions discussed up to this point have been highly reactive and short-lived. Nevertheless, 1-bromocycloheptatriene exists as an ionic salt which is stable, high-melting, and soluble in water; notice in Fig. 5-25 that its

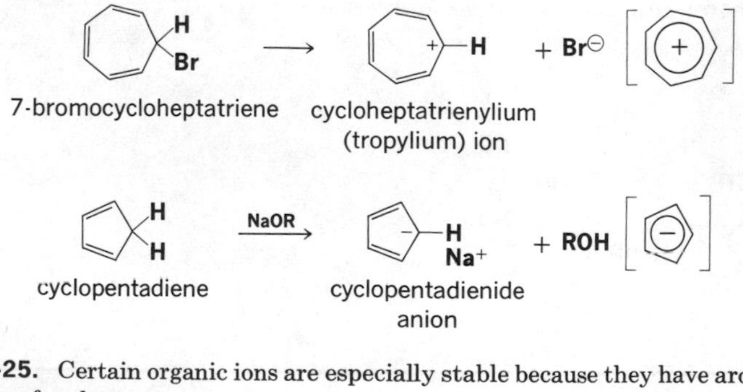

7-bromocycloheptatriene   cycloheptatrienylium
                            (tropylium) ion

cyclopentadiene   cyclopentadienide
                            anion

Fig. 5-25. Certain organic ions are especially stable because they have aromatic sextets of π electrons.

seven-membered ring contains three double bonds, has a positive charge and *six* π electrons, and is therefore aromatic. Analogously, cyclopentadiene, in contrast to nearly all other hydrocarbons, is as acidic as some alcohols, and is readily converted into its sodium salt; notice in the figure that its 5-membered ring contains two double bonds and a pair of unbonded electrons and thus has an aromatic sextet of electrons.

Prob. 5-8. Using the $4n + 2$ rule, explain why bromocyclopentadiene does not form a stable carbonium ion nor cycloheptatriene a stable anion.

Prob. 5-9. Draw structures for the following compounds:
  (a) *p*-dichlorobenzene
  (b) 1,3,5-trinitrobenzene
  (c) *m*-bromochlorobenzene
  (d) *p*-nitrobenzenesulfonic acid
  (e) isopropylbenzene
  (f) toluene
  (g) *p*-chlorostyrene
  (h) 1-nitronaphthalene

Prob. 5-10. Name the following compounds:

(a) 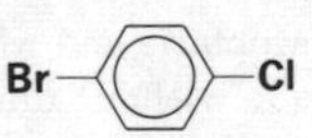 Br—⬡—Cl   (d)

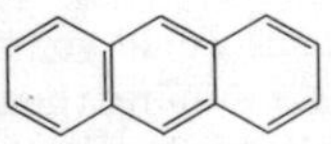

(b) 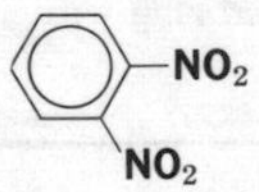 ⬡—NO₂
         |
        NO₂   (e) 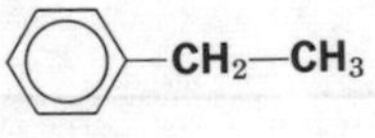 ⬡—CH₂—CH₃

(c) 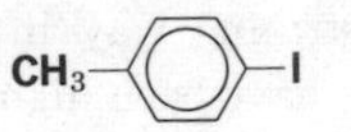 CH₃—⬡—I   (f) 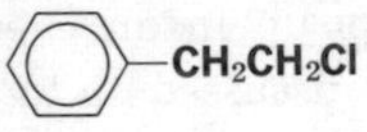 ⬡—CH₂CH₂Cl

Prob. 5-11. What would you predict to be the major product of the reaction of each of the compounds shown with chlorine and ferric chloride?

        CH₃   NO₂
(a) 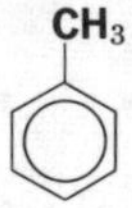   ⬡   (c) 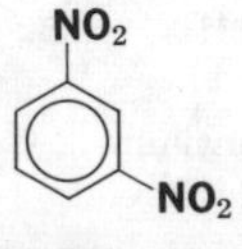   ⬡
                            NO₂

       OCH₃   OH
(b)    ⬡   (d) 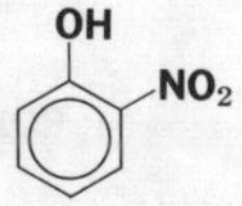   ⬡—NO₂
        Cl

Prob. 5-12.   Show how you could prepare, in the laboratory, each of the following from benzene and any other necessary organic or inorganic materials.
   (a) bromobenzene
   (b) *m*-nitrochlorobenzene
   (c) *p*-chlorobenzenesulfonic acid.

Prob. 5-13.   *p*-Cymene occurs in eucalyptus oil and oil of thyme and has been shown to be *p*-isopropyltoluene. How might this compound be prepared from toluene?

Prob. 5-14.   Natural musk (muscone) is obtained from a small male musk deer. The structure of muscone was given in Fig. 2-11. Artificial musk is 3-*tert*-butyl-2,4,6-trinitrotoluene. Draw its structure.

Prob. 5-15.   The three isomeric dimethylbenzenes are known as xylenes and are obtained from coal oil or, by a special cracking process, from petroleum. The three have very similar boiling points and so are difficult to separate by distillation. A process for separating them has been devised; it depends for its success on the fact that *m*-xylene undergoes aromatic substitution reactions more rapidly than the other two isomers. Review what has been said about the ease of aromatic substitution and explain why the *m*-isomer reacts faster than the *o*- and *p*-isomers.

CHAPTER

ALCOHOLS, PHENOLS, ETHERS

Despite the extensive attention we have accorded the hydrocarbons, they are not typical molecules; instead, they are the exceptions. Most organic molecules contain elements other than carbon and hydrogen, and the presence of these other elements profoundly influences the chemical and physical behavior of the compounds.

First, there are the alcohols. A compound is designated an alcohol when oxygen in the form of a hydroxyl group (—OH) appears in an aliphatic system. The best-known member of the class is ethyl alcohol, CH_3CH_2OH. The general formula for an alcohol is ROH, the R representing the aliphatic portion of the molecule; alcohols may be regarded as derivatives of water, in which an alkyl group replaces one hydrogen atom. The alcohols bear some physical resemblance both to the hydrocarbons and to water; ethyl alcohol is soluble in both water and in gasoline. Its boiling point is lower than that of water, although its molecular weight is much greater.

Similarly, the amines, whose general formula may be RNH_2, R_2NH, or R_3N, can be considered derivatives of ammonia (NH_3); the mercaptans, RSH, can be said to derive from hydrogen sulfide (H_2S). This is quite apparent in the parallels between the derivatives and their dissociation constants (see Table 6-1). Methyl alcohol, like water, is neutral; ethylamine, like ammonia, is basic; and ethyl mercaptan, like hydrogen sulfide, is acidic. The terms in Table 6-1 (K_a, pK_a, K_b, pK_b) are defined as follows: For an acid HA, the *acidic dissociation constant*

$$K_a = \frac{(H^+)(A^-)}{(HA)} \; ;$$

for base B the *basic dissociation constant*

Table 6-1.   Parallels between Derivatives and Their Dissociation Constants

Compound	Formula	K_a	pK_a	K_b	pK_b
water	HOH	2.0×10^{-16}	15.7		
methyl alcohol	CH_3OH	3.2×10^{-16}	15.5		
ammonia	NH_3			1.8×10^{-5}	4.7
ethylamine	$C_2H_5NH_2$			4.3×10^{-4}	3.4
hydrogen sulfide	H_2S	1.0×10^{-7}	7.0		
ethyl mercaptan	C_2H_5SH	3.2×10^{-11}	10.5		

$$K_b = \frac{(BH^+)(OH^-)}{(B)};$$

$pK_a = -\log K_a$ and $pK_b = -\log K_b$. Note that K_a increases with increasing acid strength and K_b increases with increasing base strength, while the reverse is true of pK_a and pK_b.

PHYSICAL PROPERTIES OF ALCOHOLS

The chemical behavior of alcohols is almost entirely determined by the hydroxyl group, since the alkyl portion of the molecule is unreactive. Nevertheless, the latter does affect the physical properties of an alcohol, especially such properties as boiling point and solubility in water. The student should note that the solubility of an alcohol in water decreases as the size of its alkyl group increases (Table 6-2). Within the homologous series of *normal* alcohols, the boiling point increases with greater molecular weight.

Table 6-2.   Correlation of the Size of the Alkyl Group in Alcohols with the Solubility in Water and Boiling Point

Name	Alcohol	Solubility in water, g/100 ml	B.p.,°
methyl alcohol	CH_3OH	∞	64.9
ethyl alcohol	CH_3CH_2OH	∞	78.5
n-propyl alcohol	$CH_3CH_2CH_2OH$	∞	97.2
n-butyl alcohol	$CH_3(CH_2)_2CH_2OH$	9	117.5
n-pentyl alcohol	$CH_3(CH_2)_3CH_2OH$	2.7	138.0
n-hexyl alcohol	$CH_3(CH_2)_4CH_2OH$	0.6	158.0

Just as they do in water, the hydroxyl groups in alcohols form *hydrogen bonds* with one another—that is, they form loose bonds between the hydrogen atom of one hydroxyl group and the oxygen atom of another. This hydrogen bonding accounts for the high boiling point of ethanol (78°) compared to that of propane ($-42°$), even though both have about the same molecular weight (Fig. 6-1). Hydrogen bonding is not as extensive in ethanol as in water, and so the boiling

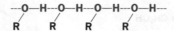

Fig. 6-1. The acidic hydrogen attached to the oxygen atom in an alcohol forms a weak bond (called a hydrogen bond) to the oxygen atom of another molecule. In order to vaporize an alcohol molecule, these hydrogen bonds must be broken. As a consequence, boiling points of alcohols are much higher than those of hydrocarbons of the same molecular weight.

point is lower, despite its greater molecular weight. Ethanol is completely soluble in water, but when a liter of ethanol is added to a liter of water at 20°, only 1.93 liters of the mixture is produced. Since the hydrocarbon-like ethyl groups of the alcohol cannot hydrogen bond, they slip into holes in the water structure and do not increase the total volume quite proportionally.

When two or more hydroxyl groups are present in an organic molecule, hydrogen bonding increases, and the boiling point rises sharply. Common examples are ethylene glycol ($HOCH_2CH_2OH$, b.p. 197°) and glycerol, also called glycerine ($HOCH_2CHCH_2OH$, b.p. 290°).
$$OH$$

NOMENCLATURE OF ALCOHOLS

The compounds in the homologous series of alcohols illustrate one method of naming alcohols. This method is the so-called substituent or group system. In this system an alcohol is named by adding the word alcohol to the name of the alkyl group. All of the group names learned in Table 1-2 may be used for naming alcohols. A few other groups are also frequently encountered (Fig. 6-2).

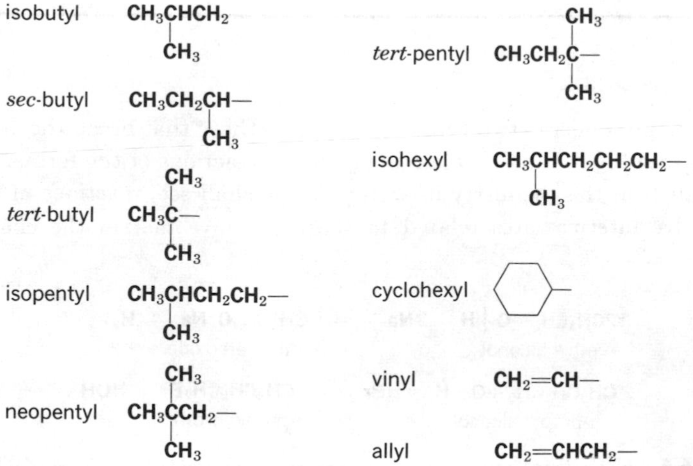

isobutyl CH_3CHCH_2
               CH_3

sec-butyl CH_3CH_2CH-
                 CH_3

             CH_3
tert-butyl CH_3C-
             CH_3

isopentyl $CH_3CHCH_2CH_2-$
              CH_3

            CH_3
neopentyl CH_3CCH_2-
              CH_3

                     CH_3
tert-pentyl CH_3CH_2C-
                     CH_3

isohexyl $CH_3CHCH_2CH_2CH_2-$
                 CH_3

cyclohexyl

vinyl $CH_2=CH-$

allyl $CH_2=CHCH_2-$

Fig. 6-2. The names of the groups shown are encountered frequently, and if any extensive study of chemistry or biochemistry is contemplated, they should be committed to memory.

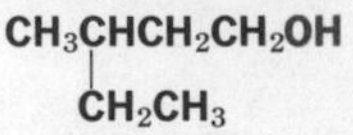

CH₃CHCH₂CH₂OH
    |
    CH₂CH₃
3-methyl-1-pentanol

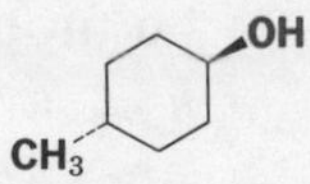

trans-4-methylcyclohexanol

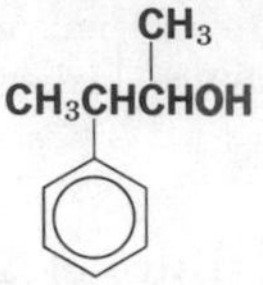

        CH₃
        |
CH₃CHCHOH
    |
    (benzene ring)

3-phenyl-2-butanol

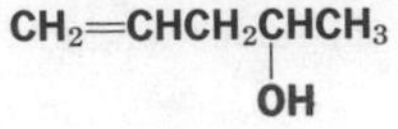

CH₂=CHCH₂CHCH₃
              |
              OH
4-penten-2-ol
(not 1-penten-4-ol)

Fig. 6-3. Application of the IUPAC system of nomenclature to alcohols is illustrated by the compounds shown.

In the IUPAC system for naming alcohols, the characteristic ending is -ol, and the system is numbered in order to give the carbon atom carrying the hydroxyl group its smallest number (Fig. 6-3). For an introduction to the nomenclature of alcohols see the Appendix, Questions 30 through 32.

Prob. 6-1. Name the following alcohols by the IUPAC system and arrange them in order of increasing predicted boiling points.

(a) 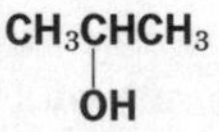 CH₃CHCH₃
         |
         OH

(b) 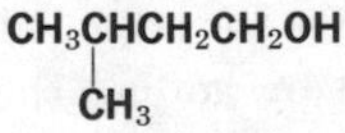 CH₃CHCH₂CH₂OH
         |
         CH₃

(c) 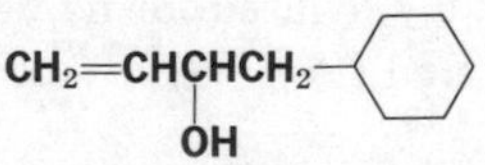 CH₂=CHCHCH₂—⬡
            |
            OH

(d) 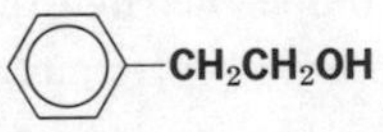 ⬡—CH₂CH₂OH

ALCOHOLS AS ACIDS

Alcohols mainly undergo two types of reactions: those that break the O—H bond and those that break the C—O bond (Fig. 6-4). Reactions of the former type find their parallels in the chemistry of water. As we shall see, reactions of the C—O bond involve intermediates related to those we have met in the chemistry of alkenes.

2CH₃CH₂—O⧸H + 2Na ⟶ 2CH₃CH₂O⁻Na⁺ + H₂↑
ethyl alcohol   sodium ethoxide

CH₃CH₂CH₂⧸O—H + HBr ⟶ CH₃CH₂CH₂Br + HOH
n-propyl alcohol   n-propyl bromide

Fig. 6-4. Alcohols may undergo reactions which involve the breaking of either the C—O or O—H bond. The evolution of bubbles of hydrogen gas when a piece of sodium metal is added provides a good visual test for the presence of an O—H group in an organic molecule.

The sodium salt of an alcohol, conveniently formed by reaction of an alcohol with metallic sodium, is the organic analog of sodium hydroxide, and in alcoholic solution is often used in organic reactions where a water-free basic solution is needed. It can be used in the same way as sodium hydroxide to neutralize an acid

$$RO^- Na^+ + H^+X^- \longrightarrow ROH + NaX$$

$$ROH + Na^+OH^- \rightleftharpoons RO^-Na^+ + H_2O$$

Fig. 6-5. Sodium alkoxides are strong bases and react with acids.

(Fig. 6-5) and has a slightly greater basic strength than sodium hydroxide. If sodium hydroxide is dissolved in ethyl alcohol, an equilibrium is established instantaneously with sodium ethoxide.

Prob. 6-2. Suppose that you have three bottles of chemicals, one bottle containing 1-pentanol, one, 1-hexene, and one, *n*-hexane. Somehow the labels of these three bottles become lost, so you do not know which compound was in which bottle. Describe simple chemical tests which you could apply to small samples of each in order to determine which was which. The chemical tests should produce a *visible* change if positive. Describe what you would see in each test.

In discussing the chemistry of alcohols it is convenient to classify them as primary (1°) alcohols if the hydroxyl group is attached to a primary carbon (see Fig. 1-24), secondary (2°) if it is attached to a secondary carbon, and tertiary (3°) if it is attached to a tertiary carbon. As acids, primary alcohols are about as weak as water, while secondary and tertiary alcohols are weaker. Conversely, the salt of a tertiary alcohol (for instance, potassium *tert*-butoxide) is a considerably stronger base than sodium hydroxide. Some alcohols and their corresponding alkoxides are compared as acids and bases in Fig. 6-6.

	Alcohols	Alkoxides	
Acidic strength increases ↑	HOH	HO$^-$	Basic strength increases ↓
	CH$_3$OH	CH$_3$O$^-$	
	CH$_3$CH$_2$OH	CH$_3$CH$_2$O$^-$	
	(CH$_3$)$_2$CHOH	(CH$_3$)$_2$CHO$^-$	
	(CH$_3$)$_3$COH	(CH$_3$)$_3$CO$^-$	

Fig. 6-6. Since methyl and other alkyl groups are electron donors, their attachment to an alcohol decreases the degree of dissociation.

Prob. 6-3. Classify the alcohols of Fig. 6-3 and Prob. 6-1 as primary, secondary, or tertiary.

Prob. 6-4. On which side would you expect the position of equilibrium to lie in each of the following reactions (see Table 6-1 and Fig. 6-6)?

$$CH_3O^-Na^+ + (CH_3)_3COH \rightleftharpoons CH_3OH + (CH_3)_3CO^-Na^+$$

$$Na^+OH^- + CH_3CH_2SH \rightleftharpoons H_2O + CH_3CH_2S^-Na^+$$

$$NH_4^+Cl^- + (CH_3)_2CHO^-Na^+ \rightleftharpoons NH_3 + (CH_3)_2CHOH + NaCl$$

ESTERS

By elimination of a molecule of water, primary and secondary alcohols react with sulfuric acid to form alkyl hydrogen sulfates. Molecules of this type are known as *esters*. This reaction is reversible, as we saw in Fig. 3-20. Analogous esters may be formed from nitric and nitrous acid, and from organic acids (Chapter 11). In the formation of these esters the acid loses a hydroxyl group and the alcohol a proton. Thus, only the O—H bond of the alcohol is broken.

Among these esters is nitroglycerine, a pale yellow oily liquid first discovered in 1846 (Fig. 6-7). Nitroglycerine is sensitive to shock and detonates on impact with

$$CH_3CH_2OH + HOSOH \rightleftharpoons CH_3CH_2OSOH + H_2O$$

ethyl alcohol   ethyl hydrogen sulfate

$$CH_3CHCH_2CH_2OH + HON{=}O \rightleftharpoons CH_3CHCH_2CH_2ONO + H_2O$$
$$| \phantom{HON{=}O} |$$
$$CH_3 \phantom{CHCH_2CH_2OH + HON{=}O \rightleftharpoons CH_3C} CH_3$$

isopentyl alcohol   isopentyl nitrite

$$HOCH_2CHCH_2OH + 3HONO_2 \rightleftharpoons O_2NOCH_2CHCH_2ONO_2 + 3H_2O$$
$$| |$$
$$OH ONO_2$$

glycerol   glyceryl trinitrate (nitroglycerine)

$$CH_3(CH_2)_{10}CH_2OH + HOSO_2OH \rightleftharpoons CH_3(CH_2)_{10}CH_2OSO_2OH$$
1-dodecanol
(lauryl alcohol) $\downarrow$ NaHCO_3

$$CH_3(CH_2)_{10}CH_2OSO_2O^-Na^+$$
sodium lauryl sulfate

Fig. 6-7. Alcohols react with acids to form esters. Among useful esters of inorganic acids isopentyl nitrite is used for the relief of pain in certain heart conditions, glyceryl trinitrate is the correct name for nitroglycerine, and sodium lauryl sulfate is a detergent used in toothpaste.

the ground when a container encasing the compound is dropped. It was used very little until Alfred Nobel of Sweden discovered, in 1866, that a mixture of the liquid with diatomaceous earth, sawdust, or other materials left its explosive properties intact but removed its sensitivity to shock. In this form, known as dynamite, it even can be burned without exploding.* A small amount of a shock-

* Reportedly. The authors have not verified this by experiment, and do not recommend its verification.

sensitive explosive (called a detonator) will cause dynamite to explode (Fig. 6-8). Today nitroglycerine is used in combination with nitrocellulose in gunpowder and solid propellants. Nobel amassed a great fortune and left the bulk of it for the establishment of the Nobel prizes, and income from the investment of this fortune still provides the money for these prizes.

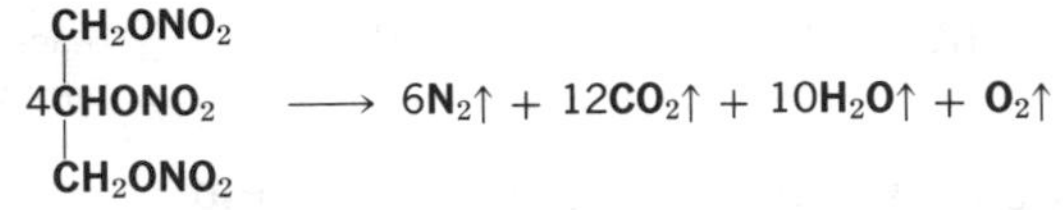

$$
4\underset{\underset{CH_2ONO_2}{|}}{\overset{\overset{CH_2ONO_2}{|}}{CHONO_2}} \longrightarrow 6N_2\uparrow + 12CO_2\uparrow + 10H_2O\uparrow + O_2\uparrow
$$

nitroglycerine

$$
O_2NOCH_2-\underset{\underset{CH_2ONO_2}{|}}{\overset{\overset{CH_2ONO_2}{|}}{C}}-CH_2ONO_2
$$

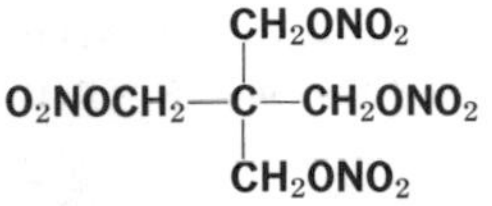

pentaerythrityl tetranitrate (PETN)

Fig. 6-8. Nitroglycerine explodes by a process of internal oxidation-reduction, liberating large amounts of gas and heat. Nitrate esters of a number of other polyhydroxy compounds, including PETN, are also used as explosives.

Prob. 6-5. Esters of phosphoric acid (H_3PO_4) play important roles in biological systems. Genes, for instance, which carry hereditary information, have phosphate esters as an integral part of their structure. It is possible to replace all three hydrogen atoms in phosphoric acid by alkyl groups. Write equations for the formation of ethyl dihydrogen phosphate, diethyl hydrogen phosphate and triethyl phosphate from ethyl alcohol and phosphoric acid.

ALKYL HALIDES AND ALKENES FROM ALCOHOLS

One of the characteristic and important reactions of the carbon–oxygen bond of an alcohol is the replacement of the hydroxyl group by a halogen atom. The formation of *n*-propyl bromide from *n*-propyl alcohol and hydrogen bromide has already been mentioned (Fig. 6-4). Primary, secondary, and tertiary alcohols all undergo this reaction, but the conditions required to bring about conversion are quite different for each. These differences form the basis of the *Lucas test,* which is used to differentiate the three types of alcohols. When a tertiary alcohol is dissolved in a solution of zinc chloride in strong hydrochloric acid, an immediate reaction occurs and a distinct layer of the tertiary chloride separates. With the same reagents secondary alcohols usually react within five minutes, while primary alcohols require a much longer time for any evidence of reaction (Fig. 6-9).

The same order of reactivity—tertiary $>$ secondary $>$ primary alcohols—is observed in another reaction of alcohols with acid. Heating an alcohol with sulfuric acid results in loss of water and formation of an alkene. The alkyl hydrogen sulfate is the usual intermediate, and the net result is the reversal of the reactions by which sulfuric acid adds to an alkene (Fig. 3-12). Other dehydrating agents such

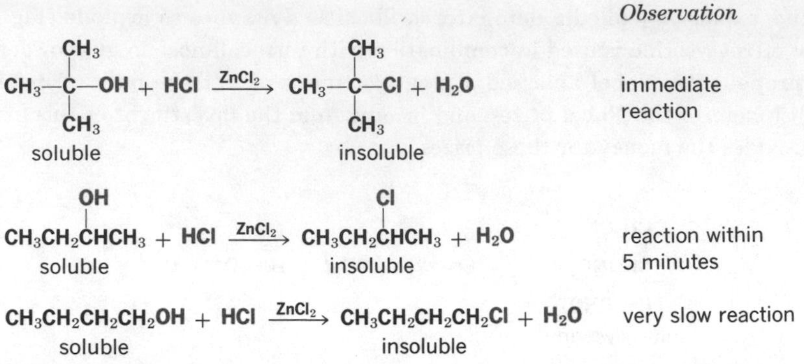

Observation

$$CH_3-\underset{\underset{CH_3}{|}}{\overset{\overset{CH_3}{|}}{C}}-OH + HCl \xrightarrow{ZnCl_2} CH_3-\underset{\underset{CH_3}{|}}{\overset{\overset{CH_3}{|}}{C}}-Cl + H_2O$$

immediate
reaction

soluble   insoluble

$$CH_3CH_2\overset{\overset{OH}{|}}{C}HCH_3 + HCl \xrightarrow{ZnCl_2} CH_3CH_2\overset{\overset{Cl}{|}}{C}HCH_3 + H_2O$$

reaction within
5 minutes

soluble   insoluble

$$CH_3CH_2CH_2CH_2OH + HCl \xrightarrow{ZnCl_2} CH_3CH_2CH_2CH_2Cl + H_2O$$

very slow reaction

soluble   insoluble

Fig. 6-9. The Lucas test differentiates primary, secondary, and tertiary alcohols by their varying ease of conversion to chlorides. A separate layer of alkyl chloride is observed in a positive test.

as phosphoric acid or alumina can also be used. In many cases the dehydration may proceed in more than one direction. The major product may then be predicted by *Saytzeff's rule,* which says that *the alkene with the fewest hydrogen atoms attached to the double bond is formed in greatest amount* (Fig. 6-10).

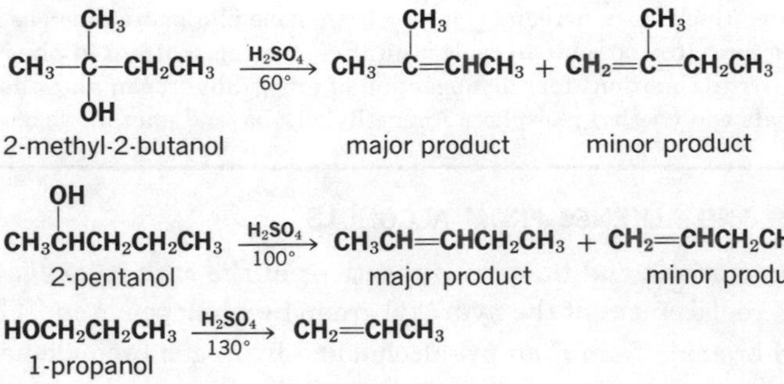

$$CH_3-\underset{\underset{OH}{|}}{\overset{\overset{CH_3}{|}}{C}}-CH_2CH_3 \xrightarrow[60°]{H_2SO_4} CH_3-\overset{\overset{CH_3}{|}}{C}=CHCH_3 + CH_2=\overset{\overset{CH_3}{|}}{C}-CH_2CH_3$$

2-methyl-2-butanol   major product   minor product

$$CH_3\overset{\overset{OH}{|}}{C}HCH_2CH_2CH_3 \xrightarrow[100°]{H_2SO_4} CH_3CH=CHCH_2CH_3 + CH_2=CHCH_2CH_2CH_3$$

2-pentanol   major product   minor product

$$HOCH_2CH_2CH_3 \xrightarrow[130°]{H_2SO_4} CH_2=CHCH_3$$

1-propanol

Fig. 6-10. Alcohols are dehydrated when heated with sulfuric acid or other dehydrating agents. A greater amount of the alkene with the fewer hydrogens on the double bond is formed. A higher temperature is required to dehydrate a primary alcohol than a secondary alcohol and a higher temperature for a secondary than a tertiary alcohol.

The close relationship among *tert*-butyl alcohol, isobutylene, and *tert*-butyl chloride is summarized in Fig. 6-11. In the formation of all three, the trimethyl-carbonium ion plays a central role. A positive charge can be placed with relative ease on a tertiary carbon compared to a secondary or primary carbon, since methyl groups have more electrons than hydrogen atoms with which to stabilize a positive charge. This same effect was noted in analyzing Markownikoff's rule.

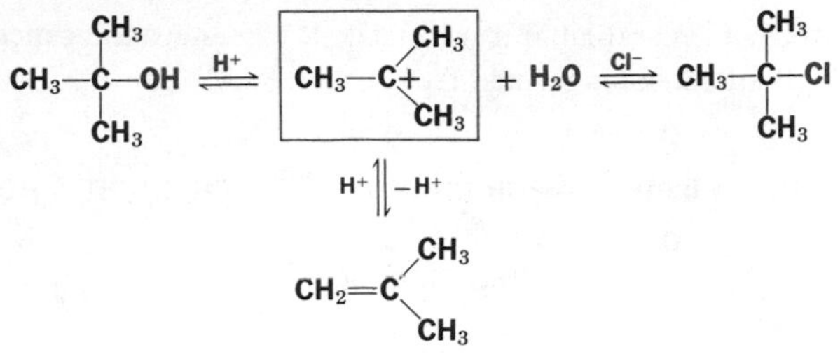

Fig. 6-11. Carbonium ions are intermediates in many acid-catalyzed reactions of alcohols, alkenes, and halides.

OXIDATION OF ALCOHOLS

Primary and secondary alcohols are readily attacked by oxidizing agents to form acids and ketones, respectively. Tertiary alcohols do not react, since the point of attack is usually the hydrogen atom attached to the carbon bearing the hydroxyl group (Fig. 6-12).

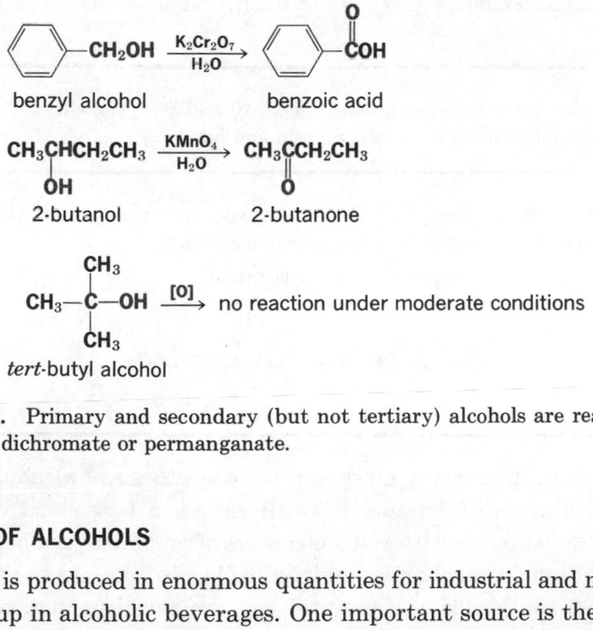

Fig. 6-12. Primary and secondary (but not tertiary) alcohols are readily oxidized by dichromate or permanganate.

SYNTHESES OF ALCOHOLS

Ethyl alcohol is produced in enormous quantities for industrial and medicinal uses. It also turns up in alcoholic beverages. One important source is the fermentation of grain, a process whose details will be discussed in Chapter 14. Today, however, more than half of the industrial alcohol is produced from ethylene (Fig. 6-13). Ethyl hydrogen sulfate, formed by the addition of sulfuric acid to ethylene, is allowed to react with water. Ethanol forms and sulfuric acid is regenerated. Produced in this way, ethanol sells for only a few cents a gallon. Forming an alcohol by adding sulfuric acid to a double bond, and then hydrolyzing the resulting hydrogen sulfate, is a general laboratory method. The steps are exactly the reverse of those by which an alkene is formed from an alcohol.

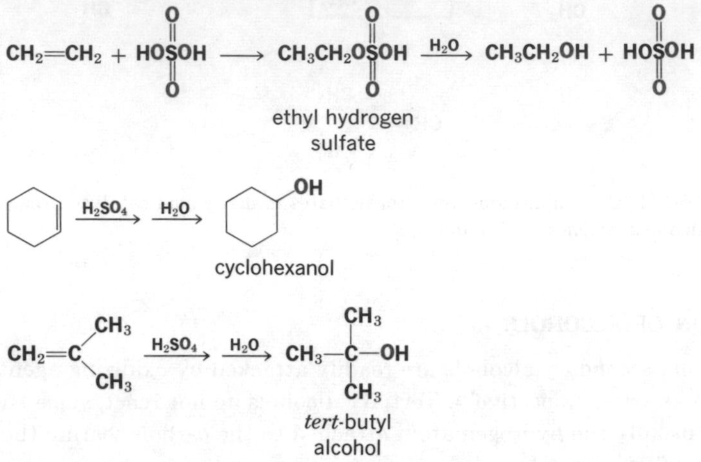

$$CH_2{=}CH_2 + HO\overset{\overset{O}{\parallel}}{\underset{\underset{O}{\parallel}}{S}}OH \longrightarrow CH_3CH_2O\overset{\overset{O}{\parallel}}{\underset{\underset{O}{\parallel}}{S}}OH \xrightarrow{H_2O} CH_3CH_2OH + HO\overset{\overset{O}{\parallel}}{\underset{\underset{O}{\parallel}}{S}}OH$$

ethyl hydrogen
sulfate

cyclohexanol

$$CH_2{=}C\overset{CH_3}{\underset{CH_3}{\big<}} \xrightarrow{H_2SO_4} \xrightarrow{H_2O} CH_3{-}\overset{\overset{CH_3}{|}}{\underset{\underset{CH_3}{|}}{C}}{-}OH$$

tert-butyl
alcohol

Fig. 6-13. Hydration of ethylene is now the main source of pure ethyl alcohol. Two additional examples are shown of the hydration of alkenes promoted by sulfuric acid.

Prob. 6-6. Making use of the reactions of Figs. 6-10 and 6-13, show how 1-propanol can be converted to 2-propanol, using only sulfuric acid and water.

Prob. 6-7. What reagents and conditions could you use to carry out the following conversions? In both cases two separate reactions are necessary.

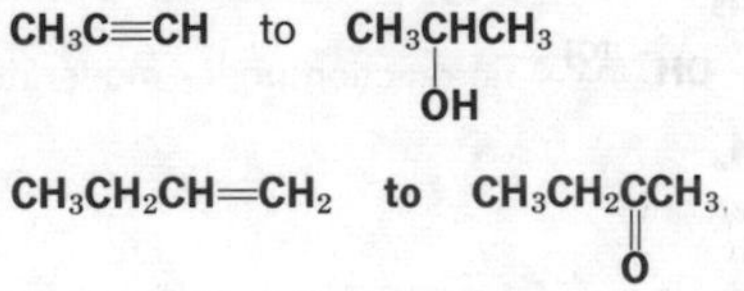

$$CH_3C{\equiv}CH \quad to \quad CH_3\underset{\underset{OH}{|}}{C}HCH_3$$

$$CH_3CH_2CH{=}CH_2 \quad to \quad CH_3CH_2\underset{\underset{O}{\parallel}}{C}CH_3$$

A second general laboratory method for the synthesis of alcohols involves the reaction of an alkene with borane (BH_3). Borane is a Lewis acid which exists as diborane, B_2H_6, and reacts with the π electrons of an alkene, adding to the double bond. The resultant organoborane may be oxidized to an alcohol with hydrogen peroxide (Fig. 6-14). Yields in these reactions are excellent and, since the boron atom is the attacking acid, the net result is addition of the elements of water in anti-Markownikoff fashion.

Prob. 6-8. Refer to the table of electronic structure in Chapter 1 (Fig. 1-10) and write the electronic formula for BH_3. Why is it a Lewis acid?

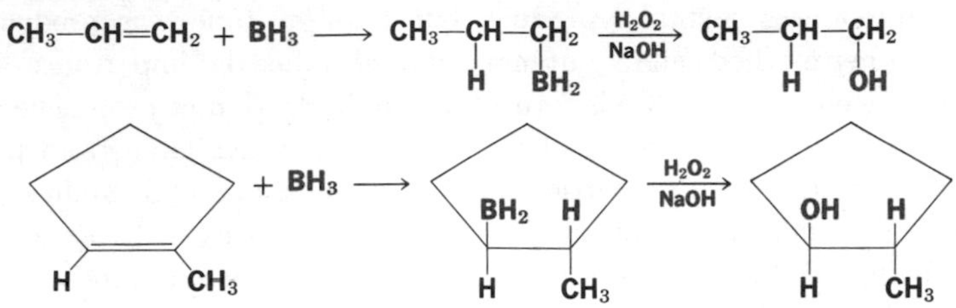

CH$_3$—CH=CH$_2$ + BH$_3$ $\longrightarrow$ CH$_3$—CH—CH$_2$ $\xrightarrow[\text{NaOH}]{\text{H}_2\text{O}_2}$ CH$_3$—CH—CH$_2$
                                                  | | | |
                                                  H   BH$_2$ H   OH

1-methylcyclopentene   trans-2-methylcyclopentanol

Fig. 6-14. Addition of borane to a double bond followed by oxidation to an alcohol results in a net hydration in an anti-Markownikoff manner. Note that the result is a *cis* addition of the elements of water.

Another common alcohol is methanol, which is sometimes called wood alcohol since it was formerly made by heating wood in the absence of air. Methanol is now produced industrially by special processes, one of which is the hydrogenation of carbon monoxide (Fig. 6-15). Methanol is said to have been first recognized as

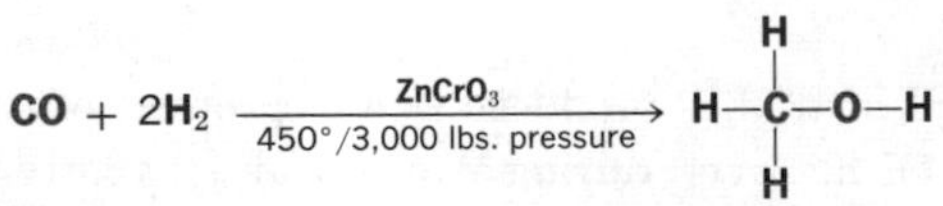

$$\text{CO} + 2\text{H}_2 \xrightarrow[450°/3{,}000 \text{ lbs. pressure}]{\text{ZnCrO}_3} \begin{array}{c} \text{H} \\ | \\ \text{H}—\text{C}—\text{O}—\text{H} \\ | \\ \text{H} \end{array}$$

Fig. 6-15. Hydrogenation of carbon monoxide gives methanol. It is also synthesized industrially by the controlled oxidation of methane.

a distinct substance by Robert Boyle in 1661; its structure was proved in 1834. It is widely used as a nonpermanent antifreeze, and is converted industrially into formaldehyde and a variety of other molecules.

Like ethanol, methanol is inebriating. However, it is much more poisonous, probably because it is oxidized in the body to formaldehyde and formic acid. For this reason methanol is sometimes added to ethanol to denature it, that is, to make it unfit for drinking. Death from methanol poisoning occurs from respiratory paralysis preceded by visual disturbances; blindness can result in nonfatal cases. Both may sometimes be prevented by administration of sodium bicarbonate or other bases.

A few other alcohols derive from agricultural sources. Among these are *n*-pentyl and isopentyl alcohols (3-methyl-1-butanol). These are the principal constituents of fusel oil, a fermentation product which flavors many liquors but leads to hangovers. Another is *n*-butyl alcohol, produced in the special fermentation of carbohydrates originally developed by Chaim Weizmann before World War I for the production of acetone; this compound was needed in the manufacture of the smokeless propellant known as Cordite (a nitroglycerine-guncotton mixture).* Ini-

* Weizmann continued as professor of chemistry at the University of Manchester, England until after World War II, when he became President of the new state of Israel, whose independence he had been instrumental in establishing. He died in 1952.

tially, 1-butanol was just a byproduct, but later acetone was produced more cheaply by other methods and 1-butanol acquired industrial importance.

Isopropyl alcohol (b.p. 82.4°) is formed by the hydration of propylene with sulfuric acid; propylene, in turn, is cheap because it is available from petroleum cracking. The good solvent properties of isopropyl alcohol and its ability to absorb water make it useful as an industrial solvent and also as a deicer for airplane wings. Rubbing alcohol is isopropyl alcohol. n-Propyl alcohol is industrially synthesized by the controlled oxidation of propane.

Ethylene glycol, used as permanent antifreeze, is made from ethylene by addition of hypochlorous acid, followed by replacement of the chlorine atom with base (Fig. 6-16). An alternative preparation is shown in Fig. 6-35 (see page 114). Large amounts of ethylene glycol are used in the manufacture of Dacron.

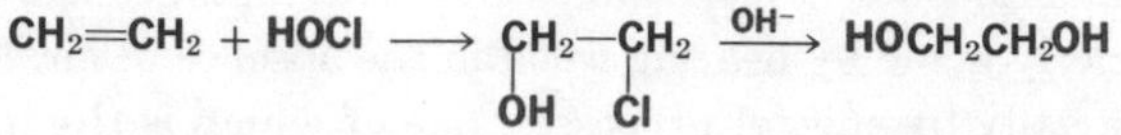

$$CH_2{=}CH_2 + HOCl \longrightarrow \underset{\underset{OH \quad Cl}{|\qquad|}}{CH_2{-}CH_2} \xrightarrow{OH^-} HOCH_2CH_2OH$$

Fig. 6-16. Ethylene glycol is formed from ethylene by addition of hypochlorous acid followed by basic hydrolysis.

Glycerol, the simplest triol, is produced as a byproduct of the hydrolysis of fats and oils (Chapter 11); however, during World War II, vastly more glycerine was needed than could be supplied from this source, in spite of extensive fat-saving programs. To meet the needs for glycerine, the Shell Oil Company developed the Shell process (Fig. 6-17). At high temperatures, chlorine reacts with propylene by substitution rather than by addition, to produce allyl chloride. Replacement of the chlorine atom by a hydroxyl group, addition of hypochlorous acid, and further reaction with base completes the synthesis.

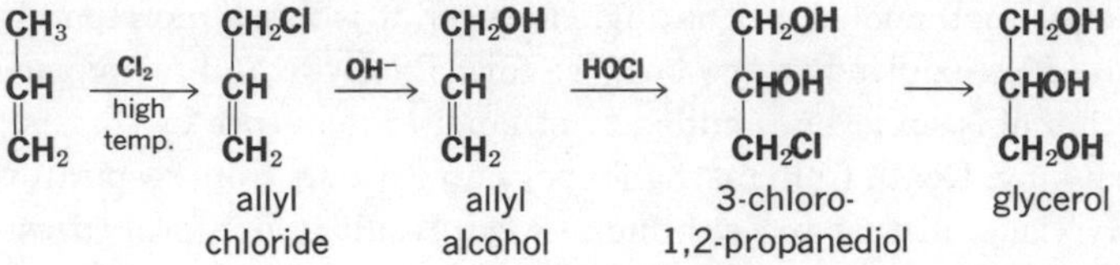

Fig. 6-17. The Shell process for the synthesis of glycerol from propylene.

Glycerine is sweet and has a great affinity for water. It is added to tobacco as a humectant. Certain medicines, such as eardrops, may contain anhydrous glycerine to reduce swelling by removing water from the tissues. The use of glycerine in the preparation of nitroglycerine has already been mentioned.

ACIDITY OF PHENOLS

Phenols are a class of compounds containing hydroxyl groups that are directly attached to aromatic nuclei (Fig. 6-18). They are closely related to alcohols, but

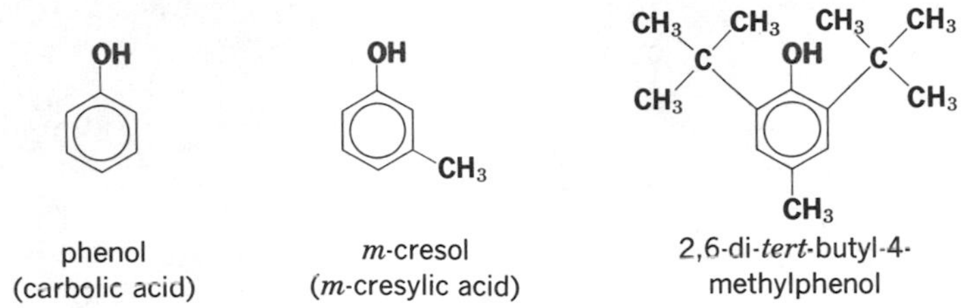

phenol
(carbolic acid)

m-cresol
(*m*-cresylic acid)

2,6-di-*tert*-butyl-4-
methylphenol

Fig. 6-18. Some common phenols. The characteristic functional group is a hydroxyl group attached to an aromatic ring. The development of a deep color in the presence of a solution of ferric chloride is a visual chemical test for phenols.

the aromatic nucleus exerts a strong modifying effect on the properties of the hydroxyl group. For example, phenols are acidic, as attested by the name carbolic acid for phenol itself and cresylic acids for the methylphenols (cresols).

The most striking modification which the benzene ring achieves on the properties of the hydroxyl group is shown by comparing the acidity of phenol with that of aliphatic alcohols. Phenol is approximately 10^6 (1,000,000) times more acidic than ethanol. It is about the same amount less acidic than acetic acid. As a consequence of this acidity, phenol forms the salt sodium phenoxide when treated with sodium hydroxide (Fig. 6-19). Because of this salt formation, phenols are soluble in aqueous sodium hydroxide solution, even if they do not dissolve in water.

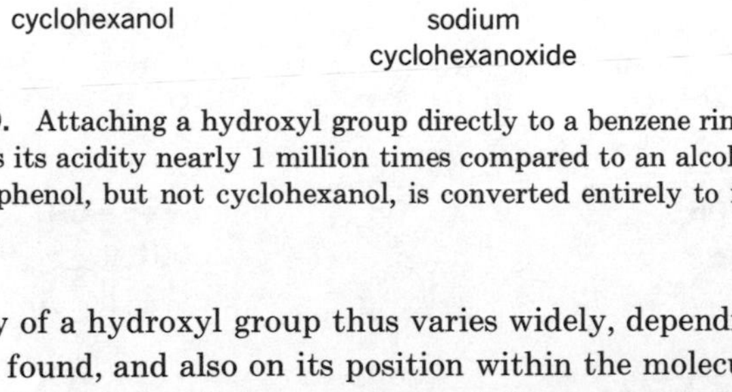

phenol

sodium
phenoxide

cyclohexanol

sodium
cyclohexanoxide

Fig. 6-19. Attaching a hydroxyl group directly to a benzene ring, as in phenol, increases its acidity nearly 1 million times compared to an alcohol. As a consequence, phenol, but not cyclohexanol, is converted entirely to its salt in basic solution.

The acidity of a hydroxyl group thus varies widely, depending on the molecule in which it is found, and also on its position within the molecule. The correlation of acidity with structure is best understood if we consider the ionized species (Fig. 6-20). In some ions, like alkoxide and hydroxide, the full negative charge is localized on the oxygen atom, and there is no special stabilization of the anion. These oxide ions are strongly basic, and the corresponding acid ROH is very weak. In less basic oxide ions, like the nitrate and phenoxide ions, the full negative charge is no longer localized on one oxygen atom, but is delocalized over other

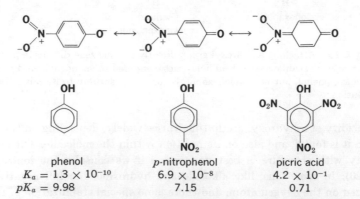

Fig. 6-20. In an aliphatic alkoxide, as in the hydroxide ion itself, a full negative charge is localized on one oxygen atom, so its affinity for a proton is high. In the phenoxide ion, as in the nitrate ion, the negative charge can be shared by a number of atoms, thus reducing its intensity at any single site and lessening its attraction for a proton.

parts of the molecule. Delocalization of the charge stabilizes the oxide and shifts the ionization equilibrium to favor the anion (phenoxide or nitrate ion).

The resonance theory nicely accounts for this delocalization of the phenoxide ion's negative charge. We can see that several structures involving only the delocalization of electrons can be written for the phenoxide ion. In three of these the negative charge is on a carbon atom of the benzene ring rather than on the oxygen atom. The actual molecule is a hybrid of these structures, so that the charge is delocalized over several centers.

If electronegative groups are attached to the benzene ring, the negative charge may be further delocalized, and the phenol becomes more acidic. *p*-Nitrophenol, for example, is 800 times more acidic than phenol itself, because the negative charge in the phenoxide ion may be delocalized into the nitro group (Fig. 6-21);

phenol	*p*-nitrophenol	picric acid
$K_a = 1.3 \times 10^{-10}$	6.9×10^{-8}	4.2×10^{-1}
$pK_a = 9.98$	7.15	0.71

Fig. 6-21. Attachment of a nitro group to phenol increases its acidity. In the *p*-nitrophenolate ion, the charge can be shared by the oxygens of the nitro group. Picric acid is a strong acid, almost as strong as hydrochloric acid.

2,4,6-trinitrophenol (picric acid), in which all three nitro groups can help stabilize the negative charge, is nearly as strong as hydrochloric acid.

Prob. 6-9. Apply the concepts of Figs. 6-20 and 6-21 to explain the following sequence of acidities:

$$RSOH < RSO_2H < RSO_3H$$

REACTIONS OF PHENOLS

Just as the benzene ring affects the acidity of a hydroxyl group attached to it, so does it modify other reactions of the functional group, sometimes drastically and sometimes subtly. In particular, the hydroxyl group is much more firmly attached to the benzene ring than to an alkyl group, so that replacement reactions of the entire —OH group by cleavage of the C—O bond do not occur with phenols. For example, phenol cannot be converted to a halobenzene with hydrogen halides.

In reactions that involve the O—H bond, phenols resemble alcohols. They liberate hydrogen when treated with sodium and they also form esters with many acids (Fig. 6-22). The interaction of a hydroxyl and a phenyl group is, of course, a

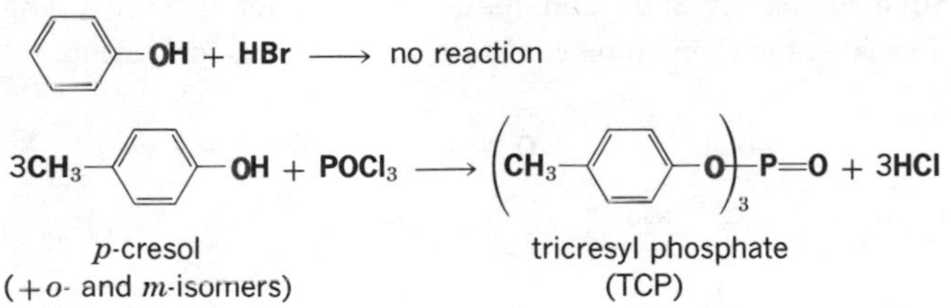

p-cresol
(+*o*- and *m*-isomers)

tricresyl phosphate
(TCP)

Fig. 6-22. Phenols do not undergo the reactions of alcohols which involve breaking of the C—O bond, but do undergo those which involve the O—H bond, as illustrated by preparation of the gasoline additive TCP.

mutual one, and the benzene ring in phenol differs in reactivity from benzene itself. In particular, phenol is much more reactive than benzene toward substitution reactions (Fig. 6-23). Even with dilute nitric acid, phenol is nitrated at 25°. (Remember that benzene requires concentrated nitric acid, added sulfuric acid as catalyst, and 50°.) As another example, bromine (without catalyst) rapidly trisubstitutes the ring.

SYNTHESIS OF PHENOLS

The hydroxyl group cannot be introduced directly into a benzene ring, so that phenol synthesis always require at least two steps (Fig. 6-24). The commonest laboratory preparation of a phenol involves, first, sulfonation of the ring and then fusion (melting together) of the sulfonate with sodium hydroxide. High temperatures are required but, since both reactants and products are high-boiling salts, no special apparatus is needed. A great deal of phenol is made industrially from

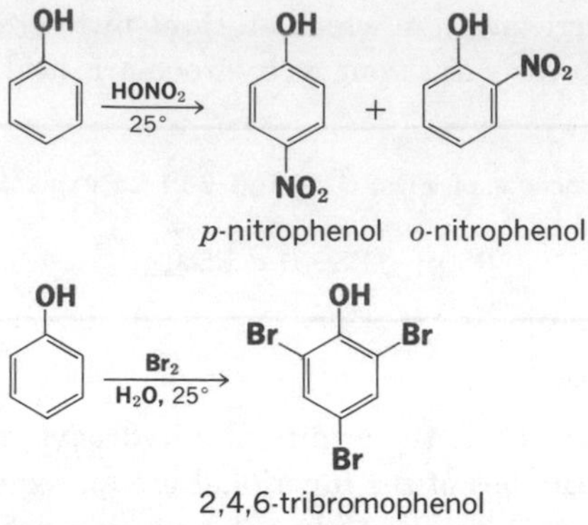

p-nitrophenol   o-nitrophenol

2,4,6-tribromophenol

Fig. 6-23. Phenol undergoes substitution reactions of the benzene nucleus much more readily than benzene itself. Bromination is so rapid that it is difficult to stop until all *ortho-para* positions are substituted.

chlorobenzene and sodium hydroxide. The reaction must be carried out under pressure, or else the chlorobenzene would boil away. In order to make the process continuous, chlorobenzene and aqueous sodium hydroxide are fed together into a mile-long tube heated at 300° and maintained under intense pressure. Sodium phenolate forms and is then converted into phenol by acidification.

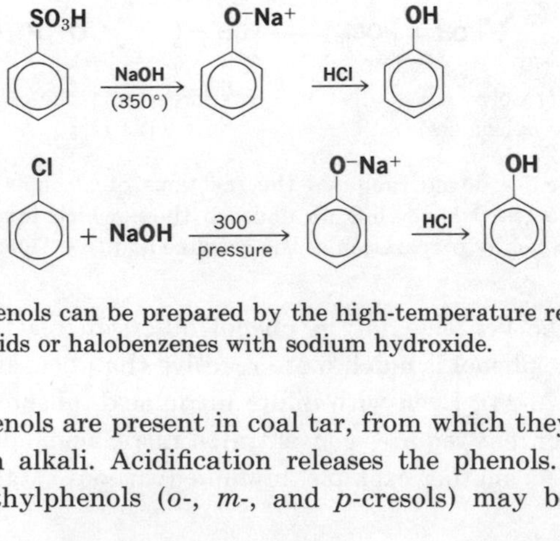

Fig. 6-24. Phenols can be prepared by the high-temperature reaction of benzenesulfonic acids or halobenzenes with sodium hydroxide.

A number of phenols are present in coal tar, from which they may be separated by extraction with alkali. Acidification releases the phenols. Phenol itself, and *o*-, *m*-, and *p*-methylphenols (*o*-, *m*-, and *p*-cresols) may be obtained in this way (Fig. 6-25).

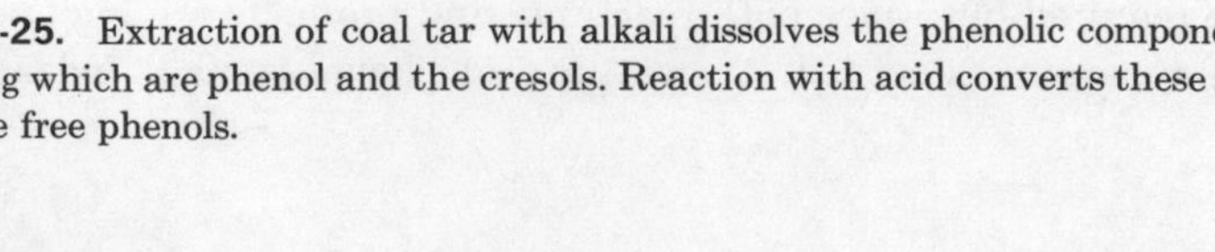

(also *m*- and *p*-isomers)

Fig. 6-25. Extraction of coal tar with alkali dissolves the phenolic components, among which are phenol and the cresols. Reaction with acid converts these salts to the free phenols.

Prob. 6-10. Suggest a method for making resorcinol (*m*-dihydroxybenzene) from benzene, sulfuric acid, and sodium hydroxide.

OXIDATION OF PHENOLS

A simple phenol cannot be oxidized in quite the same way as a 1° or 2° alcohol, since the hydroxyl group is not on a carbon atom bearing a hydrogen atom. Phenols are easily oxidized, but their products are often complex. This oxidation may occur with air alone (auto-oxidation) or with other oxidizing agents. The reaction of phenols with oxygen in the air is exploited industrially by the use of phenols as antioxidants in gasoline, rubber, and other products. The phenols react with oxygen more readily than most other organic compounds, and protect them from oxidation.

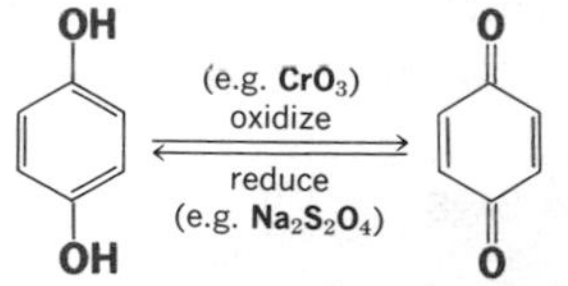

p-hydroquinone   *p*-quinone
(colorless)   (yellow)

Fig. 6-26. The quinone-hydroquinone oxidation-reduction system is common in biological systems.

In the special case where two hydroxyl groups are in the *para* position relative to each other, the compound (*p*-hydroquinone) may be easily, selectively, and reversibly oxidized to a diketone, *p*-benzoquinone, representative of a class of compounds called quinones (Fig. 6-26); *p*-benzoquinone itself is yellow, and substituted quinones are often the coloring material in naturally occurring systems, particularly in molds and fungi (Fig. 6-27). Similarly, *o*-dihydroxybenzene (catechol) is oxidized to the unstable *o*-benzoquinone.

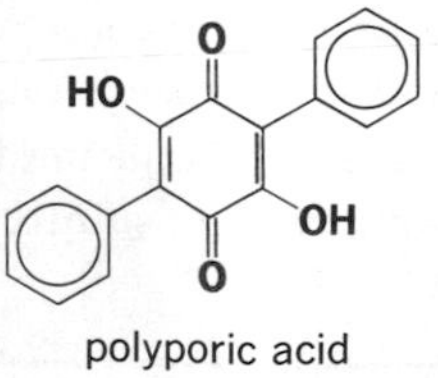

polyporic acid   juglone
(brown-violet)   (yellow-brown)

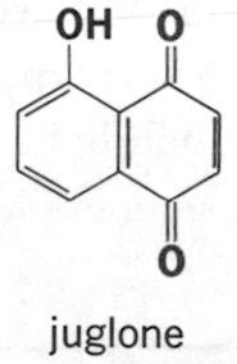

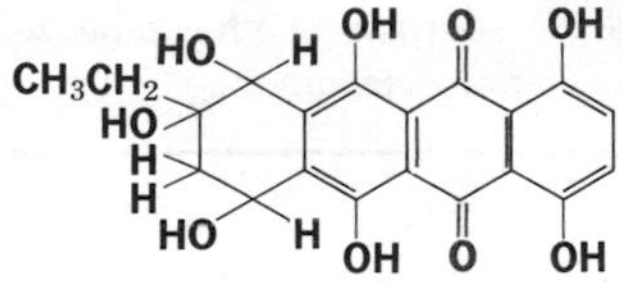

β-rhodomycinone
(red)

Fig. 6-27. Quinones often occur as natural coloring matters.

USES OF PHENOLS

Phenol (m.p. 41°) is a toxic solid with a characteristic "hospital" odor. In sufficiently high concentrations it corrodes the human skin. It finds extensive use as a
preservative and antiseptic, although substituted phenols, like hexylresorcinol, are
more powerful (Fig. 6-28). A great deal of phenol is used in reactions with formaldehyde to make plastics like Bakelite. The cresols are used as wood preservatives

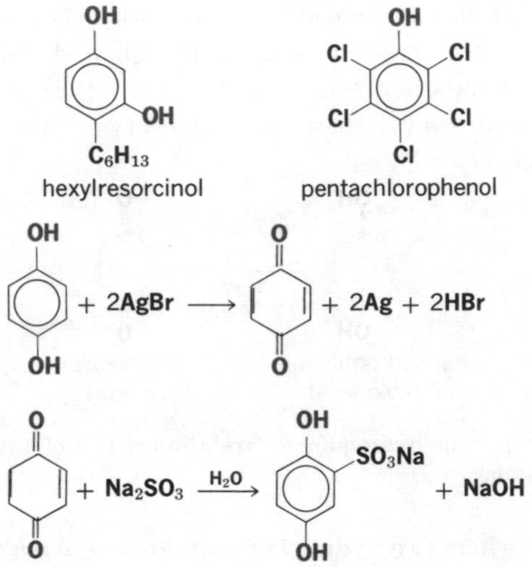

OH

OH
C6H13
hexylresorcinol

OH
Cl   Cl
Cl   Cl
Cl
pentachlorophenol

OH

OH
+ 2AgBr ⟶

O

O
+ 2Ag + 2HBr

O

O
+ Na2SO3 —H2O→

OH
SO3Na

OH
+ NaOH

Fig. 6-28. Hexylresorcinol is an antiseptic and pentachlorophenol is used in
killing barnacles and other mollusks. Hydroquinone and sodium sulfite are used
in photographic developers.

for fenceposts and railroad ties (creosote). Hydroquinone (m.p. 172°) occurs in
nature, combined with the sugar glucose as *arbutin*. Industrially, it is obtained
from aminobenzene (aniline) by oxidation to quinone and reduction. Hydroquinone
is principally used as a photographic developer, since it has the ability to reduce
exposed grains of silver halide in a photographic emulsion faster than unexposed
grains. Photographic developers also contain sodium sulfite, which reacts with the
quinone formed.

Prob. 6-11. Write a balanced equation for the oxidation of catechol (*o*-hydroquinone)
by chromic oxide (CrO_3) in acidic solution to give *o*-benzoquinone. Why does resorcinol
(*m*-dihydroxybenzene) not give an analogous quinone?

ETHERS

If both hydrogen atoms of the water molecule are replaced by alkyl or aryl groups,
compounds known as *ethers* are formed. The commonest ether is diethyl ether,

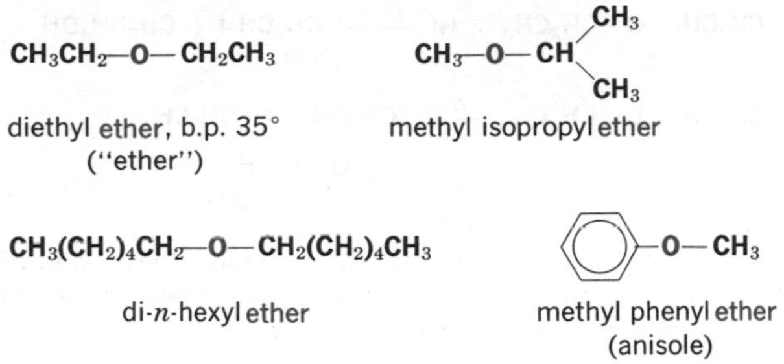

$$CH_3CH_2-O-CH_2CH_3$$

$$CH_3-O-CH \begin{matrix} CH_3 \\ \\ CH_3 \end{matrix}$$

diethyl ether, b.p. 35°
("ether")

methyl isopropyl ether

$$CH_3(CH_2)_4CH_2-O-CH_2(CH_2)_4CH_3$$

di-*n*-hexyl ether

⬡—O—CH₃

methyl phenyl ether
(anisole)

Fig. 6-29. Ethers are usually inert substances with good solvent properties. Since they cannot form hydrogen bonds, their boiling points are close to those of hydrocarbons of the same molecular weight.

usually called simply "ether," and used as an anesthetic and a solvent (Fig. 6-29). Notice the system of nomenclature, in which the groups retain their radical names. If both groups are the same, as they are in *diethyl ether*, the ether is *symmetrical* and is commonly produced by reaction of the corresponding alcohol with sulfuric acid. Mixed ethers are prepared by the *Williamson ether synthesis*, in which the salt of an alcohol reacts with an alkyl halide (Fig. 6-30). This reaction will be discussed in more detail in the next chapter.

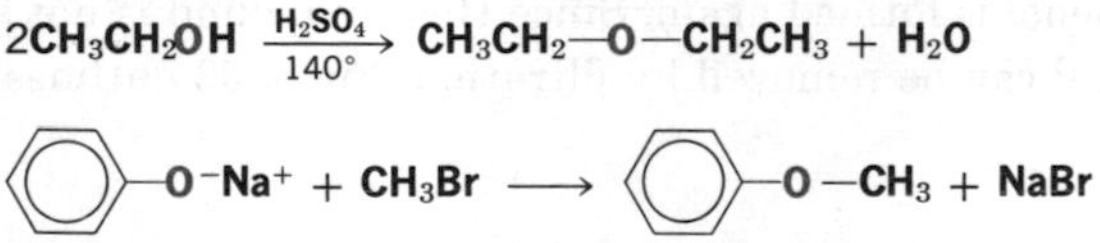

$$2CH_3CH_2OH \xrightarrow[140°]{H_2SO_4} CH_3CH_2-O-CH_2CH_3 + H_2O$$

⬡—O⁻Na⁺ + CH₃Br ⟶ ⬡—O—CH₃ + NaBr

Fig. 6-30. Symmetrical ethers are prepared by reactions of alcohols with sulfuric acid at high temperatures. Mixed ethers are prepared by the Williamson ether synthesis.

Prob. 6-12. Why can mixed ethers not be prepared satisfactorily by causing a reaction of a mixture of alcohols with sulfuric acid? Answer by showing what products would be expected if a mixture of 1-propanol and ethanol were converted to ethers with sulfuric acid.

For an ether to undergo reaction, a C—O or a C—H bond must be broken; however, both of these processes are ordinarily difficult. Strong heating of diethyl ether with concentrated hydriodic acid converts it into ethyl iodide, and ether which is exposed to oxygen and light undergoes air oxidation to become a *peroxide* (Fig. 6-31). These peroxides are highly explosive: Great care must be taken in using ether which has been standing exposed to air for some time.

Because it is quite unreactive, diethyl ether makes an excellent solvent for many organic reactions. Many more organic compounds will dissolve in ether than in hydrocarbons, because the oxygen atom in ethers imparts some polar character to

$$CH_3CH_2—O—CH_2CH_3 + HI \xrightarrow{120°} CH_3CH_2I + CH_3CH_2OH$$
$$\text{ethyl iodide}$$

$$CH_3CH_2—O—CH_2CH_3 \xrightarrow[\text{light}]{O_2} CH_3CH—O—CH_2CH_3$$
$$\overset{|}{O—O—H}$$
$$\text{a peroxide}$$

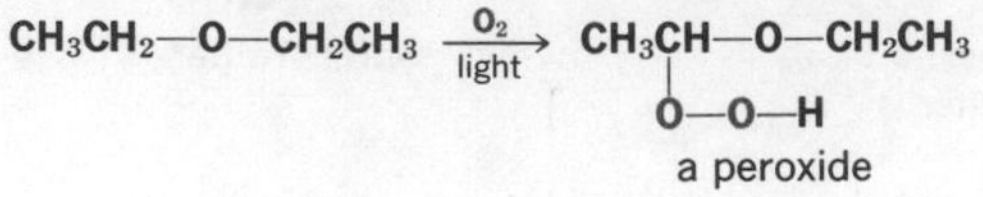

Fig. 6-31. Ethers are inert to most chemical reactions. However, heating with concentrated acids eventually cleaves ethers, and exposure to air and light generates small amounts of highly explosive peroxides.

the ether molecule. Gaseous hydrogen chloride, for example, is rather soluble in ether, because the proton of hydrogen chloride forms a highly polar hydrogen bond with the oxygen atom of ether, $R_2O \cdots HCl$, helping to keep the acid in solution. Ether and water are not miscible with each other, so that ether is often used in the separation of mixtures of organic compounds. Suppose, for example, that one had a mixture of p-chlorophenol and p-dichlorobenzene and wished to separate these two compounds, obtaining each in a pure state. If the mixture is added to a mixture of ether and aqueous sodium hydroxide solution, the alkali will react with the phenol, forming sodium phenoxide which will dissolve in the water. The dichlorobenzene dissolves in the ether. Separation of the layers and evaporation of the ether gives pure dichlorobenzene. If enough hydrochloric acid is added to neutralize the base, p-chlorophenol is formed again. Since this compound is not soluble in water, it precipitates and can be removed by filtration. Fig. 6-32 outlines the steps in the separation.

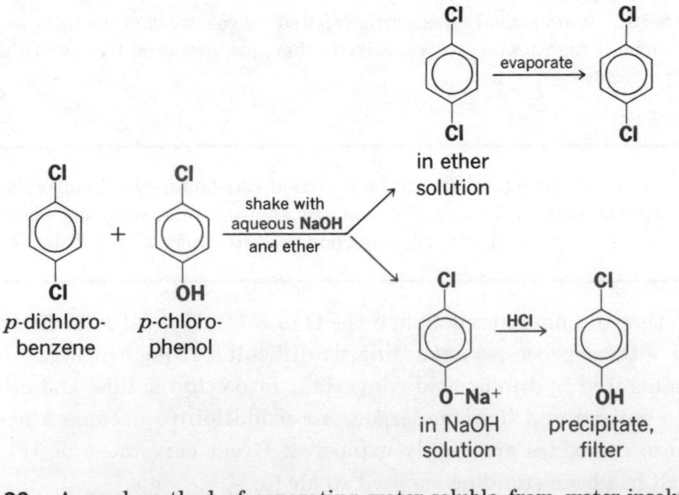

Fig. 6-32. A good method of separating water-soluble from water-insoluble organic compounds is to shake them with a mixture of water and ether. In this example, the sodium hydroxide in the water converts p-chlorophenol to its water-soluble sodium salt.

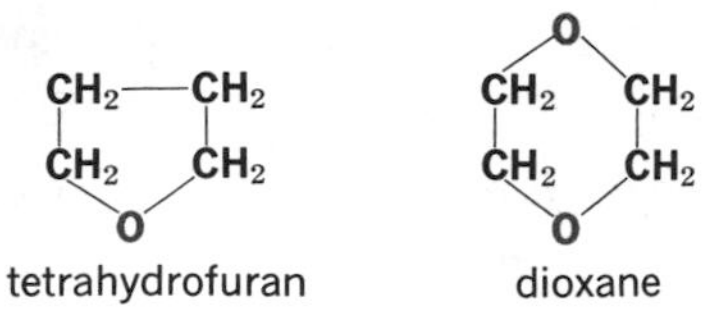

Fig. 6-33. Two water-soluble ethers make useful solvents.

Few simple ethers have great commercial significance, although a few besides diethyl ether are widely used as solvents (Fig. 6-33). Tetrahydrofuran may be synthesized from furfuraldehyde, which in turn is obtained by treating corn cobs with acid. Tetrahydrofuran is useful both because it is somewhat higher boiling (65°) than diethyl ether (35°), and because it is completely soluble in water. Dioxane is also soluble in water and is still higher boiling (101°).

Aromatic ethers occur more widely, especially in wood extracts. Guaiacol, the monomethyl ether of catechol (o-dihydoxybenzene), occurs in beechwood, while the herbicide 2,4-D and the insecticide methoxychlor both contain ether linkages (Fig. 6-34).

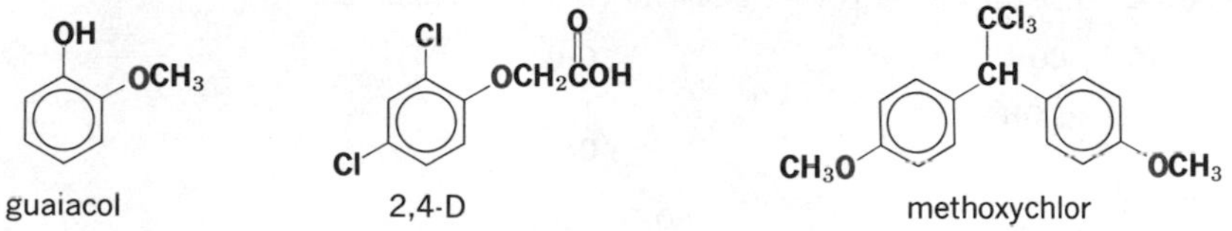

Fig. 6-34. Three important ethers. 2,4-D is an abbreviation for 2,4-dichloro-phenoxyacetic acid, while methoxychlor is a close relative of DDT.

EPOXIDES

It will be recalled that saturated hydrocarbons, like ethers, are largely unreactive and find their principal use as solvents. This lack of reactivity is true *except* for those cycloalkanes in which the carbon atoms are joined in a small ring (cyclopropane or cyclobutane); there the angle strain makes the molecules quite reactive. The same is true of cyclic ethers with three atoms in the ring, which are called *epoxides*. These compounds are named as "oxides" of the corresponding alkenes; by far the most important is ethylene oxide.

Ethylene oxide is an important industrial compound: Its ring opens in dilute aqueous acid to give ethylene glycol; in alcoholic acid to give ether alcohols, called cellosolves; and in ammonia to form ethanolamine (Fig. 6-35).

In the presence of only a trace of moisture, ethylene oxide polymerizes to polyethylene oxide, $-(CH_2CH_2O)_{\overline{n}}$. Ethylene oxide is made from ethylene, either by addition of hypochlorous acid and base or by oxidation with air over silver.

$$CH_2{=}CH_2 \xrightarrow[\text{or Ag + O}_2]{\text{HOCl, NaOH}}$$

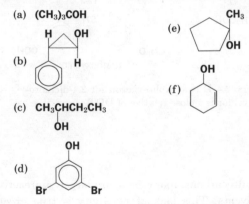

ethylene
oxide

$\xrightarrow[\text{H}^+]{\text{H}_2\text{O}}$ HOCH$_2$CH$_2$OH
ethylene glycol

$\xrightarrow[\text{H}^+]{\text{CH}_3\text{CH}_2\text{OH}}$ CH$_3$CH$_2$OCH$_2$CH$_2$OH
ethyl cellosolve

$\xrightarrow{\text{NH}_3}$ H$_2$NCH$_2$CH$_2$OH
ethanolamine

Fig. 6-35. Ethylene oxide is very reactive, and is useful in the preparation of commercially important solvents and of the polymer polyethylene oxide —(CH$_2$CH$_2$O)$_{\overline{n}}$.

Prob. 6-13. Write the structure of each of the following:
(a) 3-methyl-2-butanol
(b) *cis*-2-methylcyclohexanol
(c) *trans*-4-hexen-2-ol
(d) 3,3-dimethyl-1,2-butanediol
(e) glycerol
(f) *m*-isopropylphenol
(g) resorcinol
(h) 1,4-naphthoquinone
(i) neopentyl alcohol
(j) benzyl alcohol
(k) allyl phenyl ether
(l) cyclohexene oxide

Prob. 6-14. Give the correct IUPAC name for each of the following:

(a) (CH$_3$)$_3$COH

(b) [structure: cyclopropane ring fused to benzene with H, OH, and H substituents]

(c) CH$_3$CHCH$_2$CH$_3$
         |
        OH

(d) [structure: phenol with two Br substituents, OH at top, Br at bottom positions]

(e) [structure: cyclopentane ring with CH$_3$ and OH]

(f) [structure: cyclohexenol]

Prob. 6-15. Show all the reagents and conditions necessary to make each of the following from 1-butene:
(a) 2-butanol
(b) 1-butanol
(c) 1-butene oxide
(d) 2-butene
(e) di-*n*-butyl ether

Prob. 6-16. Show all the reagents and conditions necessary to make each of the following from phenol:
(a) *o*-nitrophenol
(b) anisole
(c) sodium phenoxide
(d) 2,4,6-tribromophenol

Prob. 6-17. Suppose you had a mixture of 4-*tert*-butylcyclohexanol and *p-tert*-butylphenol. Explain how you could separate the two compounds, using only ether (in which both are soluble), water (in which both are insoluble), sodium hydroxide, and hydrochloric acid.

Prob. 6-18. Describe simple, visual chemical tests which would allow you to distinguish among the following:

(a) cyclohexene, cyclohexanol, 1-methylcyclohexanol

(b) picric acid, cyclohexanol, anisole

(c) allyl alcohol, ethylene glycol, 2-hexene

Prob. 6-19. Making use of the Williamson ether synthesis, how could you synthesize the herbicide 2,4-D (Fig. 6-34)?

CHAPTER

CONFIGURATIONAL ISOMERISM
AND ORGANIC HALIDES

To learn how alkyl halides* react, we must first understand a third kind of isomerism: *configurational isomerism.* Two types of isomers have already been introduced, structural in Chapter 1, and geometrical in Chapter 2. In structural isomers such as ethyl alcohol and dimethyl ether or *n*-propyl and isopropyl alcohols, we saw that atoms bonded in different order in two isomers often produce dramatic distinctions in both physical and chemical properties of the two molecules; for example, ethyl alcohol reacts with sodium, but dimethyl ether does not. Geometrical isomerism, a form of stereoisomerism, is subtler. The *cis-* and *trans-*2-butenes, geometrical isomers, in which groups are joined together in the same order but at different distances, are almost always similar, differing from one another only in physical properties such as boiling and melting points (Fig. 7-1).

Some molecules exist, however, in two isomeric forms, one of which mirrors the other. These molecules are called *configurational isomers,** because they differ from each other in configurational or three-dimensional arrangement of their atoms. Molecules that are mirror images of each other are known as *enantiomers.*

The relationship between enantiomers is the same as that of the left hand to the right (Fig. 7-2). Through this analogy, one isomer is called the D-isomer (from the Greek *dextro* meaning right) and the other, the L-isomer (*levo* meaning left). The compound 2-butanol, which fits this pattern, thus consists of D-2-butanol and L-2-butanol. Converting an object into its mirror image should have no effect on its physical properties; D- and L-2-butanols do have exactly the same boiling point,

---

* Halide is the generic name for fluorides, chlorides, bromides, and iodides.
* For reasons to become apparent shortly, such molecules are also called *optical isomers.*

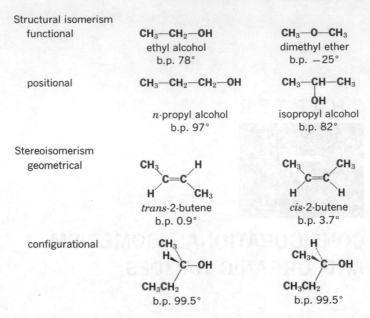

Structural isomerism
functional

$CH_3—CH_2—OH$
ethyl alcohol
b.p. 78°

$CH_3—O—CH_3$
dimethyl ether
b.p. −25°

positional

$CH_3—CH_2—CH_2—OH$

$CH_3—CH—CH_3$
     |
     OH

n-propyl alcohol
b.p. 97°

isopropyl alcohol
b.p. 82°

Stereoisomerism
geometrical

trans-2-butene
b.p. 0.9°

cis-2-butene
b.p. 3.7°

configurational

b.p. 99.5°

b.p. 99.5°

Fig. 7-1. Isomerism among organic compounds may be arranged in order of subtlety. Structural isomers are usually quite different, stereoisomers quite similar.

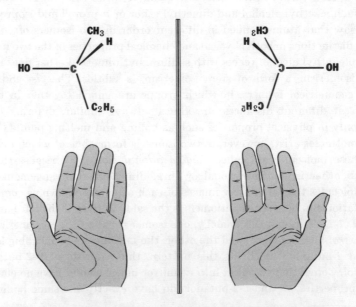

Fig. 7-2. Configurational isomers bear the same mirror-image relationship to one another as do the left and right hands.

melting point, solubility, density, etc. Similarly, the chemical properties of D- and L-isomers are indistinguishable through ordinary reagents; both react with the same rapidity with hydrogen bromide, sodium, thionyl chloride, and other standard chemicals.

Prob. 7-1. Which of these things are capable of existing in D- and L- forms: a sphere, a cube, a foot, a spearfish, a spiral staircase (called a helix), a tree, a one-armed paperhanger? Can you make any generalization about the types of objects which are likely to be identical to their mirror image and thus incapable of existing in D- and L-isomers?

How, then, may we distinguish D- from L-isomers? Again the analogy of the left and right hands applies. If we assume that a man's hands are exact mirror images, the two would have the same mass and same melting point, and would dissolve equally well in concentrated sulfuric acid. Moreover, the two hands would fit with equal facility into a paper bag or similar container. However, if the attempt were made to insert both hands into a right-handed glove, a vast difference would arise. The right hand would go in easily, the left hand only with difficulty. If the analogy is sound, left- and right-handed molecules should differ in their interactions with left- and right-handed surroundings.

SEPARATION OF D- AND L-ISOMERS

Since D- and L-isomers have identical physical properties, we might expect their separation to be difficult. The first separation of an equal mixture of D- and L-isomers into two distinct forms was accomplished by the great French scientist Louis Pasteur in 1848. Working with a mixture of the sodium ammonium salts of D- and L-tartaric acids (Fig. 12-17), known as sodium ammonium racemate, he discovered that he could separate two different types of crystals by hand. The crystals were mirror images of each other and one type proved to be the known sodium ammonium salt of L-tartaric acid. The other crystals were the corresponding salt of the previously unknown D-tartaric acid. The acids were liberated from the salts; mixed together in equal amounts, they furnished what had been known as racemic acid and which we now call racemic tartaric acid.*

The differences in reactivity between mirror images are enormously important in biological systems, because almost all the organic compounds that occur in living organisms are either pure left-handed or pure right-handed molecules. Most things we eat, for example, must be of the correct "handedness" to be used most efficiently by the body, and medicines are much more active in one mirror image form than the other. Enzymes, which are biological catalysts, are particularly selective in their reactions with D- and L-isomers (Fig. 7-3). For a molecule to react on an enzyme surface, the groups indicated by the same color must come into contact with one another. In only one of the isomers is this possible; therefore one

---

* It is only rarely that D- and L-isomers form separate crystals. In nearly every case they precipitate together from solution in the same crystal.

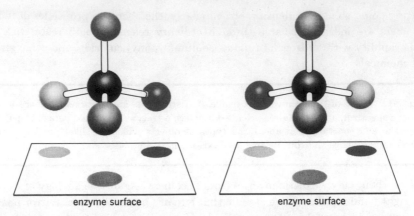

enzyme surface   enzyme surface

Fig. 7-3. The enzyme (organic catalyst) shown is capable of reacting with the molecule on the left but not with that on the right, since the reactive sites in the enzyme surface match the arrangement of groups on the left.

isomer reacts much more readily than the other in the system. Pasteur first used this in another preparation of D-tartaric acid. Observing that yeast organisms were able to use L-tartaric acid in their metabolism, he added racemic tartaric acid to a yeast broth. The organism consumed the L-isomer but did not touch the D-isomer, which he was able to reisolate from the solution. Evidently, the L-isomer can fit onto some enzyme surface where reaction takes place but the D-isomer cannot. Another more general method of separation of optical isomers will be discussed in Chapter 10.

ROTATION OF THE PLANE OF POLARIZED LIGHT

The identical character of nearly all the physical properties of D- and L-isomers makes it difficult to tell the two apart. Here physics comes to the aid of chemistry by providing a simple method for distinguishing the two. The principal agent in this process is polarized light. Because polarized light is used, the D- and L-isomers are sometimes known as optical isomers.

The ordinary light beam is a mass of light waves which vibrate in all directions as in Fig. 7-4a. When the beam strikes a certain object, for example a Nicol prism,* only those waves vibrating in a specific plane with respect to the axis of the prism may pass through; all others are denied passage. Upon emergence from the prism the light beam is fully polarized as in Fig. 7-4b. All of its waves vibrate in a single plane in a single direction which can be changed only by rotation of the prism as in Fig. 7-4c. When such polarized light passes through a solution of one configurational isomer of a compound (for instance, L-2-butanol) the plane of rotation of the light changes, so that the light emerging from the solution, though still polarized, has a new angle. Now suppose a second prism were placed parallel to the first a distance away. If something occurred to change the angle of the light beam's path

---

* Formed by cutting diagonally a crystal of Iceland spar (calcium carbonate) and cementing the pieces together with Canada balsam.

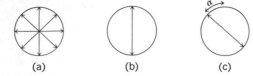

(a)   (b)   (c)

Fig. 7-4. An ordinary beam of light contains waves vibrating in all directions (a). The beam can be polarized by passing it through certain crystals giving polarized light (b). Such a polarized beam, after passing through a (−) isomer, vibrates in a new plane, having been rotated α degrees to the left (c). After passing through an equal amount of the (+) isomer instead, the beam would vibrate in a plane rotated α degrees to the right.

en route to the second prism after its polarization by the first, the waves would be unable to penetrate the second prism until its angle were made to correspond to the new angle of the beam.

This same principle is applied in a polarimeter, an instrument for detecting and measuring polarized light. An ordinary beam of light is polarized by being passed through a Nicol prism. A second Nicol prism, with its axis parallel to the first, is located about a meter away and the instrument is adjusted so that the polarized beam passes freely through the second prism. Then a tube containing the compound to be tested, either in pure liquid form or, more commonly, in solution, is placed in the beam. If the compound does not exhibit configurational isomerism or if it is an equal mixture of D- and L-isomers (a *racemic mixture*) it will have no effect on the angle of polarization and the beam will still emerge from the second prism. However, if the compound is a single isomer (either D- or L-), or if it contains more of one isomer than the other, the plane of polarization will be changed by passage through the solution and the light will not be able to pass through the second prism. This prism is then rotated until the light beam passes freely through it again. The angle through which the prism must be turned is called the *angle of rotation* of the solution.

SPECIFIC ROTATION

If a given isomer rotates the plane of polarized light to the left it is designated as (−), if it rotates the plane to the right the isomer is designated as (+). Unfortunately, there is no easy correlation between "handedness" (D- and L-) and the direction of rotation of a plane of polarized light. Though it might seem that a right-handed molecule (D-) should rotate the plane of polarized light to the right and a left-handed molecule (L-) should rotate it to the left, in fact this is not necessarily the case. The direction of rotation may even change from (+) to (−) for the same isomer if the wavelength of the light being used to measure the rotation, the solvent, or the temperature is changed. In addition, the actual magnitude of the rotation depends on the amount of substance in the light beam (that is, the concentration of the compound in the solution and the length of the tube containing the solution). All these variables are specified in the *specific rotation* [α]

$$[\alpha]_D^{25} = 45.2° \ (1.5\%, \text{ in } \mathbf{CHCl_3})$$

$$[\alpha]_\lambda^t = \frac{\alpha V}{gl} \ (\text{conc., in solvent})$$

Fig. 7-5. The specific rotation $[\alpha]_\lambda^t$ is a characteristic physical constant of a molecule. In the above formula, α is the observed rotation of a solution of g grams of compound in V ml of solution in a cell l decimeters long, t is the temperature, and λ is the wavelength of light used (usually the D-line of a sodium lamp, 5890 Å).

as indicated in Fig. 7-5. Once all the conditions of the measurement are defined, the specific rotation of an optically active molecule is a useful physical constant, like its melting or boiling point.

Prob. 7-2. A solution of 20 g/l of 2-butanol in ethanol rotated a polarized beam of light at the sodium D line +0.24° at 25° in a 1-decimeter tube. What is its specific rotation?

ABSOLUTE CONFIGURATION

If we cannot tell the "handedness" of a molecule from the direction it rotates a plane of polarized light, how do we arrive at the designations D- and L- for a particular isomer? By special x-ray methods crystallographers deduced the actual, three-dimensional structure of that isomer of glyceraldehyde, a colorless syrup, which rotates polarized light to the right. In other words, they discovered the *absolute configuration* of (+)-glyceraldehyde. This molecule has been *defined* as having the D- configuration, so we call it D-(+)-glyceraldehyde. In order to determine the absolute configuration of any other molecule we must relate it by a sequence of known steps to D-(+)-glyceraldehyde.

For example, it is possible to prepare 2-butanol from D-(+)-glyceraldehyde in the manner schematically outlined (Fig. 7-6). If this is done, the 2-butanol formed

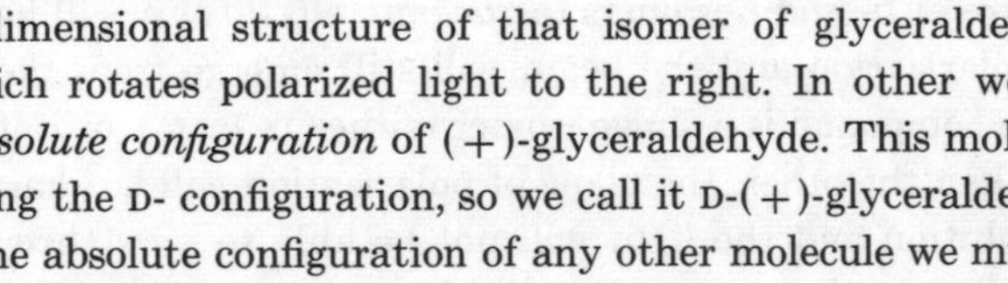

Fig. 7-6. (+)-Glyceraldehyde with the configuration shown has been arbitrarily defined as D-. It may be converted, as shown schematically, into (+)-2-butanol, which then must have the structure shown and can also be called D-.

is D-2-butanol. Since this 2-butanol rotates polarized light to the right it is D-(+)-2-butanol. The butanol formed from L-(−)-glyceraldehyde by the same sequence of reactions would be L-2-butanol. Other compounds prepared from

D-(+)-glyceraldehyde might rotate the plane of polarized light to the left and still be D- compounds. It is perfectly possible, indeed not unusual, to have a D-(−) or an L-(+) compound. The (+) or (−) prefix comes from experimental observation related to the direction of the rotation. The D- or L- prefix relates the actual three-dimensional arrangement of the atoms to those in glyceraldehyde.

ASYMMETRIC CARBON ATOMS

For a molecule to rotate the plane of polarized light, it must differ from its mirror image. The simplest and commonest situation in which this will be the case is when a compound contains an *asymmetric carbon atom,* a carbon atom that is bonded to four different atoms or groups (Fig. 7-7). In 2-butanol, C-2 is an asymmetric car-

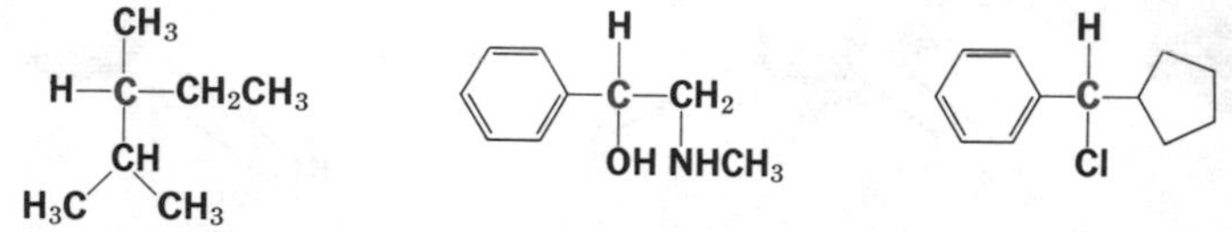

Fig. 7-7. Each of these molecules contains one (and only one) asymmetric carbon atom, in red. Hence, each is capable of existing as a D- and an L-isomer.

bon, since it is bonded to a methyl group, a hydrogen atom, a hydroxyl group, and an ethyl group. A little thought will show that symmetrical things are unchanged by reflection in a mirror, and that unsymmetrical objects are altered. So it is with molecules; if they are symmetrical they cannot give rise to configurational isomers.

One way to recognize symmetry in a molecule is to look for some plane which will cut the molecule into two mirror halves. Butane is a simple example. Two planes can be found which divide the molecule into identical parts (Fig. 7-8). Such a *plane of symmetry* is absent in molecules which exist in D- and L- forms, however. In 2-chlorobutane no plane of symmetry exists and the molecule has D- and L- forms. The ultimate test for the existence of configurational isomerism is to see whether or not a molecule is identical to its mirror image. Nonidentity can best be established by constructing models of the molecule and its mirror image and attempting to *superimpose* the two structures—that is, to lay one on top of the other so that the positions of all the atoms correspond in the two structures. In dibromofluorochloromethane the molecule is superimposable on its mirror image and so is incapable of exhibiting configurational isomerism. On the other hand, iodobromofluorochloromethane does not have superimposable mirror images. Additional examples of symmetric and asymmetric molecules are found in Fig. 7-9.

Prob. 7-3. Identify a plane of symmetry through each of the symmetric molecules in Fig. 7-9. Draw the mirror image of 3-methylcyclohexene and show that it cannot be superimposed on the original. (Molecular models may help you visualize this.)

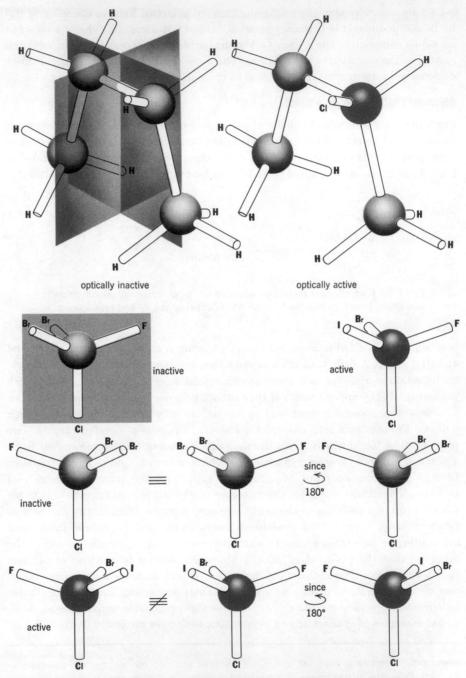

Fig. 7-8. Most optically inactive compounds have planes of symmetry. Optically active compounds do not. For each optically active compound there exists a mirror image which is not superimposable on the original compound. For optically inactive materials, the mirror image is superimposable.

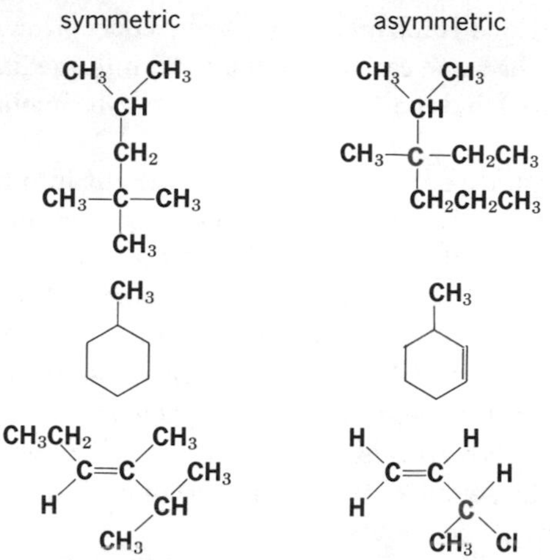

Fig. 7-9. Three examples of symmetric molecules (incapable of existing as D- and L-isomers) and three of asymmetric molecules, which can exist as configurational isomers. Asymmetric carbon atoms are shown in red.

ORGANIC HALIDES

In later chapters we shall find examples of the importance of optical activity in molecules obtained from nature. Among simple molecules, optical activity can be a useful tool for the investigation of the paths of organic reactions. Alcohols react with hydrogen bromide, hydrogen chloride, and hydrogen iodide to give alkyl halides. Because the order of reactivity is $3° > 2° > 1°$, it was suggested that carbonium ions were intermediates in these reactions. If pure D-2-butanol were used as the starting material, is optical activity to be expected in the 2-bromobutane formed by reaction with hydrogen bromide? With a carbonium ion as intermediate, the asymmetry of D-2-butanol would be lost in forming this symmetrical intermediate. The carbonium ion will react with bromide ion to produce an equal amount of D- and L-2-bromobutanes (Fig. 7-10). This is indeed what is found, and

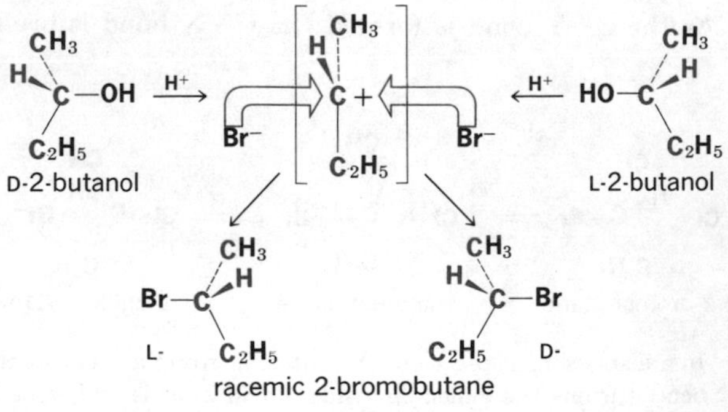

Fig. 7-10. When either pure D- or pure L-2-butanol reacts with hydrogen bromide, it is converted into racemic 2-bromobutane, by way of the symmetrical carbonium-ion intermediate.

the result serves as added confirmation that our conception of the course of this reaction fits reality. The same carbonium ion is an intermediate in the addition of hydrogen bromide to 1-butene, so that racemic 2-bromobutane must also be formed in the reaction.

Studies with configurational isomers can give insight into many other chemical transformations. In the *displacement reaction* a primary or secondary halide is allowed to react with nearly any anion Y^-. As a result, halide is replaced by Y (Fig. 7-11). It is immediately evident that displacement reactions differ from those studied so far. In the first place the reagents are bases or anions, whereas acids or radicals have been involved in earlier reactions. Secondly, tertiary halides do not undergo the displacement reaction, and the order of reactivity among the halides is $1° > 2° \gg 3°$, the reverse of that found in, for instance, the Lucas reaction with alcohols. The details of the process become clearer if we examine a reaction of optically active 2-bromobutane.

$$CH_3CH_2Br + OH^- \longrightarrow CH_3CH_2OH + Br^-$$

$$CH_3CH_2I + SH^- \longrightarrow CH_3CH_2SH + I^-$$

$$CH_3CH_2Cl + CN^- \longrightarrow CH_3CH_2CN + Cl^-$$

$$CH_3CH_2Br + I^- \longrightarrow CH_3CH_2I + Br^-$$

Fig. 7-11. Four examples of the displacement reaction in which a halide is replaced by a group Y. Y may be nearly any anion, and some neutral molecules with unbonded electrons, like NH_3, are also effective. Tertiary halides do not undergo this reaction.

If pure D-2-bromobutane reacts with chloride ion, the product is pure L-2-chlorobutane. Not only has optical activity been retained, but a right-handed molecule has been converted to a left-handed one. Results like these clearly rule out a carbonium-ion intermediate and indicate a different pathway, one in which the molecule is literally turned inside out by a process known as Walden inversion (Fig. 7-12). The incoming group Y attacks the rear of the C—X bond and pushes X out from the rear. As the C—Y bond is formed the C—X bond is broken, and at an

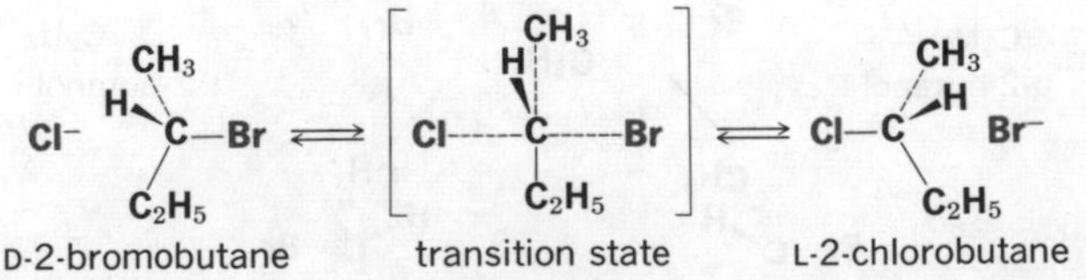

D-2-bromobutane   transition state   L-2-chlorobutane

Fig. 7-12. In a displacement reaction, the entering group attacks at the rear of the C—Br bond, turning the molecule inside out in what is known as a Walden inversion. Large groups about the C—Br bond (as in a tertiary halide) prevent the reaction.

intermediate point in the reaction both bonds are about half-made, half-broken. The other three groups at this point lie in a plane containing the central carbon atom. This high energy state, in which the transformation of reactants to products is about half over, is called the *transition state* of the reaction. It does not represent a molecule that can be isolated, but rather the path the reaction takes. This reaction mechanism is in good accord with the order of reactivity $1° > 2° \gg 3°$, since an increase in the number of alkyl groups around the C—Br bond will make it increasingly difficult for the chloride to approach the rear of the carbon atom. Other examples of displacement are shown in Fig. 7-13.

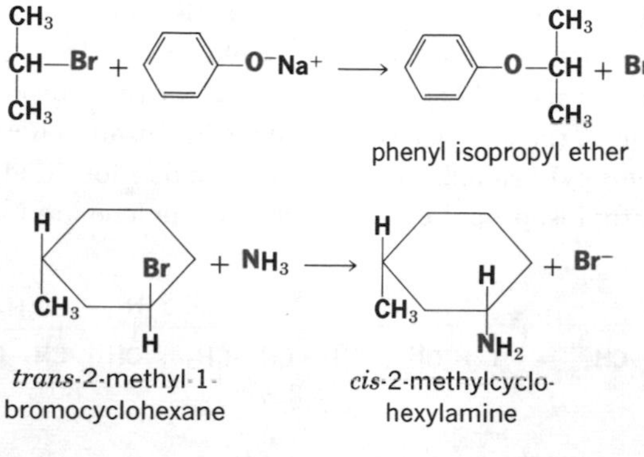

Fig. 7-13. Three examples of the displacement reaction. All these reactions proceed with Walden inversion, although only in the second case is this obvious from the structure of the product.

Prob. 7-4. If pure D-2-bromobutane is allowed to react with sodium bromide rather than sodium chloride, the product is racemic 2-bromobutane. Explain.

Prob. 7-5. Suppose you wanted to prepare ethyl *tert*-butyl ether, $C_2H_5OC(CH_3)_3$, by a reaction using the first example in Fig. 7-13 as an analogy. There are two different combinations of halide and alkoxide you might use. Explain why one combination would give the product wanted and the other would not.

NOMENCLATURE

In the IUPAC system of naming organic compounds, halogen atoms are not regarded as functional groups, so there is no characteristic ending for halides. Instead, a halogen atom is treated as a substituent and is indicated in a prefix (fluoro-, chloro-, bromo-, iodo-) to the name of the parent hydrocarbon. This was discussed in Chapter 1 and examples have been encountered in subsequent ones. Aromatic halides, such as bromobenzene, are named similarly, by affixing a prefix indicating the halogen atom to the name of the compound.

We can also name organic halides by the group name method used earlier for alcohols. Thus, bromoethane is ethyl bromide and *tert*-butyl bromide is the same compound as 2-bromo-2-methylpropane. Numerous instances of both methods of naming halides are found in the figures of this chapter. Additional exercises may be found in the Appendix, for example Questions 8, 22 and 23.

ELIMINATION REACTIONS OF HALIDES

Alkyl halides sometimes react with anions to give alkenes. This type of reaction is known as an *elimination reaction.* The best yield results from treatment with a base, and hydroxide or alkoxide is frequently used for this purpose. With primary and secondary halides, the two reactions, displacement and elimination, are competitive. When isopropyl bromide reacts with ethoxide ion in ethanolic solution, for instance, 20% ethyl isopropyl ether and 80% propylene are formed (Fig. 7-14).

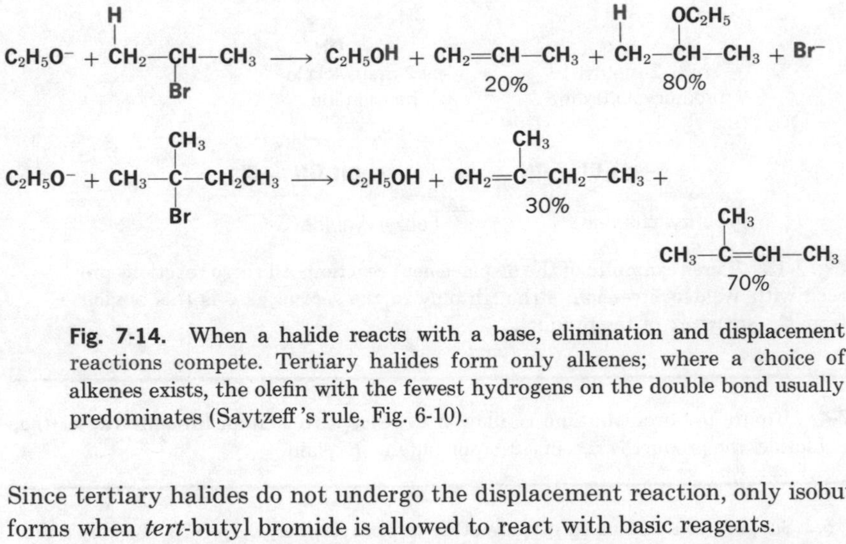

$$C_2H_5O^- + CH_2\!-\!\underset{\underset{Br}{|}}{\overset{\overset{H}{|}}{C}H}\!-\!CH_3 \longrightarrow C_2H_5OH + \underset{20\%}{CH_2\!=\!CH\!-\!CH_3} + \underset{80\%}{CH_2\!-\!\overset{\overset{H \quad OC_2H_5}{|\quad\;\;|}}{C}H\!-\!CH_3} + Br^-$$

$$C_2H_5O^- + CH_3\!-\!\underset{\underset{Br}{|}}{\overset{\overset{CH_3}{|}}{C}}\!-\!CH_2CH_3 \longrightarrow C_2H_5OH + \underset{30\%}{CH_2\!=\!\overset{\overset{CH_3}{|}}{C}\!-\!CH_2\!-\!CH_3} +$$

$$\underset{70\%}{CH_3\!-\!\overset{\overset{CH_3}{|}}{C}\!=\!CH\!-\!CH_3} + Br^-$$

Fig. 7-14. When a halide reacts with a base, elimination and displacement reactions compete. Tertiary halides form only alkenes; where a choice of alkenes exists, the olefin with the fewest hydrogens on the double bond usually predominates (Saytzeff's rule, Fig. 6-10).

Since tertiary halides do not undergo the displacement reaction, only isobutylene forms when *tert*-butyl bromide is allowed to react with basic reagents.

The elimination and displacement reactions proceed by related pathways. In both, approach by the base precedes the reaction, but the attack in elimination is on the hydrogen atom located on the carbon atom adjacent to that bearing the halogen atom. The oxygen–hydrogen bond and the carbon–carbon double bond form, whereas the hydrogen–carbon and carbon–halogen bonds break. When elimination can take place in more than one direction, a mixture of products usually results.

Elimination reactions occur most readily if the hydrogen and halogen atoms are *trans* to one another. This stereochemical requirement has its most striking effect

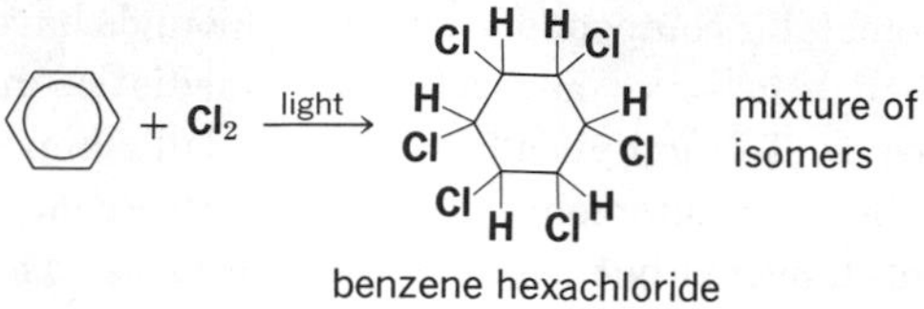

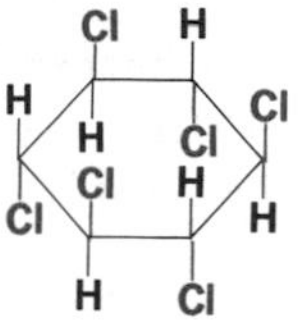

Fig. 7-15. Chlorination of benzene under special conditions results in a mixture of stereoisomers of 1,2,3,4,5,6-hexachlorocyclohexane (benzene hexachloride). When treated with potassium hydroxide solution, all isomers except one lose hydrogen chloride. The unreactive isomer (shown) has no hydrogen and chlorine atoms *trans* to each other.

in cyclic systems. An example is found in the chemistry of hexachlorocyclohexanes (Fig. 7-15). A mixture of isomers is formed from the light-catalyzed chlorination of benzene. One of these isomers is an insecticide which is marketed as Lindane. If the mixture of isomers is treated with potassium hydroxide at 80°, hydrogen chloride is eliminated rather readily from all isomers except one. X-ray analysis shows that in this unreactive isomer all chlorine atoms are *trans* to one another; that is, there are only *cis* hydrogens and chlorines. All other isomers have at least one *trans* hydrogen-chlorine pair. It should be clear from this example, and from the examples of the Walden inversion, that stereochemistry can have a profound effect on chemical reactivity.

Prob. 7-6. Write the structures of *all* the products (substitution and/or elimination) you would expect to be formed in the following reactions:

$$CH_3CH_2CH_2Br + C_2H_5O^-Na^+ \longrightarrow$$

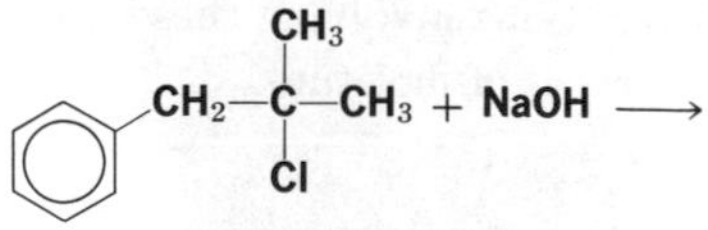

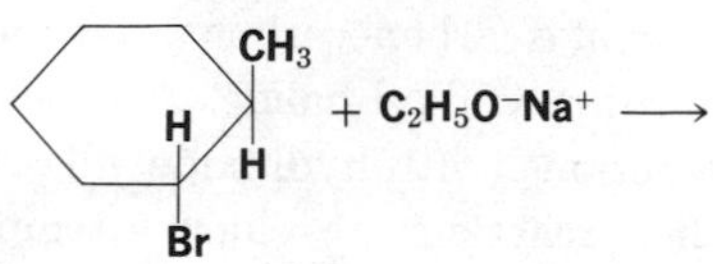

REACTIONS OF HALIDES WITH METALS

By reaction with anions alkyl halides may be converted into a wide variety of other functionally substituted compounds. Halides also react with a number of metals to give organometallic compounds. These compounds have a number of practical applications and also serve as useful intermediates in the synthesis of other organic molecules. Tetraethyllead is commercially important as the commonest antiknock additive for automobile gasoline. Other organometallic compounds are also good antiknock agents but cannot be removed as easily from the engine after combustion.

For organic synthesis, more reactive organometallic compounds than tetraethyllead are needed. Organomagnesium compounds form from the reaction, in ether, of alkyl or aryl halides with metallic magnesium (Fig. 7-16). These compounds are

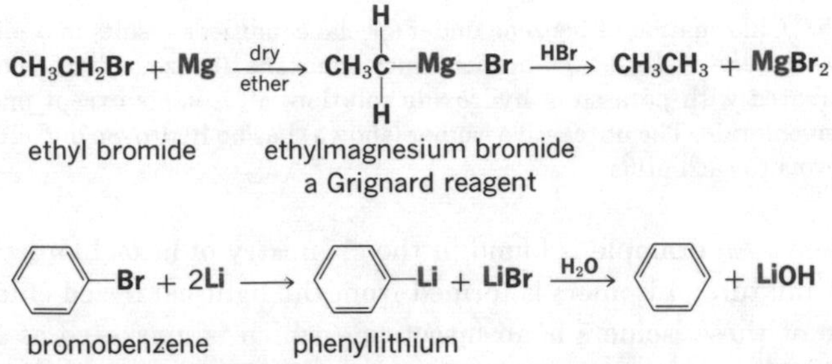

$$CH_3CH_2Br + Mg \xrightarrow[\text{ether}]{\text{dry}} CH_3\overset{\overset{\displaystyle H}{|}}{\underset{\underset{\displaystyle H}{|}}{C}}-Mg-Br \xrightarrow{HBr} CH_3CH_3 + MgBr_2$$

ethyl bromide   ethylmagnesium bromide
                          a Grignard reagent

$$\langle\!\!\!\bigcirc\!\!\!\rangle\!-Br + 2Li \longrightarrow \langle\!\!\!\bigcirc\!\!\!\rangle\!-Li + LiBr \xrightarrow{H_2O} \langle\!\!\!\bigcirc\!\!\!\rangle + LiOH$$

bromobenzene   phenyllithium

Fig. 7-16. Most organic chlorides, bromides, and iodides react with magnesium (to give Grignard reagents) or with lithium. The resultant organometallic compounds react vigorously with water, acids, or other sources of protons to form hydrocarbons.

more commonly called Grignard reagents after their discoverer, the French chemist Victor Grignard (Nobel Prize 1912). Organolithium compounds, formed by the reaction of organic halides with metallic lithium, are also useful. Most carbon–metal bonds are not particularly ionic, but to interpret their reactions it helps to think of them as reacting as if they were $\rangle C^-Mg^{++}Br^-$ or $\rangle C^-Li^+$. Both of these organometallics readily combine with any source of a proton (from water, acid, alcohol, etc.) to give $\rangle C$—H. Consequently, all reactions involving these intermediates must be carried out in the absence of even traces of moisture.

ARYL AND VINYL HALIDES

A halogen atom attached directly to a carbon atom of a carbon–carbon unsaturated bond has a great deal less reactivity than an ordinary alkyl halide. Specifically, aryl and vinyl halides undergo displacement reactions (with hydroxide, alkoxide, etc.) only under such stringent conditions that these reactions are seldom attempted in the laboratory. Elimination reactions of vinyl halides are less difficult, and vinyl bromide is converted to acetylene by heating with base (Fig. 7-17). If an aromatic halide is allowed to react with a strong base like sodium amide ($NaNH_2$), elimination also takes place. The resulting intermediate is called a *benzyne* and is highly strained. Benzynes cannot be isolated, since they react readily with either excess amide or with themselves to give a dimer.

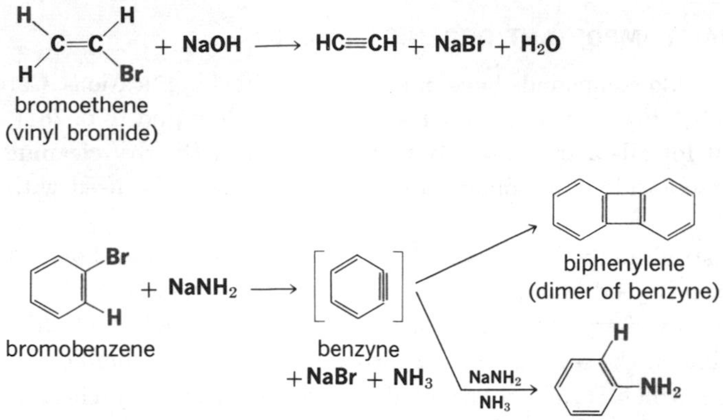

bromoethene
(vinyl bromide)

$$H_2C=CHBr + NaOH \longrightarrow HC\equiv CH + NaBr + H_2O$$

bromobenzene

benzyne
+NaBr + NH$_3$

biphenylene
(dimer of benzyne)

Fig. 7-17. Halogen atoms attached to a double bond or aromatic ring are quite unreactive in displacement reactions. Vinyl and aryl halides form acetylenes on treatment with strong base, but those from aryl halides, called benzynes, are quite unstable. One of the products from this elimination reaction of halobenzenes is the dimer of benzyne.

Both aryl and vinyl halides form organometallic compounds with magnesium, and these reagents, like their alkyl counterparts, react rapidly with protons and other reagents. Halobenzenes undergo further aromatic substitution reactions, as discussed in Chapter 5. The halogens are *ortho-para* directing in aromatic substitution (Fig. 7-18).

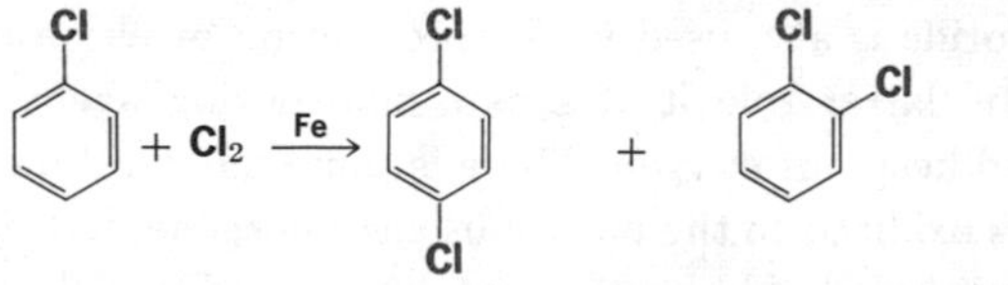

p-dichlorobenzene   *o*-dichlorobenzene

Fig. 7-18. Halobenzenes are *ortho-para* directing. Chlorination of chlorobenzene (or dichlorination of benzene) gives a mixture of *o*- and *p*-dichlorobenzenes. The *para* isomer is sold as a moth repellent.

Several methods for the synthesis of alkyl halides were given in earlier chapters, but it may do to summarize them here. They include:

(1) halogenation of saturated alkyl groups (Fig. 1-1)
(2) addition of hydrogen bromide to double bonds by
   a. Markownikoff addition (Fig. 3-15)
   b. anti-Markownikoff addition (Fig. 4-4)
(3) addition of halogen to double bonds (Fig. 3-14)
(4) replacement of hydroxyl groups by halogen (Fig. 6-4).

Aromatic halides are prepared by direct halogenation (Fig. 7-18) or from aromatic amines by a method to be presented in the next chapter.

COMMERCIALLY IMPORTANT ORGANIC HALIDES

A number of halo compounds have important practical applications. Carbon tetrachloride (CCl_4), for example, is a dense nonflammable liquid (b.p. 78°) which is a good solvent for oils and greases. It finds wide use in the dry cleaning industry. Carbon tetrachloride is poisonous, and so should always be used with adequate ventilation.

Two industrial methods are available for the synthesis of carbon tetrachloride, and they furnish good examples of some of the economic factors which play a role in industrial chemistry. The simplest method involves the direct chlorination of methane, while in the second method carbon and sulfur are combined to give carbon disulfide, which is then chlorinated to furnish carbon tetrachloride. Twice as much chlorine is required for chlorination of methane to carbon tetrachloride as for chlorination of carbon disulfide. Most companies have uses for the hydrogen chloride produced as a byproduct in the first reaction, or can sell it, but if they do not, the synthesis from carbon disulfide is cheaper (Fig. 7-19).

(a) $CH_4 + 4Cl_2 \longrightarrow CCl_4 + 4HCl$

(b) $CS_2 + 2Cl_2 \longrightarrow CCl_4 + 2S$

Fig. 7-19. Two industrial syntheses of carbon tetrachloride. If a market were not readily available for hydrogen chloride, the second reaction would be the more economical since carbon disulfide is synthesized from carbon and sulfur, two cheap raw materials.

Carbon tetrachloride is also used in the production of chloroform and as a fire extinguisher. In the latter role it acts as a smothering agent; its dense vapors blanket the fire and keep out oxygen. There is some danger, however, because carbon tetrachloride is oxidized to the poisonous gas phosgene, $COCl_2$. A carbon tetrachloride fire extinguisher should be used only with good ventilation.

Prob. 7-7. During World War II, many fire bombs were used which were primarily powdered magnesium metal. This metal burns fiercely and the bombs caused great destruction. Why were people warned not to use carbon tetrachloride fire extinguishers on such fires?

Chloroform, a sweet colorless liquid (b.p. 61°), is prepared industrially by the reduction of carbon tetrachloride with iron. Like nearly all halo compounds, chloroform is somewhat toxic. As it is especially apt to cause damage to the liver, it is now seldom used as a general anesthetic, although it is still used as a mild sedative in cough syrups, cough drops, or liniments. Ethyl chloride (b.p. 12°) is also commonly used as a topical anesthetic. It owes its effect to its physical rather than its chemical properties: When sprayed on the skin, ethyl chloride evaporates rapidly, cooling the skin and nerve endings.

More complex chlorine-containing organic molecules are often violent poisons and some find wide use as insecticides. Benzene hexachloride has been mentioned in this connection (see Fig. 7-15). The most famous such compound is DDT, an abbreviation for the somewhat illegitimate name *di*chloro*di*phenyl-*tri*chloroethane; this compound is formed by the reaction of chlorobenzene with chloral (see Fig. 7-20). DDT is active against a wide variety of insects and proved its usefulness

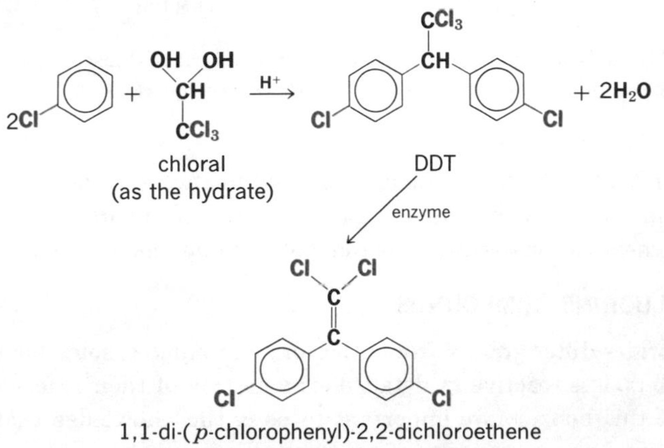

chloral
(as the hydrate)   DDT

1,1-di-(*p*-chlorophenyl)-2,2-dichloroethene

Fig. 7-20. DDT (Dichlorodiphenyl-trichloroethane, not a correct IUPAC name) was the first really potent synthetic insecticide. Many insects have developed an enzyme system (called DDT dehydrochlorinase) which inactivates DDT by converting it to the ethylene derivative shown.

in striking fashion when, after World War II, nearly all the residents of Naples were dusted with DDT to bring a typhus epidemic to a halt. It has also been used to eradicate malaria from many parts of the world.

Unfortunately, when millions of insects are treated with DDT, a few survive. Naturally, those few are the most resistant to DDT, and some are able to pass on this resistance to their progeny. Over many generations, whole species of insects have become resistant to DDT, and cannot be killed by it. These resistant insects apparently contain an enzyme which deactivates DDT by causing an elimination of the elements of hydrogen chloride from the molecule.

Prob. 7-8. Production of DDT by the Friedel-Crafts reaction shown in Fig. 7-20 actually leads to three isomeric DDT molecules, only one of which is shown. Suggest structures for the other two isomers based upon your knowledge of the directive effect of chlorine in aromatic substitution reactions.

After the discovery of DDT, a wide search was made among other chlorinated hydrocarbons for insecticidal properties. Aldrin, a compound more toxic than DDT, was one result. Insects have an enzyme system which converts Aldrin to Dieldrin. Dieldrin is a more powerful insecticide than Aldrin (Fig. 7-21), so that

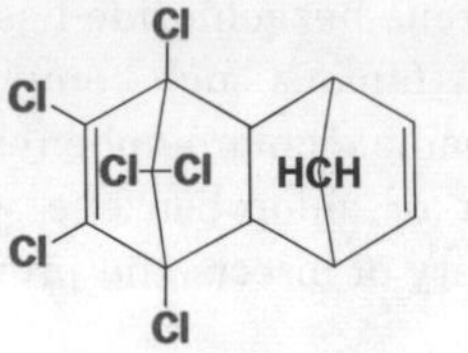

Fig. 7-21. Aldrin and Dieldrin are two powerful chlorinated insecticides. Almost nothing is known about the way in which these substances kill insects.

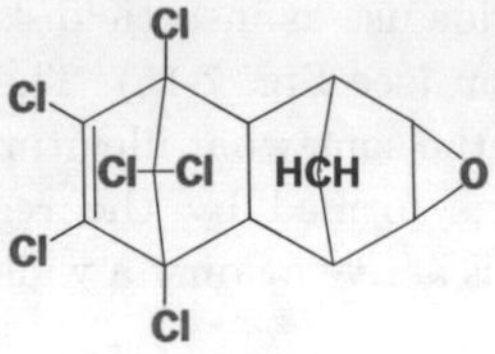

in this instance the insects' enzyme systems aid in their own destruction. Dieldrin can also be produced by oxidation of Aldrin. However, many insects have become resistant to these two insecticides, by some little-understood method.

ORGANIC FLUORINE COMPOUNDS

Organic fluorides differ greatly from other organic halides, some being more reactive and others, less reactive. A detailed examination of their reactivity is beyond the scope of this book. More important to us is the knowledge that compounds containing two or more fluorine atoms on the same carbon atom are extremely resistant to chemical attack. Tetrafluoroethylene, for instance, can be polymerized to Teflon (Fig. 7-22), which is an extremely inert, high-melting plastic. It is used to

$$F_2C{=}CF_2 \longrightarrow \ {-}CF_2{-}CF_2{-}(CF_2{-}CF_2)_n CF_2{-}CF_2{-}$$

tetrafluoroethylene   Teflon

Fig. 7-22. Polytetrafluoroethylene (Teflon) is the completely fluorinated analog of polyethylene. It is stable to 380° and completely inert to boiling acids and bases, and to many oxidizing agents.

coat the insides of frying pans and the bottoms of skis to prevent sticking; it also has many industrial and scientific applications, such as being made into bearings to be exposed to a corrosive atmosphere.

Completely fluorinated hydrocarbons—fluorocarbons—have unusual physical and chemical properties. In particular, their boiling points are much lower than hydrocarbons of the same molecular weight. Perfluoro-n-butane (C_4F_{10}, mol. wt. 138) has a boiling point even lower ($-1.7°$) than that of n-butane (mol. wt. 58, b.p. $-0.5°$).

Sodium monofluoroacetate is a powerful rat-killing agent, whereas freon, CF_2Cl_2, is a completely nontoxic gas used in refrigerators and as a propellant in aerosol sprays. Satisfactory methods for preparing a variety of completely fluorinated hydrocarbons were discovered in the late 1930's, just in time to be used in the atomic energy program developed during the war years. The great unreactivity of these hydrocarbons made them valuable in contact with uranium hexafluoride and this use gave great impetus to investigations of their syntheses and properties.

Fluorinated compounds are still quite expensive, but industrial applications are increasing.

Prob. 7-9. Which of the following compounds are capable of exhibiting optical isomerism?

(a) $CH_3CHBrCH_3$

(b) $C_2H_5CHOHCH_3$

(c) $(C_2H_5)_2CHCH_2CH(C_2H_5)_2$

(d) $CH_2=CH-CH(CH_3)CH_2CH_3$

(e)

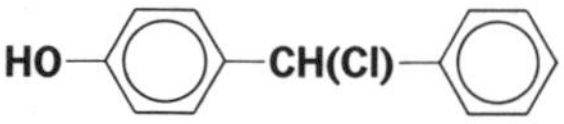

HO—⟨benzene ring⟩—CH(Cl)—⟨benzene ring⟩

(f) 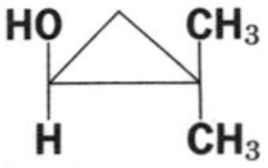 HO ⟨cyclopropane with CH_3⟩ CH$_3$
    H   CH$_3$

(g) CH$_3$ CH$_3$
    ⟨cyclopentane⟩
    H   H

(h) CH$_3$ H
    ⟨cyclopentane⟩
    H   CH$_3$

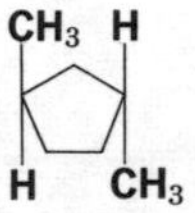

(i) 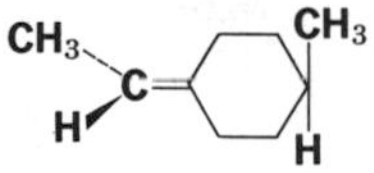 CH_3 ╲ CH_3
          C=⟨cyclohexane ring⟩
     H ╱   H

(j) 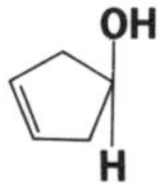 ⟨cyclopentene ring⟩ OH
                         H

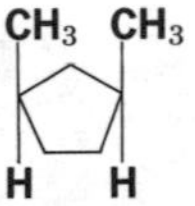

Prob. 7-10. Would you expect the product of each of the following reactions to be optically active or optically inactive?

(a) $CH_2=CHCH_2CH_3 + Br_2 \longrightarrow$

(b) 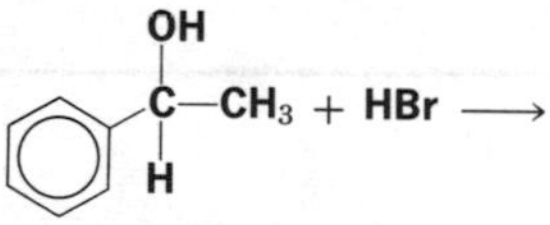
     OH
     |
⟨benzene ring⟩—C—CH$_3$ + HBr $\longrightarrow$
     |
     H
     D-isomer

(c) 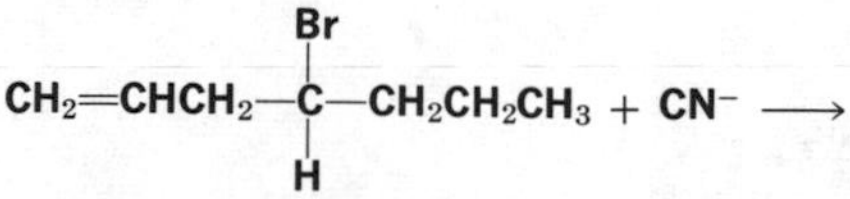
          Br
          |
(c) $CH_2=CHCH_2-C-CH_2CH_2CH_3 + CN^- \longrightarrow$
          |
          H
        D-isomer

(d) 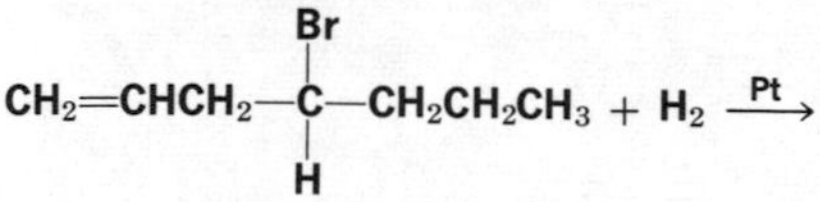
          Br
          |
(d) $CH_2=CHCH_2-C-CH_2CH_2CH_3 + H_2 \xrightarrow{Pt}$
          |
          H
        D-isomer

(e) 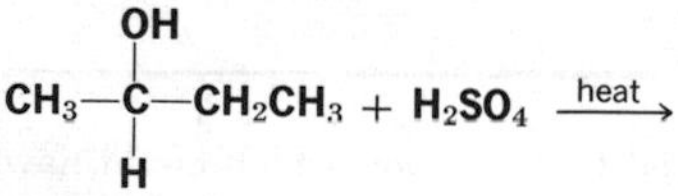
        OH
        |
(e) $CH_3-C-CH_2CH_3 + H_2SO_4 \xrightarrow{heat}$
        |
        H
      D-isomer

Prob. 7-11. Give all the organic products that you would expect to be produced in the following reactions.

(a) 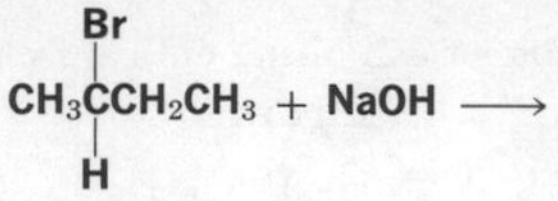
$$
\begin{array}{c}
\text{Br} \\
| \\
\text{CH}_3\text{CCH}_2\text{CH}_3 \\
| \\
\text{H}
\end{array}
+ \text{NaOH} \longrightarrow
$$
D-isomer

(b) 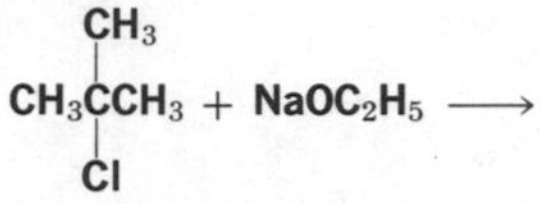
$$
\begin{array}{c}
\text{CH}_3 \\
| \\
\text{CH}_3\text{CCH}_3 \\
| \\
\text{Cl}
\end{array}
+ \text{NaOC}_2\text{H}_5 \longrightarrow
$$

(c) + NaOC$_2$H$_5$ ⟶

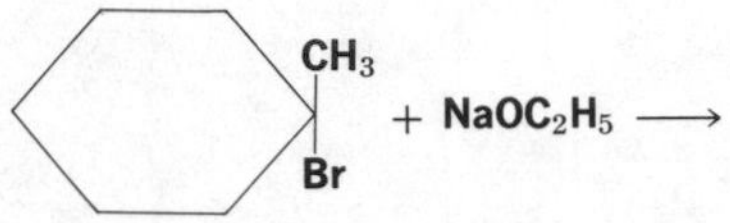

(d) 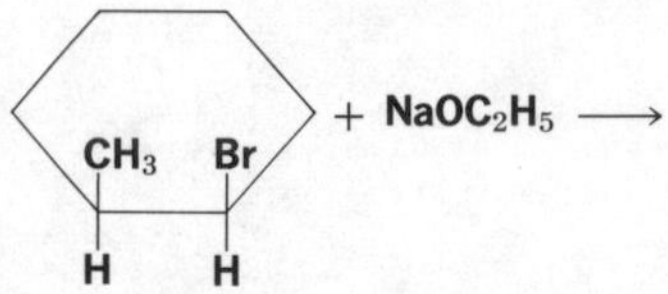 + NaOC$_2$H$_5$ ⟶

(e) 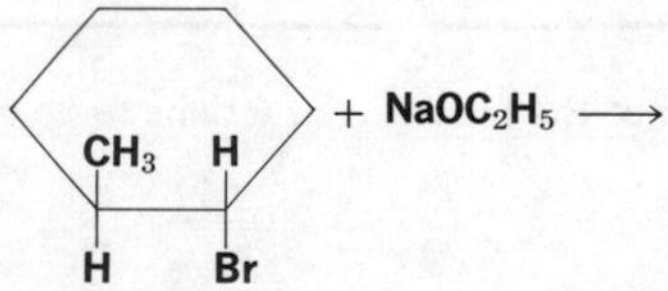 + NaOC$_2$H$_5$ ⟶

Prob. 7-12. Complete the following reactions.

(a) 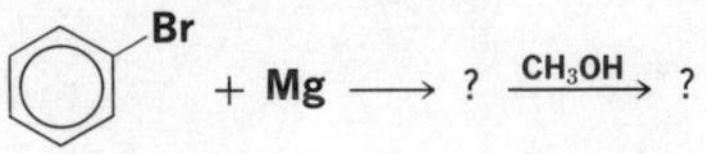 + Mg ⟶ ? $\xrightarrow{\text{CH}_3\text{OH}}$?

(b) 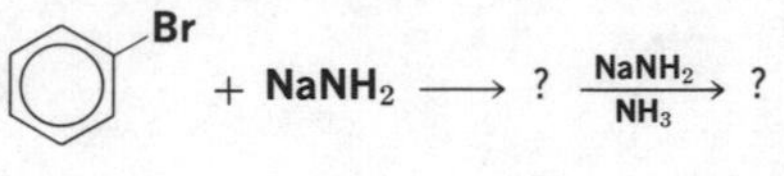 + NaNH$_2$ ⟶ ? $\xrightarrow[\text{NH}_3]{\text{NaNH}_2}$?

(c)  + HNO$_3$ $\xrightarrow{\text{H}_2\text{SO}_4}$?

(d) 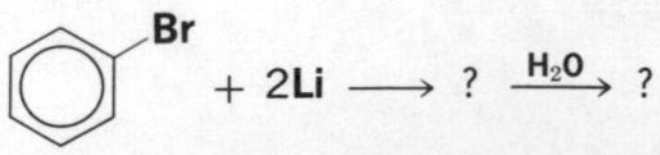 + 2Li ⟶ ? $\xrightarrow{\text{H}_2\text{O}}$?

Prob. 7-13. What is the smallest acyclic saturated hydrocarbon which could have optical isomers? The smallest alkene? The smallest cyclic saturated hydrocarbon?

Prob. 7-14. Deduce the structures of compounds A through G.

$A(C_5H_{11}Br)$ $\xrightarrow[\text{(2) H}_2\text{O}]{\text{(1) Mg, Et}_2\text{O}}$ $B(C_5H_{12})$

optically   inactive
active

$A \xrightarrow{\text{NaOH}} C(C_5H_{12}O) + D(C_5H_{10}) + E(C_5H_{10})$

active   inactive   inactive

$E + HBr \longrightarrow A$

$D + HBr \longrightarrow F(C_5H_{11}Br)$

$F \xrightarrow{\text{NaOH}} D + G(C_5H_{10})$

Prob. 7-15. Draw the structure of each of the following commercially important compounds.

(a) 1,1-di-(*p*-chlorophenyl)-ethanol (DMC, useful in killing mites)
(b) 3-chloro-2-methylpropene (methallyl chloride, an insecticide for grain weevils)
(c) hexachloroethane (used in smoke pots)
(d) 1,1-dihydroxy-2,2,2-trichloroethane (chloral hydrate, a hypnotic)

CHAPTER

8

AMINES AND THEIR DERIVATIVES

The organic derivatives of ammonia (NH_3) perform an important role in organic chemistry, particularly with reference to biological systems. These derivatives include amino acids, the materials from which proteins are constructed, and many of the most important drugs and medicines. One group of them is a set of bases known as amines. As we saw in Chapter 6, amines may be represented by the general formula RNH_2, R_2NH, or R_3N. No matter how they are symbolized, amines contain nitrogen and relate to ammonia just as alcohols and ethers relate to water. Much of the organic chemistry of amines springs from their weak basicity. This characteristic results from the presence of a nonbonded pair of electrons on the nitrogen atom (Fig. 8-1).

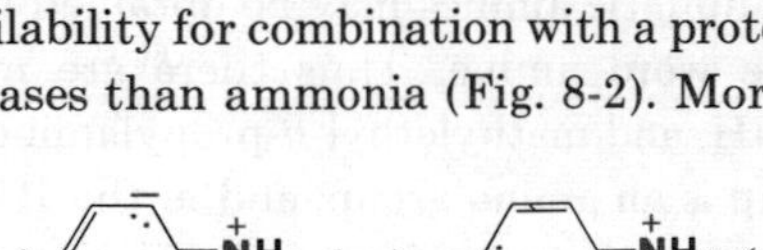

$$\begin{matrix} & R & & & R & \\ & | & & & | & \\ R-\!\!&N&\!\!:\; + \;HOH & \rightleftharpoons & R-\!\!&N&\!\!\overset{+}{-}H \;+\; OH^- \\ & | & & & | & \\ & R & & & R & \end{matrix}$$

Fig. 8-1. Amines, like ammonia, are weak bases.

In an aromatic amine the unshared electrons are *delocalized* into the aromatic ring, reducing their availability for combination with a proton, and making aromatic amines much weaker bases than ammonia (Fig. 8-2). Moreover, the effect of sub-

Fig. 8-2. In an aromatic amine like aniline the nonbonded electrons on the nitrogen atom are partially delocalized into the aromatic ring.

139

Table 8-1.   Relative Basicity of Alkyl Amines, Ammonia,
and Aromatic Amines

Amine	K_b	pK_b
NH_3	1.26×10^{-5}	4.90
CH_3NH_2	2.82×10^{-4}	3.55
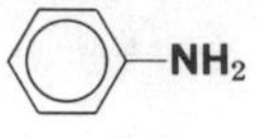 ⬡—NH_2 aniline	2.57×10^{-10}	9.59
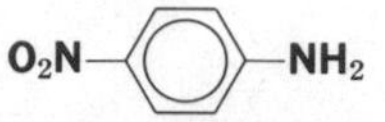 O_2N—⬡—NH_2 *p*-nitroaniline	7.08×10^{-14}	13.15

stituents such as nitro groups on the basic dissociation constants of aromatic amines is similar to their effect on the acidic dissociation constants of the phenols, except that a group which makes a phenol a *stronger acid* makes an aromatic amine a *weaker base*. This is illustrated in the K_b's of Table 8-1.

Owing to their basicity, amines form salts when treated with acids, and an amine that is insoluble in water usually dissolves readily in dilute aqueous solutions of hydrochloric or other strong mineral acids (Fig. 8-3).

$$CH_3(CH_2)_6CH_2NH_2 + HCl \longrightarrow CH_3(CH_2)_6CH_2\overset{+}{N}H_3 + Cl^-$$

insoluble in water   soluble in water

Fig. 8-3. When treated with mineral acids, amines are converted into water-soluble salts.

Prob. 8-1. Suppose you were given a mixture of *n*-hexylamine, $CH_3(CH_2)_5NH_2$, and 1-hexanol, $CH_3(CH_2)_5OH$, and were asked to obtain each in its pure form. Explain how you would accomplish this, modeling your answer after that of Fig. 6-32.

NOMENCLATURE OF AMINES

The common names of aliphatic amines may be obtained by joining the names of the alkyl groups to the word amine. Thus there are methylamine, CH_3NH_2, dimethylamine, $(CH_3)_2NH$, and methylethyl-*n*-propylamine, $CH_3CH_2CH_2N(CH_3)$-CH_2CH_3. The NH_2 group is an amino group, and in the IUPAC system of nomenclature it is treated as a substituent. Thus, $CH_3CH(NH_2)CH_3$ is properly called either isopropylamine (common name) or 2-aminopropane (IUPAC name).

Among aromatic amines, the parent is aniline, $C_6H_5NH_2$. Since some confusion might arise over whether a substituent is attached to the nitrogen atom or the aromatic ring, the prefix N- precedes the name for nitrogen substituents; for example, $C_6H_5NHCH_3$ is properly called N-methylaniline.

It is convenient to classify amines according to the number of alkyl or aryl groups attached to the nitrogen atom. An amine having only a single organic group, like methylamine or aniline, belongs to the general class of primary (1°) amines. Amines with two or three organic groups are classified as secondary (2°) or tertiary (3°) amines, respectively. Amine derivatives containing a tetrasubstituted nitrogen atom are known as quaternary (4°) ammonium salts. These classifications are illustrated in Fig. 8-4.*

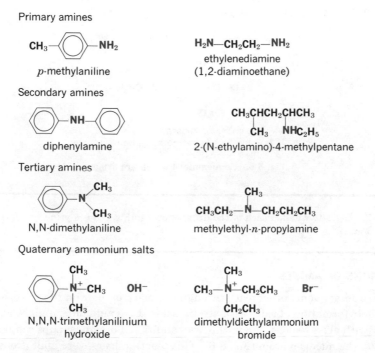

Fig. 8-4. Names of some typical amines and quaternary ammonium salts.

Organic derivatives of the positively charged ammonium ion are named as such. Thus, tetramethylammonium bromide is $(CH_3)_4\overset{+}{N}Br^-$ and methylethylammonium chloride is $CH_3(C_2H_5)\overset{+}{N}H_2Cl^-$. Salts of aniline are similarly known as anilinium salts. Problems dealing with amine nomenclature are found in the Appendix.

Amines are important compounds, especially in biology, where amino acids constitute the monomeric units from which proteins and many hormones are made

---

* It may be useful to point out the structural difference between 1°, 2°, and 3° as applied to alcohols and halides on the one hand and to amines on the other. For example, *tert*-butyl alcohol is a tertiary alcohol, while *tert*-butylamine is a primary amine containing a tertiary carbon atom.

and where amines are some of the most potent drugs. Most of these biologically, important compounds are rather complex, and so they usually have common names. Names for the amino acids will be found in Chapter 13. A few common drugs are shown in Fig. 8-5. Benzedrine is the ingredient of "pep-pills," adrenaline is a heart stimulant, and mescaline produces hallucinations.

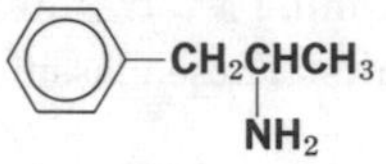

benzedrine
(amphetamine; 1-phenyl-2-aminopropane)

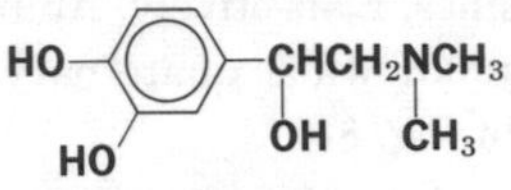

adrenaline
[epinephrine; 1-(3,4-dihydroxy-
phenyl)-1-hydroxy-2-dimethyl-
aminoethane]

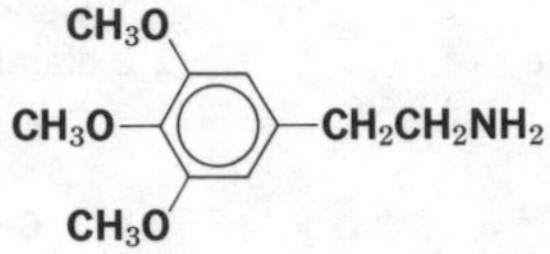

mescaline
1-amino-2-(3,4,5-trimethoxyphenyl)-ethane

Fig. 8-5. Some amines which are drugs.

Prob. 8-2. Indicate whether each of the drugs shown in Fig. 8-5 is a primary, secondary, or tertiary amine.

REACTIONS OF AMINES

Amines and ammonia often react through the electron pair on the nitrogen atom, as in their formation of salts with strong acids. Like ammonia, amines also react readily with alkyl halides, and in this way additional organic groups can be substituted on the nitrogen atom (Fig. 8-6). This reaction has severe limitations from a

$$H-\underset{\underset{H}{|}}{\overset{\overset{H}{|}}{N}}: + C_2H_5Br \longrightarrow C_2H_5NH_2 + HBr \xrightarrow{C_2H_5Br} (C_2H_5)_2NH + HBr$$

Fig. 8-6. Ammonia and amines react with alkyl halides.

synthetic standpoint, however, because the amines which are products of the reaction can react further with the alkyl halide, leading to a mixture of 1°, 2°, 3°, and 4° compounds (Fig. 8-7). These reactions of amines with halides belong to the general class of *displacement reactions* (Chapter 7) and so do not take place with tertiary or aromatic halides.

$$(C_2H_5)_2NH + C_2H_5Br \longrightarrow (C_2H_5)_3N \xrightarrow{C_2H_5Br} (C_2H_5)_4N^+ \ Br^-$$

Fig. 8-7. Continued reaction of ethyl bromide with amines leads eventually to the formation of a quaternary ammonium salt.

Primary and secondary amines may be converted into *amides* upon treatment with acid derivatives. The reaction of aniline with acetyl chloride is a straightforward example (Fig. 8-8). During the reaction, a molecule of hydrogen chloride is

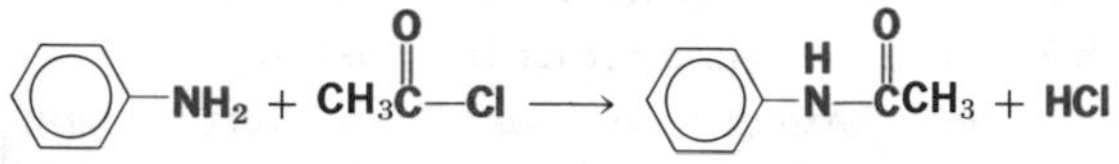

aniline   acetyl chloride   acetanilide

Fig. 8-8. An amide is formed from a 1° or 2° amine and an acid chloride.

eliminated; since 3° amines have no hydrogen attached to the nitrogen atom, no amide can form. Amides can also be formed through the reaction of acid anhydrides or esters with primary or secondary amines (Fig. 8-9). These reactions will be discussed in more detail in Chapter 11.

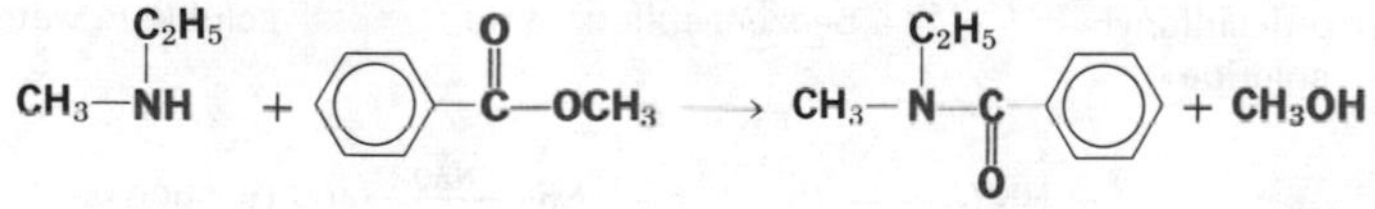

methylethylamine   methyl benzoate   N-methyl-N-ethyl-
benzamide

Fig. 8-9. An ester and an amine will react to form an amide, although the reaction is often slow. Acid anhydrides or acid chlorides are more commonly used.

Although amines are bases, amides are neutral molecules. The basicity of an amine depends upon the availability of the electron pair on the nitrogen atom for combination with a proton. In an amide, the electron pair is partially delocalized by resonance onto the oxygen atom of the carbonyl group, rather than being localized on the nitrogen atom (Fig. 8-10). An amide, therefore, shows little or no tendency toward salt formation.

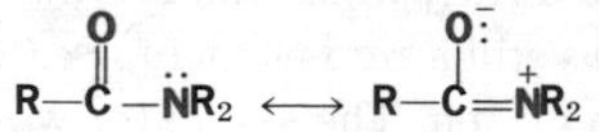

Fig. 8-10. In an amide, the electron pair on the nitrogen atom is shared by the oxygen atom, reducing the basicity of the nitrogen.

Amides of sulfonic acids can similarly be formed by reaction of amines with

sulfonyl chlorides. The sulfonyl group, $-\overset{\displaystyle O}{\underset{\displaystyle O}{S}}-$,

is so strongly electron-withdrawing that sulfonamides, $(-\overset{\displaystyle O}{\underset{\displaystyle O}{S}}-N\Big\langle\,)$,

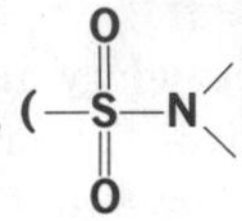

are actually acidic if a hydrogen atom is attached to the nitrogen atom. The property of a sulfonamide with a hydrogen atom on its nitrogen atom to be acidic and to react with bases to give salts forms the basis of a test (the Hinsberg test) which distinguish among primary, secondary, and tertiary amines. A primary amine reacts with benzenesulfonyl chloride to give a precipitate of a benzene-sulfonamide which dissolves in base, since the hydrogen atom on the nitrogen atom is acidic. A secondary amine also gives a precipitate with benzenesulfonyl chloride, but this sulfonamide, lacking an N—H group, is insoluble in base. A tertiary amine does not form a sulfonamide (Fig. 8-11).

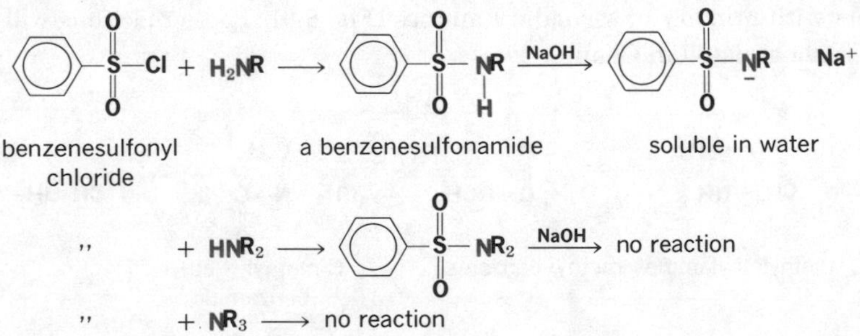

Fig. 8-11. Primary and secondary amines react with benzenesulfonyl chloride to give sulfonamides. The *Hinsberg test* distinguishes among primary, secondary, and tertiary amines.

SUBSTITUTION REACTIONS OF AROMATIC AMINES

Aniline and its derivatives undergo aromatic substitution reactions with great ease; ordinarily it is difficult to stop such a reaction until all available *ortho* and *para* positions have been substituted. This great reactivity is due to the partial distribution of the electron pair of nitrogen onto the aromatic ring, as shown in Fig. 8-2. The reactivity of aniline found early industrial use in the recovery of bromine from the ocean, when bromine was still a rare element. Sea water contains about 0.015% bromine in the form of bromide ion. The sea water was oxidized to bromine by the addition of chlorine and then aniline was added. Even at this low concentration, bromine forms the insoluble solid 2,4,6-tribromoaniline; this compound can be easily isolated so that the bromine can be recovered from it. Although this process has now been supplanted by less expensive methods, it illustrates the great reactivity of the aromatic ring in aniline toward electrophilic reagents like bromine (Fig. 8-12).

The reactivity of aniline is greatly reduced if the amino group has an electron-withdrawing group attached to it. Acetanilide, for example, can be monosubstituted easily, because a portion of the electrons of the amino group in it are delocalized onto the oxygen of the carbonyl group.

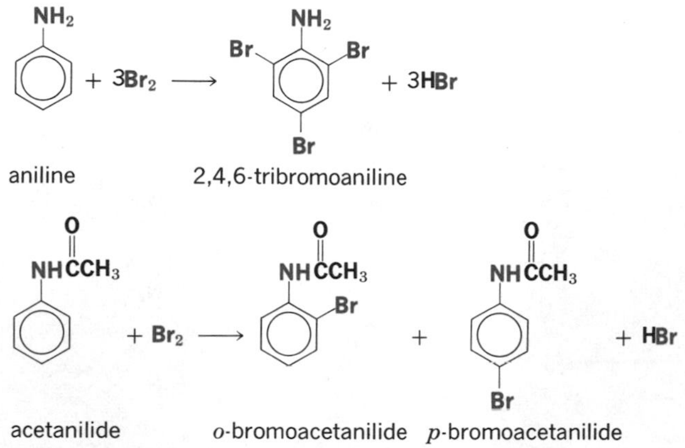

aniline   2,4,6-tribromoaniline

acetanilide   o-bromoacetanilide   p-bromoacetanilide

Fig. 8-12. Aniline is so reactive toward aromatic substitution that the reaction is difficult to stop before trisubstitution has occurred. Acetanilide is less reactive, and monosubstitution products are easily obtained.

Prob. 8-3. Would you expect aniline to react more or less readily with bromine in a solution of hydrogen bromide? Why?

DIAZONIUM SALTS

When treated with nitrous acid, primary aromatic amines are converted into *diazonium salts* (Fig. 8-13). Benzenediazonium chloride, obtained in solution by the treatment of aniline with sodium nitrite and hydrochloric acid, is the simplest example of these useful compounds. Diazonium salts are unstable and can explode

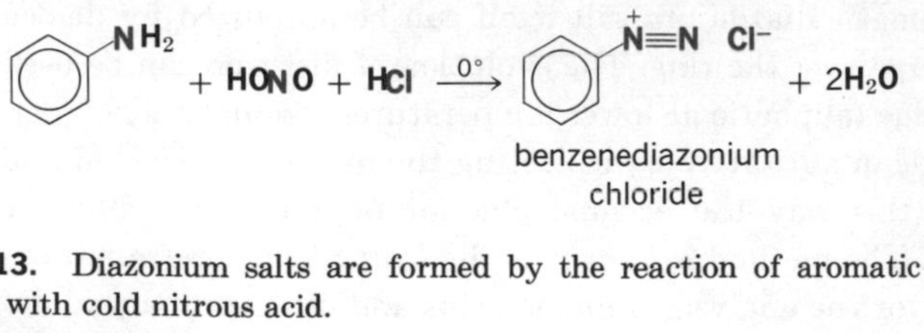

benzenediazonium
chloride

Fig. 8-13. Diazonium salts are formed by the reaction of aromatic primary amines with cold nitrous acid.

when dry. They also decompose with the evolution of nitrogen gas when their solutions are allowed to warm to room temperature. Phenols are the organic products of this reaction in solution, and the sequence aniline $\longrightarrow$ diazonium salt $\longrightarrow$ phenol is one of the best for the synthesis of substituted phenols.

If diazonium salts are allowed to warm up in the presence of cuprous bromide or cuprous chloride, an aromatic bromide or chloride forms instead of a phenol. Cuprous cyanide similarly gives an aromatic cyanide. In this way, an aromatic amine can be converted into a large number of other aromatic derivatives and play a role as a very useful intermediate (Fig. 8-14).

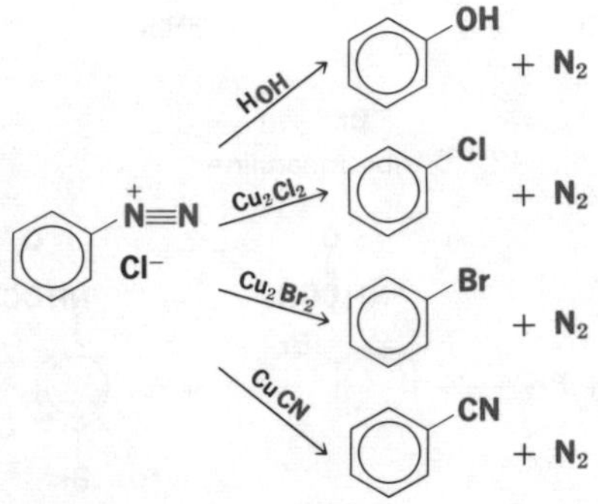

Fig. 8-14. Aromatic diazonium salts are readily transformed into a variety of substituted aromatic compounds.

Aliphatic diazonium compounds are much less stable than their aromatic counterparts; even at 0° they immediately decompose, with nitrogen gas being liberated. Because of their great instability, they are not useful synthetically, but the reaction of an amine with nitrous acid can be used to distinguish a primary aromatic amine from a primary aliphatic amine. When treated with nitrous acid at 0°, the latter (but not the former) gives off bubbles of nitrogen gas. If no gas is liberated at 0°, warming the solution to room temperature will cause nitrogen to evolve from an aromatic diazonium salt.

The difference in stability between aromatic and aliphatic diazonium salts can be ascribed to the electron-attracting character of an aromatic ring, which makes it more difficult for the nitrogen molecule to depart with its pair of electrons; by contrast an alkyl group is electron-donating and eases the loss of nitrogen. Then, too, the aromatic diazonium salt itself can be stabilized by delocalization of the positive charge over the ring. The evolution of nitrogen can be used as a test for a primary amine (aliphatic at lower temperatures, aromatic at higher ones); the test may be made quantitative by collecting the nitrogen liberated and measuring its volume. In this way the original amount of a primary amine present can be determined. The method is known as the *Van Slyke* determination, and it is commonly used for the analysis of amino acids and other primary amines.

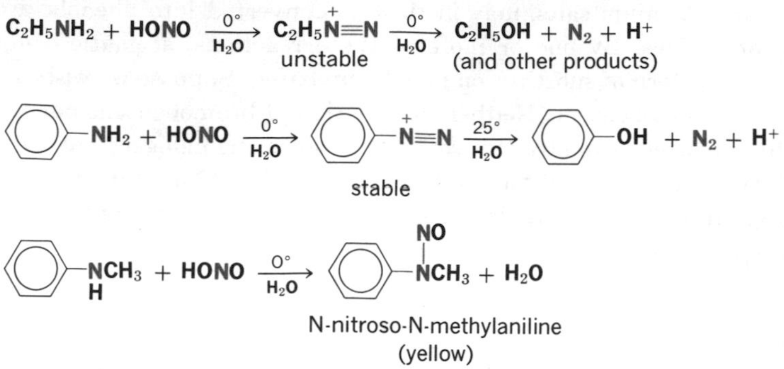

$$C_2H_5NH_2 + HONO \xrightarrow[H_2O]{0°} C_2H_5\overset{+}{N}\equiv N \xrightarrow[H_2O]{0°} C_2H_5OH + N_2 + H^+$$

unstable   (and other products)

stable

N-nitroso-N-methylaniline
(yellow)

Fig. 8-15. Nitrous acid is a useful reagent for distinguishing, by a visual chemical test, among 1° aromatic, 1° aliphatic, and other amines.

The reaction with nitrous acid can be used to distinguish between secondary and tertiary amines as well as to identify primary amines (Fig. 8-15). Secondary amines do not liberate nitrogen gas, but give yellow, usually oily, precipitates of N-nitroso compounds. Tertiary amines give neither nitrogen nor yellow oils.

SYNTHESIS OF AMINES

The reaction of an alkyl halide with ammonia or an amine usually yields a mixture of products. However, the simplicity of the reaction often renders it synthetically useful in spite of the mixtures. Reductive methods, however, usually lead to purer products. For example, reduction of a cyanide or of a nitro compound gives a primary amine, uncontaminated by secondary and tertiary amines (Fig. 8-16).

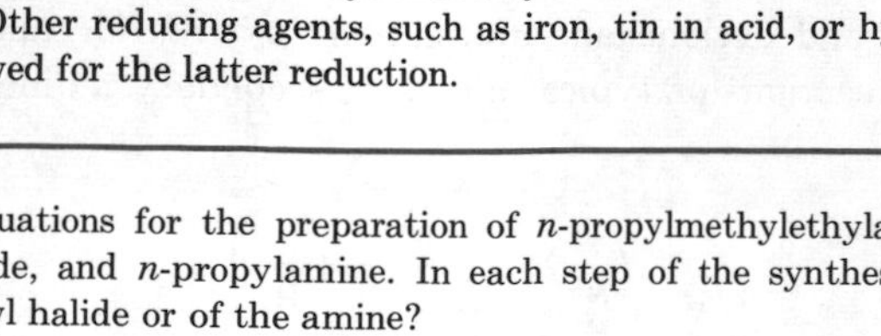

$$CH_3(CH_2)_4C\equiv N \xrightarrow[LiAlH_4]{H_2 \text{ or}} CH_3(CH_2)_4CH_2NH_2$$

n-hexylamine

Fig. 8-16. Reductive methods are important for the preparation of pure amines. Aromatic amines are nearly always made by the reduction of aromatic nitro compounds. Other reducing agents, such as iron, tin in acid, or hydrogen gas, can be employed for the latter reduction.

Prob. 8-4. Give equations for the preparation of *n*-propylmethylethylamine from methyl iodide, ethyl bromide, and *n*-propylamine. In each step of the synthesis, should one use an excess of the alkyl halide or of the amine?

Since nitro groups are easily introduced on a benzene ring, their reduction affords the best method for the synthesis of aromatic amines. Aromatic amines, by way of their diazonium salts, may in turn be converted into phenols, aromatic cyanides, or halides. By one or more of these reactions, aromatic compounds of nearly any pattern of substitution may be prepared. Suppose we wished to prepare *m*-chlorobromobenzene. Neither chlorination of bromobenzene nor bromination of chlorobenzene can give this compound, since the halogens are *ortho-para* directing. However, bromination of nitrobenzene will yield *m*-bromonitrobenzene; the nitro group can then be replaced by a chlorine atom by using the reduction-diazotization-cuprous chloride process (Fig. 8-17).

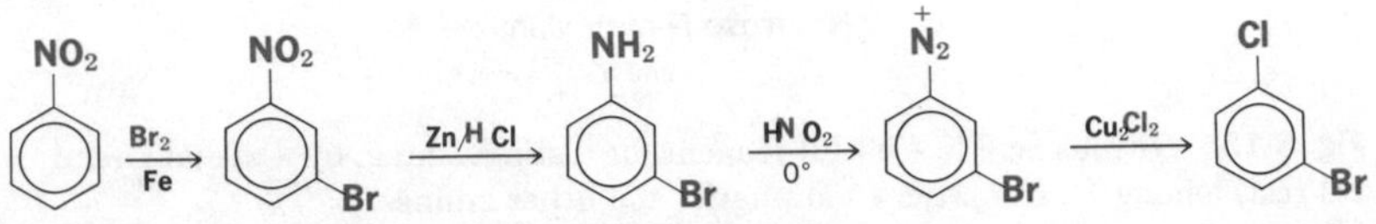

Fig. 8-17. An example of the use of an aromatic amine in the indirect synthesis of an aromatic halide.

Prob. 8-5. Explain why it is often preferable to synthesize primary amines by reducing nitriles instead of by treating alkyl halides with ammonia. Why are aromatic amines usually made by reduction of nitro compounds rather than by the reaction of an aryl halide with ammonia?

Prob. 8-6. Through what sequence of reactions could one prepare *m*-bromoaniline from benzene?

HETEROCYCLIC AMINES

If the nitrogen atom of an amine is incorporated as part of a ring, the resulting amine is said to be a *heterocyclic compound,* one of a group of compounds whose rings contain at least one element other than carbon. Heterocyclic compounds containing oxygen, sulfur, or other elements are also known; we have, for example, already encountered ethylene oxide, tetrahydrofuran and dioxane in Chapter 6. However, heterocyclic nitrogen compounds are the most common.

Saturated heterocyclic amines behave much the same as their acyclic analogs, just as *n*-hexane and cyclohexane are similar; *pyrrolidine* and *piperidine* both undergo all the reactions of typical aliphatic secondary amines (Fig. 8-18). If a

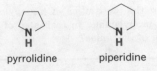

pyrrolidine   piperidine

Fig. 8-18. Two common saturated nitrogen heterocycles. In chemical and physical properties they resemble open-chain amines.

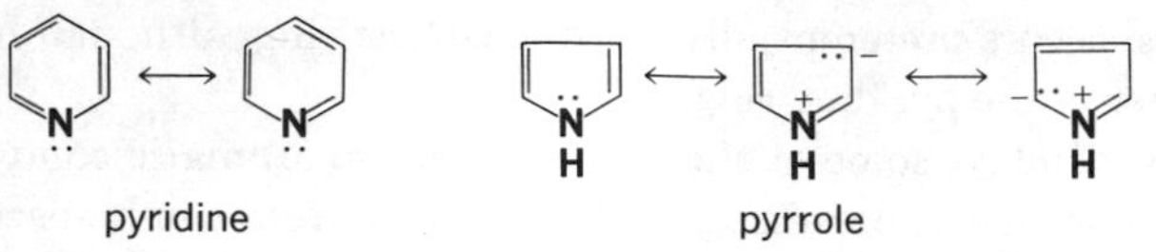

Fig. 8-19. Two unsaturated heterocyclic compounds. The electrons making up the aromatic sextet are shown in red.

heterocyclic ring is highly unsaturated, however, it may acquire unusual properties all its own. For this reason, heterocyclic chemistry is often treated as a special subject. Often heterocyclic compounds have aromatic properties reminiscent of those of benzene. *Pyridine* and *pyrrole* are the most common examples (Fig. 8-19). Pyridine is the direct heterocyclic analog of benzene, in which one carbon atom and its attached hydrogen atom have been replaced by a nitrogen atom. The aromatic sextet of electrons, the closed π-electron system, is complete in pyridine without using the pair of p electrons on the nitrogen atom. Pyridine is still basic, since it has this free electron pair on the nitrogen atom. Similarly, alkylation takes place on the nitrogen atom to give a quaternary salt (Fig. 8-20).

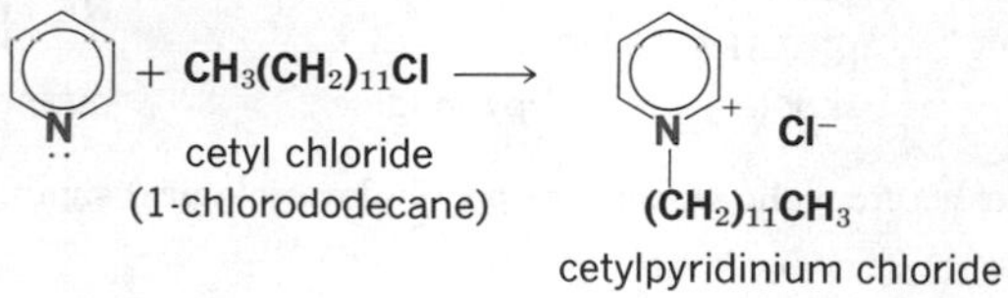

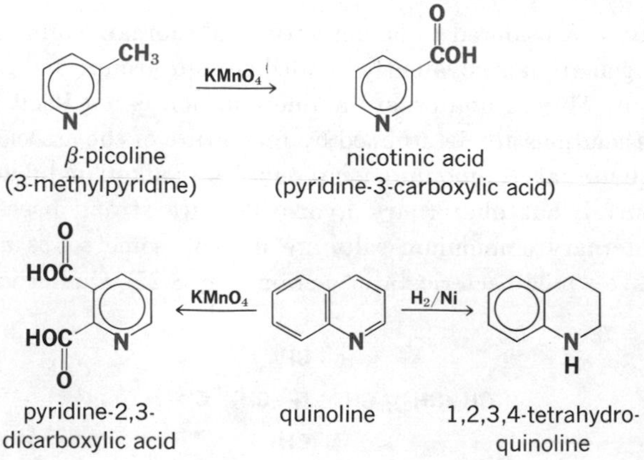

Fig. 8-20. Pyridine is a base, but it also behaves like an aromatic compound.

Evidence of pyridine's aromatic stability is found in the resistance of the ring to oxidation. A methyl group on a pyridine ring can, for example, be oxidized to a carboxyl group. In fact, oxidation of quinoline, which contains both benzene and pyridine rings, occurs preferentially at the benzene ring, although hydrogenation takes place first in the pyridine ring.

Pyrrole also displays some of the properties of an aromatic compound because the two electrons that it possesses on the nitrogen atom can be used to complete an aromatic sextet, when combined with the four electrons of the double bonds (Fig. 8-19). In pyrrole, the unshared pair of electrons on the nitrogen atom is very much a part of the aromatic system, and so the compound is the heterocyclic analog of the cyclopentadiene anion (see Fig. 5-25). As a consequence, pyrrole does not behave as a base, since combination of this electron pair with a proton would disrupt the aromatic system.

A vast number of heterocyclic compounds are known, because nearly any carbon atom in any ring system can be replaced by a nitrogen atom; in addition, oxygen, sulfur, and other elements can similarly be introduced. Four heterocyclic compounds whose ring systems are of special importance in life processes are shown in Fig. 8-21. The first two, imidazole and indole, are found widely in proteins; the last two, pyrimidine and purine, are the basic ring systems found in genes.

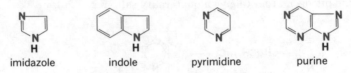

| imidazole | indole | pyrimidine | purine |

Fig. 8-21. Four heterocyclic systems of particular biological significance.

QUATERNARY AMMONIUM SALTS

These salts may be considered to be derivatives of inorganic ammonium salts, in which the nitrogen atom is covalently bonded to four groups and no longer has a free electron pair. Thus, a quaternary ammonium ion is not itself basic, and the properties of its solutions are determined by the nature of the associated anions. In this respect, a quaternary ammonium ion resembles an alkali metal ion. Quaternary halides are neutral, but quaternary hydroxides are strong bases, like sodium hydroxide. Quaternary ammonium salts are used in some soaps and antiseptics because they have a mild bacteriostatic* action (Fig. 8-22). Quaternary ammonium

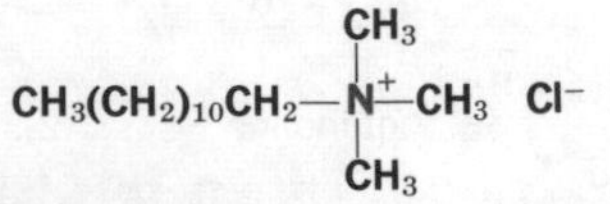

$$CH_3(CH_2)_{10}CH_2 \overset{\overset{\displaystyle CH_3}{|}}{\underset{\underset{\displaystyle CH_3}{|}}{N^+}} CH_3 \quad Cl^-$$

trimethyl-*n*-decylammonium chloride

Fig. 8-22. A quaternary ammonium salt which has a positively charged group attached to a long alkyl group can be used as a disinfectant and soap.

---

* Bacteriostatic agents inhibit the growth of bacteria. Agents that kill bacteria are called bactericidal.

salts also play special roles in human physiology. One of the most important of these is that played by choline and acetylcholine. Acetylcholine is present in a combined form in nerve cells and is released when a nerve cell is stimulated; the acetylcholine in turn stimulates an adjacent nerve cell, which releases acetylcholine and so transmits the nerve impulse (Fig. 8-23).

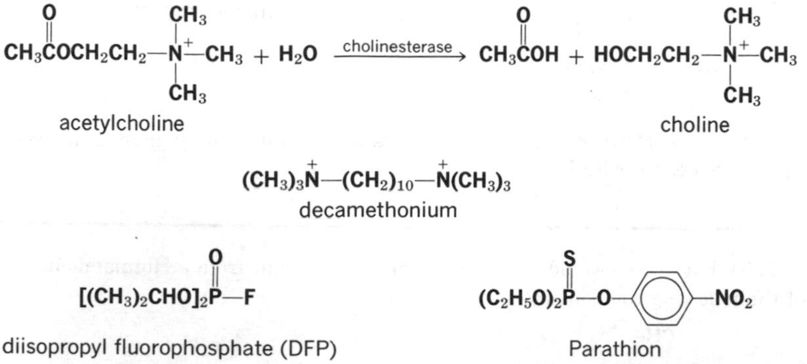

Fig. 8-23. Acetylcholine is active in the transmission of nerve impulses. Decamethonium, DFP, and Parathion interfere with this transmission.

After it has done its job of stimulating an adjacent nerve cell, acetylcholine must be quickly deactivated. This deactivation is accompanied by hydrolysis of the acetylcholine by the enzyme cholinesterase into choline and acetic acid. Anything that interferes with this deactivation short-circuits nerve impulse transmission and leads quickly to paralysis or death. Some drugs contain quaternary ammonium groups which simply compete with acetylcholine and block the sites of nerve-impulse transmission. One of the most effective of these is hexamethyldecamethylenediammonium ion (decamethonium), which is used as a muscle relaxant. Another is curare, a complex base (an alkaloid) put on the tips of arrows to render them lethal.

Other compounds function differently, by reacting with cholinesterase to prevent it from hydrolyzing acetylcholine. These compounds have structures completely unrelated to that of choline, and include the venom of some snakes and also nerve gases like diisopropyl fluorophosphate. When humans take these compounds, death follows from respiratory failure. Insecticides like Parathion have a similar effect on insects (and on farmers who apply it carelessly).

Quaternary ammonium salts undergo an important synthetic reaction: On heating with alkali, they form alkenes. The reaction, known as the *Hofmann elimination,* is analogous to the formation of alkenes from alkyl halides by reaction with base (see Fig. 7-14). In the case of the Hofmann elimination the alkene which is formed in greatest amount is the one which is *least substituted* with alkyl groups (Fig. 8-24).

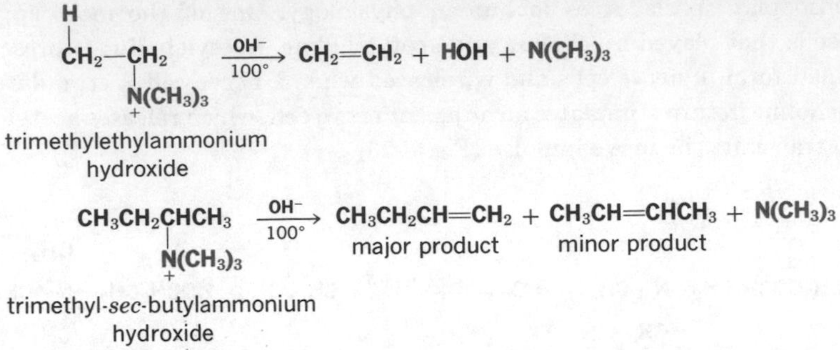

$$\underset{\substack{\displaystyle| \\ \overset{+}{N}(CH_3)_3}}{\overset{\displaystyle H}{\underset{\displaystyle |}{CH_2-CH_2}}} \xrightarrow[100°]{OH^-} CH_2{=}CH_2 + HOH + N(CH_3)_3$$

trimethylethylammonium
hydroxide

$$\underset{\substack{| \\ \overset{+}{N}(CH_3)_3}}{CH_3CH_2CHCH_3} \xrightarrow[100°]{OH^-} \underset{\text{major product}}{CH_3CH_2CH{=}CH_2} + \underset{\text{minor product}}{CH_3CH{=}CHCH_3} + N(CH_3)_3$$

trimethyl-*sec*-butylammonium
hydroxide

Fig. 8-24. A Hofmann elimination results when a quaternary ammonium compound is heated with base.

Prob. 8-7. What alkene would be formed in greater amount from a Hofmann elimination of each of the following compounds?

(a) $\underset{\substack{| \\ CH_3}}{\overset{\substack{CH_3 \\ |}}{CH_3CH_2-\underset{}{C}-\overset{+}{N}(CH_3)_3}}$ $\bar{O}H$ (b)

[structure: N-methylpyrrolidinium with N,N-dimethyl, OH⁻]

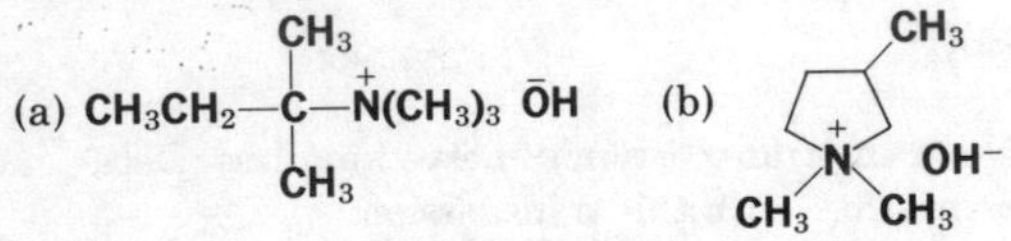

Prob. 8-8. Name each of the following compounds:

(a) $(CH_3)_2NH$

(b) [diphenylamine structure] —NH—

(c) $\underset{\substack{| \\ CH_3}}{C_2H_5-N-C_2H_5}$

(d) $\underset{\substack{| \\ CH_3}}{\overset{\substack{C_2H_5 \\ |}}{CH_3-\overset{+}{N}-C_2H_5}}$ OH^-

(e) Br—[benzene ring]—NHC_2H_5

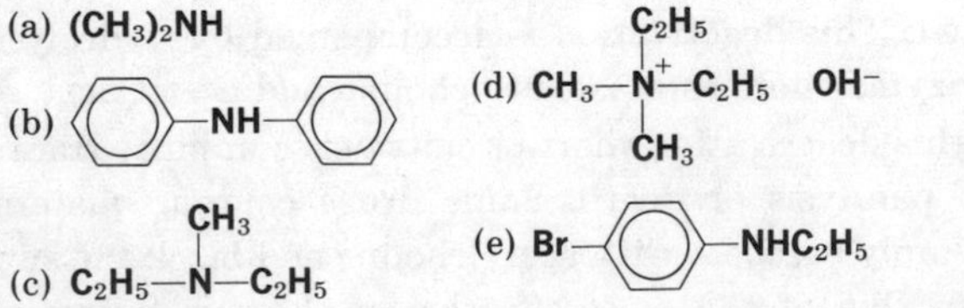

Prob. 8-9. How could you separate a mixture of the following compounds: *p*-bromophenol, *m*-bromoaniline, *p*-dichlorobenzene, and trimethylanilinium bromide?

Prob. 8-10. If you had unlabeled bottles containing aniline, cyclohexylamine and N-methylaniline, how could you distinguish among them by simple visual chemical tests?

Prob. 8-11. How could you convert aniline into each of the following compounds?
    (a) phenol   (b) trimethylanilinium chloride   (c) chlorobenzene

---

Prob. 8-12. How would you convert benzene into each of the following? Several steps may be required.
    (a) *m*-bromophenol
    (b) *m*-diaminobenzene

Prob. 8-13. Devise a synthesis of choline from ethylene and any other reagents you desire.

Prob. 8-14. Complete the following reactions:

(a) 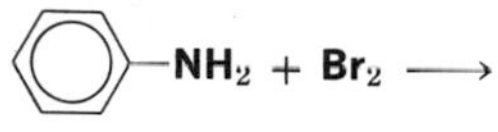   ⬡—NH_2 + Br_2 ⟶

(b) 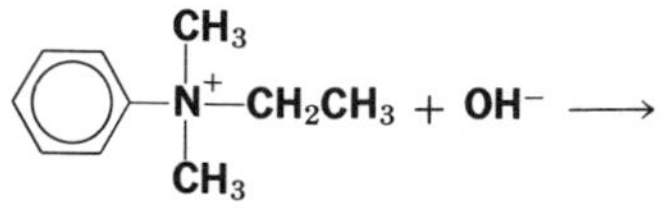
$$\begin{array}{c} CH_3 \\ | \\ \text{⬡—N}^+\text{—CH}_2CH_3 + OH^- \longrightarrow \\ | \\ CH_3 \end{array}$$

Prob. 8-15. Muscarine is a constituent of a number of poisonous mushrooms. Suggest a reason why this compound might be so deadly.

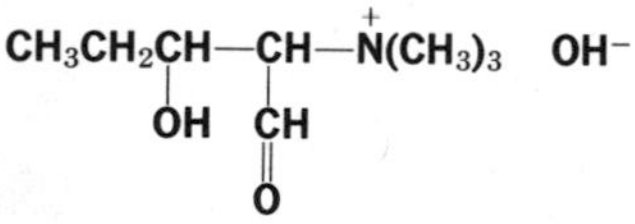

$$CH_3CH_2CH\!-\!CH\!-\!\overset{+}{N}(CH_3)_3 \quad OH^-$$
$$\qquad\quad |\qquad\ |$$
$$\qquad\quad OH\quad CH$$
$$\qquad\qquad\qquad\ \|$$
$$\qquad\qquad\qquad\ O$$

muscarine

CHAPTER

ALDEHYDES AND KETONES

Aldehydes and ketones bring us for the first time to the chemistry of the carbon-oxygen double bond (C=O), known as the carbonyl group. In aldehydes and ketones the carbonyl group appears in its simplest form, with only a hydrogen or a carbon atom attached directly to the carbonyl carbon. The behavior of molecules in which other atoms—oxygen, nitrogen, or halogen—are attached to the carbonyl group is considerably altered by these attachments. These compounds, which

include acids (R—$\overset{\text{O}}{\overset{\|}{\text{C}}}$OH), esters (R—$\overset{\text{O}}{\overset{\|}{\text{C}}}$OR), acid chlorides (R—$\overset{\text{O}}{\overset{\|}{\text{C}}}$Cl), and amides

(R—$\overset{\text{O}}{\overset{\|}{\text{C}}}NH_2$), will be discussed later.

In an aldehyde, at least one hydrogen atom is attached to the carbonyl group, whereas in a ketone both remaining valences of the carbonyl carbon are joined to other carbon atoms. Some familiar substances that are aldehydes or ketones are shown in Fig. 9-1. Glucose, also called dextrose, is a sugar found in honey and also in blood. Of the aldehydes, cinnamaldehyde, benzaldehyde, vanillin, and piperonal have the odors of cinnamon, almonds, vanilla, and heliotrope, respectively. Among the ketones, menthone, found in peppermint; carvone, from caraway; and camphor have familiar odors. Progesterone and cortisone (steroids) are both hormones.

NOMENCLATURE

Both common and IUPAC names of aldehydes are in general use. Frequently we must know both (Fig. 9-2), because the common names are almost always used for the lower members of the series. Fortunately, the same combining forms are used in the common names of the acids (Chapter 11) and the aldehydes. In the IUPAC

155

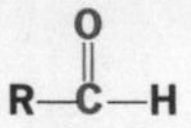

$$\text{R}\overset{\overset{\text{O}}{\|}}{\text{C}}\text{H}$$ aldehyde

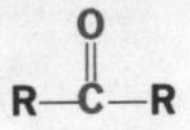

$$\text{R}\overset{\overset{\text{O}}{\|}}{\text{C}}\text{R}$$ ketone

$$\text{H}\overset{\overset{\text{O}}{\|}}{\text{C}}\text{H}$$ formaldehyde

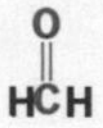

$$\text{CH}_3\overset{\overset{\text{O}}{\|}}{\text{C}}\text{CH}_3$$ acetone

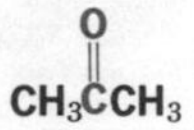

$$\text{CCl}_3\overset{\overset{\text{O}}{\|}}{\text{C}}\text{H}$$ chloral

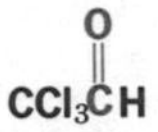

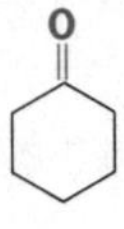

cyclohexanone

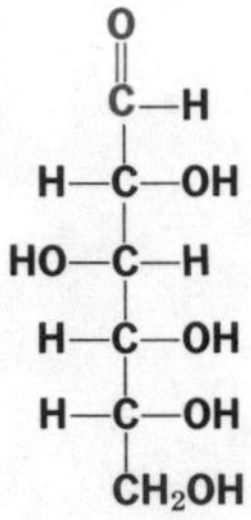

D-glucose

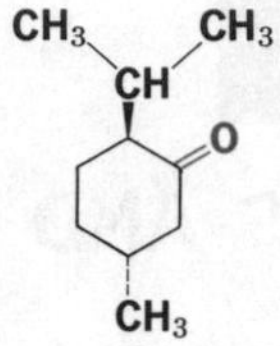

menthone

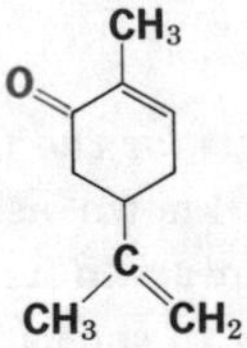

$$\begin{array}{c}\text{CH}_3\\\text{C}\\\text{CH}_3\end{array}\!\!=\!\text{CHCH}_2\text{CH}_2\text{CHCH}_2\overset{\overset{\text{O}}{\|}}{\text{C}}\text{H}$$

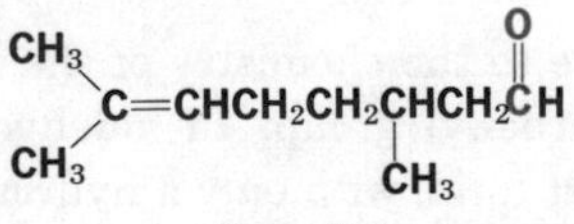

citronellal

carvone

$$\begin{array}{c}\text{CH}_3\\\text{C}\\\text{CH}_3\end{array}\!\!=\!\text{CHCH}_2\text{CH}_2\text{C}\!=\!\text{CHC}\text{H}$$

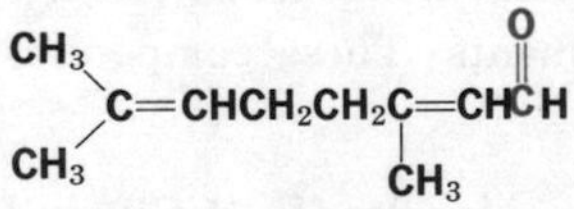

citral

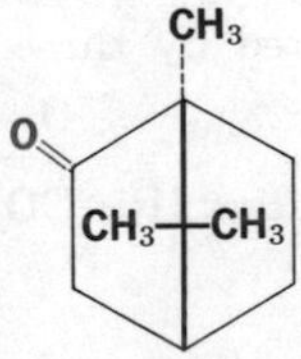

(+)-camphor

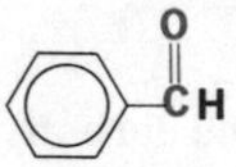

benzaldehyde

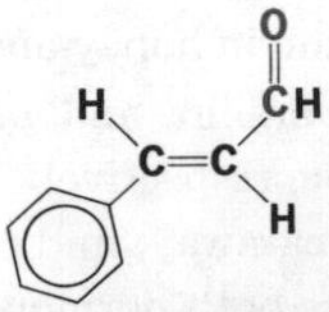

cinnamaldehyde

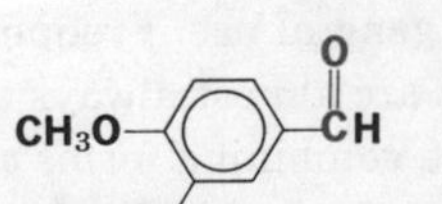

vanillin

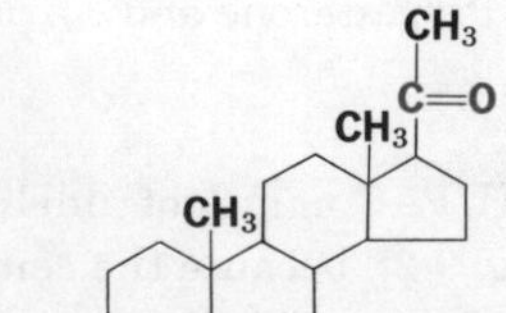

progesterone

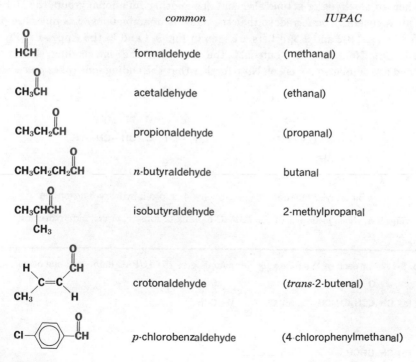

Fig. 9-1. Some familiar aldehydes and ketones. The carbonyl groups are indicated in red.

system, the ending *-al* is applied to the name of the compound, and the aldehyde functional group takes precedence over all groups discussed in earlier chapters. Thus, the aldehyde carbon is usually numbered one.

Both common and systematic names are also frequently used for ketones. The IUPAC ending is *-one* (Fig. 9-3), and the ketone group takes precedence over alkene, hydroxyl, and most other groups, though not over aldehyde groups. In general, common names are constructed by naming the groups attached to the carbonyl group and adding the word "ketone."

	common	*IUPAC*
O‖ HCH	formaldehyde	(methanal)
O‖ CH₃CH	acetaldehyde	(ethanal)
O‖ CH₃CH₂CH	propionaldehyde	(propanal)
O‖ CH₃CH₂CH₂CH	*n*-butyraldehyde	butanal
O‖ CH₃CHCH CH₃	isobutyraldehyde	2-methylpropanal
H C=C CH₃ CH	crotonaldehyde	(*trans*-2-butenal)
Cl—⟨ ⟩—CH	*p*-chlorobenzaldehyde	(4-chlorophenylmethanal)

Fig. 9-2. Common and systematic names for some aldehydes. The names in parentheses, although technically correct, are seldom used.

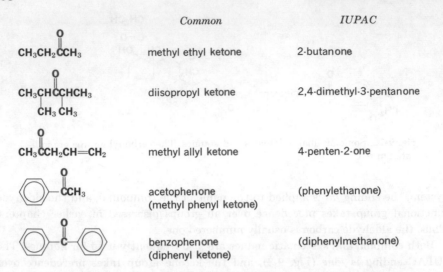

Fig. 9-3. Ketones are given the systematic ending -one. Alternatively, one of these compounds may be called a "ketone" with two group names indicated. The names in parentheses, although technically correct, are hardly ever used.

When an aldehyde or ketone also contains another functional group, the IUPAC system is generally preferred, so that the name is unambiguous. Examples are presented in Figs. 9-2 and 9-3; others are seen in Fig. 9-4 and in the Appendix (Probs. 37 and 38). Note that in "butenal," the final e of the -ene ending is dropped to avoid the cumbersome -eneal. Note further that the ending *-one* takes precedence over *-ol*.

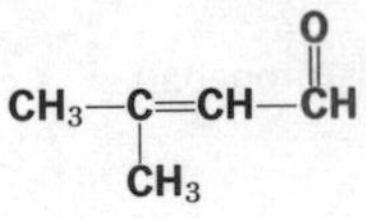

$$CH_3-\underset{\underset{CH_3}{|}}{C}=CH-\overset{\overset{\text{O}}{\|}}{CH} \qquad CH_3-\underset{\underset{C_6H_5}{|}}{CH}-\overset{\overset{\text{O}}{\|}}{C}-\underset{\underset{Cl}{|}}{CH}-\underset{\underset{OH}{|}}{CH}-CH_3$$

3-methyl-2-butenal 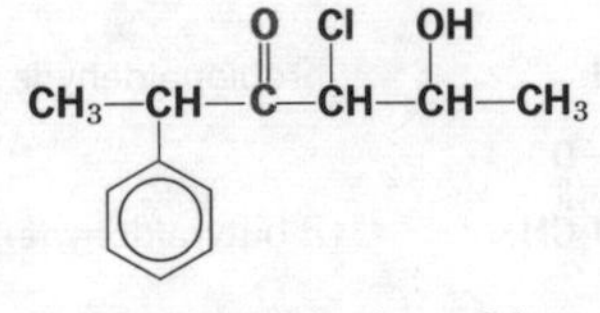   2-phenyl-4-chloro-5-hydroxy-3-hexanone

Fig. 9-4. Two examples of the IUPAC naming of more complex aldehydes and ketones.

Prob. 9-1. For each of the following compounds give the IUPAC name and one other name.

(a) $CH_3\overset{\overset{\text{O}}{\|}}{C}CH_2CH_2CH_3$ (c) $Cl-\langle\bigcirc\rangle-\overset{\overset{\text{O}}{\|}}{C}CH_3$

(b) $CH_3\underset{\underset{CH_3}{|}}{CH}\overset{\overset{\text{O}}{\|}}{CH}$ (d) $CH_3\overset{\overset{\text{O}}{\|}}{C}CH_3$

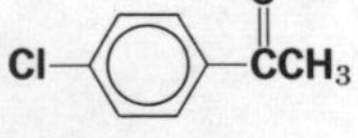

Prob. 9-2. Name each of the following by the IUPAC method.

(a) CH₃CHCH
    |
    OH
with O above the second carbon

(c) CH₃CCH₂CCH₃
with two O above

(b) CH₃CH=CHCCH₃
with O above the C

(d) a benzene ring with Cl substituent and CH group with O (benzaldehyde derivative)

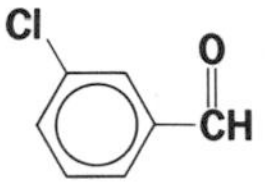

Prob. 9-3. Name the following compounds from Fig. 9-1 by the IUPAC system: chloral, D-glucose, cinnamaldehyde, menthone.

SYNTHESIS OF ALDEHYDES AND KETONES

Aldehydes and ketones are most easily prepared by the oxidation of alcohols; this is especially true for ketones of low molecular weight, which may be prepared from inexpensive secondary alcohols. For example, acetone can be prepared in enormous quantities by oxidation (Fig. 9-5) of isopropyl alcohol, obtained from the petrochemical propylene.

$$CH_3CH=CH_2 \xrightarrow{H_2SO_4} \xrightarrow{H_2O} CH_3CHCH_3 \xrightarrow{O_2} CH_3CCH_3$$
(with OH above CH and O above the C)

Fig. 9-5. The preparation of acetone from propylene via isopropyl alcohol.

Prob. 9-4. Show the preparation of methyl ethyl ketone from 1-butene by the series of reactions of Fig. 9-5. Could methyl ethyl ketone also be prepared from 2-butene?

Primary alcohols can sometimes be oxidized to aldehydes, although this is a delicate reaction, since aldehydes are themselves easily oxidized. Special conditions are usually employed, such as dehydrogenation over copper at high temperatures. Aromatic aldehydes are conveniently produced by hydrolysis of 1,1-dichloro compounds (Fig. 9-6).

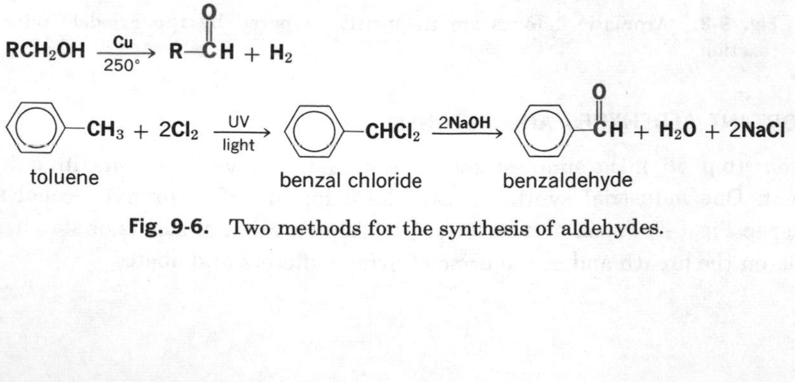

$$RCH_2OH \xrightarrow[250°]{Cu} R-CH + H_2$$
(with O above the C)

benzene-CH₃ + 2Cl₂ $\xrightarrow[light]{UV}$ benzene-CHCl₂ $\xrightarrow{2NaOH}$ benzene-CH + H₂O + 2NaCl
(with O above the last CH)

    toluene   benzal chloride   benzaldehyde

Fig. 9-6. Two methods for the synthesis of aldehydes.

Both aldehydes and ketones can be formed by the action of ozone on alkenes. The initial product is an adduct called an ozonide. If this is treated with hydrogen and a catalyst, or with zinc, it is reduced to give two moles of carbonyl compounds, as shown in Fig. 9-7.

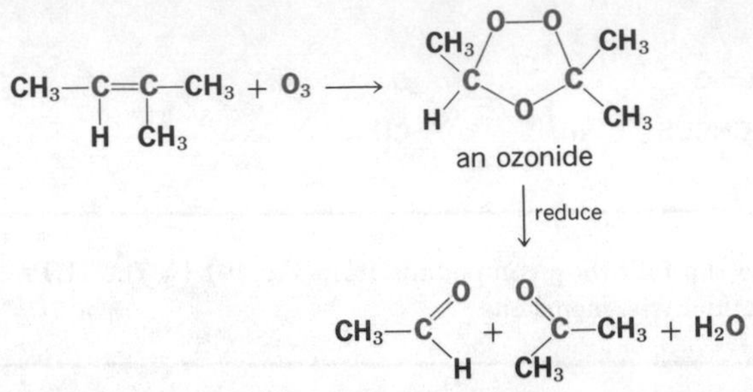

$$CH_3-\underset{\underset{H}{|}}{C}=\underset{\underset{CH_3}{|}}{C}-CH_3 + O_3 \longrightarrow$$

an ozonide

reduce

$$CH_3-\underset{\underset{H}{\diagdown}}{\overset{\overset{O}{\diagup}}{C}} + \underset{\underset{CH_3}{\diagdown}}{\overset{\overset{O}{\diagup}}{C}}-CH_3 + H_2O$$

Fig. 9-7. Reaction of an alkene with ozone, followed by reduction, yields aldehydes and ketones as products.

Ozonolysis, as this process is called, is useful not only in synthesizing aldehydes and ketones, but also in locating carbon–carbon double bonds, since the position of the carbonyl bonds in the products defines that of the carbon–carbon double bond in the alkene.

Prob. 9-5. If an alkene gives 2-butanone and propanal when treated with ozone followed by palladium and hydrogen, what might its structure be?

An important reaction for synthesizing aromatic ketones involves the use of an acid chloride like acetyl chloride in the Friedel-Crafts reaction (Fig. 9-8). Substitution nearly always occurs in the *para* position relative to an electron-donating substituent. The reaction does not occur when the ring contains electron-withdrawing substituents.

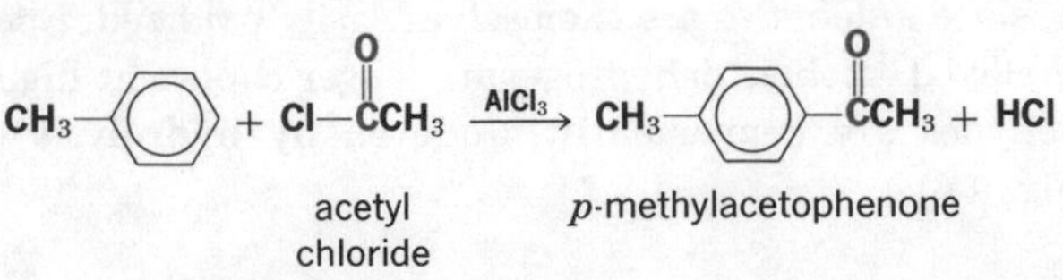

$$CH_3-\langle\bigcirc\rangle + Cl-\overset{\overset{O}{\|}}{C}CH_3 \xrightarrow{AlCl_3} CH_3-\langle\bigcirc\rangle-\overset{\overset{O}{\|}}{C}CH_3 + HCl$$

acetyl   *p*-methylacetophenone
chloride

Fig. 9-8. Aromatic ketones are frequently prepared by the Friedel-Crafts reaction.

IMPORTANT ALDEHYDES AND KETONES

Acetone (b.p. 56°), the simplest ketone, is an inexpensive (7–9 cents/lb) industrial solvent. One industrial synthesis uses the oxidation of isopropyl alcohol shown earlier in Fig. 9-5. It can also be formed by fermentation of sugars or starch, and is found on the breath and in the urine of many sufferers of diabetes.

Methyl ethyl ketone (b.p. 80°) shows many of acetone's desirable solvent properties and is used when a solvent with a higher boiling point is needed. It is approximately twice as expensive as acetone; however, in many processes the solvent is recovered and reused, so that the greater initial expense is not especially important.

Acetaldehyde (b.p. 20°) is formed readily by the hydration of acetylene and is used mainly as a raw material for the synthesis of other organic compounds (Fig. 9-9), among them acetic acid by reaction with oxygen. Chlorination of acetaldehyde gives chloral; chloral in the form of its hydrate is a hypnotic, the well-known "Mickey Finn," and is also used to prepare DDT (Fig. 7-20).

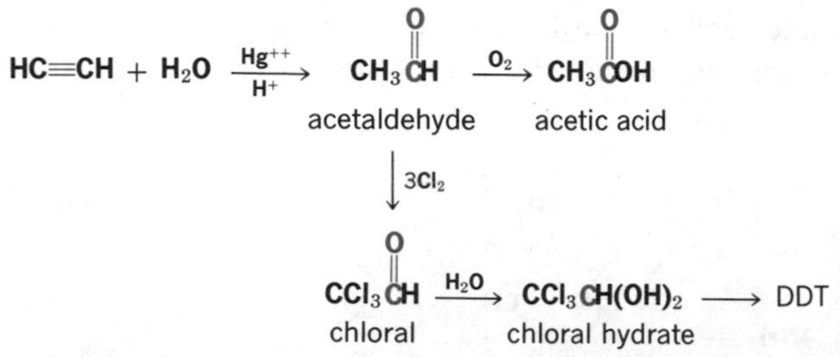

$$HC{\equiv}CH + H_2O \xrightarrow[H^+]{Hg^{++}} CH_3\overset{\overset{\textstyle O}{\|}}{C}H \xrightarrow{O_2} CH_3\overset{\overset{\textstyle O}{\|}}{C}OH$$
acetaldehyde   acetic acid

$$\downarrow 3Cl_2$$

$$CCl_3\overset{\overset{\textstyle O}{\|}}{C}H \xrightarrow{H_2O} CCl_3CH(OH)_2 \longrightarrow DDT$$
chloral   chloral hydrate

Fig. 9-9. Acetaldehyde is an intermediate in the synthesis of a variety of useful products.

n-Butyraldehyde (b.p. 75°), formed from oxidation of *n*-butyl alcohol, is widely used in the production of safety glass (Fig. 9-15).

From a commercial standpoint, the simplest aldehyde, *formaldehyde,* is also the most important. Pure formaldehyde is a gas (b.p. −21°) which can be neither readily isolated nor handled in this state. It is prepared from controlled oxidation of methanol over a metal catalyst and is sold as a 37% solution in water (formalin) and also as a solid polymer (paraformaldehyde), from which it can be recovered by heating (Fig. 9-10). Candles of paraformaldehyde are used as fumigating agents.

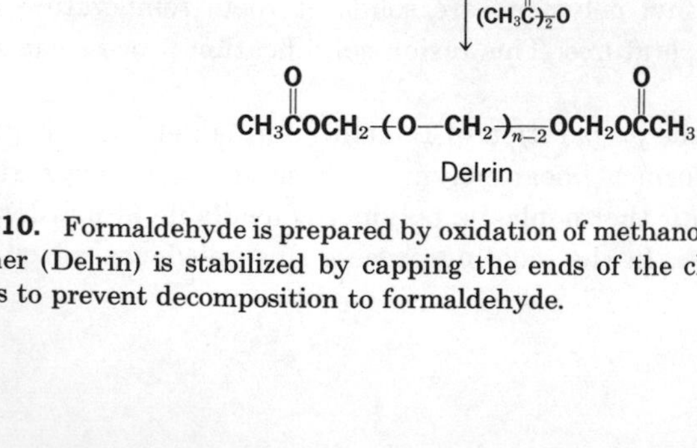

$$CH_3OH + {\textstyle\frac{1}{2}}O_2 \xrightarrow[250°]{Ag} H\overset{\overset{\textstyle O}{\|}}{C}H + H_2O$$

$$H_2O + nH\overset{\overset{\textstyle O}{\|}}{C}H \longrightarrow H\,OCH_2{\left(O{-}CH_2\right)}_{\overline{n-2}}O{-}CH_2\,OH$$
polyformaldehyde

$$\downarrow (CH_3\overset{\overset{\textstyle O}{\|}}{C})_2O$$

$$CH_3\overset{\overset{\textstyle O}{\|}}{C}OCH_2{\left(O{-}CH_2\right)}_{\overline{n-2}}OCH_2O\overset{\overset{\textstyle O}{\|}}{C}CH_3$$
Delrin

Fig. 9-10. Formaldehyde is prepared by oxidation of methanol. A formaldehyde polymer (Delrin) is stabilized by capping the ends of the chain with acetate groups to prevent decomposition to formaldehyde.

Since formaldehyde can be produced inexpensively and polymerizes readily (to paraformaldehyde), a great deal of effort has gone into investigations of its use in the preparation of commercial polymers. The problem in using pure polyformaldehyde has been to prevent its decomposition to formaldehyde, which is poisonous. It can be shown that the decomposition begins at the ends of the chains, but when these free hydroxyl groups are converted into ester groups a stable polymer results. Polyformaldehyde is now being produced and sold under the trade name *Delrin;* its useful properties promise a wide market for this inexpensive material.

Formaldehyde and ammonia react to form the cagelike compound hexamethylenetetramine, which liberates formaldehyde upon treatment with acid (Fig. 9-11). Hexamethylenetetramine is medicinally useful as a urinary antiseptic (urotropine) and is also oxidized by nitric acid to the important military explosive cyclonite (RDX).

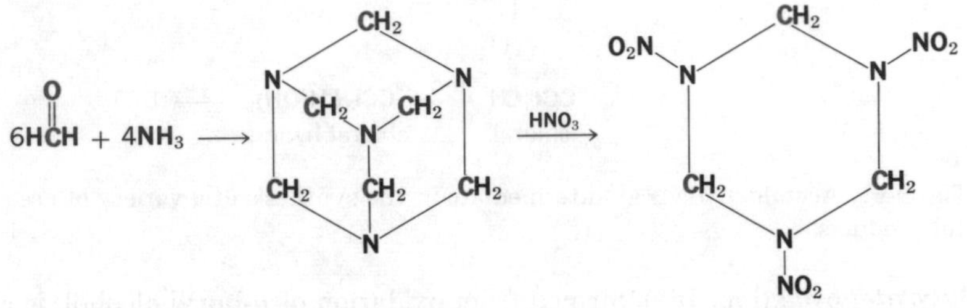

hexamethylenetetramine
(urotropine)

cyclonite
(RDX)

Fig. 9-11. Formaldehyde and ammonia form hexamethylenetetramine, a source of the explosive cyclonite.

Prob. 9-6. Draw a conformational picture of hexamethylenetetramine. Hint: See the drawing of adamantane in the answer to Prob. 2-4.

The largest commercial use of formaldehyde is in the preparation of phenol-formaldehyde resins for molded articles (Bakelite) and for use in plywood (Fig. 9-12). These resins are thermosetting; this means that in the course of the manufacture of an article the phenol-formaldehyde resin melts, and then, under the influence of heat and pressure, resolidifies to become permanently infusible. The properties of thermosetting polymers contrast with those of thermoplastic polymers. The latter, which include most vinyl polymers, are solids at room temperature but can be molded at higher temperatures. This fusion-solidification process can be repeated numerous times.

In one method for the preparation of Bakelite, formaldehyde is heated with an excess of phenol to form a linear polymer whose structure approximates that shown in Fig. 9-12. This thermoplastic polymer is available in powdered form for the molding of articles. In the molding process this powder is mixed with hexa-

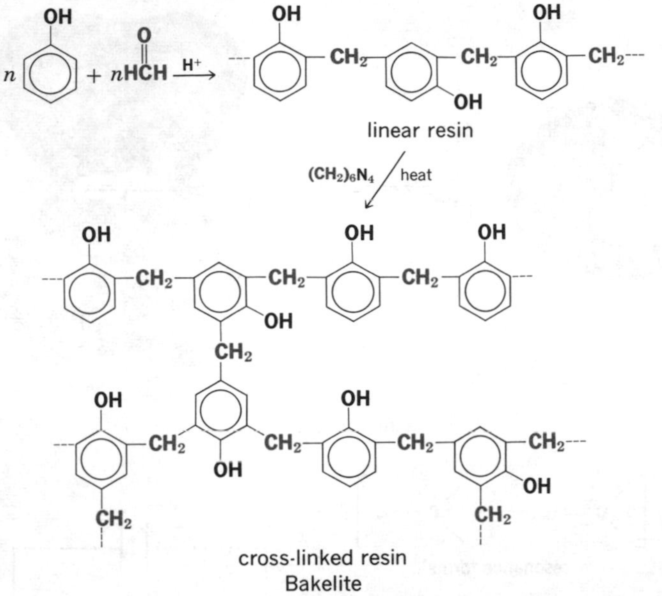

Fig. 9-12. Bakelite can be made by heating a linear phenol-formaldehyde resin with hexamethylenetetramine.

methylenetetramine, which serves as a source both of more formaldehyde and of ammonia, a basic catalyst. The mixture is melted in a mold where further polymerization takes place, this time *between* the chains. This converts the individual linear polymer molecules into a single gigantic molecule, by a process known as *cross-linking.* The plastic resolidifies in the mold, since the molecular weight has increased enormously.

PROPERTIES OF ALDEHYDES AND KETONES

In electronic structure, a carbon–oxygen double bond closely resembles a carbon–carbon double bond. Like the latter, it may be considered a combination of σ and π bonds, as shown in Fig. 9-13. The σ bond is formed from overlap of an sp^2 orbital of carbon and a p_y orbital of oxygen. This bond is cylindrically symmetrical about the line between the carbon and oxygen centers. The π bond is formed from overlap of p_z orbitals of carbon and oxygen and is localized in the region above and below this line, just as it was for the carbon–carbon double bond.

However, there is one important respect in which C=C and C=O bonds differ. An oxygen atom has two more protons (and two more neutrons) in its nucleus than a carbon atom. As a consequence of this greater nuclear positive charge, oxygen has a greater attraction for the shared electrons than does carbon; oxygen is more electronegative, so the electronic distribution is not symmetrical.

A carbon–oxygen double bond is therefore *polarized;* that is to say, the carbon atom has a slight positive charge and the oxygen atom a slight negative charge.

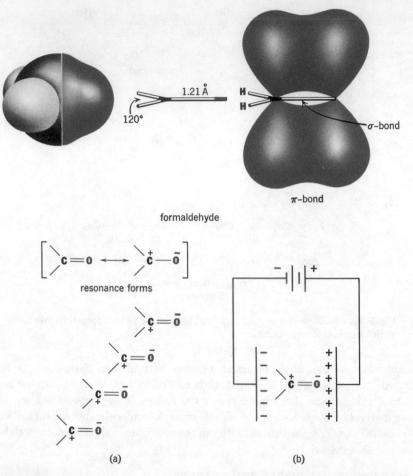

formaldehyde

resonance forms

(a)

(b)

Fig. 9-13. The carbonyl bond is composed of a σ bond and a π bond. Aldehydes and ketones have *dipole moments* and so align themselves in an electric field (a). They also have higher boiling points than hydrocarbons due to dipolar attraction between molecules (b).

This can be expressed as the sum of two resonance forms, a neutral form and a doubly charged form. If placed in an electric field, the molecules of an aldehyde or a ketone would line up with their oxygen atoms facing the positive pole, their carbon atoms facing the negative pole. This is what we mean when we say that carbonyl compounds have *dipole moments*. Molecules with only carbon–carbon double bonds seldom have dipole moments. The polarity of a carbon–oxygen double bond also has an effect on the boiling points of aldehydes and ketones. The partial charges in the bond are attracted to opposite charges on nearby molecules, which tend to adhere to one another. These *dipolar forces,* which must be overcome before evaporation can take place, are ordinarily not as strong as hydrogen bonds.

As a result, aldehydes and ketones have boiling points between those of hydro-carbons and alcohols of the same molecular weight.

ADDITION REACTIONS

As might be expected from the unsaturated nature of the carbonyl group, addition is a predominant reaction just as it is for alkenes. For example, hydrogen adds to a carbon–oxygen double bond so that aldehydes give primary alcohols, and ketones secondary alcohols on hydrogenation (Fig. 9-14). However, many typical addition reactions of alkenes do not give stable products when carried out on carbon–oxygen double bonds. An example is the addition of water to a carbonyl group.

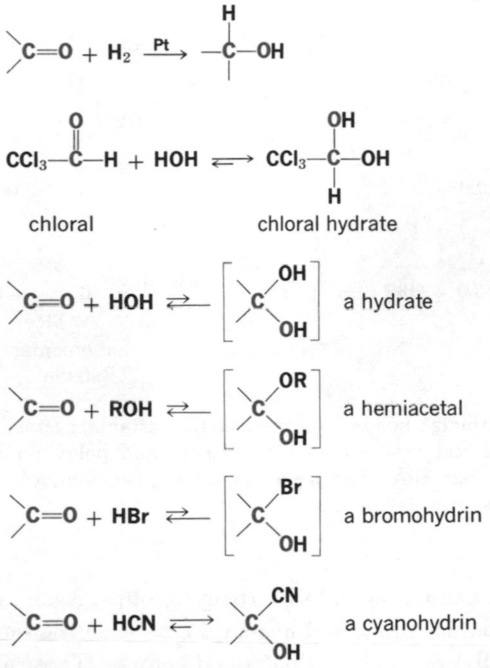

$$>C=O + H_2 \xrightarrow{Pt} -\overset{\overset{\displaystyle H}{|}}{\underset{|}{C}}-OH$$

$$CCl_3-\overset{\overset{\displaystyle O}{\|}}{C}-H + HOH \rightleftharpoons CCl_3-\overset{\overset{\displaystyle OH}{|}}{\underset{|}{C}}-OH$$

chloral   chloral hydrate

$$>C=O + HOH \rightleftharpoons \left[>C\overset{OH}{\underset{OH}{<}} \right] \quad \text{a hydrate}$$

$$>C=O + ROH \rightleftharpoons \left[>C\overset{OR}{\underset{OH}{<}} \right] \quad \text{a hemiacetal}$$

$$>C=O + HBr \rightleftharpoons \left[>C\overset{Br}{\underset{OH}{<}} \right] \quad \text{a bromohydrin}$$

$$>C=O + HCN \rightleftharpoons >C\overset{CN}{\underset{OH}{<}} \quad \text{a cyanohydrin}$$

Fig. 9-14. Hydrogen adds to carbonyl groups as it does to carbon–carbon double bonds. Additions of water, alcohols, and acids, except in special cases like chloral, do not lead to stable products, although cyanohydrins are usually stable. The positive part of the reagent always adds to the oxygen atom.

This addition takes place in an acid-catalyzed reaction like the hydration of alkenes to alcohols. In a few cases the resultant diol is moderately stable, like chloral hydrate. Ordinarily, however, the hydrated form of a carbonyl compound cannot be isolated, water being lost and the C=O double bond reforming.

These simple adducts can often be stabilized if the very reactive —OH group is converted into the much more stable ether group, —OR. Thus, addition of an alcohol ROH to an aldehyde gives a hemiacetal, which is ordinarily much too

unstable to be isolated. If the free hydroxyl group in the hemiacetal is etherified
by further heating with the alcohol, the molecule is converted to an acetal,

$$-\text{CH} \overset{\displaystyle \text{OR}}{\underset{\displaystyle \text{OR}}{\diagdown}}$$. Acetals are ordinarily quite stable and easily isolated. The adhesive used

in safety glass is an acetal of a polyol (Fig. 9-15).

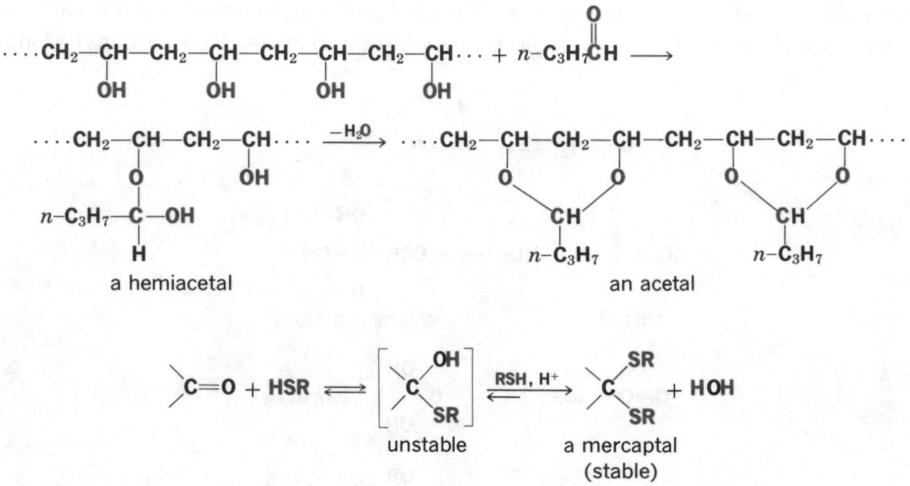

Fig. 9-15. Although hemiacetals are usually unstable, acetals are stable compounds. An acetal between *n*-butyraldehyde and polyvinyl alcohol is used
in preparing safety glass. Analogous compounds, called mercaptals, are formed
from aldehydes and mercaptans.

Amines and ammonia also add to carbonyl groups. Again, the initially formed
products, which contain amino and hydroxyl groups on the same carbon atom, are
unstable and rapidly revert to aldehydes and ketones. These adducts can stabilize
themselves in another way, however, by the loss of water to give imino groups
($>$C$=$N$-$), with formation of carbon–nitrogen double bonds (Fig. 9-16). This
latter reaction is also an equilibrium, but if the group attached to the nitrogen
atom is properly chosen the carbonyl group is converted in high yield to the imine.
The reaction finds its principal use in the conversion of aldehydes and ketones,
which are usually liquid, into solid *derivatives* for purification and identification.
Three common reagents for preparing derivatives of aldehydes and ketones are
presented in Fig. 9-16. Phenylhydrazones and semicarbazones of even simple
carbonyl compounds are usually solids. For instance, although acetone and acetophenone are liquids, acetone semicarbazone melts at 191° and acetophenone
phenylhydrazone at 106°.

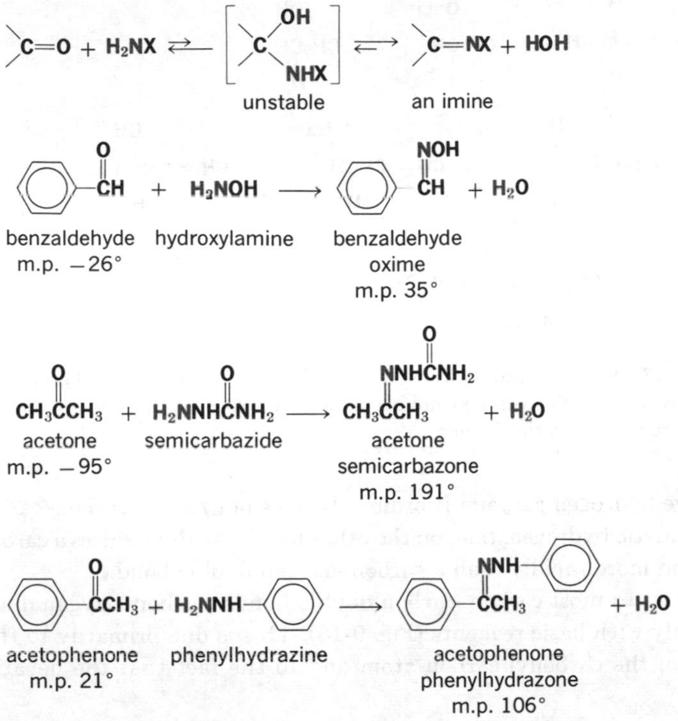

Fig. 9-16. The initial adducts of carbonyl groups and substituted ammonias stabilize themselves by loss of water and formation of carbon–nitrogen double bonds. Aldehydes and ketones form *oximes* when treated with hydroxylamine, *semicarbazones* when treated with semicarbazide, and *phenylhydrazones* when treated with phenylhydrazine.

Prob. 9-7. Write equations for the formation of 2-butanone semicarbazone and benzaldehyde phenylhydrazone. 2,4-Dinitrophenylhydrazine forms even higher melting derivatives. Write an equation for the preparation of cyclohexanone 2,4-dinitrophenylhydrazone.

Some addition reactions of carbon–oxygen double bonds are not readily reversible, and result in stable products without the necessity of a further reaction like dehydration. Two examples have already been given: hydrogenation and addition of hydrogen cyanide. The adducts are most likely to be stable when new carbon–carbon or carbon–hydrogen bonds are formed in the product. Certain metal hydrides, for instance, lithium aluminum hydride ($LiAlH_4$) or sodium borohydride ($NaBH_4$), are particularly useful for the reduction of carbon–oxygen double bonds in the laboratory (Fig. 9-17). For water-soluble compounds sodium borohydride is used, because the reagent reacts only slowly with water. Reduction with metal hydrides has two great advantages over catalytic hydrogenation: It avoids the use

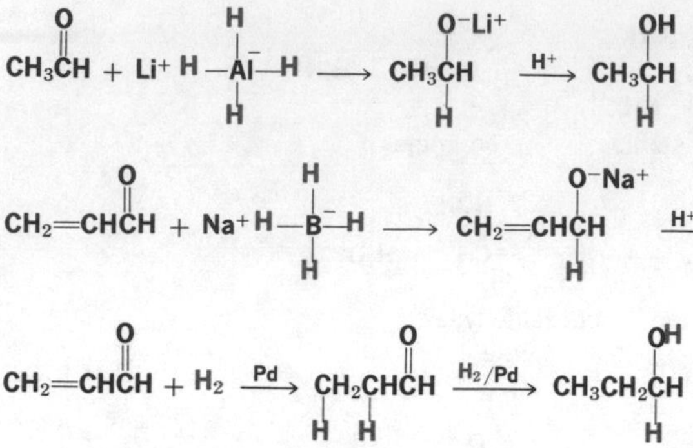

Fig. 9-17. Metal hydrides form stable adducts and reduce carbonyl groups more readily than carbon–carbon double bonds. Hydrogenation reduces the latter more rapidly than the former.

of explosive hydrogen gas, and it ordinarily does not reduce carbon–carbon double bonds. Catalytic hydrogenation, on the other hand, usually reduces a carbon–carbon double bond more rapidly than a carbon–oxygen double bond.

In contrast to most carbon–carbon double bonds, carbon–oxygen double bonds react readily with basic reagents (Fig. 9-18). This is due primarily to the positive character of the carbonyl carbon atom and to the fact that the negative charge

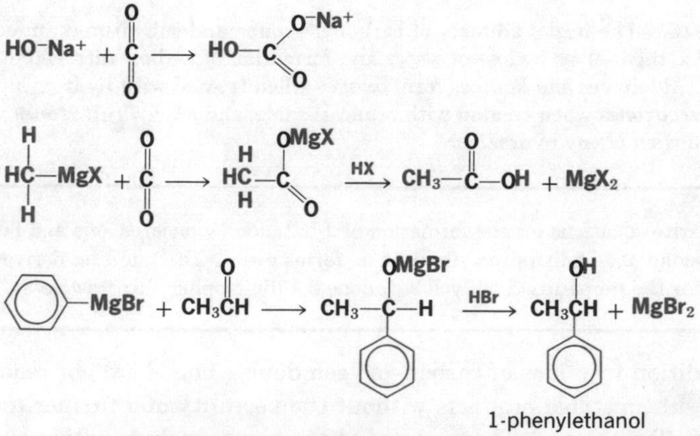

1-phenylethanol

Fig. 9-18. Carbon–oxygen double bonds add basic reagents. The formation of bicarbonate ion from carbon dioxide and hydroxide and the reactions of Grignard reagents are examples.

introduced by the addition can be placed on an oxygen atom. A simple example of the addition of an anion to a carbonyl group is found in the reaction of carbon dioxide with sodium hydroxide, which indicates why carbon dioxide dissolves more readily in alkali than in water.

In discussing Grignard reagents we noted that these organometallic compounds might be considered to have negatively charged carbon atoms. As might be expected, Grignard reagents also add rapidly to the carbonyl groups of aldehydes and ketones. On acidification, the adducts yield alcohols. For organic chemistry, the addition of a Grignard reagent to a carbonyl group is extremely important, since a new carbon–carbon bond forms in the process. This means that large molecules can be prepared from small ones (Fig. 9-19). Note that reaction with formal-

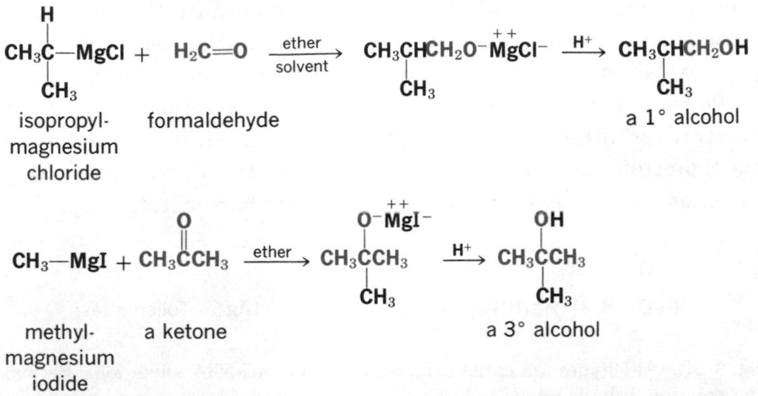

Fig. 9-19. Two additional examples of the synthesis of alcohols by addition of Grignard reagents to carbonyl groups of aldehydes and ketones.

dehyde leads to a primary alcohol, that all other aldehydes yield secondary alcohols, and that ketones give tertiary alcohols. The Grignard reagent is prepared from the corresponding organic chloride, bromide, or iodide. Exactly the same reactions can be carried out with organolithium reagents, although the greater reactivity of the lithium reagents makes organomagnesium reagents easier to handle.

Other organometallic compounds also add to carbon–oxygen double bonds. Sodium acetylide, for example, is used commercially to prepare unsaturated alcohols (Fig. 9-20).

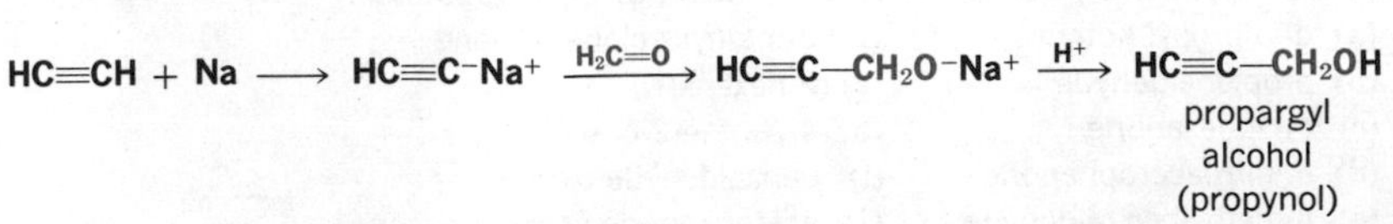

Fig. 9-20. Sodium acetylide forms stable adducts with carbonyl groups.

Prob. 9-8. Give three different ways you could prepare

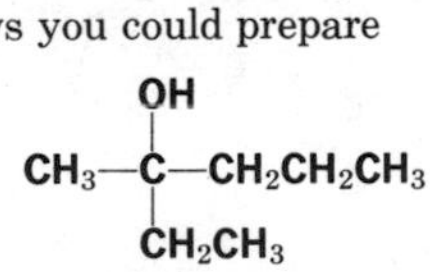

$$CH_3-\underset{\underset{CH_2CH_3}{|}}{\overset{\overset{OH}{|}}{C}}-CH_2CH_2CH_3$$

by the reaction of a ketone with a Grignard reagent.

OXIDATION OF ALDEHYDES

The carbonyl group of an aldehyde has attached to it a hydrogen atom which is easily oxidized; a ketone, lacking a carbonyl-hydrogen bond, is not oxidized as readily. The difference is similar to that between oxidizable primary and secondary alcohols and oxidation-stable tertiary alcohols. Even the oxygen of air can oxidize an aldehyde to the corresponding acid. Powerful oxidizing agents like potassium permanganate or potassium dichromate perform the job very well, but milder reagents are often used to avoid oxidation of other parts of the molecule. Testing for oxidation by one of these mild reagents can show whether a compound that reacts with phenylhydrazine is an aldehyde or a ketone. If a reaction with ammoniacal silver nitrate (Tollen's reagent) is carried out in a clean test tube, the silver metal precipitates in a thin film on the walls and produces a mirror (Fig. 9-21). For this reason the reaction is often called the silver mirror test.

$$\underset{\text{R--C--H}}{\overset{\text{O}}{\|}} + 2\overset{+}{\text{Ag}}(\text{NH}_3)_2 \xrightarrow[\text{H}_2\text{O}]{\text{OH}^-} \underset{\text{R--C--O}^-}{\overset{\text{O}}{\|}} + 2\text{Ag}\downarrow \quad \text{Tollen's test}$$

Fig. 9-21. Aldehydes are easily oxidized to salts of acids by silver ions. Because the reaction only proceeds in basic solution, the silver ion must be complexed with ammonia to prevent its precipitation.

Prob. 9-9. How could you distinguish, by visual chemical tests, among

$$\text{CH}_3(\text{CH}_2)_6\text{CH}_3, \quad \text{CH}_3\underset{\overset{\|}{\text{O}}}{\text{C}}\text{CH}_2\text{CH}_3, \quad \text{and} \quad \text{CH}_3(\text{CH}_2)_4\underset{\overset{\|}{\text{O}}}{\text{C}}\text{H}?$$

Among 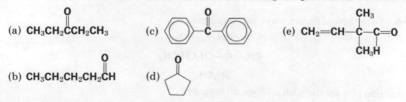 ?

Prob. 9-10. Draw the structure of each of the following compounds:

    (a) di-*n*-propyl ketone   (f) 3-methylcyclopentanone

    (b) propionaldehyde   (g) 2-hexenal

    (c) cyclohexanone   (h) 4-penten-2-one

    (d) *m*-nitroacetophenone   (i) benzaldehyde oxime

    (e) *p*-methylbenzaldehyde   (j) acetophenone semicarbazone

---

Prob. 9-11. Give the IUPAC name for each of the following compounds:

(a) $\text{CH}_3\text{CH}_2\underset{\overset{\|}{\text{O}}}{\text{C}}\text{CH}_2\text{CH}_3$

(b) $\text{CH}_3\text{CH}_2\text{CH}_2\text{CH}_2\underset{\overset{\|}{\text{O}}}{\text{C}}\text{H}$

(c) (benzophenone structure)

(d) (cyclopentanone structure)

(e) $\text{CH}_2{=}\text{CH}{-}\underset{\underset{\text{CH}_3}{|}}{\overset{\overset{\text{CH}_3}{|}}{\text{C}}}{-}\underset{\text{H}}{\overset{\text{O}}{\underset{}{\text{C}}}}{=}\text{O}$

Prob. 9-12. What would be the product of the reaction of benzaldehyde with each of the following reagents?

(a) H_2/Pt   (d) LiAlH$_4$

(b) 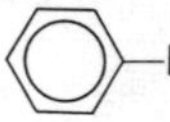 ⬡—MgBr   (e) Ag$^+$(NH$_3$)$_2$

(c) NH$_2$OH   (f) CH$_3$SH,H$^+$

Prob. 9-13. What would be the structures of the alkenes or alkadienes which give the following products on ozonolysis?

$$\text{(a) } H_2C{=}O \text{ and } CH_3\overset{O}{\overset{\|}{C}}CH_3$$

$$\text{(b) } CH_3\overset{O}{\overset{\|}{C}}CH_2CH_2CH_2CH_2\overset{O}{\overset{\|}{C}}CH_3$$

(c) $CH_3\overset{O}{\overset{\|}{C}}CH_3$, $H\overset{O}{\overset{\|}{C}}CH_2CH_2\overset{O}{\overset{\|}{C}}H$, and $CH_3CH_2\overset{O}{\overset{\|}{C}}H$ in equal amounts.

Prob. 9-14. What would be the product, after hydrolysis with water and acid, of the reaction of methylmagnesium bromide with each of the following reagents?

(a) H_2O (d) methyl ethyl ketone

(b) CO_2 (e) HCl

(c) 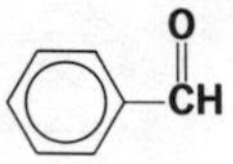 ⬡—$\overset{O}{\overset{\|}{C}}H$ (f) formaldehyde

---

Prob. 9-15. How could each of the following compounds be formed by making use of a Grignard reaction? More than one way may be possible.

(a) 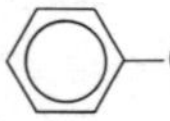 ⬡—CH$_2$OH   (c) n-hexane

(b) CH$_3\overset{OH}{\overset{|}{C}}HCH_3$ (d) 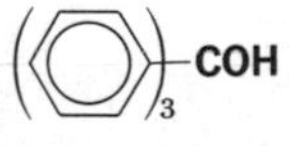 (⬡)$_3$—COH

Prob. 9-16. Suppose you had unlabeled bottles containing all of the following chemicals in each group. How could you distinguish among them by simple, visual chemical tests?

(a) 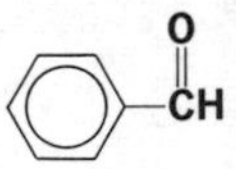 ⬡—$\overset{O}{\overset{\|}{C}}H$ and ⬡—$\overset{O}{\overset{\|}{C}}CH_3$

(b) (cyclohexanone), (cyclohexene), and (cyclohexane)

(c) ⬡—CH=CH$_2$, ⬡—$\overset{OH}{\overset{|}{C}}HCH_3$, and ⬡—$\overset{O}{\overset{\|}{C}}CH_3$.

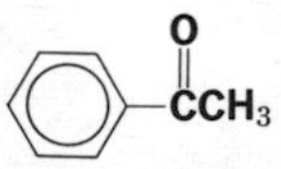

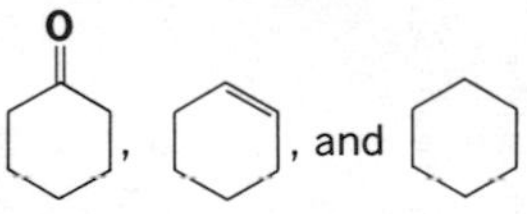

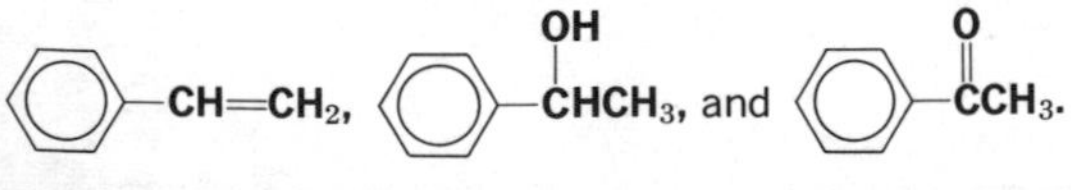

CHAPTER

CARBOHYDRATES, COMPLEX STEREOISOMERS

In nutrition and agriculture perhaps the most important aldehydes and ketones are the carbohydrates. This major class of compounds includes the sugars of blood, fruits, and cane, and also cellulose and starch. The name *carbohydrates* derives from their molecular formulas, which approximate the composition $(CH_2O)_n$. Despite their name, carbohydrates are actually multihydroxy aldehydes and ketones. Glucose, also known as dextrose, is the familiar sugar of the blood; it is the most widely distributed carbohydrate.

STRUCTURE OF GLUCOSE

Glucose is a pentahydroxy aldehyde, and as such, would be expected to have most of the properties of aldehydes and alcohols; we shall see that it does. It differs importantly, however, from most simple aldehydes and ketones because it forms stable hemiacetals. Although the equilibrium in the reaction of most aldehydes and alcohols favors the reactants rather than the hemiacetal, in glucose both reactants are parts of the same molecule and cannot escape from each other into the solution. Moreover, they can form 5- and 6-membered rings, which are stable. It is probably easiest to see that this is possible if one looks at a molecular model of D-glucose. As Fig. 10-1 shows, the oxygen atoms of both the C-5 and C-4 hydroxyl groups can be quite close to the carbonyl group of glucose. Adding the C-5 hydroxyl produces a 6-membered ring, called a pyranose ring after the heterocycle pyran, whereas adding the C-4 hydroxyl gives a 5-membered furanose ring, named for the heterocycle furan. Glucose exists almost entirely in the pyranose form, although other sugars form stable furanoses.

173

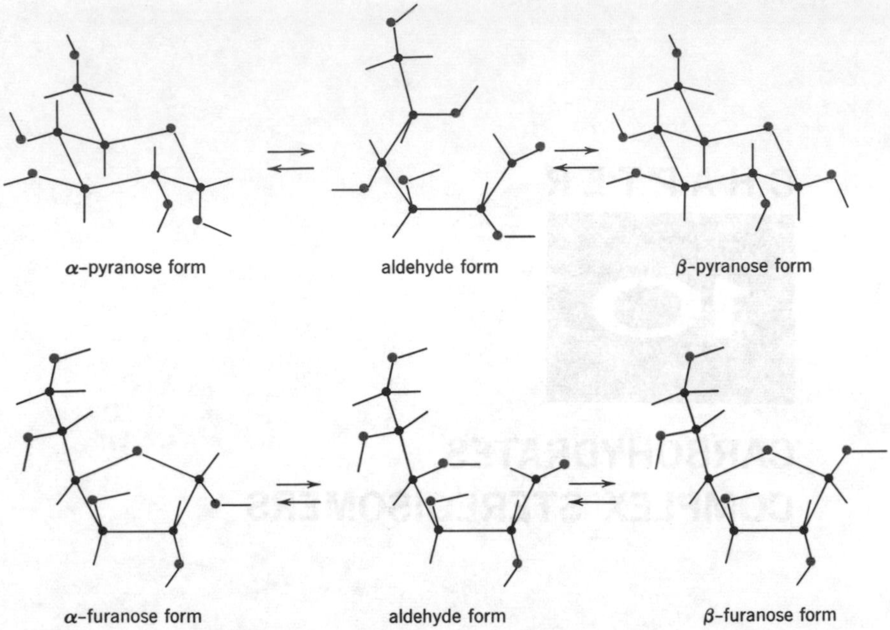

α–pyranose form   aldehyde form   β–pyranose form

α–furanose form   aldehyde form   β–furanose form

Fig. 10-1. Dreiding-type models of D-glucose, showing the ease of formation of 5-membered (furanose) and 6-membered (pyranose) rings. In these drawings of the models, a red atom attached at one end only represents —O—H, a red atom attached at both ends represents —O—.

When a hemiacetal is produced by addition to the carbonyl group, a new asymmetric center is created, and two isomers of either the pyranose or furanose may form. Notice that in the β form, the new hydroxyl group (in red) is drawn on the top side of the ring, *trans* to the hydroxyl group on C-2. In the α forms these two hydroxyls are *cis*.

There are three common ways of representing D-glucose: by Fischer, Haworth, and conformational formulas (Fig. 10-2). Note that a substituent (hydrogen or hydroxyl) which is shown on the right in the Fischer formula appears below the ring in either the Haworth or the conformational formula. Of the three representations, the conformational drawings most accurately represent the true shape of the molecules as indicated by the Dreiding-type models of Fig. 10-1, but they are rather inconvenient to draw. The Fischer formulas are misleading with their straight chains and long C—O bonds. We shall therefore compromise and usually employ Haworth formulas to represent sugars. It should be emphasized at the outset, however, that the pyranose rings are not really planar.

REACTIONS OF GLUCOSE

Many of the reactions of glucose are reactions of the stable pyranose form (Fig. 10-3). For example, glucose reacts with methanol and hydrochloric acid to provide

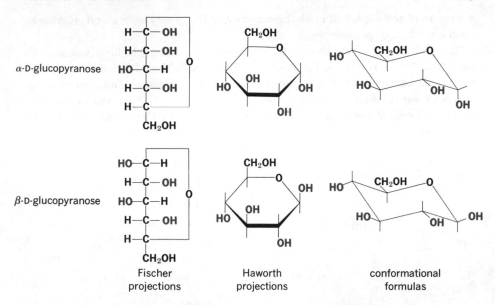

α-D-glucopyranose

β-D-glucopyranose

Fischer projections

Haworth projections

conformational formulas

Fig. 10-2. Three ways of drawing D-glucopyranose. In this book, we shall usually employ the Haworth projections.

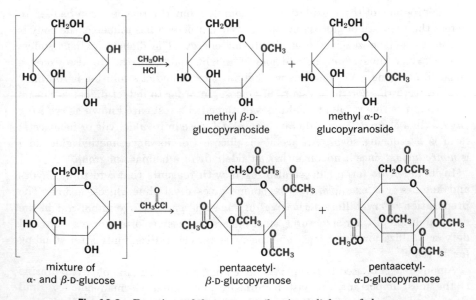

methyl β-D-glucopyranoside

methyl α-D-glucopyranoside

mixture of α- and β-D-glucose

pentaacetyl-β-D-glucopyranose

pentaacetyl-α-D-glucopyranose

Fig. 10-3. Reactions of the pyranose (hemiacetal) form of glucose.

a mixture of acetals, called methyl glucosides; it also reacts with acetyl chloride to form a mixture of pentaesters.

Although 99.9% of all glucose is hemiacetal, the aldehyde form can also be demonstrated by reactions. For example, the aldehyde form of glucose is reduced by sodium borohydride to a hexahydroxy compound, sorbitol, and is oxidized by Tollen's reagent (silver-ammonia complex, Fig. 9-21), or even by a weaker oxidizing agent composed of cupric ion mixed with a buffer (Benedict's or Fehling's solution) (Fig. 10-4).

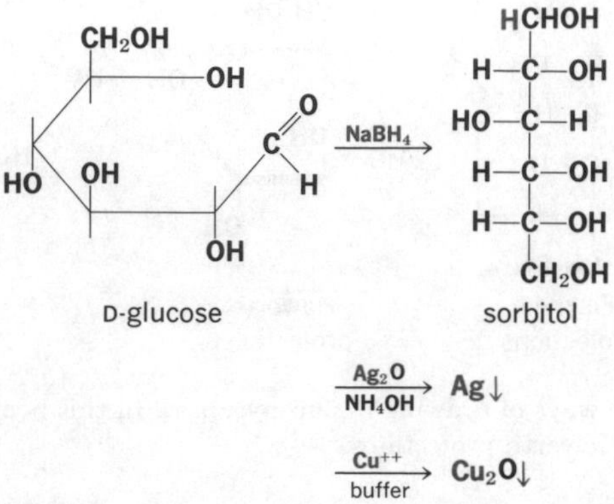

Fig. 10-4. Reactions of the aldehyde form of glucose. Tollen's reagent as well as Fehling's, or Benedict's reagent (cupric ion in citrate or tartrate solution) can be used to detect the presence of glucose in blood or urine.

The products of these oxidations are complex, but the reagents can be used to detect the presence of glucose in nature. When a person has diabetes, the body is unable to metabolize glucose efficiently for energy. The diabetic patient suffers from extreme thirst, hunger, and loss of weight and strength. He also excretes sugar in his urine; as a consequence, Fehling's or Benedict's solution is routinely used to test urine for the presence of glucose, in order to detect diabetes. Sugars that yield positive results to Fehling's or Benedict's tests are known as *reducing sugars* (in a chemical, not a dietary, sense). Glucose in its aldehyde or hemiacetal form is a reducing sugar. An acetal of glucose (for instance, methyl glucoside) is *nonreducing,* since it no longer has an aldehyde or a hemiacetal group.

In its aldehyde form, glucose also reacts with reagents that add to aldehydes and ketones. For example, hydroxylamine gives crystalline glucose oxime. The preparation of crystalline derivatives of sugars is particularly important in the determination of their structures, since sugars themselves often form syrups and defy crystallization. In at least one case, a sugar crystallized only after standing for 35 years!

Among reagents used to form crystalline adducts with sugars, phenylhydrazine is the most important, at least historically. The great German chemist Emil Fischer, who won the Nobel Prize in 1902 for his brilliant work in elucidating the

structures of many of the sugars, called phenylhydrazine his "first and most last-
ing chemical love," even though he became violently allergic to it. The reaction of
phenylhydrazine with a sugar is somewhat more complex than its reaction with a
simple carbonyl compound, because sugars are easily oxidized and phenylhydrazine
is a mild oxidizing agent. The initially formed phenylhydrazone consumes a second
mole of phenylhydrazine and is oxidized at carbon-2. A third mole of phenylhydrazine adds to form a di-phenylhydrazone. Fischer coined the name *osazone*
for these compounds, which are nearly always nicely crystalline (Fig. 10-5).

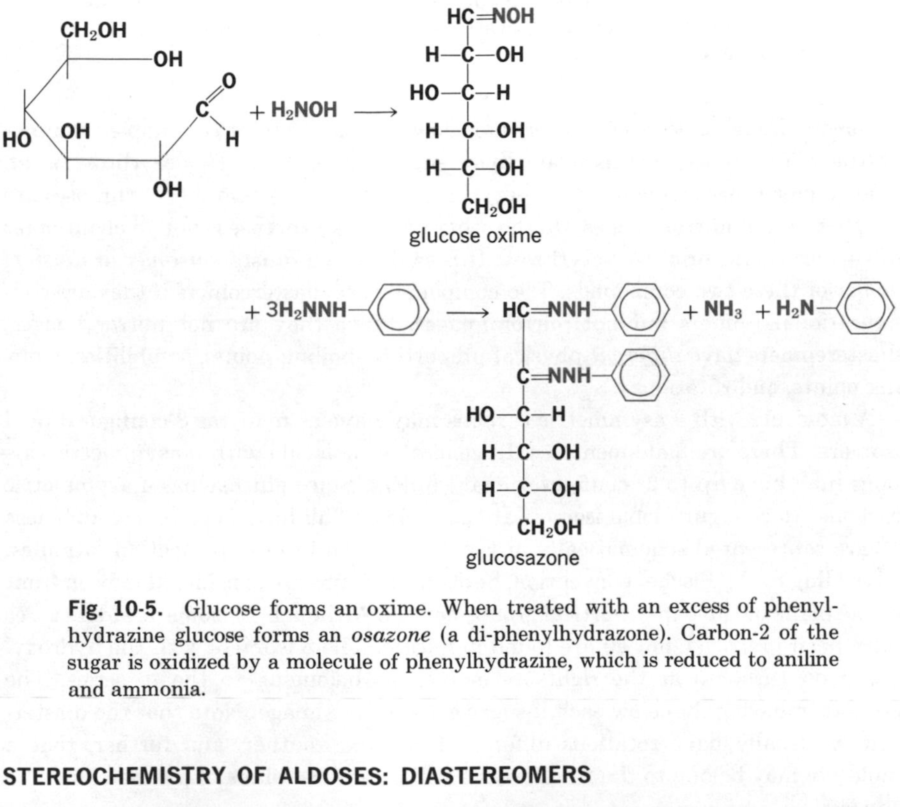

Fig. 10-5. Glucose forms an oxime. When treated with an excess of phenylhydrazine glucose forms an *osazone* (a di-phenylhydrazone). Carbon-2 of the
sugar is oxidized by a molecule of phenylhydrazine, which is reduced to aniline
and ammonia.

STEREOCHEMISTRY OF ALDOSES: DIASTEREOMERS

Although D-glucose is probably the most important carbohydrate, it is only one
member of this class of compounds. More specifically, glucose is a monosaccharide,
one of a group of carbohydrates which contain one actual or potential aldehyde or
ketone group. Still more precisely, it is an example of an aldohexose, an aldose
since it has an aldehyde group, a hexose since it has 6 carbon atoms. It differs from
other aldohexoses in its stereochemistry.

So far we have ignored the fact that glucose contains several asymmetric carbon
atoms. A molecule that contains a single asymmetric carbon can exist, as we saw
in Chapter 7, in 2 configurations, D- and L-. If 2 different asymmetric carbon atoms
are present in the same molecule, each of them can exist in 2 configurations; thus,

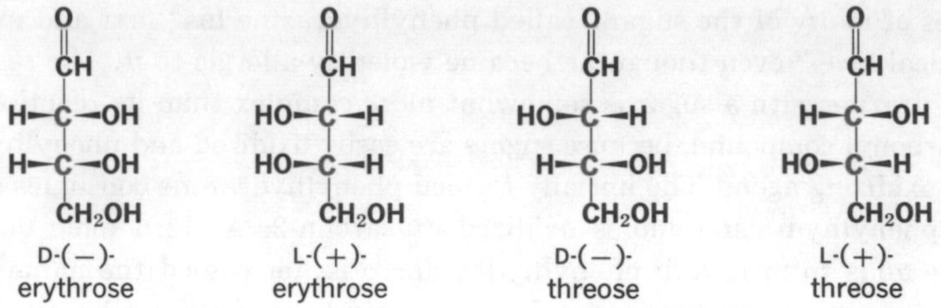

$$
\begin{array}{cccc}
\underset{\text{CH}}{\overset{\text{O}}{\|}} & \underset{\text{CH}}{\overset{\text{O}}{\|}} & \underset{\text{CH}}{\overset{\text{O}}{\|}} & \underset{\text{CH}}{\overset{\text{O}}{\|}} \\
\text{H—C—OH} & \text{HO—C—H} & \text{HO—C—H} & \text{H—C—OH} \\
\text{H—C—OH} & \text{HO—C—H} & \text{H—C—OH} & \text{HO—C—H} \\
\text{CH}_2\text{OH} & \text{CH}_2\text{OH} & \text{CH}_2\text{OH} & \text{CH}_2\text{OH} \\
\text{D-(—)-} & \text{L-(+)-} & \text{D-(—)-} & \text{L-(+)-} \\
\text{erythrose} & \text{erythrose} & \text{threose} & \text{threose}
\end{array}
$$

Fig. 10-6. Erythrose and threose are 4-carbon sugars containing 2 asymmetric carbon atoms (in red). Four optical isomers are possible; (+)- and (—)-erythrose are mirror images of each other, as are (+)- and (—)-threose. Each threose is a diastereomer of each erythrose.

4 isomers are possible. Four isomers are shown in Fig. 10-6 for the simple examples of the aldotetroses, 4-carbon aldehydo sugars. Note that (+)-erythrose is an enantiomer (mirror image) of (—)-erythrose and that (+)- and (—)-threoses are another pair of mirror images. On the other hand, (+)-threose is not an enantiomer of (+)-erythrose or of (—)-erythrose. It is said to be a *diastereoisomer* or *diastereomer* of these two compounds. Two compounds are diastereomers if they are configurational isomers but not mirror images. Since they are not mirror images, diastereomers have *different* physical properties—boiling points, solubilities, melting points, and rotations.

A molecule with 3 asymmetric carbons may have as many as 8 configurational isomers. There are 8 aldopentoses. In general, a molecule with n asymmetric carbons may have up to 2^n configurational isomers. Since glucose has 4 asymmetric carbons, 16 configurational isomers are possible and all have been prepared. These 16 are represented schematically in Fig. 10-7 in the Fischer projection formulas. According to the Fischer convention, horizontal groups are considered to be in front of the plane of the paper, vertical groups behind. Although 16 isomeric aldohexoses have been prepared, not all are found in nature. The 8 isomers with the hydroxyl group on carbon-5 at the right are defined as belonging to the D- series. The L-sugar immediately below each D-sugar is its mirror image. Note that the diastereomers usually have rotations different from one another, and further, that a molecule may belong to the D- series but still rotate the plane of polarized light to the left.

Prob. 10-1. Draw the eight aldopentoses. Indicate which are mirror images and which are diastereomers.

α- And β-D-glucopyranoses (usually called just α- and β-D-glucoses) are optical isomers but not mirror images. Hence, they are diastereomers, have different physical properties, and can be separated by crystallization. Crystallization of D-glucose from methyl alcohol gives pure α-D-glucose. A freshly prepared aqueous solution of

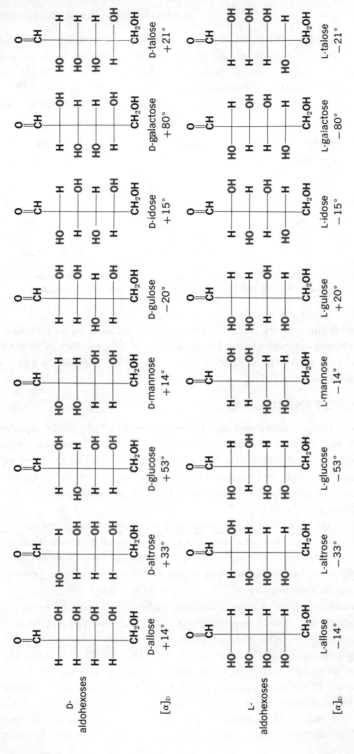

Fig. 10-7. The 16 configurational isomers of glucose are shown in their Fischer projection formulas.

α-D-glucose has $[\alpha]_D + 113°$; on standing, however, the specific rotation gradually drops to $+52.5°$. Crystallization of glucose from hot acetic acid gives pure β-D-glucose. A freshly prepared solution of β-D-glucose has $[\alpha]_D + 19°$; on standing, this specific rotation increases, until it, too, reaches $+52.5°$. This gradual change of rotation until equilibrium is reached is known as *mutarotation* (Fig. 10-8).

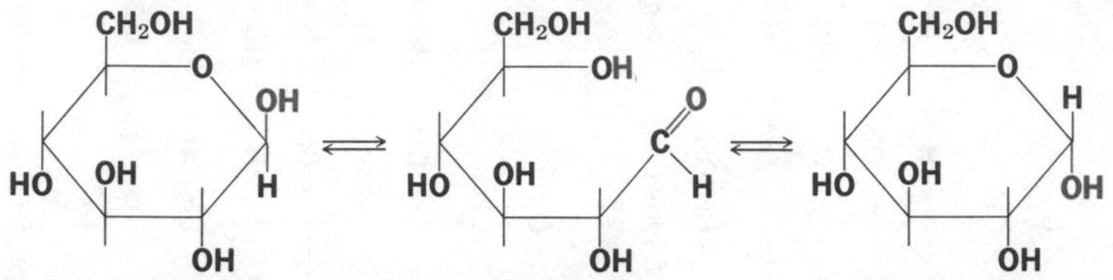

β-D-glucopyranose $[\alpha]_D^{20°} + 19°$ D-glucose (aldehyde form) α-D-glucopyranose $[\alpha]_D^{20°} + 113°$

Fig. 10-8. At equilibrium, D-glucose consists of 37% α-D-glucopyranose and 63% β-D-glucopyranose, with less than 0.05% of the free aldehyde present.

Both α- and β-glucoses are stable as solids, but in solution an equilibrium is gradually established between them. Simple arithmetic shows that in water the equilibrium mixture with $[\alpha]_D + 52.5°$ is 37% α-D-glucose (rotation $+113°$) and 63% β-D-glucose (rotation $+19°$).

RESOLUTION OF ENANTIOMERS

As we saw in the preceding section, diastereomers have physical properties which differ from one another in other ways besides optical rotation—for example, in melting points and solubilities. Difference in solubility means that two crystalline diastereomers can often be separated from each other by fractional crystallization. We have already seen this in the separation of the two diastereomers, α-D-glucose and β-D-glucose.

This means, further, that if it is possible to convert a pair of enantiomers into a pair of diastereomers, the latter can often be separated by crystallization. This is not always possible experimentally, but the possibility does provide the most generally useful procedure for separating a pair of enantiomers. This process is called *resolution of the enantiomers.*

For the diastereomers to be of maximum utility, they must be nicely crystalline and it must be possible to regenerate the starting enantiomers from them. To separate benzedrine into its D- and L-isomers, for instance, one can treat it with an optically active organic acid like mandelic acid (Fig. 10-9). Two salts are formed; these differ from each other in their stereochemistry at the amine asymmetric center, but not at the acid counterpart. Therefore, they are diastereomers, which have different solubilities and can be separated by crystallization. Treatment of the separated salts with sodium hydroxide restores the amine in pure D- and L- forms. The method is not restricted to the resolution of bases, but can be used

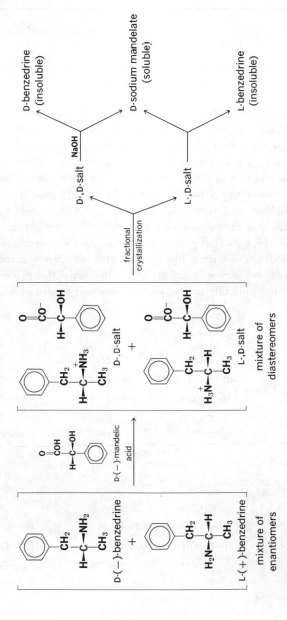

Fig. 10-9. An example of the resolution (separation into pure mirror images) of a racemic mixture of enantiomers.

181

for the separation of any pair of enantiomers, provided they can be converted to a pair of crystalline diastereomers. The resolution of enantiomeric phenols or alcohols, for example, can be effected by conversion to diastereomeric esters.

Prob. 10-2. Show a sequence of reactions by which D-mandelic acid could be obtained in pure form from a racemic mixture of D- and L-mandelic acids.

MESO ISOMERS

In the compounds discussed thus far, the number of possible isomers has equaled 2^n, where n is the number of asymmetric carbon atoms. However, we noted that this was in fact the maximum number allowed, implying that fewer isomers are sometimes found. This is indeed so, as may be seen from the reduction products of D- and L-erythrose and D- and L-threose. Reductions with sodium borohydride of D-threose and L-threose produce mirror images, D- and L-threitol, having equal but opposite rotations. However, reductions of D- and L-erythrose yield the same compound, erythritol, whose optical rotation is zero. In the two formulas written for erythritol in Fig. 10-10, note that rotation about a point midway between the central carbons converts one mirror image into another. Since a molecule must be nonidentical with its mirror image in order to rotate the plane of polarized light, erythritol is not optically active, and its rotation is zero at all wavelengths of light.

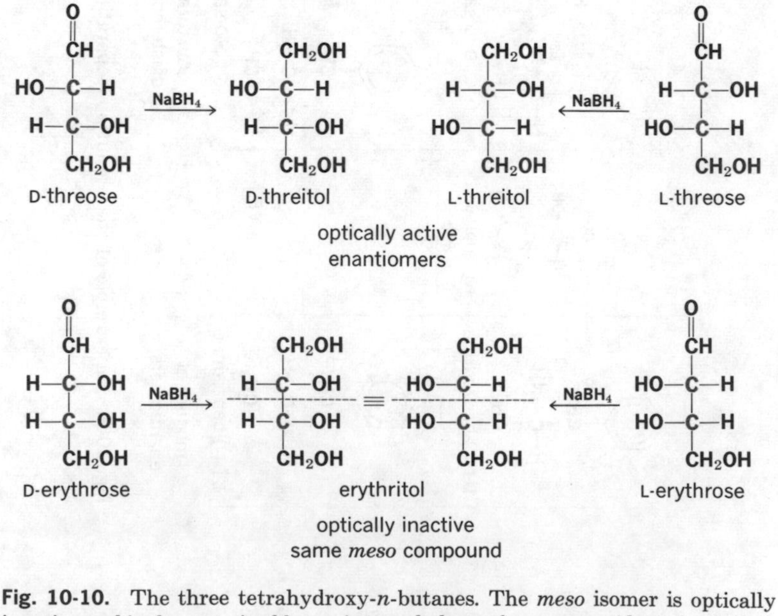

Fig. 10-10. The three tetrahydroxy-*n*-butanes. The *meso* isomer is optically inactive and is characterized by an internal plane of symmetry (dotted red line).

A molecule that contains asymmetric carbons but is identical to its mirror image is said to be *meso*. A *meso* isomer can be recognized by an element of symmetry which does not appear in optically active compounds. Thus, a plane of symmetry can be drawn through erythritol, between the two carbon atoms, but no plane of symmetry can be drawn through D- or L-threitol; these isomers will rotate the plane of polarized light.

Galactitol, obtained by sodium borohydride reduction of either D- or L-galactose, and ribitol, obtained by similar reduction of D- or L-ribose, are more complicated examples of *meso* compounds (Fig. 10-11). Although galactitol contains four asym-

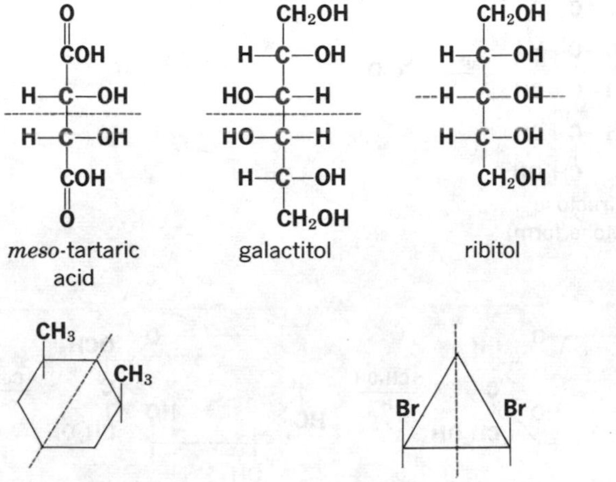

meso-tartaric acid   galactitol   ribitol

cis-1,3-dimethylcyclohexane   cis-1,2-dibromocyclopropane

Fig. 10-11. Additional examples of *meso* compounds. Planes of symmetry are indicated by dotted red lines.

metric carbon atoms and ribitol, three, they are identical with their mirror images and so are optically inactive. In these compounds planes of symmetry also can be drawn through the centers of the molecule. Similar examples can be found in cyclic compounds. These examples show that the number of possible isomers calculated by the rule (number of optical isomers = 2^n, with n = number of asymmetric carbon atoms) is a maximum which must be reduced if *meso* compounds occur.

FRUCTOSE, A KETO SUGAR

Not all sugars are aldehydes. Fructose, an important compound isomeric with D-glucose, is a ketone. Since it contains six carbon atoms, it is a ketohexose (Fig. 10-12). Because α-hydroxy ketones are easily oxidized, fructose tests positively as a reducing sugar. The carbonyl group is similar to the one in glucose; it can form a six-membered ring (a pyranose ring) or a five-membered ring (a furanose ring), with the C-5 or C-4 hydroxyl groups, respectively. These are called hemiketal forms

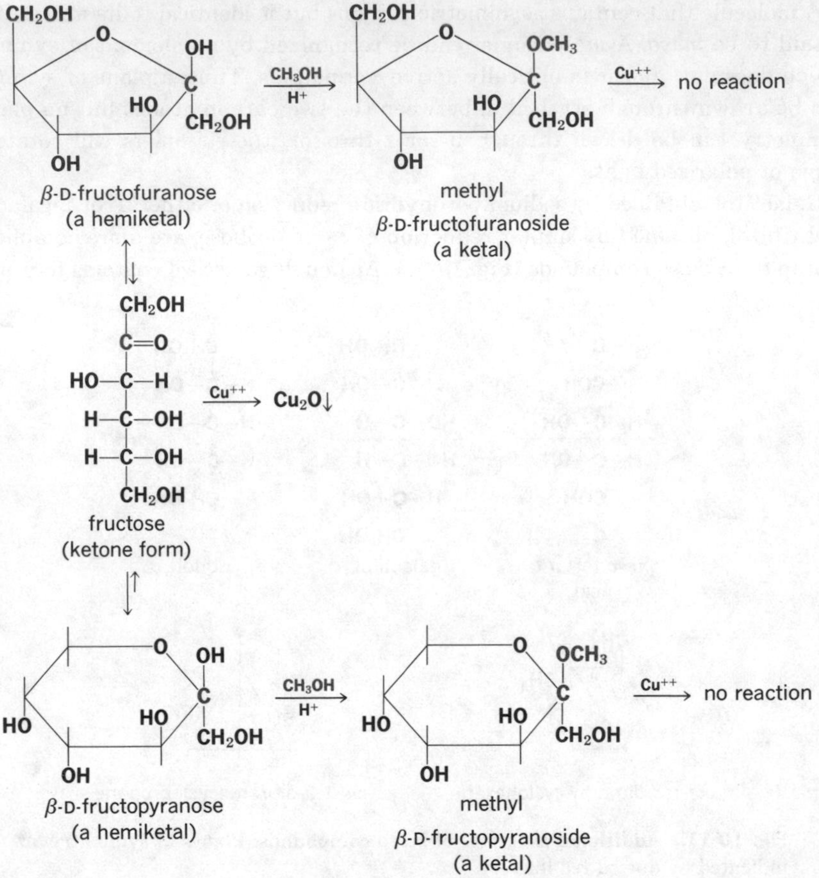

Fig. 10-12. Fructose is an example of a ketohexose, a six-carbon ketonic sugar. α-Isomers of the ketal and hemiketal are also possible.

(like hemiacetals) and can be converted to ketals. Ketals of fructose (for example, methyl fructoside) are not reducing sugars, since the α-hydroxy ketone is absent.

Glucose or dextrose, the sugar in honey, fructose, the sugar in some fruits, and sucrose, the sugar in beets and cane, are all sweet. Before proceeding, it may be helpful for us to differentiate the quality of "sweetness" from sugars. Sweetness is one of the four primary tastes which the human tongue is able to distinguish; the other three are bitterness, saltiness, and sourness. The front of the tongue is more sensitive to sweet tastes and the back of the tongue, to bitter ones; sour and salty tastes are also localized. Many sugars are indeed sweet to varying degrees, but others have little or no flavor. Conversely, some compounds that are not sugars are much sweeter than glucose or sucrose; such compounds are often used to escape the food value (calories) of sugars, since they are nonnutritive. Sucaryl calcium, for example, is 35 times as sweet as sucrose, while saccharin is 550 times

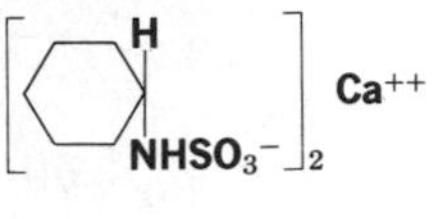

Sucaryl calcium 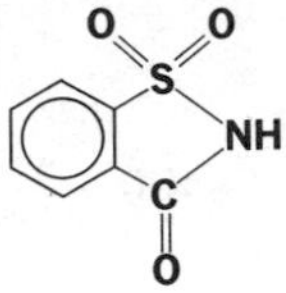   saccharin

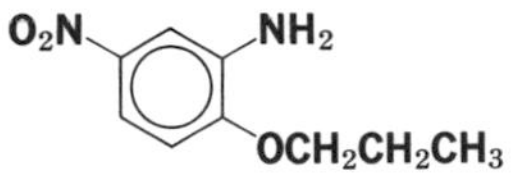

Fig. 10-13. Synthetic compounds possessing sweet tastes. Sucaryl calcium and saccharin are commercial sweeteners, but the third compound is toxic.

as sweet as sucrose (Fig. 10-13). Both of these compounds appear to be relatively nontoxic. The third compound of Fig. 10-13 is 4,100 times sweeter than sucrose and leaves no bitter aftertaste, but it is toxic.

Prob. 10-3. Give an acceptable name for the unnamed compound in Fig. 10-13.

GLUCOSIDES AND REDUCING DISACCHARIDES

Acetals of glucose are formed by the reaction of glucose with alcohols in acid solution. Hydrolysis of these glucosides with water and acid regenerates glucose. The hydrolysis can also be carried out through natural catalysts called *enzymes*, which are often highly specific. An enzyme called *emulsin*, for instance, catalyzes the hydrolysis of methyl β-D-glucoside but not methyl α-D-glucoside. *Maltase*, on the other hand, is an enzyme which catalyzes the hydrolysis of α-glucosides but not β-glucosides (Fig. 10-14). Glucosides of various types are widely distributed in nature. Arbutin, found in the blueberry, is a glucoside of hydroquinone (see Fig. 10-14). Since its hydrolysis is catalyzed by emulsin but not by maltase, it is assumed to be a β-glucoside. Indican, which produces the dye indigo (Fig. 16-5) is also a β-glucoside.

Glucose is a *monosaccharide*. In other carbohydrates two monosaccharides are joined together by the loss of a molecule of water between them. A compound of this type is called a *disaccharide*. A simple example is *maltose*, formed by the enzymatic hydrolysis of starch. Maltose has the formula $C_{12}H_{22}O_{11}$ and reduces Fehling's solution. Through further hydrolysis, which can be catalyzed by *maltase*, it splits into two molecules of glucose. *Cellobiose* is an isomer of maltose obtained by partial hydrolysis of cellulose; like maltose, it reduces Fehling's solution. Hydrolysis of cellobiose also gives two molecules of glucose; this hydrolysis can be catalyzed by emulsin but not by maltase. Thus, cellobiose is a β-glucoside and maltose an α-glucoside. Studies of the structures of these compounds have shown that in cellobiose the 4-hydroxyl group of one glucose molecule is involved in the

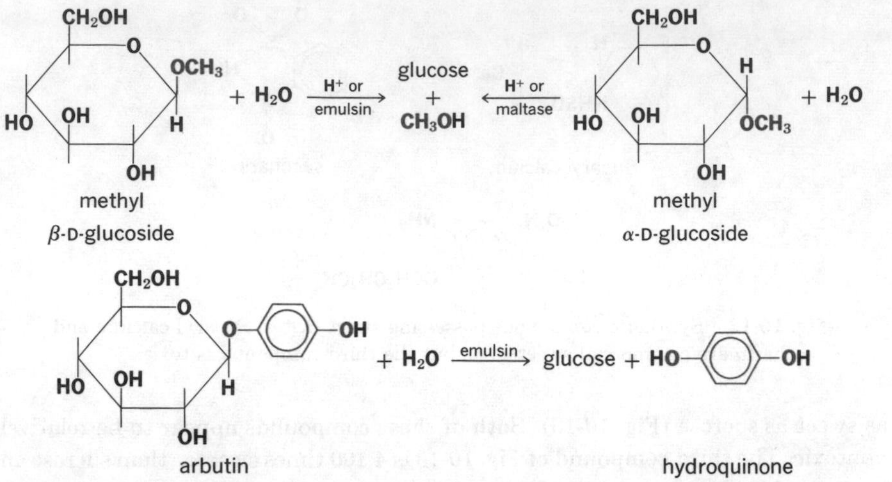

methyl
β-D-glucoside

methyl
α-D-glucoside

arbutin   hydroquinone

Fig. 10-14. Hydrolysis of an α-glucoside is catalyzed by the enzyme maltase; and hydrolysis of a β-glucoside is catalyzed by emulsion. Arbutin is a naturally occurring β-glucoside.

acetal linkage. Their structures are shown in Fig. 10-15. The common names maltose and cellobiose are much more extensively used than the scientific names.

$$\text{starch} \longrightarrow \underset{C_{12}H_{22}O_{11}}{\text{maltose}} \xrightarrow[H_2O]{\text{maltase}} 2 \text{ glucose}$$

$$\text{cellulose} \longrightarrow \underset{C_{12}H_{22}O_{11}}{\text{cellobiose}} \xrightarrow[H_2O]{\text{emulsin}} 2 \text{ glucose}$$

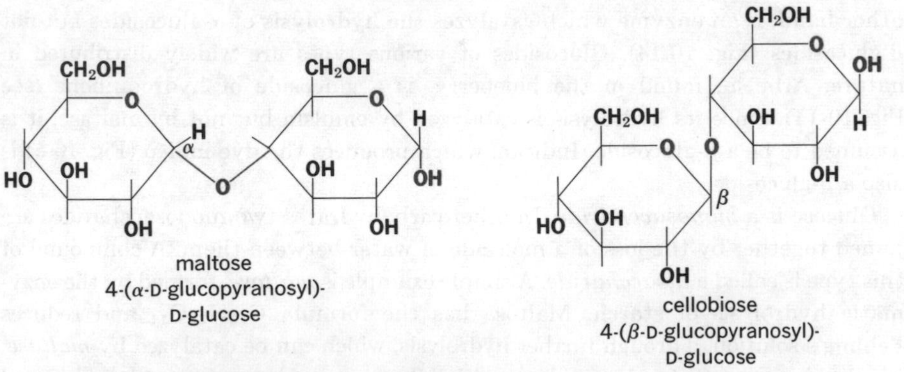

maltose
4-(α-D-glucopyranosyl)-
D-glucose

cellobiose
4-(β-D-glucopyranosyl)-
D-glucose

Fig. 10-15. Examples of reducing disaccharides. Maltose is an α-glucoside, cellobiose, a β-glucoside.

Prob. 10-4. Lactose, the sugar of cow, goat, and (in part) human milk, is a reducing sugar which, on hydrolysis by emulsin, gives one molecule of D-glucose and one of D-galactose (Fig. 10-7). Its correct name is 4-(β-D-galactopyranosyl)-D-glucose. Draw its structure.

NONREDUCING DISACCHARIDES

α,α-*Trehalose* is a disaccharide of glucose found in yeast, young mushrooms, and seaweed (Fig. 10-16). It does not react with cupric ion (Fehling's solution). Neither does it form derivatives with phenylhydrazine or hydroxylamine, as glucose, fructose, maltose, and cellobiose do. Evidently, trehalose contains neither a free carbonyl group nor its equivalent, a hemiacetal or hemiketal grouping. Since it is nonreducing, both aldehyde groups must be present as acetals, and this can occur only if the two glucose molecules are joined by an ether (acetal) linkage at their respective C-1 positions.

Sucrose, ordinary table sugar (cane or beet), is the pure organic chemical sold in greatest quantity. It is a disaccharide, which on hydrolysis gives one mole of glucose and one of fructose. Like trehalose, sucrose is a nonreducing sugar. Since the hydrolysis of sucrose is catalyzed by maltase it is evidently an α-glucoside. The hydroxyl group of the hemiketal (at C-2) of fructose must also be involved in the glucoside linkage, because if any other hydroxyl group were used, fructose would be a reducing sugar. Fructose can also be hydrolyzed by a β-fructosidase found in yeast. The complete structure of sucrose is given in Fig. 10-16.

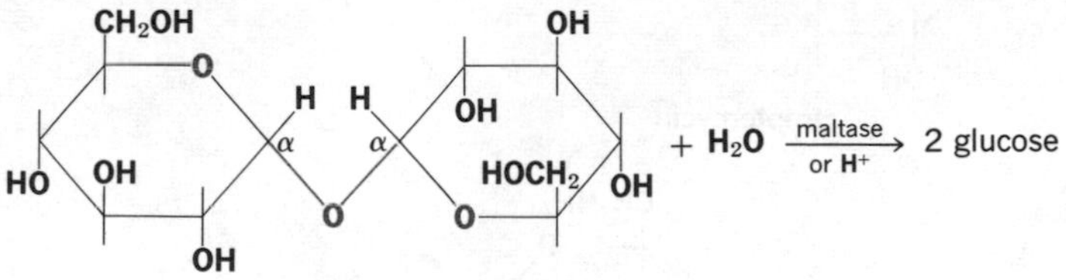

α,α-trehalose
(α-D-glucopyranosyl-α-D-glucopyranoside)

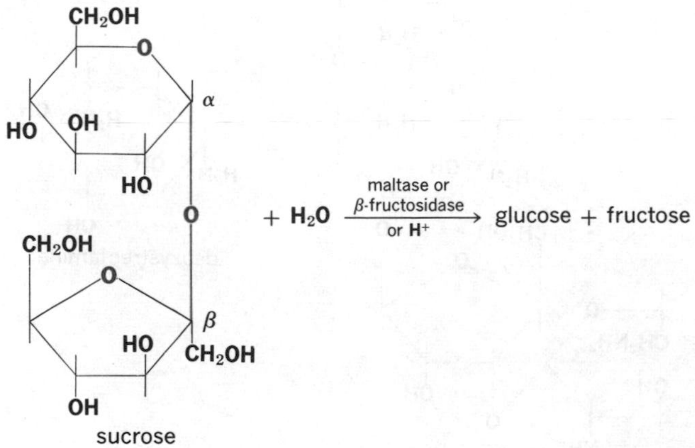

sucrose
(α-D-glucopyranosyl-
β-D-fructofuranoside)

Fig. 10-16. Examples of nonreducing disaccharides. α, α-Trehalose is a disaccharide of glucose. Sucrose is an α-glucopyranoside of glucose, and a β-fructofuranoside of fructose.

Prob. 10-5. If a nonreducing disaccharide is hydrolyzed to two molecules of glucose by emulsin but not by maltase, what is its structure? What would be its structure if it were hydrolyzed by both maltase and emulsin to glucose?

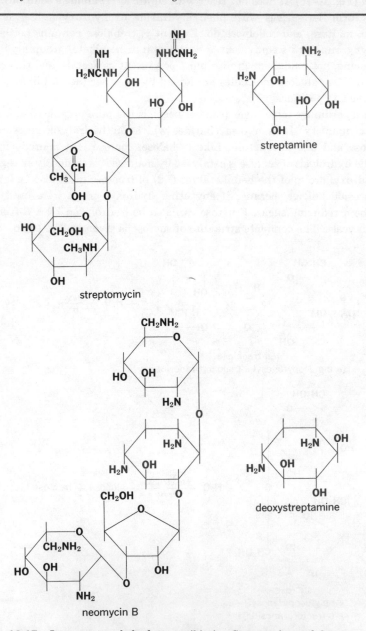

Fig. 10-17. Important carbohydrate antibiotics. Streptamine and deoxystreptamine (in red) are found in several antibiotics.

CARBOHYDRATE ANTIBIOTICS

Several widely used antibiotics either contain unusual sugars or are themselves examples of complex tri- and tetrasaccharides. The latter category includes the well-known streptomycin, used in treatment of tuberculosis and other bacterial infections, and neomycin, used topically as a component of burn ointments (Fig. 10-17). An interesting feature of each of these antibiotics is the presence of one or more aminosugars in which amino groups replace hydroxyl groups, and of a cyclohexane derivative which contains two amino groups plus three or four hydroxyl groups. These compounds, streptamine and deoxystreptamine, are not really sugars but are formed in nature from sugars.

POLYSACCHARIDES

Starch and *cellulose* are polysaccharides. They are polymers of glucose of high molecular weight. Partial hydrolysis of cellulose produces cellobiose as the only disaccharide; thus cellulose must be a polymer of β-glucose. Physical studies have shown that cellulose has a molecular weight of 300,000 to 500,000, so that each molecule has 2,000 to 3,000 glucose units in it (Fig. 10-18). Cotton and linen are good examples of relatively pure cellulose. Wood also contains large amounts of cellulose. Humans and animals do not contain the necessary enzymes for its hydrolysis, so that cellulose cannot be used as food. However, many microorganisms can hydrolyze cellulose. The termite, which does make a meal of wood, cannot digest cellulose either; however, he keeps a friendly group of bacteria in his alimentary canal which performs the hydrolysis for him. The cow keeps similar bacteria in its rumen, a "predigester"; cellulose is hydrolyzed there by the bacteria and then transferred to the stomach.

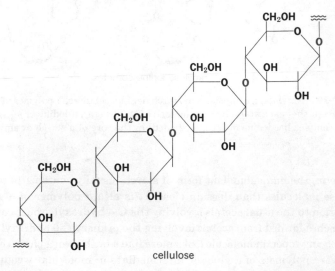

Fig. 10-18. Cellulose is a polymer of 2,000 to 3,000 β-glucose units.

Starch, a polymer of α-glucosides, is distributed widely throughout the plant kingdom, in potatoes, corn, etc. Most starch is actually a mixture of two polymers, amylose and amylopectin. Both are poly-α-glucosides; since the human body contains enzymes which can hydrolyze α-linkages, starch, unlike cellulose, is useful as food.

Amylose, the polymer usually present in a smaller amount, is a linear poly-α-glucoside exactly analogous to cellulose, though its chains are not as long, usually containing only 50 to 300 glucose molecules. When a little iodine is added to an aqueous solution of amylose, a deep blue-black color develops. It has been shown that amylose in solution curls up into a spiral or *helix,* which has just enough room down in its core for iodine molecules to fit (Fig. 10-19).

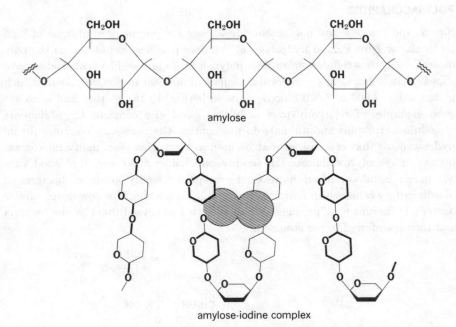

amylose

amylose-iodine complex

Fig. 10-19. Amylose, a component of starch, is, like cellulose, a polymer of glucose except that each acetal link is α instead of β. The starch-iodine or amylose-iodine complex has iodine molecules (shaded) in the core of a starch or amylose helix.

Amylopectin, the more abundant form of starch, usually contains 10 to 20 times more glucose molecules than does amylose. It is also a polymer of α-glucosides, but, in addition to the usual acetals involving the C-4 hydroxyl group, contains numerous branches formed from acetals involving the primary C-6 hydroxyl. As a consequence, the amylopectin molecule looks more like a bush than a chain (Fig. 10-20).

Dextrins are polymers of α-glucose, intermediate in molecular weight between glucose and starch. They are formed by the heating of dry starch or by the

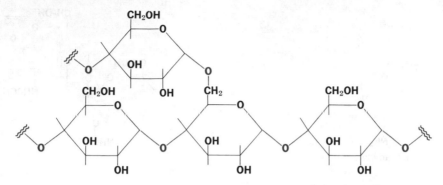

Fig. 10-20. Amylopectin is a polymer of α-glucose which contains 1,6-acetal linkages in addition to the more common 1,4-linkages.

partial hydrolysis of starch. The shiny finish imparted to a starched shirt by ironing is caused by the starch breaking down into dextrins due to the heat of the iron. In some dextrins, the glucose molecules are joined together in a ring (Fig. 10-21).

An unusual polysaccharide, the structural material of which lobster and crab shells are made, is *chitin*. This substance consists of N-acetyl-D-glucosamine

residues (a glucosamine unit with an acetyl group, $-\overset{\overset{\displaystyle O}{\|}}{C}CH_3$, on the amino group) joined by a β-linkage from the C-1 carbon of one molecule to the C-4 carbon of the next (Fig. 10-22).

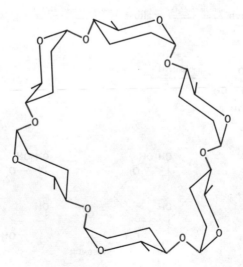

Fig. 10-21. Six glucose molecules fit nicely into a large ring. Such compounds are known as Schardinger dextrins, after the man who first isolated them.

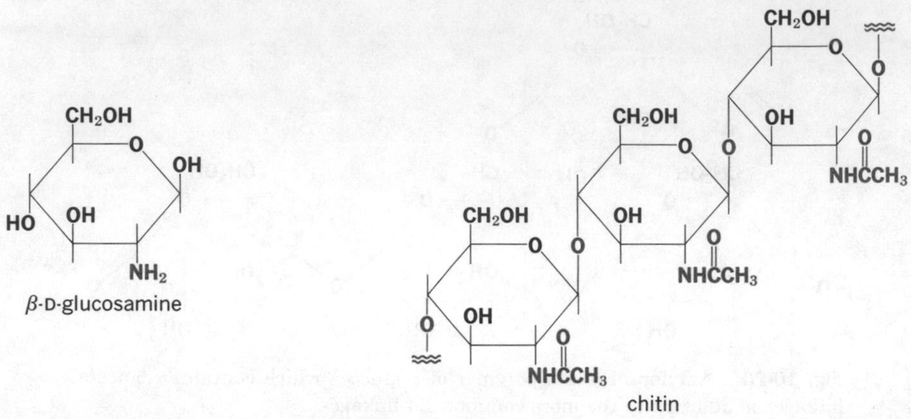

β-D-glucosamine

chitin

Fig. 10-22. Chitin, a polysaccharide found in crustaceans, is very hard; it forms the shells of these marine animals. The monosaccharide employed is N-acetyl-D-glucosamine, in which the 2-hydroxyl group of D-glucose is replaced by an acetylamino group.

CONVERSION OF STARCH TO GLYCOGEN

The enzymatic hydrolysis of starch proceeds in steps (Fig. 10-23). First, an enzyme called amylase converts the polysaccharide starch to the disaccharide maltose; this process is begun in the mouth by the amylase present in saliva and is responsible for the sweet taste of bread chewed for a few minutes. Additional amylase in the pancreatic juices of the intestine carries the polysaccharide hydrolysis to comple-

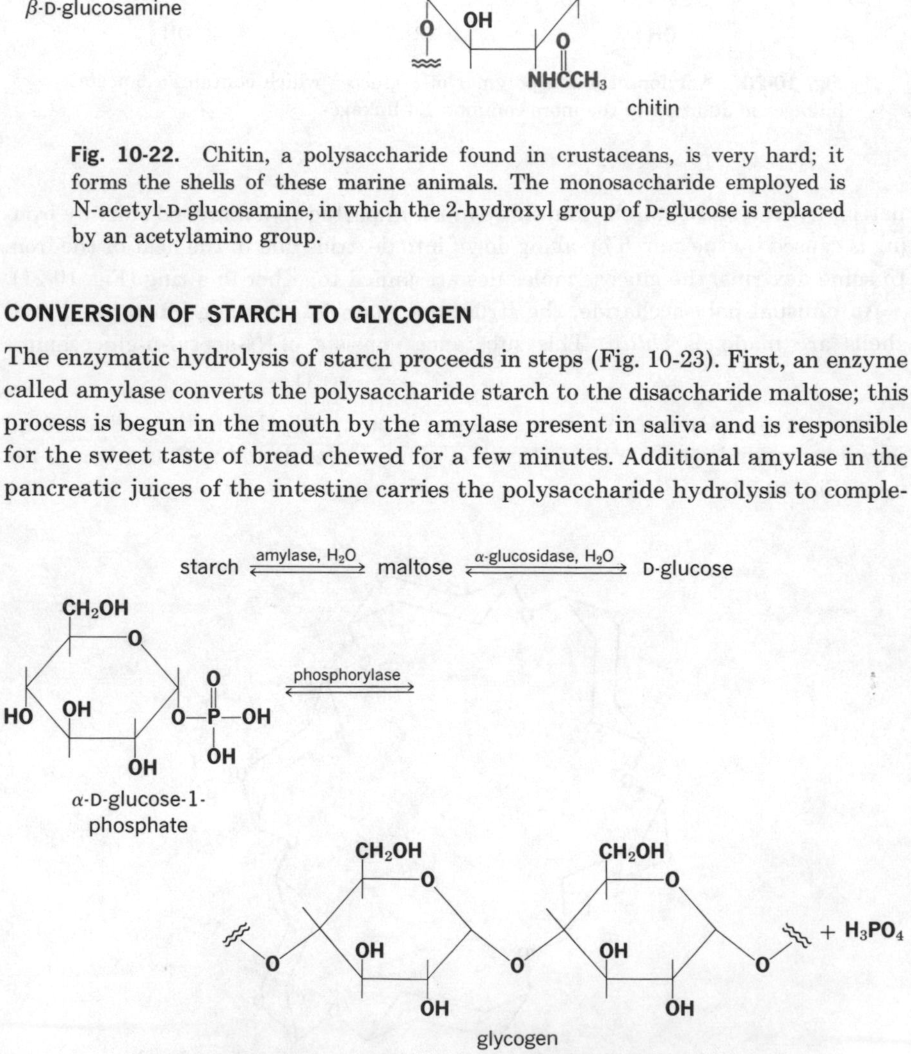

$$\text{starch} \underset{\text{amylase, H}_2\text{O}}{\rightleftharpoons} \text{maltose} \underset{\alpha\text{-glucosidase, H}_2\text{O}}{\rightleftharpoons} \text{D-glucose}$$

phosphorylase

α-D-glucose-1-phosphate

glycogen

$+ \text{H}_3\text{PO}_4$

Fig. 10-23. Starch is hydrolyzed enzymatically in the body to glucose, which is converted *via* its α-1-phosphate to glycogen, a polymer resembling starch. Glycogen is stored and can be reconverted to glucose for energy.

tion, with the assistance of another enzyme which hydrolyzes the occasional 1,6-linkages of starch. Maltose is hydrolyzed, in turn, to glucose, with the aid of an α-glucosidase of the intestines. Glucose is then absorbed from the intestine into the blood stream, in which it is transported to the liver, muscles, and other sites. At these sites it is stored as glycogen, a polymer of glucose resembling amylose, until it is needed again as glucose for conversion to energy. Formation and destruction of glycogen do not involve direct hydrolysis, but rather an equilibrium between the C-1 phosphate ester of glucose (glucose-1-phosphate) and glycogen and phosphoric acid; the reaction is catalyzed by an enzyme called a phosphorylase. Glycogen provides a great reservoir of readily available energy for animals.

RAYON AND OTHER CELLULOSE DERIVATIVES

In cotton and linen, the cellulose molecules occur as long fibers which are suitable for conversion into thread and fabric. In wood, the cellulose does not differ chemically from that in cotton and linen, but the cellulose molecules are tangled and bunched. Wood cellulose, therefore, cannot be directly used for making cloth, but it is so cheap much effort has been expended to convert it into useful forms.

The main difficulty with the modification of cellulose is its insolubility. Cellulose contains too many hydroxyl groups to be soluble in organic solvents, but it is too nonpolar to dissolve in water. In the synthesis of *viscose rayon,* this insolubility is overcome. First cellulose is mixed with strong alkali solution and then allowed to react with carbon disulfide (Fig. 10-24). A xanthate derivative of cellulose is formed by a reaction exactly analogous to the reaction of base with carbon dioxide (Fig. 9-18). This xanthate salt is ionic, so cellulose xanthate dissolves in water. The thick viscous xanthate solution of cellulose is forced through tiny holes into a solution of sulfuric acid. Just as sodium bicarbonate, when treated with acid, regenerates carbon dioxide, so cellulose xanthate regenerates carbon disulfide and

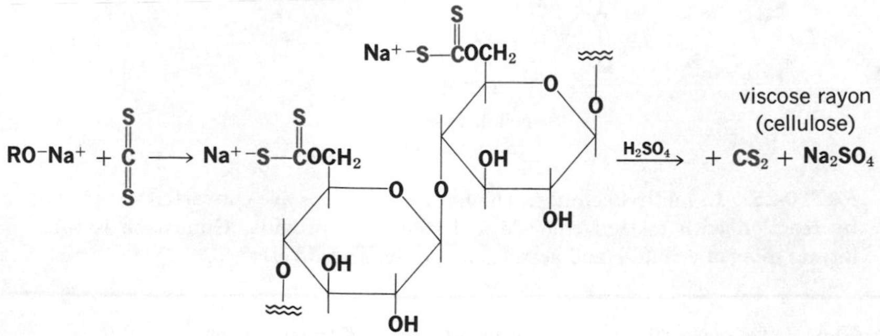

Fig. 10-24. In the preparation of viscose rayon, cellulose is brought into solution by means of its xanthate salt. Cellulose is regenerated in long threads, by forcing the xanthate through small holes into an acid solution.

precipitates cellulose in the form of a continuous thread which is drawn off and dried. Viscose rayon is then chemically identical to ordinary cellulose, although the treatment with acid and base usually results in shortening the polymer chain.

Cellulose can be made soluble in organic solvents by converting its hydroxyl groups to less polar derivatives. A cellulose ether is the simplest derivative which meets this condition. The sodium salt of cellulose can be treated, for instance, with methyl chloride to form methyl cellulose (Fig. 10-25). The resultant product does not resemble cotton or linen, but is used to impart oil and grease resistance to paper. Acetate rayon (cellulose acetate) is formed by the reaction of cellulose with acetic anhydride to yield esters of the hydroxyl groups. Guncotton is an ester of cellulose with nitric acid.

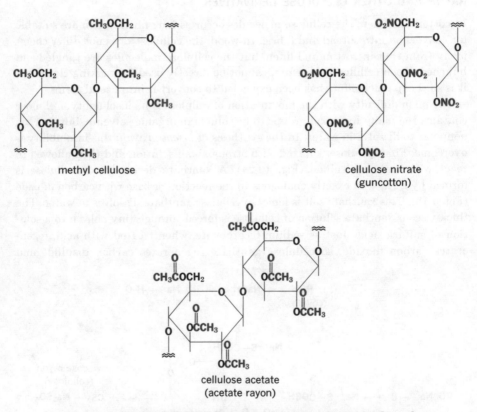

Fig. 10-25. In methyl cellulose, the hydroxyl groups are converted to ethers by reaction with methyl chloride and sodium hydroxide. Guncotton is the nitrate ester of cellulose and acetate rayon, the acetate ester.

Prob. 10-6. Give a general structural formula for each of the following:
  (a) a methyl glucoside (c) a furanose form
  (b) an osazone   (d) a xanthate salt

Prob. 10-7. What would be the product of the reaction of glucose with each of the following reagents?

(a) **NaBH$_4$**   (c) **CH$_3$OH,H$^+$**

(b) **NH$_2$OH**   (d) 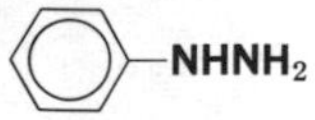 ⬡—**NHNH$_2$**

Prob. 10-8. Draw the structure of hydroxyethyl starch, formed from starch, sodium hydroxide and ethylene oxide.

Prob. 10-9. Draw a structure for any aldopentose. Draw its furanose hemiacetal in both the α- and β-forms. Draw a disaccharide of either form which would be a reducing disaccharide and another which would be a nonreducing disaccharide.

Prob. 10-10. How many configurational isomers are theoretically possible for each of the following compounds?

(a) CH$_3$—CH—CH—C$_6$H$_5$ (with OH, OH substituents)

(b) CH$_3$—CH—CH$_2$—C—CH$_3$ (with CH$_2$CH$_3$, H, C$_6$H$_5$ substituents)

(c) CH$_2$—CH—CH—CH—CH—CH—CH (with OH, OH, OH, OH, OH, OH substituents and terminal O)

(d) fructose (in the free ketone form)

Prob. 10-11. Draw all the stereoisomers (*cis-trans* as well as configurational) for

CH$_3$—CH=CH—C—CH$_3$ (with OH and H substituents)

Prob. 10-12. The structures of four disaccharides follow.

(a) Which one(s) are reducing sugars?
(b) Which one(s) would be hydrolyzed by emulsin?
(c) Which one(s) contain at least one molecule of D-glucose?
(d) Which one would properly be called 4-(β-D-glucopyranosyl)-D-glucose?

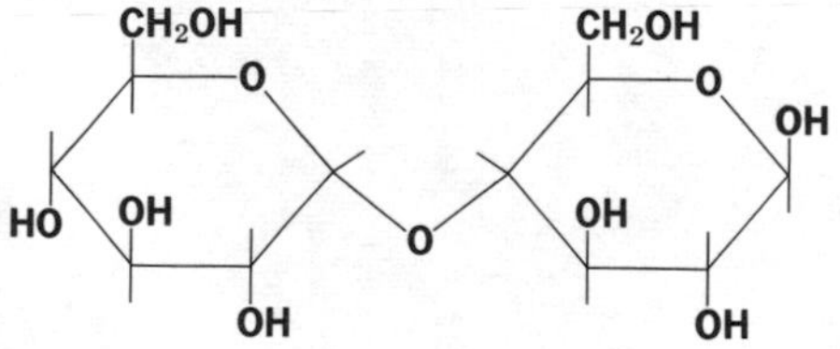

I

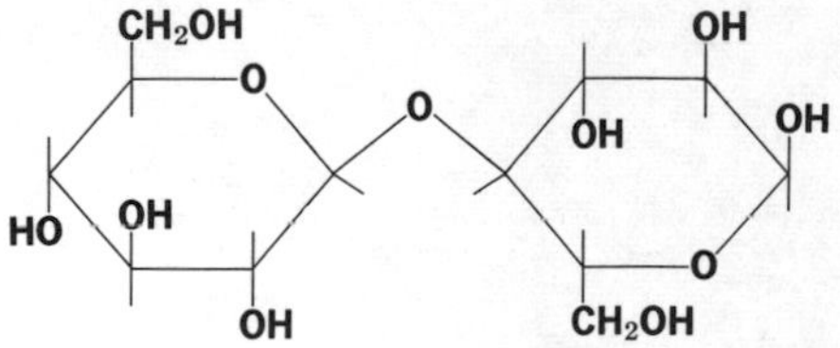

II

III

IV

CHAPTER

ACIDS AND THEIR DERIVATIVES; LIPIDS AND DETERGENTS

When a hydroxyl group is attached directly to a carbonyl carbon atom, a new

functional group results: the carboxyl group, $-\overset{\overset{\textstyle O}{\|}}{C}OH$. Compounds containing the carboxyl group are acids, because they ionize slightly in water to give a proton and are neutralized by base. Organic acids are generally weak compared to mineral acids and are only slightly dissociated in aqueous solution; nevertheless, their ability to form stable salts, even with the weak base sodium bicarbonate, gives them distinctive physical and chemical properties. Figure 11-1 lists the strengths of various hydroxylic acids.

The dissociation constant K_a* is the common measure of the strength of an acid; the percentage dissociated in a $1N$ solution is another significant quantity. From the data presented in Fig. 11-1, we can see that acetic acid, although much stronger than ethanol or phenol, is only slightly ionized compared to a strong acid like sulfuric acid. A brief examination of these compounds will help to explain the effect of structure on acidity.

When ethanol ionizes, the negative charge remains behind on a single oxygen atom. In the phenolate ion, the charge resides partly on the benzene ring (Fig. 6-20). Ionization of the carboxyl group creates the carboxylate ion, whose negative charge is spread equally over two oxygen atoms (Fig. 11-2). Both carbon–oxygen bonds in this ion are 1.27 Å long, between C=O and C—O bond lengths of 1.21 and 1.42 Å, respectively. (Compare benzene, Fig. 5-3.) The carboxylate ion

---

* For the definition of K_a see p. 93.

Acid	K_a (approximate)	% Dissociated into H$^+$ in $1N$ Solution
CH$_3$CH$_2$OH ethanol	10^{-16}	0.000001%
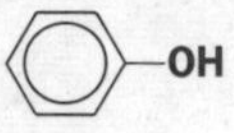 ⬡—OH phenol	10^{-10}	0.001%
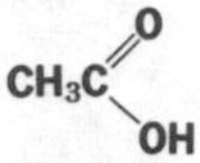 CH$_3$C(=O)OH acetic acid	10^{-5}	0.3%
ClCH$_2$COH(=O) chloroacetic acid	10^{-3}	3%
Cl$_3$CCOH(=O) trichloroacetic acid	10^{-1}	30%
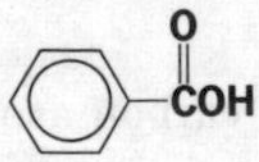 ⬡—COH(=O) benzoic acid	10^{-4}	1%
H$_2$SO$_4$ sulfuric acid	about 1	100%

Fig. 11-1. A comparison of the acidities of some typical hydroxylic acids.

is stabilized by this resonance, and has less tendency to recombine with a proton than, for instance, an alkoxide ion does.

Sulfur is more electronegative than carbon and the bisulfate ion has three oxygen atoms which help stabilize the charge; therefore, sulfuric acid is a still stronger acid. In general, the more oxygen atoms that are available for sharing the

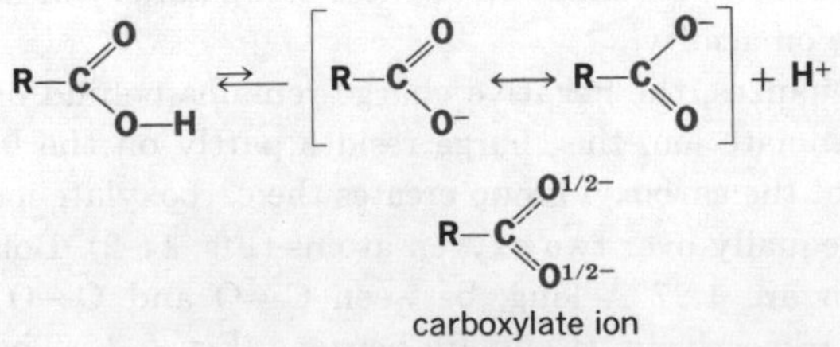

$$R-C\begin{smallmatrix}O\\O-H\end{smallmatrix} \rightleftharpoons \left[R-C\begin{smallmatrix}O\\O^-\end{smallmatrix} \longleftrightarrow R-C\begin{smallmatrix}O^-\\O\end{smallmatrix} \right] + H^+$$

$$R-C\begin{smallmatrix}O^{1/2-}\\O^{1/2-}\end{smallmatrix}$$
carboxylate ion

Fig. 11-2. Ionization of a proton from the carboxyl group yields a carboxylate ion, in which the negative charge is spread over two oxygen atoms.

charge, the stronger the acid. For that reason sulfonic acids (RSOH) are stronger

than sulfinic acids (RSOH), as we saw in Prob. 6-9.

The functional group is not the only factor responsible for the acidity of a compound. Substituents can play an important role in determining the precise K_a. We have already seen in Fig. 6-21 that 2,4,6-trinitrophenol (picric acid) is a strong acid. In carboxylic acids, the substitution of a strongly electronegative group adjacent to the carboxyl group increases its acidity. Thus, chloroacetic acid is 100 times stronger than acetic acid and trichloroacetic acid is a strong acid.

Prob. 11-1. Would you expect fluoroacetic and bromoacetic acids to be stronger or weaker acids than acetic acid?

Aromatic acids have acidic properties similar to those of their aliphatic counterparts. Benzoic acid (m.p. 121°) is a white solid whose dissociation constant is nearly the same as that of acetic acid.

The hydroxyl groups of carboxylic acids have several important influences on the properties of these compounds (Fig. 11-3). As would be expected, acids are

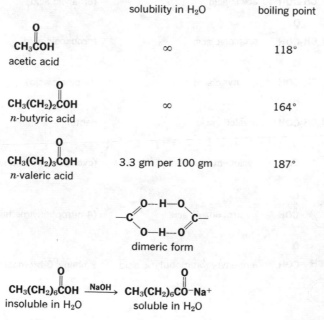

	solubility in H$_2$O	boiling point
CH$_3$COH acetic acid	∞	118°
CH$_3$(CH$_2$)$_2$COH n-butyric acid	∞	164°
CH$_3$(CH$_2$)$_3$COH n-valeric acid	3.3 gm per 100 gm	187°

dimeric form

CH$_3$(CH$_2$)$_6$COH $\xrightarrow{\text{NaOH}}$ CH$_3$(CH$_2$)$_6$CO$^-$Na$^+$
insoluble in H$_2$O   soluble in H$_2$O

Fig. 11-3. Properties of acids. The high boiling points are due to dimer formation. Most acids insoluble in water dissolve in base.

relatively soluble in water. Moreover, those acids which are insoluble in water dissolve in base, since they are converted to ionic salts. Acids have higher boiling points than their molecular weights would suggest. Acetic acid, which has a molecular weight of 60, boils at 118°; this is 20° higher than *n*-propyl alcohol (b.p. 98°), which has the same molecular weight. The reason for this is that acids usually exist as dimers, in which the hydroxyl group of one molecule is hydrogen-bonded to the carbonyl group of another.

NOMENCLATURE

The common names of the acids parallel those of the aldehydes. Acetic acid, which gives vinegar its taste and odor (*L. acetum* = vinegar), is one of many well-known examples. The simplest organic acid, formic acid, gets its name from the red ant *formica rufa* (*L.*) which stings its victims by injecting the acid through its bite. Butyric acid gives rancid butter (*L. butyrum*) its characteristic odor and flavor. Caproic acid can be obtained from the hairs of the goat (*Gr. caper* = goat). Indeed, many organic acids are stronger as odors than as acids.

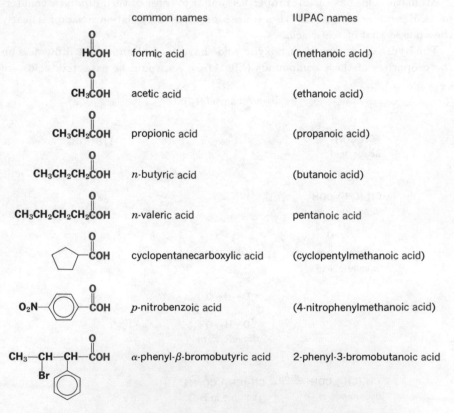

	common names	IUPAC names
HCOH	formic acid	(methanoic acid)
CH₃COH	acetic acid	(ethanoic acid)
CH₃CH₂COH	propionic acid	(propanoic acid)
CH₃CH₂CH₂COH	*n*-butyric acid	(butanoic acid)
CH₃CH₂CH₂CH₂COH	*n*-valeric acid	pentanoic acid
⬠COH	cyclopentanecarboxylic acid	(cyclopentylmethanoic acid)
O₂N—⬡—COH	*p*-nitrobenzoic acid	(4-nitrophenylmethanoic acid)
CH₃—CH—CH—COH	*α*-phenyl-*β*-bromobutyric acid	2-phenyl-3-bromobutanoic acid

Fig. 11-4. Some common and IUPAC names for acids. Names in parentheses, although technically correct, are seldom used.

In the IUPAC nomenclature, the ending -*oic acid* is added to the name of the parent straight-chain hydrocarbon (Fig. 11-4). The carboxyl group is always numbered 1. (See Appendix, Probs. 39, 40, and 41.) Substituted aliphatic acids can also be named by locating the substituent with a Greek letter: The *alpha* (α) position is *adjacent* to the carboxyl group, the *beta* (β) position is next, etc. Acid derivatives of cyclic hydrocarbons are named by attaching the suffix "carboxylic acid" to the name of the hydrocarbon.

Prob. 11-2. Draw the structures of (a) 3-methylbutanoic acid, (b) 2,4-dimethylbenzoic acid, (c) α-methylvaleric acid.

SYNTHESIS

Three general methods are available for the synthesis of simple carboxylic acids in the laboratory: oxidation, hydrolysis of a cyanide, and reaction of a Grignard reagent with carbon dioxide. The first of these methods is preferred for industrial purposes, especially if oxygen in the air can be used as the oxidant. In the laboratory potassium permanganate or sodium dichromate is more commonly used (Fig. 11-5). Aliphatic hydrocarbon groups are oxidized more easily than aromatic

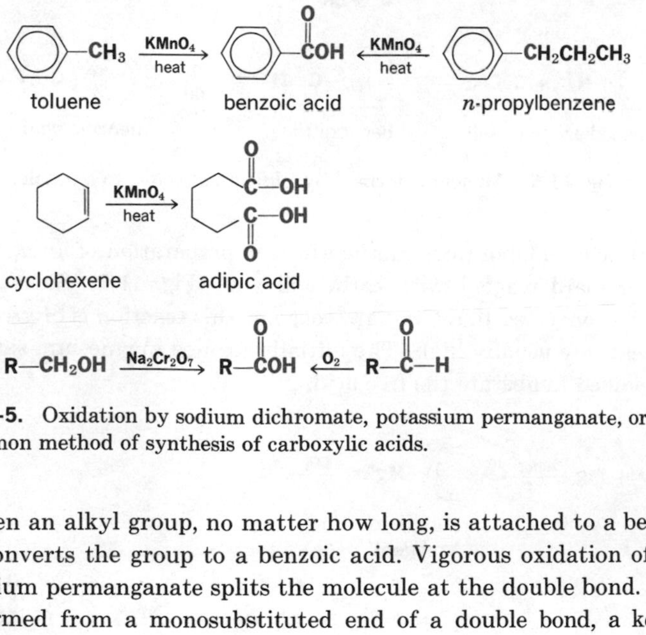

Fig. 11-5. Oxidation by sodium dichromate, potassium permanganate, or air is a common method of synthesis of carboxylic acids.

groups; when an alkyl group, no matter how long, is attached to a benzene ring, oxidation converts the group to a benzoic acid. Vigorous oxidation of an alkene with potassium permanganate splits the molecule at the double bond. A carboxyl group is formed from a monosubstituted end of a double bond, a ketone from a disubstituted end, and carbon dioxide from an unsubstituted end, and so oxidation of a cyclic alkene thus gives a dicarboxylic acid. Primary alcohols and aldehydes are also easily converted to acids by oxidation.

Prob. 11-3. Draw the alkenes that on vigorous permanganate oxidation give the following products:

(a) $CH_3\overset{O}{\overset{\|}{C}}CH_3 + CO_2$

(b) $CH_3(CH_2)_4\overset{O}{\overset{\|}{C}}OH + CH_3CH_2\overset{O}{\overset{\|}{C}}CH_2CH_3$

(c) $CH_3\overset{O}{\overset{\|}{C}}OH$ only

Acids may also be prepared by the hydrolysis of nitriles (organic cyanides), which, in turn, may be prepared by the reaction of primary or secondary halides with sodium cyanide (Fig. 11-6). Since the reaction of a halide with cyanide ion is a displacement reaction, this method cannot be applied to tertiary halides or halides attached to double bonds or benzene rings. However, aromatic nitriles are easily prepared from diazonium salts, and the nitrile hydrolysis reaction is valuable for the synthesis of aromatic acids.

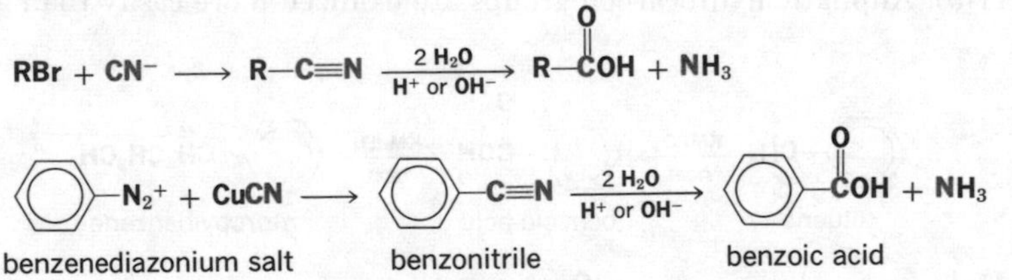

$$RBr + CN^- \longrightarrow R-C\equiv N \xrightarrow[H^+ \text{ or } OH^-]{2 H_2O} R-\overset{O}{\overset{\|}{C}}OH + NH_3$$

Fig. 11-6. An acid is formed by addition of water to a nitrile.

The most general laboratory method for the preparation of an acid is the reaction of a Grignard reagent with carbon dioxide (Fig. 11-7). Since nearly every halide can be converted to a Grignard reagent, this reaction is of great generality and the yields are usually high. The initially formed magnesium salt of the acid must be acidified to liberate the free acid.

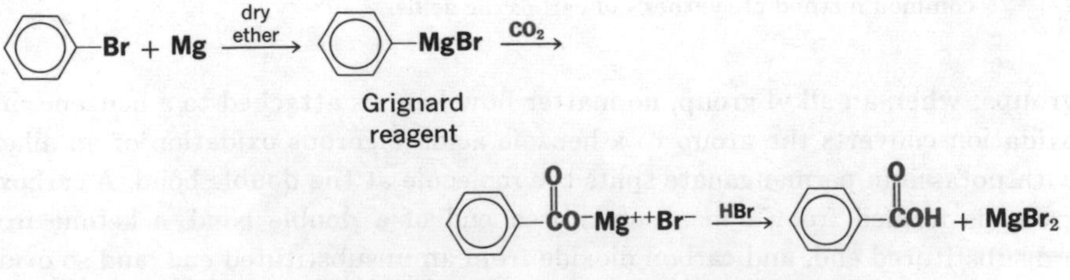

Grignard reagent

Fig. 11-7. The reaction of a Grignard reagent with carbon dioxide is a general method for the synthesis of carboxylic acids.

Prob. 11-4. Why can a Grignard reagent not be prepared from 4-bromo-1-butanol?

SOME IMPORTANT ACIDS

Formic acid (b.p. 101°) has been known since 1670. It occurs in a variety of biting and stinging plants and insects; the stinging nettle contains formic acid and we have already noted its presence in some ants. Industrially, formic acid can be readily prepared by the reaction of carbon monoxide with sodium hydroxide (Fig. 11-8).

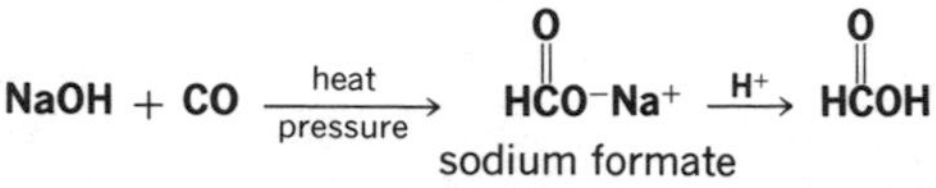

$$NaOH + CO \xrightarrow[\text{pressure}]{\text{heat}} HC\overset{O}{\underset{\text{sodium formate}}{\parallel}}O^-Na^+ \xrightarrow{H^+} HC\overset{O}{\parallel}OH$$

Fig. 11-8. The industrial synthesis of formic acid.

Acidification of the resultant sodium formate and distillation yields pure formic acid. Because it is stronger than acetic acid and is so volatile that any excess can be removed by evaporation, formic acid finds extensive use in the dyeing and textile industry. For instance, cotton cloth may be treated with a mixture of formic acid and soap in a process called "scrooping" to impart a suitable "feel" to the finished product. Formic acid is also a reducing agent, since it is readily oxidized to carbon dioxide by potassium permanganate.

Acetic acid (m.p. 17°, b.p. 118°) is the main constituent of vinegar, obtained by the fermentation of sugar in the presence of air (ethyl alcohol is the product in the absence of air). Industrially, most acetic acid is made, however, by the oxidation of acetaldehyde, which in turn is prepared by the hydration of acetylene. Acetic acid is used in the production of cellulose acetate, discussed at the end of Chapter 10, and for the synthesis of many other esters. Chlorination of acetic acid gives chloroacetic acid which, upon treatment with sodium 2,4-dichlorophenoxide gives the weed killer, 2,4-D (Fig. 11-9).

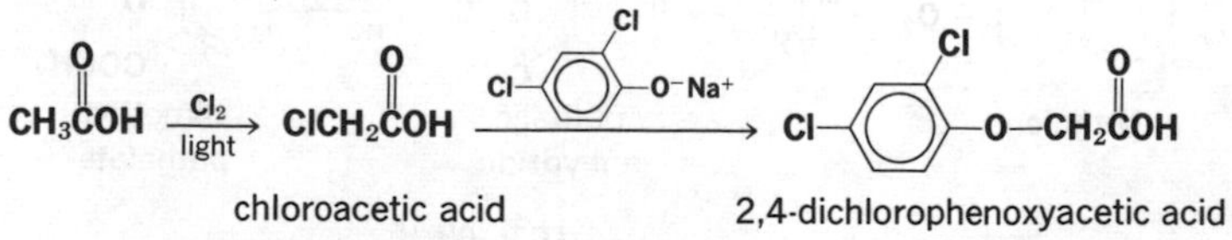

$$CH_3C\overset{O}{\parallel}OH \xrightarrow[\text{light}]{Cl_2} ClCH_2C\overset{O}{\parallel}OH \xrightarrow{} Cl\text{—}\bigcirc\text{—}O\text{—}CH_2C\overset{O}{\parallel}OH$$

chloroacetic acid 2,4-dichlorophenoxyacetic acid (2,4-D)

Fig. 11-9. The synthesis of 2,4-D uses chloroacetic acid.

Undoubtedly the most widely used drug in the world is a derivative of benzoic acid, *o*-hydroxybenzoic acid, whose common name is *salicyclic acid,* prepared from phenol and carbon dioxide (Fig. 11-10). Although the exact mode of action of salicyclic acid is not well understood, the beneficial effects of esters of this acid,

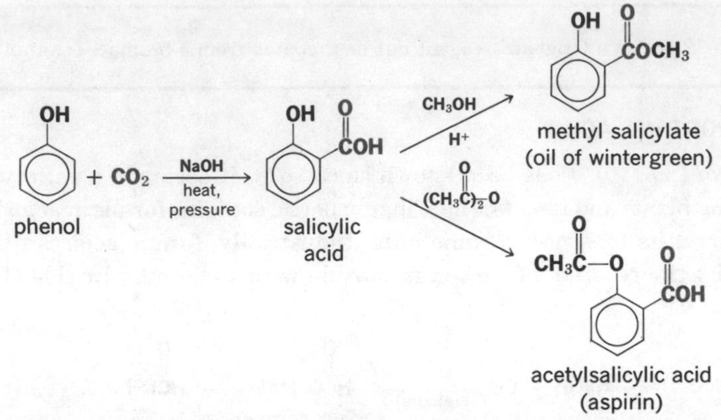

Fig. 11-10. Salicylic acid, methyl salicylate, and acetylsalicylic acids are all important medicinal compounds. The parent acid is prepared from phenol and carbon dioxide.

salicylates, have been known since antiquity: Leaves that contain sizable quantities of these pain- and fever-relieving compounds were prescribed by ancient physicians. Salicyclic acid is the active ingredient of the salicylates and is itself an analgesic or pain killer; it may be taken orally, but it is a strong enough acid to irritate the stomach. Aspirin, its ester with acetic acid, is less acidic and less irritating. The contents of the stomach itself are acidic, and aspirin passes through this organ unchanged; however, under the alkaline conditions in the intestines, it is hydrolyzed to sodium salicylate, which is absorbed through the intestinal walls. Methyl salicylate can also be taken internally or absorbed through the skin, and thus finds much use in liniments and other topical applications.

The *ortho*-dicarboxylic acid of benzene, called *phthalic acid,* is prepared (as its anhydride) by the oxidation of naphthalene by air (Fig. 11-11). This process was

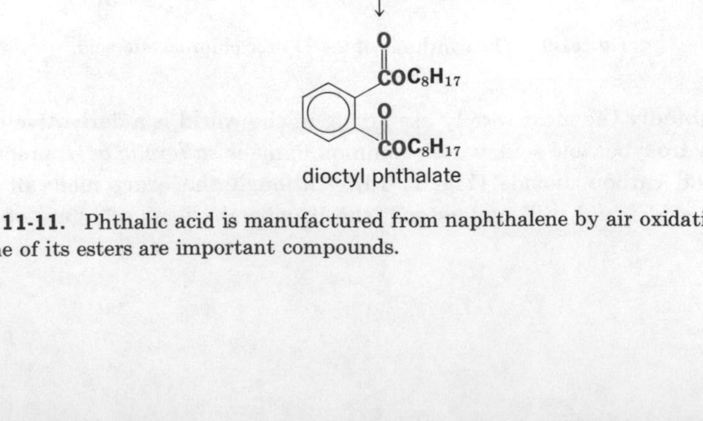

Fig. 11-11. Phthalic acid is manufactured from naphthalene by air oxidation. Some of its esters are important compounds.

developed simultaneously in Germany and in the United States. Before an idea can be patented, however, it must be "reduced to practice." An examination of research notebooks and other data led to the conclusion that the reduction to practice took place on September 4, 1916 in Germany and three days later in the United States, and the patent was therefore awarded to a German firm. Dimethyl phthalate, the ester of phthalic acid with methanol, is an insect repellent. Its diisooctyl ester, used as a plasticizer, softens many commercial polymers or makes them more flexible.

ESTERS

Alcohols react with carboxylic acids, forming organic esters analogous to the esters from alcohols and inorganic oxygen acids discussed earlier. We have seen examples of organic esters in this and prior chapters. In Fig. 11-12, we see the preparation of

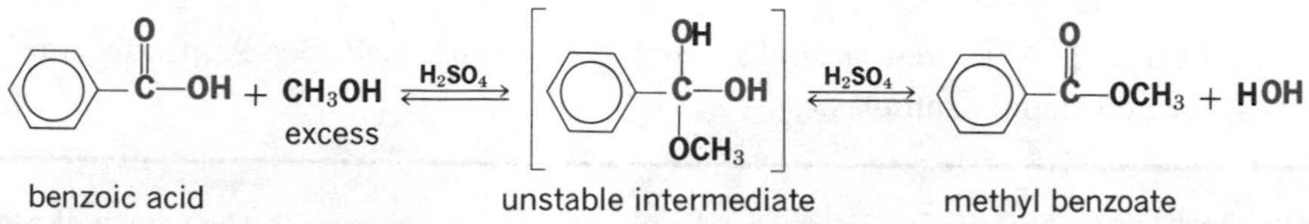

benzoic acid   unstable intermediate   methyl benzoate

Fig. 11-12. An ester is formed by heating an acid with an excess of alcohol and a mineral acid catalyst. The reaction is reversible.

an ester, where benzoic acid is heated in methyl alcohol together with a trace of strong acid catalyst to form the ester *methyl benzoate*. The hydroxyl group in the water formed arises from the carboxylic acid; the proton comes from the alcohol. Addition of the alcohol to the carbonyl group produces an unstable intermediate analogous to a hemiacetal, which loses water. The reaction is reversible. If an excess of alcohol is used, the equilibrium shifts to favor the ester (law of mass action); on the other hand, if an ester is heated with an excess of water and an acid catalyst, it is hydrolyzed to an acid and an alcohol.

Because they can be easily derived from organic acids, esters are called *derivatives* of acids; other acid derivatives will be discussed later in the chapter. Esters are among the most widely distributed organic compounds, and they provide some of our pleasantest smells. Although most of the pleasant odors in nature are due to mixtures of esters, the odor of one ester often predominates. Figure 11-13 cites some common examples, together with illustrations of the nomenclature of esters. In addition to their importance in flavoring agents and perfumes, esters are used in vast quantities commercially as solvents. Still another important use of esters is in the polyester resins, which will be discussed in the next chapter.

In naming esters, it is simplest to identify and cite first the alcohol (in red in Fig. 11-13), then the acid from which the ester is formed. For instance, oil of pineapple could be formed by reaction of *n*-butyl alcohol with *n*-butyric acid. In the ester name, the alkyl group from the alcohol is given first and the ending *-ate* is appended to the root name of the acid. The method is clearly illustrated in *methyl*

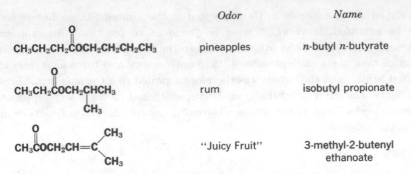

Fig. 11-13. Esters with common agreeable odors. In naming an ester, the name of the alcohol from which it is derived (in red) comes first, followed by the name of the acid with the ending -*ate*. The last compound shown is named by the IUPAC system; it has not been found in nature.

benzoate (Fig. 11-12), from *methyl* alcohol and *benzoic* acid. See Appendix, Probs. 42–44, for additional examples.

Prob. 11-5. Give the structures of the following esters, which occur in the odor indicated:
(a) methyl *n*-butyrate (apple)
(b) *n*-octyl acetate (orange)
(c) isoamyl acetate (banana)
Isoamyl alcohol, isopentyl alcohol, and 3-methyl-1-butanol are different names for the same compound.

Esters are neutral substances. They are less soluble in water and much lower boiling than acids of the same molecular weight, since carboxylic hydroxyl groups are no longer available for hydrogen bonding. For example, methyl *n*-butyrate is nearly insoluble in water, and methyl formate (molecular weight 60) has a b.p. of 32°. The most important reaction an ester undergoes is its reaction with water, which regenerates the alcohol and acid from which the ester was formed. The process is called *hydrolysis,* from the Greek words *hydro* meaning water and *lysis* meaning loosening; hydrolysis therefore means a *cleavage with water.*

In the absence of a catalyst, the reaction is slow. If acid is used as the catalyst, the reaction is much faster, but an equilibrium develops and hydrolysis is never complete. If an alkali such as sodium hydroxide is used to speed the hydrolysis, however, one of the products (the carboxylic acid) is removed from the equilibrium by conversion to its salt, which does not react with the other product, the alcohol (Fig. 11-14). In this way the equilibrium is drawn to completion by Le Chatelier's principle* and hydrolysis is complete. For this reason ester hydrolysis is usually carried out in basic solution. The mechanism of basic hydrolysis involves, first, an

---

* This famous principle states that if a stress is applied to a system at equilibrium, the system readjusts, if possible, to reduce the stress.

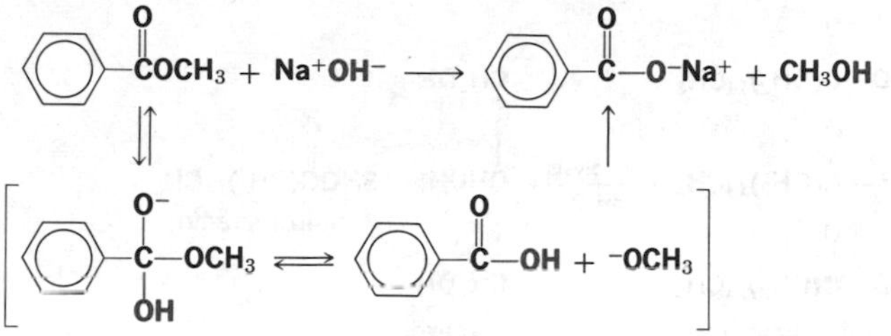

Fig. 11-14. When alkali is used to hydrolyze an ester (a process known as *saponification*), a salt of the acid is formed. Since the salt does not react with the other product (the alcohol), the reaction is forced to completion.

addition of hydroxide ion to the carbonyl group, followed by loss of alkoxide ion from the intermediate. The reaction is completed by reaction of the strong base, alkoxide ion, with the weak carboxylic acid.

LIPIDS: FATS AND OILS

The general term "lipids" includes both fats and oils. Animal and vegetable fats and oils are all esters formed from long-chain carboxylic acids and the triol glycerol (Fig. 11-15). Palm oil, for instance, contains glyceryl tripalmitate, formed from glycerol and palmitic acid. A number of other acids found naturally as esters of glycerol have been given the general name *fatty acids*. The acids may be either saturated or unsaturated. The double bonds of the unsaturated fatty acids are in the *cis* configuration. Nearly all fatty acids that occur naturally have an even number of carbon atoms.

Usually two or three different fatty acids are combined with one glycerol molecule in natural lipids. A compound of this sort is called a mixed triglyceride; one containing only one fatty acid is a simple triglyceride. In glycerides, the end positions of glycerol are referred to as α-positions, the middle position as the β-position.

Although the fatty acids listed in Fig. 11-15 are among the commonest in fats and oils, a wide variety of others have also been found. Among the unusual fatty acids recently discovered are malvalic acid, occurring in very small amounts in cottonseed oil, and sterculic acid, found in the oil of seeds from an Indian tree (Fig. 11-16). Both acids contain the exceedingly strained and reactive cyclopropene ring. The parent cyclic hydrocarbon, cyclopropene, has been prepared in the laboratory and polymerizes spontaneously at $-70°$. At high feeding levels, the two acids are toxic to chickens and pigs, and when hens are fed seed oils containing small quantities of malvalic or sterculic acid they lay eggs in which the "whites" are streaked with an unpleasant red color.

Fats are solids, whereas oils are liquids. Since the only physical difference between a fat and an oil is one of melting point, some lipids are fats in the arctic and oils in the tropics. As a rule, esters of short-chain acids have lower melting points. Moreover, esters of unsaturated fatty acids have lower melting points than those of saturated esters, so that oils usually have a high percentage of oleic,

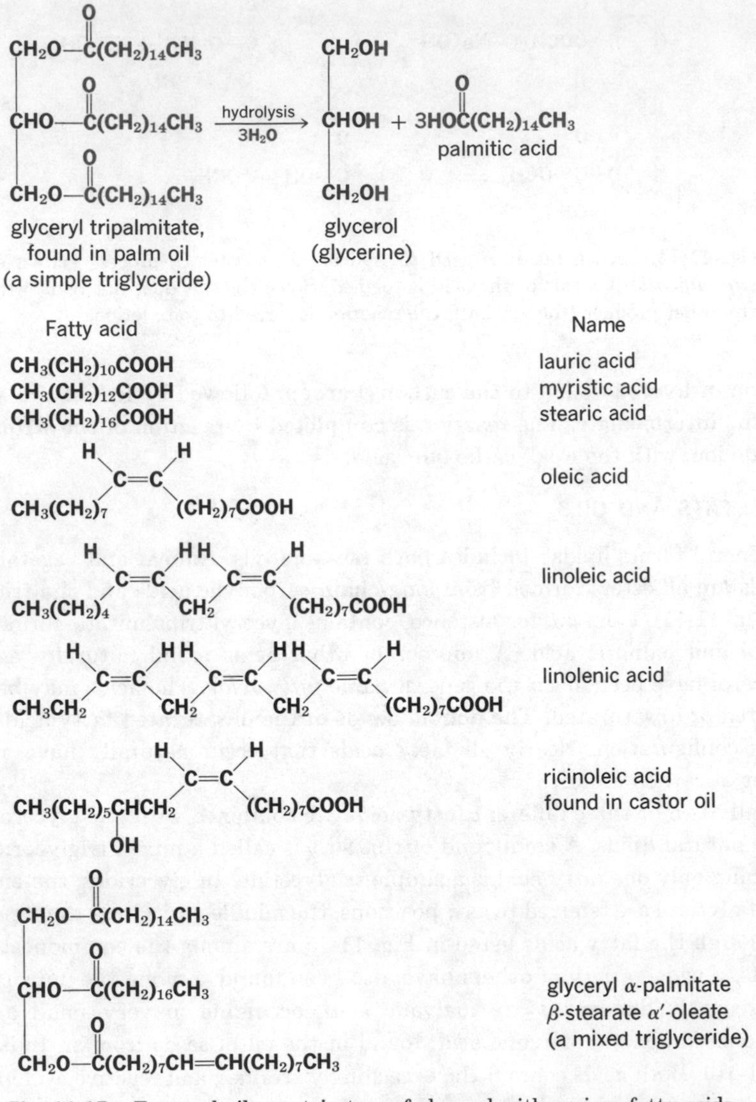

$$
\begin{array}{c}
\underset{\displaystyle \text{O}}{\text{CH}_2\text{O}-\overset{\text{O}}{\text{C}}(\text{CH}_2)_{14}\text{CH}_3} \\[4pt]
\text{CHO}-\overset{\text{O}}{\text{C}}(\text{CH}_2)_{14}\text{CH}_3 \\[4pt]
\text{CH}_2\text{O}-\overset{\text{O}}{\text{C}}(\text{CH}_2)_{14}\text{CH}_3
\end{array}
\xrightarrow[\text{3H}_2\text{O}]{\text{hydrolysis}}
\begin{array}{c}
\text{CH}_2\text{OH} \\[4pt]
\text{CHOH} \\[4pt]
\text{CH}_2\text{OH}
\end{array}
+\ 3\text{HO}\overset{\text{O}}{\text{C}}(\text{CH}_2)_{14}\text{CH}_3
$$

glyceryl tripalmitate,   glycerol   palmitic acid
found in palm oil   (glycerine)
(a simple triglyceride)

Fatty acid	Name
$CH_3(CH_2)_{10}COOH$	lauric acid
$CH_3(CH_2)_{12}COOH$	myristic acid
$CH_3(CH_2)_{16}COOH$	stearic acid

$$CH_3(CH_2)_7 \overset{\text{H}}{\underset{}{C}}=\overset{\text{H}}{\underset{}{C}}(CH_2)_7COOH$$ oleic acid

$$CH_3(CH_2)_4 \;C=C\; CH_2 \;C=C\; (CH_2)_7COOH$$ linoleic acid

$$CH_3CH_2 \;C=C\; CH_2 \;C=C\; CH_2 \;C=C\; (CH_2)_7COOH$$ linolenic acid

$$CH_3(CH_2)_5CHCH_2 \;C=C\; (CH_2)_7COOH \atop OH$$ ricinoleic acid
found in castor oil

$$
\begin{array}{c}
\text{CH}_2\text{O}-\overset{\text{O}}{\text{C}}(\text{CH}_2)_{14}\text{CH}_3 \\[4pt]
\text{CHO}-\overset{\text{O}}{\text{C}}(\text{CH}_2)_{16}\text{CH}_3 \\[4pt]
\text{CH}_2\text{O}-\overset{\text{O}}{\text{C}}(\text{CH}_2)_7\text{CH}=\text{CH}(\text{CH}_2)_7\text{CH}_3
\end{array}
$$

glyceryl α-palmitate
β-stearate α′-oleate
(a mixed triglyceride)

Fig. 11-15. Fats and oils are triesters of glycerol with various fatty acids.

linoleic, linolenic, and other fatty acids containing double bonds. Reduction of the double bonds, by hydrogenation, for instance, often converts an oil into a fat (Fig. 11-17).

Animals generally produce fats, like lard and butter, whereas plants produce oils, like corn, cottonseed, and soybean oils. Since most people living in the United States and northern Europe prefer to eat fats to oils, a major industry has developed for the hydrogenation of oils. Oleomargarine is produced in this way from cottonseed, soybean, or corn oil, and peanut oil is hydrogenated to give a peanut

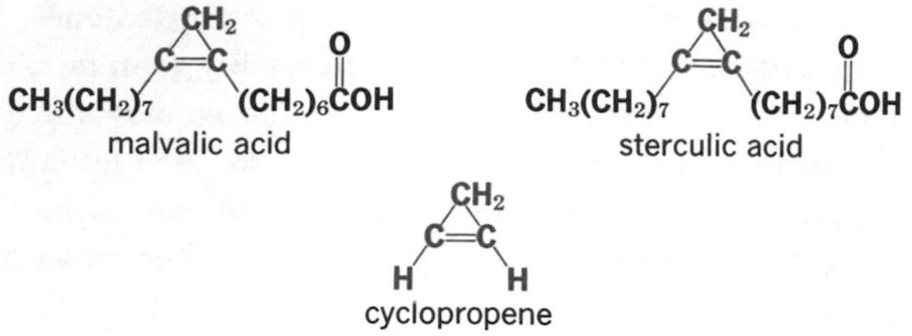

Fig. 11-16. Two unusual fatty acids found in nature, and the strained cyclic hydrocarbon to which they are related.

butter in which the oil does not separate. On the other hand, some evidence has been presented that unsaturated triglycerides are metabolized more easily than saturated ones and lead to less cholesterol in the blood. Thus, sales of highly unsaturated oils like safflower seed oil are increasing.

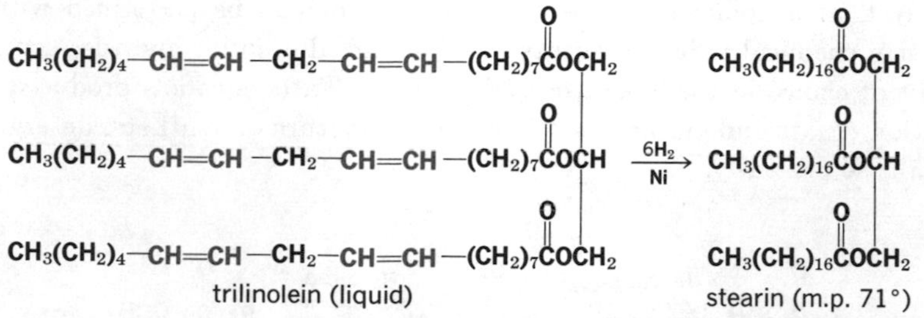

Fig. 11-17. Hydrogenation of an oil often converts it to a fat. Linoleic acid is a major constituent of the triglycerides of cottonseed oil, while stearic acid is found in the triglycerides of lard.

As might be inferred from their saturated character, fats are among the most stable of all organic compounds, rivaling petroleum in this regard. Centuries ago the Irish were in the habit of burying butter in large wooden kegs. The butter would turn rancid, but the butyric acid and other fluid or volatile products were eventually leached out or evaporated and the residue resembled cheese. Tubs of such "bog butter" buried in the eleventh to fourteenth centuries have been unearthed in modern times and found to be in edible condition.*

A similar phenomenon occurs in the decomposition of animal tissue. A waxy substance *adipocera* is often the only portion remaining from a body buried several hundred years in moist ground.†

---

* "Butter to eat with their hog
  was seven years buried in a bog"
          —*17th Century Rhyme*

† "In a hydropicall (dropsical) body ten years buried in a church yard, we met with fat concretion, where the nitre of the Earth, and the salts and lixivious liquor of the body, had coagulated large lumps of fat, into the consistence of the hardest castle-soap (Castile soap), whereas part remaineth with us"—Sir Thomas Browne (1658)

Unsaturated molecules oxidize more easily than saturated ones. Therefore, oils turn rancid by air oxidation during storage more readily than fats, though natural fats also contain some unsaturated esters and undergo slow air oxidation. This tendency of oils to react with oxygen can be put to good advantage in certain cases. Since oxygen has unpaired electrons, it is able to initiate a free-radical polymerization of highly unsaturated oils. These oils, known as drying oils, are used in paints, varnishes, and lacquers. When spread in a thin film by painting, the individual molecules are exposed to oxygen, polymerization ensues, and the whole surface is converted into gigantic molecules. Certain metallic salts, such as cobaltic stearate, are commonly added to catalyze the polymerization. Linoleum is produced by polymerizing unsaturated esters into a high molecular weight plastic together with other materials which add body to the product (binders) or color it (pigments).

Reduction of an acid produces an alcohol, and reduction of an ester, two alcohols. This can be carried out cheaply by high temperature hydrogenation, using a catalyst, as is commonly done commercially, or can be performed with more expensive chemical reducing agents like lithium aluminum hydride, usually the reagent of choice in the laboratory (Fig. 11-18). Fatty alcohols produced by the reduction of fats and oils are used in the manufacture of synthetic detergents, as we shall see presently.

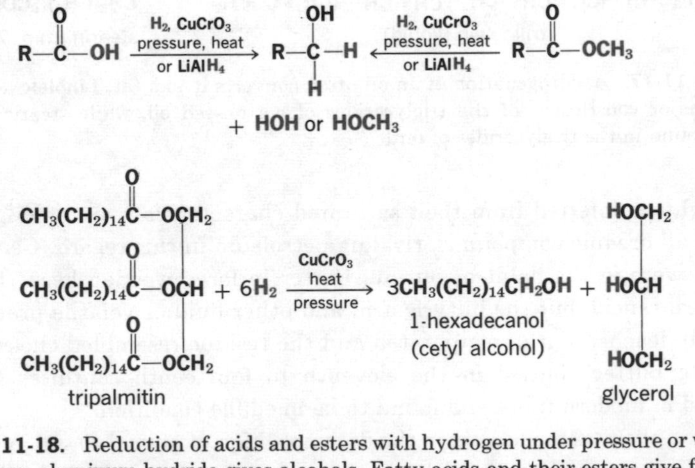

Fig. 11-18. Reduction of acids and esters with hydrogen under pressure or with lithium aluminum hydride gives alcohols. Fatty acids and their esters give fatty alcohols, as shown.

Fatty alcohols are also found in nature as components of *waxes*. Plant waxes are usually complex mixtures of organic materials of high molecular weight which coat leaves and stems in hot or arid regions and reduce evaporation of moisture. *Carnauba wax,* used as floor wax and in carbon paper, coats the leaves of the carnauba palm which grows along river banks in Brazil. The leaves are cut up and beaten against saw horses in airtight buildings to collect the wax. *Beeswax* is secreted by eight wax glands of the bee. Approximately one pound of wax is produced for each eight pounds of honey. Since insects have a high surface to volume ratio, many are coated with a protective layer of wax to retard evaporation of moisture.

Although waxes are usually complex mixtures of compounds, esters composed of long-chain fatty acids and long-chain fatty alcohols are always important constituents. Cetyl palmitate, an ester of cetyl alcohol, $CH_3(CH_2)_{14}CH_2OH$, and palmitic acid is the wax *spermaceti* from the sperm whale.

SALTS: SOAPS AND SYNTHETIC DETERGENTS

If an organic acid is treated with a base, a salt is formed, just as with an inorganic acid (Fig. 11-19). Organic salts, the most readily prepared acid derivatives, are named by indicating the positive ion first, and then appending -*ate* to the name of

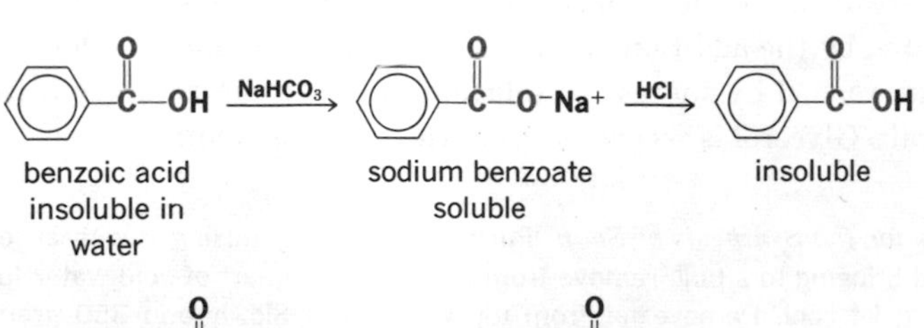

benzoic acid
insoluble in
water

sodium benzoate
soluble

insoluble

$$CH_3\overset{O}{\overset{\|}{C}}O^-\ \overset{+}{N}H_4$$
ammonium acetate

$$CH_3CH_2\overset{O}{\overset{\|}{C}}O^-\ \overset{+}{H_3}NCH_2CH_3$$
ethylammonium propionate

Fig. 11-19. Salts are prepared from acids by treatment with bases, including ammonia and organic bases. The acid is regenerated on treatment of the salt with mineral acid.

the acid. Salts have a bacteriostatic action, so that calcium and sodium propionate are added to bakery goods to prevent mold growth and sodium benzoate is a preservative for cider. Although the simplest carboxylate salts are formed from inorganic bases, there are also salts of carboxylic acids and amines, such as ethylammonium propionate.

Prob. 11-6. How could you separate, by using ether and hydrochloric acid, sodium hydroxide and sodium bicarbonate solutions, a mixture of benzoic acid, *p*-cresol (*p*-methylphenol), and *p*-xylene (*p*-dimethylbenzene)?

Salts of long-chain fatty acids are known as soaps. Hydrolysis of a fat or oil with alkali produces a soap and glycerol (Fig. 11-20). The process of soap-making has been known since antiquity, when the necessary lye was leached from the ashes of a fire. Even now, the home production of soap makes an interesting, economical (the cost is only a few cents a cake), and instructive experiment. (See recipe given

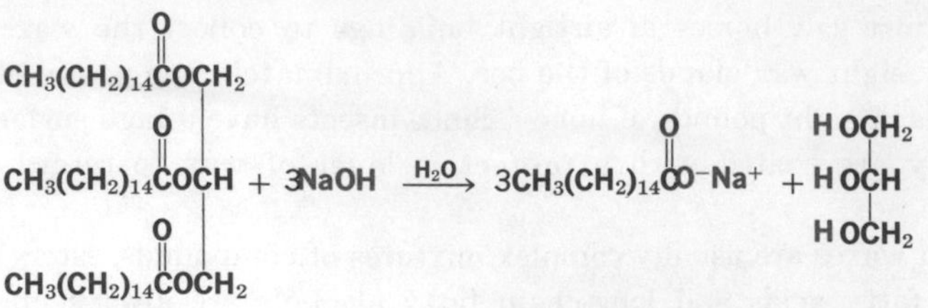

$$
\begin{array}{c}
\quad\quad\quad\overset{O}{\underset{\|}{}} \\
CH_3(CH_2)_{14}COCH_2 \\
\quad\quad\quad\overset{O}{\underset{\|}{}}\quad\quad\quad\quad\quad\quad\quad\quad O\quad\quad\quad H\,OCH_2 \\
CH_3(CH_2)_{14}COCH + 3NaOH \xrightarrow{H_2O} 3CH_3(CH_2)_{14}CO^-Na^+ + H\,OCH \\
\quad\quad\quad\overset{O}{\underset{\|}{}}\quad\quad\quad\quad\quad\quad\quad\quad\quad\quad\quad\quad\quad\quad H\,OCH_2 \\
CH_3(CH_2)_{14}COCH_2
\end{array}
$$

tripalmitin   sodium palmitate   glycerol
                                                   a soap

Fig. 11-20. Basic hydrolysis of a fat gives glycerol and the salts of the fatty acids, which are soaps.

below; Fig. 11-21). Industrially, molten tallow (the fat of cattle and sheep) is treated with a slight excess of alkali in large vats. The mixture is heated through coils, and steam is bubbled through it. After hydrolysis is complete, the soap is precipitated by the addition of an inorganic salt like sodium chloride and is then filtered and washed by successive solution in water and reprecipitation with the inorganic salt. Glycerol is recovered from the aqueous solutions.

■ *A Recipe for the Synthesis of Soap:* Purify bacon fat by mixing it with an equal amount of water and bringing to a boil; remove from fire, add one quart of cold water for each gallon of liquid, and let cool. Remove fat from top when firm. Slowly add 350 grams of sodium hydroxide to 1200 ml of cold water. Melt six pounds (2700 grams) of fat, cool it to 30° (85°F), pour the lye solution at 24° (75°F) into the melted fat in a slow steady stream with slow even stirring. Continue stirring for ten minutes until the material has the texture of thick honey. Pour into a wooden or heavy cardboard box lined with damp cotton cloth and cover with an old blanket or rug to retain heat. Let stand 24 hours, cut into bars and let age in a dry place for two weeks. *Warning:* Do not use glass, stoneware, or aluminum containers.

Fig. 11-21. Assuming that the consumption of bacon is not increased to get the fat, one can make soap in this way for only a few cents a cake.

Potassium salts of fatty acids are the usual liquid soaps. Aluminum salts of fatty acids form gels; mixed with gasoline, these gels are used in flame-throwers and napalm bombs.

Calcium, magnesium, and iron salts of fatty acids are insoluble, and precipitate. So-called "hard water" contains appreciable quantities of one or more of these three ions. When a sodium or potassium soap is put in hard water, the calcium, magnesium, or iron salt precipitates, forming a deposit on clothes or bathtub. Water is "softened" by removing calcium, iron, and magnesium ions, usually by replacing them with sodium ions in a water softener.

Soap cleans, primarily, because of its ability to emulsify fats, oils, greases, and other organic molecules. Most dirt, for instance, is held to clothes by a thin film of oil. If the oil is removed, the dirt can be rinsed away. A suspension of tiny oil droplets in water is an emulsion. If pure oil and water are shaken together briefly and allowed to stand, the two layers are regenerated after a short time. However, if a little soap is added to the mixture before shaking, a cloudy emulsion forms, with the oil dispersed in the form of tiny droplets throughout the water. This emulsion is indefinitely stable, showing no tendency to separate into layers of oil and water.

Soap owes its remarkable ability to act as an emulsifying agent to the curious combination of polar and nonpolar sites in its structure. Regarded from one end, a soap is a highly ionic salt, attracted to water (hydrophilic) and repelled by organic solvents (lipophobic). From the other end, a soap is a long-chain hydrocarbon, repelling water (hydrophobic) and attracting organic solvents (lipophilic). If a little soap is added to water, the hydrophilic carboxylate ends dissolve in the water, but the hydrophobic hydrocarbon ends do not. As a consequence, soap makes a film on water one molecule thick, and accumulates on the surface of water. The surface tension of water is drastically reduced by this film. Therefore, water containing a little soap will wet glass, for instance, more readily than will pure water.

Soap also seeks out the interface between a layer of oil and water, with the carboxylate end dissolved in the water and the hydrocarbon end dissolved in the oil. If the oil is dispersed into tiny droplets throughout the water by shaking or stirring, soap molecules arrange themselves around the surface of each drop (Fig. 11-22). Since the surface of each drop is negatively charged, the drops repel one another and do not coalesce into a separate oil layer. The oil is then emulsified in the water.

To be effective, a soap must be only moderately soluble in water, and so the short-chain and the extremely long-chain fatty acids are ruled out; soaps containing 12 to 20 carbon atoms are the most useful. Ordinarily soap has a higher specific gravity than water, but this can be reduced by blowing air into molten soap; in this way floating soaps are manufactured.

For many purposes, the tendency of soaps to form insoluble precipitates in hard water is a great disadvantage. It was recognized many years ago that if the

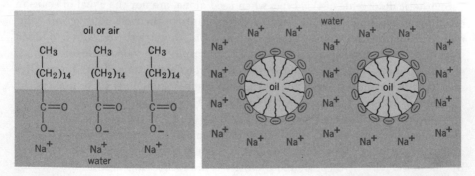

Fig. 11-22. The carboxylate end of a soap molecule dissolves in water; the hydrocarbon end dissolves in oil or is attracted to other molecules of the same composition.

carboxyl group of a soap could be replaced by a sulfonate group, $-\overset{\overset{O}{\parallel}}{\underset{\underset{O}{\parallel}}{S}}-O^-$,

an equally good detergent would be produced, whose calcium and magnesium salts would not precipitate. Two general methods are commercially important for the manufacture of synthetic detergents (Fig. 11-23). In the first and historically earlier method, a long-chain alcohol is allowed to react with sulfuric acid to form

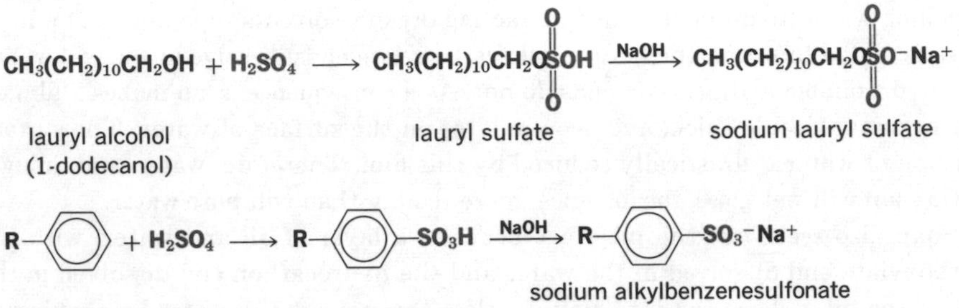

$$CH_3(CH_2)_{10}CH_2OH + H_2SO_4 \longrightarrow CH_3(CH_2)_{10}CH_2O\overset{\overset{O}{\parallel}}{\underset{\underset{O}{\parallel}}{S}}OH \xrightarrow{NaOH} CH_3(CH_2)_{10}CH_2O\overset{\overset{O}{\parallel}}{\underset{\underset{O}{\parallel}}{S}}O^- Na^+$$

lauryl alcohol   lauryl sulfate   sodium lauryl sulfate
(1-dodecanol)

$$R-\langle \bigcirc \rangle + H_2SO_4 \longrightarrow R-\langle \bigcirc \rangle-SO_3H \xrightarrow{NaOH} R-\langle \bigcirc \rangle-SO_3^- Na^+$$

sodium alkylbenzenesulfonate

Fig. 11-23. Two important commercial methods for the synthesis of synthetic detergents. The group R is a long-chain alkyl group.

an alkyl sulfate ester. Neutralization with sodium hydroxide then gives a synthetic detergent. As early as 1860, a commercial process was in use to produce a synthetic detergent from castor oil, which has a high percentage of the hydroxyl-containing fatty acid, ricinoleic acid (Fig. 11-15). More recently, pure fatty alcohols from the hydrogenation of fats and oils have been used. In the commonest type of synthetic detergent, a benzene ring containing a long-chain alkyl group is sulfonated with concentrated sulfuric acid. This method of synthesis can be quite inexpensive, because the alkene needed for the alkyl group R, usually a mixture of isomers and homologs, can be obtained from petroleum.

Synthetic detergents of this type, when used alone, are not the equal of soaps in cleaning power, but two important additives improve their cleaning power enormously. Sodium tripolyphosphate is used as a *builder;* it has the ability to break up and suspend certain clays, pigments, and other finely divided solids in aqueous solution and also to form complexes with numerous metal ions. Other phosphates also have detergent action of their own, and when combined with sulfonates the cleansing powers of both are greatly enhanced. Heavy duty household detergents also contain ½ to 1% of carboxymethylcellulose (CMC), prepared by the reaction of cellulose and chloroacetic acid in basic solution. This polymeric material has the ability to prevent redeposition of the dirt on the fabric once it has been removed by the detergents. Other common additives are whitening agents and sudsing enhancers or repressors; and, if the product is a powder, varying amounts of a granular salt like sodium sulfate are added to provide a satisfactory consistency.

The sulfonate detergents (sometimes called sulfonics) have been plagued, unfortunately, by a major and increasing problem—disposability. Soaps may be removed from waste water by precipitation or by degradation by bacteria in sewage treatment plants; many sulfonate detergents, which are neither precipitated nor readily metabolized, cannot be removed this way. They remain indestructibly in suspension, foaming away, clogging municipal waste disposal plants, polluting streams. Many companies and government agencies have joined in seeking to solve this problem.

The chief difficulty lies in the nature of the alkyl group R- in the alkylbenzene-sulfonates. Microorganisms in sewage disposal plants can attack straight-chain alkyl groups and oxidize them, ultimately, to carboxyl groups; the resulting benzoic acids do not foam. However, these microorganisms cannot degrade highly branched alkyl groups, like that resulting from alkylation with tetrapropylene (Fig. 3-23); these semi-insoluble alkylbenzenesulfonates foam. The solution has been to employ straight-chain alkenes like 1-dodecene in alkylation. Although these are somewhat more expensive at the present time, increased research and greater demand will bring their price down.

In general, any molecule having a long hydrocarbon tail and a water soluble head has soaplike properties. "Invert" or "cationic" soaps are another interesting class of detergents (Fig. 11-24). In these molecules, the positively charged ammo-

$$CH_3(CH_2)_{14}CH_2-\overset{\overset{\displaystyle CH_3}{|}}{\underset{\underset{\displaystyle CH_3}{|}}{N^+}}-CH_3 \ Cl^-$$

trimethyl-*n*-hexadecylammonium chloride

$$CH_3(CH_2)_{14}\overset{\overset{\displaystyle O}{\|}}{C}-OCH_2-\overset{\overset{\displaystyle CH_2OH}{|}}{\underset{\underset{\displaystyle CH_2OH}{|}}{C}}-CH_2OH$$

pentaerythrityl palmitate

Fig. 11-24. Two synthetic detergents: a cationic soap and an ester of the tetra-hydroxy alcohol, pentaerythritol. In each case, the end of the molecule shown in red is soluble in water.

nium group is attached to a long-chain hydrocarbon. These molecules are usually toxic to bacteria, and are used in medicinal soaps. Since they are positively charged, they cannot precipitate with metal ions. Some soaps are not salts at all, but owe their hydrophilic properties to an accumulation of hydroxyl groups at one end. A typical example is formed from palmitic acid and pentaerythritol.

Prob. 11-7. Show how one could prepare the compounds of Fig. 11-24 from palmitic acid and any other desired compounds.

OTHER DERIVATIVES OF ACIDS

The hydroxyl portion of the carboxyl group may be replaced by a number of groups other than alkoxyl to form new derivatives of acids (Fig. 11-25). Replacement by halogens leads to *acid halides* and replacement by amino groups gives *amides*. Compounds formed from two carboxyl groups with loss of water (two carboxyl groups joined through an oxygen atom) are known as *acid anhydrides*.

derivative	ending	example	boiling point
$R\overset{O}{\underset{}{-\!\overset{\|}{C}\!-}}Cl$	-yl chloride or -oyl chloride	$CH_3\overset{O}{\underset{}{\overset{\|}{C}}}\!-\!Cl$ acetyl chloride	52°
$R\overset{O}{\underset{}{-\!\overset{\|}{C}\!-}}O\overset{O}{\underset{}{-\!\overset{\|}{C}\!-}}R$	-ic anhydride or -oic anhydride	$CH_3\overset{O}{\overset{\|}{C}}\!-\!O\!-\!\overset{O}{\overset{\|}{C}}CH_3$ acetic anhydride	140°
$R\overset{O}{\underset{}{-\!\overset{\|}{C}\!-}}OR'$	-ate or -oate	$CH_3\overset{O}{\overset{\|}{C}}\!-\!OCH_3$ methyl acetate	57°
$R\overset{O}{\underset{}{-\!\overset{\|}{C}\!-}}NH_2$	-amide	$CH_3\overset{O}{\overset{\|}{C}}\!-\!NH_2$ acetamide	222°

Fig. 11-25. A summary of the common derivatives of acids. The derivatives are arranged in decreasing order of reactivity.

Acid halides are the most reactive of the common derivatives of acids; they are also much lower boiling than the acids from which they are prepared, just as alkyl chlorides are much lower boiling than the alcohols from which they are prepared. In general, the methods of synthesizing acid chlorides parallel those of synthesizing alkyl chlorides, except that hydrogen chloride is not effective in the preparation of acid chlorides (Fig. 11-26). Acid halides have strong, acrid odors, and are extremely painful to the eyes. Since they are so reactive, they are exceedingly

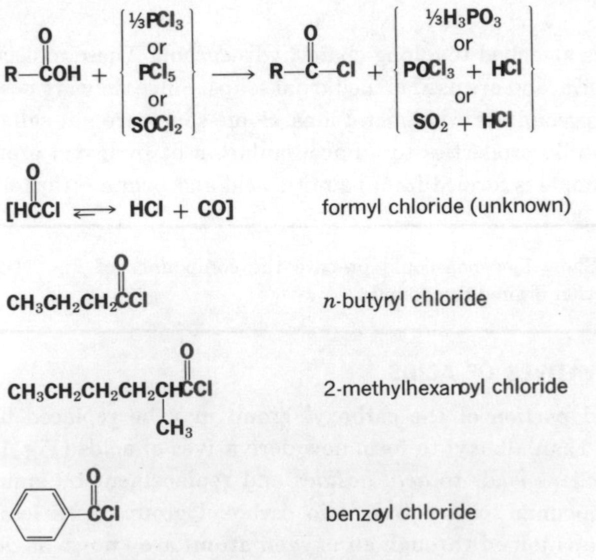

$$R\overset{O}{\overset{\|}{-COH}} + \begin{Bmatrix} \tfrac{1}{3}PCl_3 \\ or \\ PCl_5 \\ or \\ SOCl_2 \end{Bmatrix} \longrightarrow R\overset{O}{\underset{}{-\overset{\|}{C}-}}Cl + \begin{Bmatrix} \tfrac{1}{3}H_3PO_3 \\ or \\ POCl_3 + HCl \\ or \\ SO_2 + HCl \end{Bmatrix}$$

$[H\overset{O}{\overset{\|}{C}}Cl \rightleftharpoons HCl + CO]$ formyl chloride (unknown)

$CH_3CH_2CH_2\overset{O}{\overset{\|}{C}}Cl$ n-butyryl chloride

$CH_3CH_2CH_2CH_2\underset{\underset{CH_3}{|}}{CH}\overset{O}{\overset{\|}{C}}Cl$ 2-methylhexanoyl chloride

$\underset{}{\bigcirc}\overset{O}{\overset{\|}{C}}Cl$ benzoyl chloride

Fig. 11-26. Synthesis and nomenclature of acid chlorides.

useful in preparing other compounds; they react with alcohols to form esters, with ammonia to form amides, and with water to form acids.

Acid anhydrides are formed by elimination of a molecule of water between two molecules of acid, or by loss of sodium chloride in reaction of an acid chloride with a sodium salt (Fig. 11-27). Acid anhydrides react readily with water and alcohols to form acids and esters, respectively. With ammonia or amines they form amides.

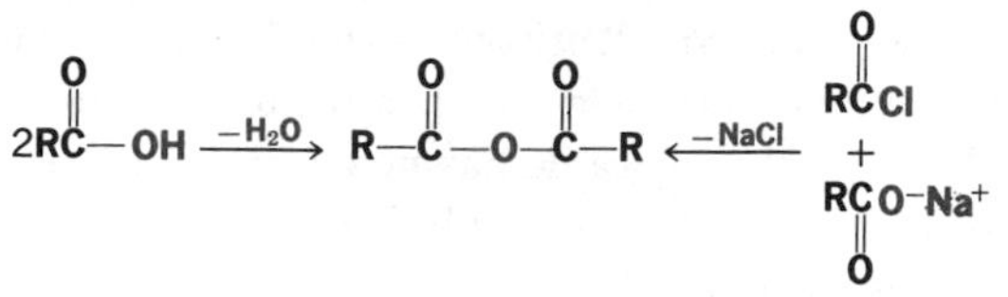

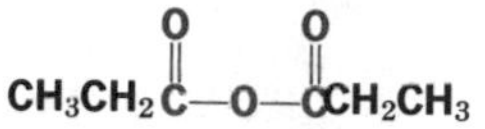

CH₃CH₂C—O—CCH₂CH₃   propionic anhydride

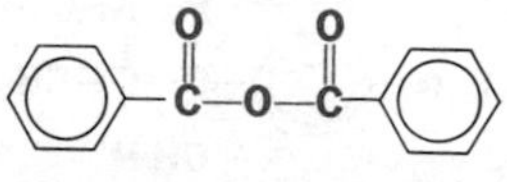

benzoic anhydride

Fig. 11-27. Acid anhydrides may be formed by dehydration of acids or by reaction of an acid halide with the salt of an acid.

When the hydroxyl group of an acid is replaced by an —NH₂ group, —NHR group, or —NR₂ group, an *amide* is produced. These compounds are neutral, as noted in Fig. 8-10. The amide linkage is strong, and amide groups constitute

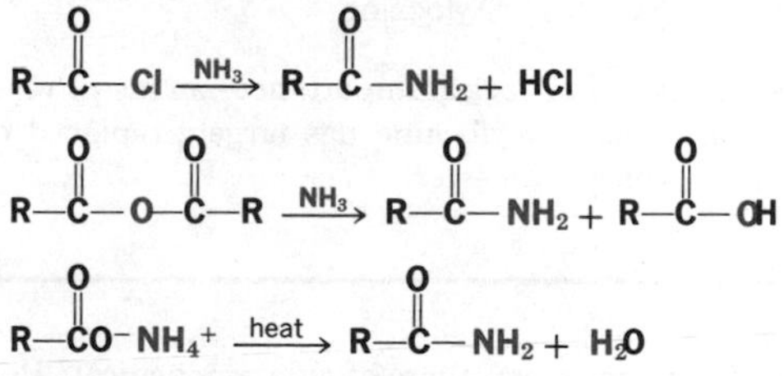

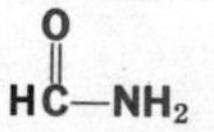

HC—NH₂   formamide

CH₃C—NHCH₂CH₃   N-ethylacetamide

HOCH₂CH₂C—NH₂   3-hydroxypropanamide

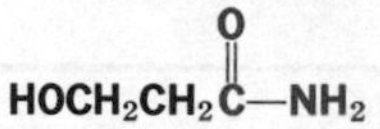

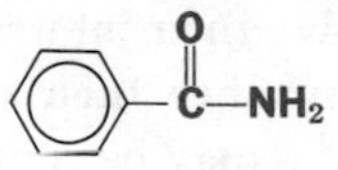

benzamide

Fig. 11-28. Amides may be synthesized by the reaction of acid halides, anhydrides, or esters with ammonia or amines. Amides are also prepared by heating ammonium salts of organic acids.

the repeating units in the backbone of protein molecules,* in Nylon, and in other industrial polymers. They are prepared by treating the more reactive acid derivatives with ammonia or amines or by heating an amine salt of a carboxylic acid above its melting point. Figure 11-28 shows three methods for the synthesis of amides and contains examples of their nomenclature.

Many relatively simple amides are also important in biology. For example, one of the most effective insect repellents is the N,N-diethyl amide of m-toluic acid; the commonest local anesthetic in dentistry, Xylocaine, is the 2,6-dimethylphenylamide of N,N-diethylaminoacetic acid; and the antibiotic chloramphenicol has the structure shown (Fig. 11-29). Xylocaine has now largely replaced the older Novocaine, because body enzymes rapidly hydrolyze an ester linkage of the latter compound, rendering it inactive.

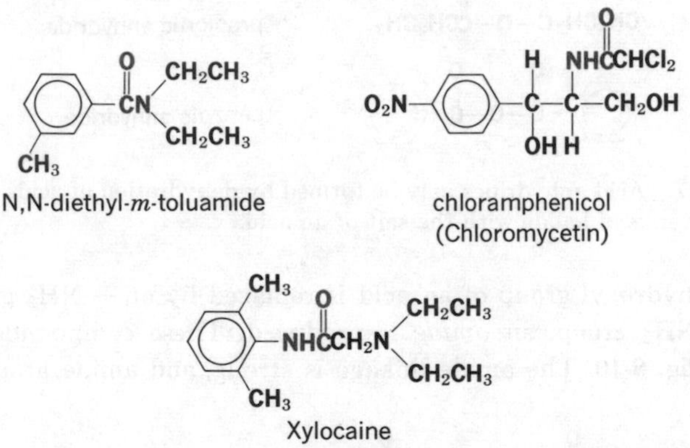

N,N-diethyl-m-toluamide   chloramphenicol
                                             (Chloromycetin)

Xylocaine

Fig. 11-29. Three amides of biological importance—an insect repellent, an antibiotic, and a local anesthetic. Xylocaine has largely replaced the older local anesthetic Novocaine, which is an ester.

Prob. 11-8. How many diastereomers are there of chloramphenicol? How many are optically active?

Prob. 11-9. Suggest an IUPAC name for chloramphenicol.

Many of the reactions of acid derivatives involve their interconversion. In learning these interconversions, it is helpful to remember their order of reactivity, which is summarized in Fig. 11-30. Any derivative may be converted to any other below it by reaction with the appropriate reagent on the left. In order to go up the

* See Chapter 13.

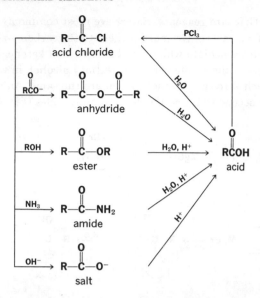

Fig. 11-30. In this chart, the common derivatives of acids are arranged in order of decreasing reactivity.

scale, the free acid must be prepared first. The most reactive derivative, an acid halide, may be converted into an anhydride, an ester, or an amide in one step, simply by reaction with an acid salt, an alcohol, or ammonia. An anhydride readily forms an ester or amide, but cannot be converted directly into an acid halide in the laboratory. An ester gives an amide with ammonia, but cannot be converted into an anhydride or acid halide.

Prob. 11-10. Using Fig. 11-30, show how you would convert (a) benzoic anhydride to N-methylbenzamide, (b) ethyl propionate to propionic anhydride.

REACTIONS WITH GRIGNARD REAGENTS

Since a carboxylic acid contains an acidic hydrogen atom, its reaction with a Grignard reagent forms the salt of the acid and a hydrocarbon. A similar reaction takes place with an amide (Fig. 11-31). Other derivatives of acids give alcohols

$$R-\overset{O}{\underset{|}{C}}-OH + CH_3MgBr \longrightarrow R-\overset{O}{\underset{|}{C}}-O^-Mg^{++}Br^- + CH_4\uparrow$$

$$R-\overset{O}{\underset{|}{C}}-NH_2 + CH_3MgBr \longrightarrow R-\overset{O}{\underset{|}{C}}-NH^-Mg^{++}Br^- + CH_4\uparrow$$

Fig. 11-31. Acids and amides give salts and hydrocarbons with Grignard reagents.

in reactions with Grignard reagents. Esters are most commonly used in this synthesis. Addition of one mole of Grignard reagent to the carbon–oxygen double bond gives an unstable intermediate which breaks down to a ketone. A second mole of Grignard then adds to the ketone, giving a tertiary alcohol, in which at least two of the groups attached to the carbinol carbon are the same. An exactly analogous series of reactions occurs with acid halides and anhydrides (Fig. 11-32).

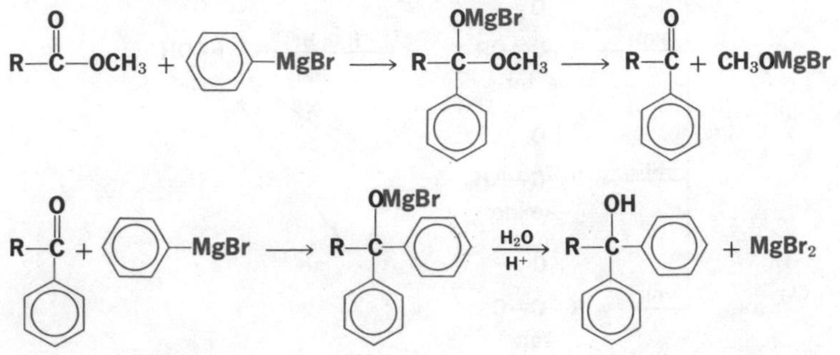

Fig. 11-32. An ester (or an acid halide or an anhydride) reacts with *two* moles of a Grignard reagent to form a tertiary alcohol.

Ordinarily it is not possible to make and isolate a ketone through reaction of an ester or other acid derivative with only one mole of Grignard reagent. However, other organometallic reagents can carry out this useful conversion (Fig. 11-33). An organocadmium compound, for instance, formed from a Grignard reagent by reaction with cadmium chloride, yields a ketone when treated with an acid chloride. Furthermore, an organolithium reagent is able to react with the salt of an acid to form, after hydrolysis, a ketone. A Grignard reagent is not reactive enough to react under ordinary conditions with the already negatively charged carboxylate ion.

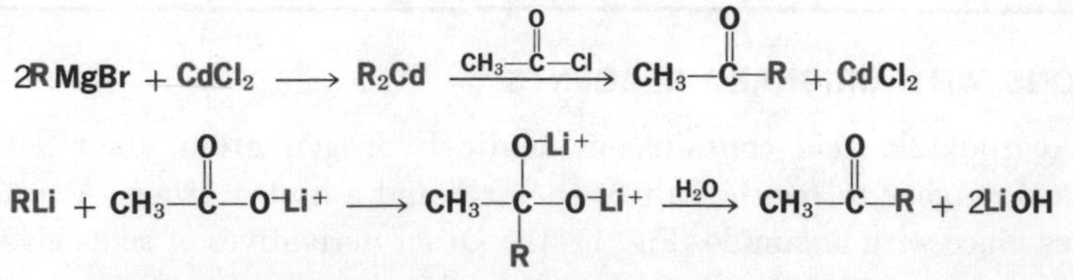

Fig. 11-33. Two methods for the synthesis of ketones from acid derivatives.

NITRILES

Nitriles do not contain carbonyl groups like the other acid derivatives of this chapter. Nevertheless, they can be derived from acids and it is convenient at this point to consider their reactions, which show many similarities to those of esters.

CH$_3$C≡N   acetonitrile

CH$_3$CH$_2$C≡N   propionitrile

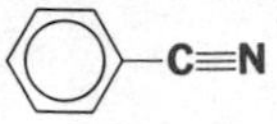

⬡—C≡N   benzonitrile

$$RC≡N \underset{POCl_3}{\overset{H_2O,\ H^+}{\rightleftharpoons}} R\overset{O}{\overset{\|}{C}}NH_2 \overset{H_2O}{\underset{H^+}{\longrightarrow}} R\overset{O}{\overset{\|}{C}}OH$$

$$R—C≡N + CH_3MgBr \longrightarrow R—\underset{CH_3}{\overset{}{C}}=NMgBr \overset{H_2O}{\longrightarrow} R—\underset{CH_3}{\overset{}{C}}=NH \overset{H_2O}{\longrightarrow} R—\overset{O}{\overset{\|}{C}}—CH_3$$

$$R—C≡N \underset{LiAlH_4}{\overset{H_2/Pd}{\underset{or}{\longrightarrow}}} R—CH_2NH_2$$

Fig. 11-34. In addition to their usefulness as intermediates in the synthesis of acids and amides, nitriles give good yields of ketones when treated with Grignard reagents; they may also be reduced to primary amines.

Nitriles are most conveniently formed by the reaction of halides with cyanide ion or of diazonium salts with cuprous cyanide. Their hydrolysis to acids, which has been discussed before, may be stopped at the amide stage after the addition of one molecule of water (Fig. 11-34).

Prob. 11-11. Give the electronic structures of sodium cyanide and of acetonitrile, showing all valence electrons and charges.

Prob. 11-12. Draw the structure of each of the following:

(a) 2-methylhexanoic acid   (e) palmitic anhydride
(b) ethyl propionate   (f) glyceryl tribenzoate
(c) pentanoyl bromide   (g) potassium propionate
(d) p-nitrobenzamide   (h) isopropyl propionate

Prob. 11-13. Name each of the following:

(a) CH$_3$CHCOH
       | $\overset{O}{\overset{\|}{}}$
       Br

(b) CH$_3$CHCOH
       | $\overset{O}{\overset{\|}{}}$
       CH$_2$CH$_3$

(c) CH$_3$CH$_2$CH$_2$O$\overset{O}{\overset{\|}{C}}CH_3$

(d) ⬡—C$\overset{O}{\overset{\|}{}}$Cl
    with O$_2$N substituent

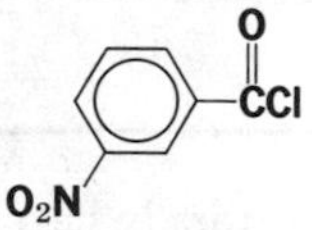

(e) CH$_3$CHCN(CH$_3$)$_2$
       | $\overset{O}{\overset{\|}{}}$
       CH$_3$

Prob. 11-14. What reagents (organic, inorganic, or both) would you use to carry out the following conversions?

(a)

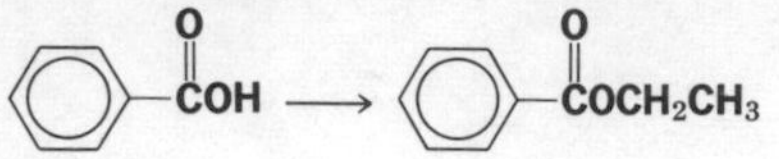

(b) $CH_3(CH_2)_4\overset{O}{\underset{\|}{C}}OCH_3 \longrightarrow CH_3(CH_2)_4CH_2OH$

(c)

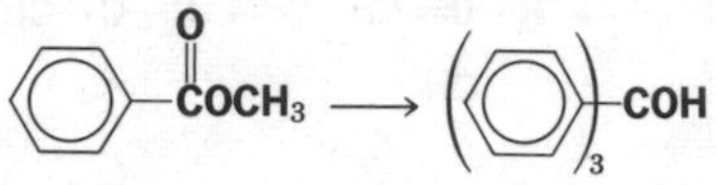

(d) $CH_3(CH_2)_3C\equiv N \longrightarrow CH_3(CH_2)_3\overset{O}{\underset{\|}{C}}OH$

(e)

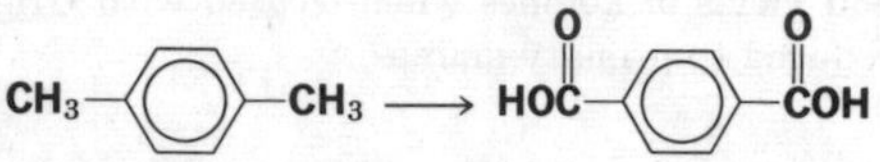

Prob. 11-15. How could you distinguish among the following compounds by simple, visual chemical tests?

(a) $CH_3\overset{O}{\underset{\|}{C}}CH_2CH_2CH_3$, $CH_3CH_2\overset{O}{\underset{\|}{C}}OCH_3$, and $CH_3CH_2\overset{O}{\underset{\|}{C}}OH$

(b)

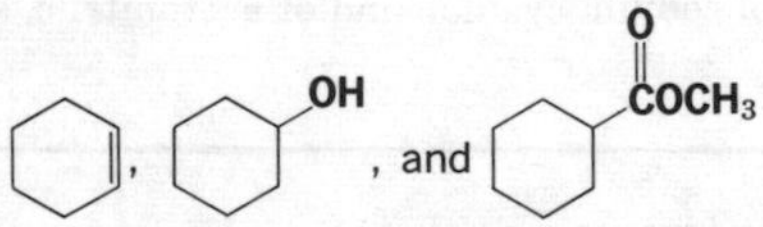

Prob. 11-16. Explain why sodium hydroxide is preferred to hydrochloric acid for use in the hydrolysis of an ester.

Prob. 11-17. It was mentioned on p. 214 that castor oil could, by reaction with sulfuric acid, be converted into a synthetic detergent. Castor oil can also be hydrolyzed to sodium ricinoleate (see ricinoleic acid, Fig. 11-15). Suggest a reason why sodium ricinoleate makes a poor soap.

Prob. 11-18. Most fatty acids that occur naturally have an even number of carbon atoms.

Suggest a method by which a naturally occurring acid $CH_3(CH_2)_{14}\overset{O}{\underset{\|}{C}}OH$ could be converted

to $CH_3(CH_2)_{15}\overset{O}{\underset{\|}{C}}OH$.

Prob. 11-19. How would you carry out each of the following conversions? More than a single step may be required.

(a) C₆H₅—COOH ⟶ (3-bromophenyl)—COOH

(b) C₆H₅—CH₂COOH ⟶ C₆H₅—COOH

(c) C₆H₅—CH₃ ⟶ (3-nitrophenyl)—COOH

CHAPTER

12

DIFUNCTIONAL AND POLYFUNCTIONAL COMPOUNDS. ENOLATE REACTIONS.

Most of the compounds presented thus far have had only a single functional group. In the few cases in which the compound contained more than one functional group, we ordinarily assumed that the groups behaved independently of one another. When such groups are separated from one another, they usually do behave in exactly this manner. For example, a steroid with functional groups in different rings undergoes the reactions expected of each (Fig. 12-1).

Fig. 12-1. The steroid shown, in which the functional groups are well separated from one another, is acetylated like other alcohols, hydrogenated like other alkenes, and forms an oxime like other ketones.

On the other hand, when functional groups are close together, they often affect one another's reactions. We have already seen some examples of such intergroup influences. In conjugated dienes, where two double bonds are adjacent to each other, 1,4-addition usually takes place at the ends of the conjugated system. Sugars exist entirely as hemiacetals, because the hydroxyl and aldehyde groups in the same molecule can easily form 5- and 6-membered rings. This chapter examines in greater detail the results of having two or more functional groups in the same molecule.

UNSATURATED ACIDS

In unsaturated acids such as the naturally occurring fatty acids in Fig. 11-15, in which the double bond and the carboxyl group are separated, the two functional groups react normally. Undecylenic acid (see Fig. 12-2) readily brominates and esterifies. In conjugated unsaturated acids, in which the double bond and carboxyl group are adjacent, there is a mutual interaction, leading to a change in reactivity for both groups. It is possible to brominate and esterify selectively a nonconjugated unsaturated acid in the presence of a conjugated one, because nonconjugated acids react more rapidly in both processes. On the other hand, free-radical catalyzed vinyl polymerization occurs more readily with a vinyl group conjugated to an acid

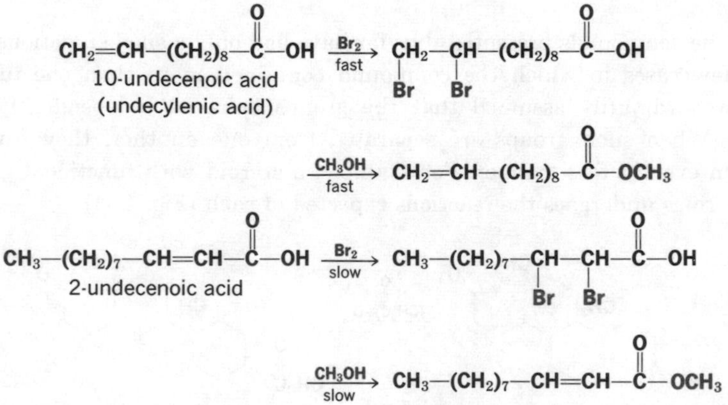

Fig. 12-2. Conjugated unsaturated acids react less readily than unconjugated acids with bromine or alcohol.

or ester group than with an unconjugated double bond. *n*-Butyl acrylate is polymerized between layers of glass in the preparation of some types of safety glass (Fig. 12-3), and methyl methacrylate is a monomer for the synthesis of Lucite and Plexiglass.

Unsaturated acids and their derivatives are usually prepared by dehydration reactions. A sequence which is particularly important in industry is the one which

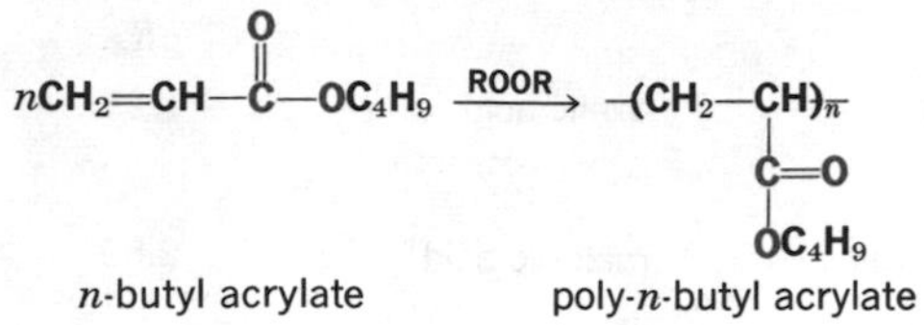

$$nCH_2=CH-\overset{\overset{\displaystyle O}{\|}}{C}-OC_4H_9 \xrightarrow{ROOR} -(CH_2-CH)_{\overline{n}}$$

$$\underset{\substack{| \\ C=O \\ | \\ OC_4H_9}}{}$$

n-butyl acrylate   poly-n-butyl acrylate

Fig. 12-3. Esters of conjugated acids polymerize readily. The polymerization of n-butyl acrylate is used in the preparation of safety glass.

leads to methyl methacrylate. In the first step of this synthesis, hydrogen cyanide is added to acetone to give the hydroxynitrile (cyanohydrin) shown in Fig. 12-4. When this is heated with refluxing methanolic hydrogen chloride, the nitrile is converted to the methyl ester and the alcohol is simultaneously dehydrated.

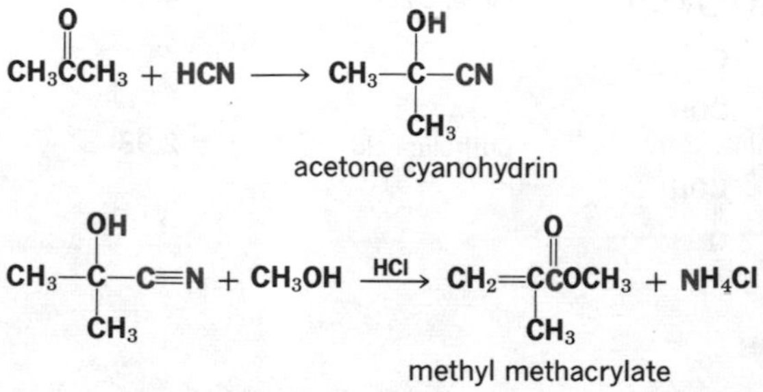

$$CH_3\overset{\overset{\displaystyle O}{\|}}{C}CH_3 + HCN \longrightarrow CH_3-\overset{\overset{\displaystyle OH}{|}}{\underset{\underset{\displaystyle CH_3}{|}}{C}}-CN$$

acetone cyanohydrin

$$CH_3-\overset{\overset{\displaystyle OH}{|}}{\underset{\underset{\displaystyle CH_3}{|}}{C}}-C\equiv N + CH_3OH \xrightarrow{HCl} CH_2=\overset{\overset{\displaystyle O}{\|}}{\underset{\underset{\displaystyle CH_3}{|}}{C}}COCH_3 + NH_4Cl$$

methyl methacrylate

Fig. 12-4. An unsaturated acid or acid derivative is often prepared by dehydration of an alcohol. The preparation of methyl methacrylate involves two steps, the formation of acetone cyanohydrin and its subsequent methanolysis and dehydration.

DIACIDS

Compounds containing two carboxyl groups in the same molecule provide excellent examples of group interactions. These compounds are *diacids*. As simple a property as the degree of dissociation of an acid (as measured by the dissociation constant) is extremely sensitive to the proximity of a second carboxyl group in the same molecule (Fig. 12-5). Thus, oxalic acid, in which these groups are adjacent, is nearly 3,000 times stronger than adipic acid in which the carboxyl groups are separated by four methylene groups. This large increase in acidity is caused by the strong electron-attracting nature of a carboxyl group that stabilizes an adjacent carboxylate anion. This stabilizing effect decreases rapidly with distance and nearly disappears when the two groups are three or four carbon atoms apart.

Several of the diacids are important constituents of *condensation polymers,* that is, polymers formed by the simultaneous elimination of a small molecule like water or alcohol (in contrast to vinyl *addition polymers*). Polyethylene terephthalate, best known as Dacron, is formed from terephthalic acid and ethylene glycol and is an

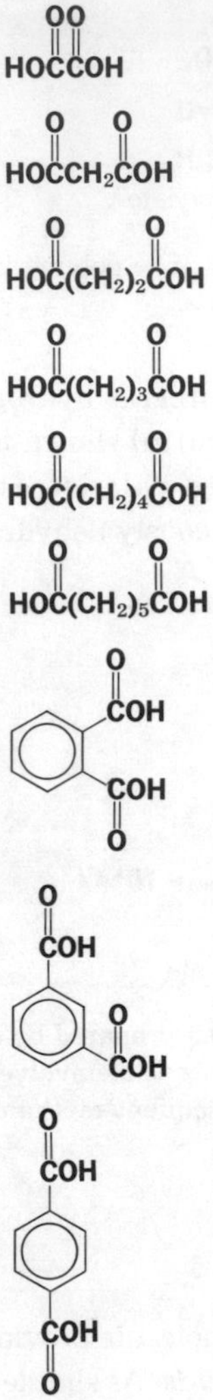

		pK_{a_1}	pK_{a_2}
$\underset{\text{HOCCOH}}{\overset{\text{O O}}{\parallel\parallel}}$	oxalic acid	1.23	4.19
$\underset{\text{HOCCH}_2\text{COH}}{\overset{\text{O O}}{\parallel~~\parallel}}$	malonic acid	2.83	5.69
$\underset{\text{HOC(CH}_2)_2\text{COH}}{\overset{\text{O O}}{\parallel~~~\parallel}}$	succinic acid	4.19	5.48
$\underset{\text{HOC(CH}_2)_3\text{COH}}{\overset{\text{O O}}{\parallel~~~\parallel}}$	glutaric acid	4.34	5.42
$\underset{\text{HOC(CH}_2)_4\text{COH}}{\overset{\text{O O}}{\parallel~~~\parallel}}$	adipic acid	4.42	5.41
$\underset{\text{HOC(CH}_2)_5\text{COH}}{\overset{\text{O O}}{\parallel~~~\parallel}}$	pimelic acid	4.48	5.42
phthalic acid structure	phthalic acid	2.98	5.28
isophthalic acid structure	isophthalic acid	3.46	4.46
terephthalic acid structure	terephthalic acid	3.51	4.82

Fig. 12-5. Examples of important dicarboxylic acids. One carboxyl group is electron-attracting and increases the dissociation of a neighboring acid group. The dissociation of a second proton (as reflected in pK_{a_2}) is more difficult, since a dianion is being produced.

example of this type of polymer. It is formed by heating together dimethyl terephthalate (or terephthalic acid) and ethylene glycol (Fig. 12-6). Methyl alcohol (or water) is split out and a polyester is formed.

Dacron is a linear polymer which typically contains about 80 units per chain, a solid which can be melted without decomposition. The molten polymer is forced through tiny holes in a spinneret and cools and solidifies in the form of a thin fiber. These fibers are then stretched to about five times their original length. During the stretching process the individual polymer molecules become aligned so that

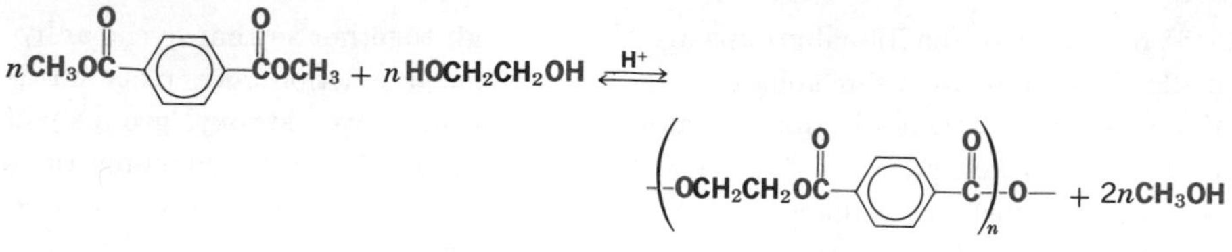

$$n \text{ CH}_3\text{OC} - \bigcirc - \overset{\text{O}}{\underset{}{\text{C}}}\text{OCH}_3 + n \text{ HOCH}_2\text{CH}_2\text{OH} \underset{}{\overset{\text{H}^+}{\rightleftharpoons}}$$

$$\left(-\text{OCH}_2\text{CH}_2\text{OC} - \bigcirc - \overset{\text{O}}{\underset{}{\text{C}}} \right)_n - \text{O} - + 2n\text{CH}_3\text{OH}$$

Fig. 12-6. Polyethylene terephthalate (Dacron) is a polyester prepared from a diester and a diol.

they all lie parallel to the fiber axis; this allows the molecules to pack closely together, making the yarn stronger. Closer packing of the polymer molecules also makes it more difficult for other molecules to penetrate the fiber, and drawn Dacron is more chemically resistant and absorbs less water than the undrawn polymer. For the same reason it is difficult to dye Dacron, since the dye molecules cannot find room between the polyester chains. In the form of a film, this same polyester, polyethylene terephthalate, is known commercially as Mylar. In Europe, this polyester is called Terylene, and the fibers Fortrel and Kodel made in the United States have similar structures. Still other polyesters are prepared from aliphatic diacids.

Formation of a polyester from a triol instead of a diol gives rise to a polymer that is not linear like Dacron but rather highly cross-linked and three dimensional. Common members of this class are the *glyptals,* made from *glyc*erol and *phthalic* acid.

Prob. 12-1. Draw a portion of the structure of a glyptal polymer from phthalic acid and glycerol.

The reactions described thus far for diacids have differed only in degree from those expected for any acid or acid derivative. When two carboxyl groups are close together, however, completely new reactions may occur. This can be seen most clearly by comparing the products formed from heating a number of dicarboxylic acids. The first two members of the series, oxalic and malonic acids, react quite differently from the others, decomposing with the formation of carbon dioxide (Fig. 12-7). All other members of the series lose water with the formation of anhydrides.

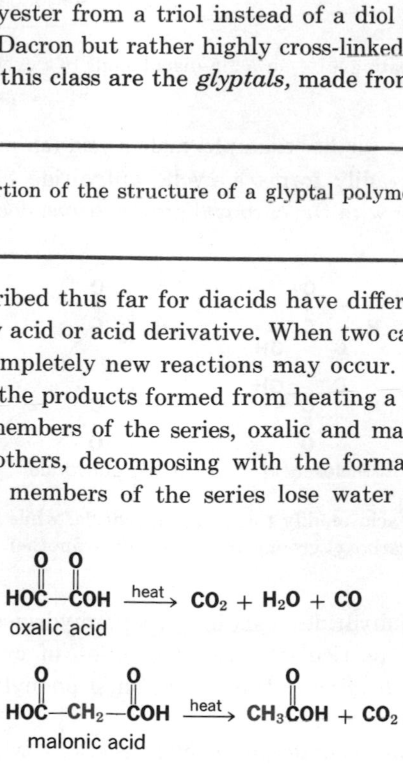

$$\underset{\text{oxalic acid}}{\text{HOC}-\text{COH}} \overset{\text{heat}}{\longrightarrow} CO_2 + H_2O + CO$$

$$\underset{\text{malonic acid}}{\text{HOC}-\text{CH}_2-\text{COH}} \overset{\text{heat}}{\longrightarrow} \text{CH}_3\text{COH} + CO_2$$

Fig. 12-7. Heating oxalic and malonic acids results in the evolution of carbon dioxide.

When the two functional groups are close enough together so that cyclic anhydrides containing 5- or 6-membered rings can be formed, reaction takes place intramolecularly. Separated by four or more carbon atoms, two carboxyl groups will undergo intermolecular reactions. The tendency to form 5- and 6-membered rings is strong in most compounds in which two functional groups are suitably located for interaction (Fig. 12-8). Such intramolecular reactions are especially easy, because the functional groups involved are close to each other and the rings formed

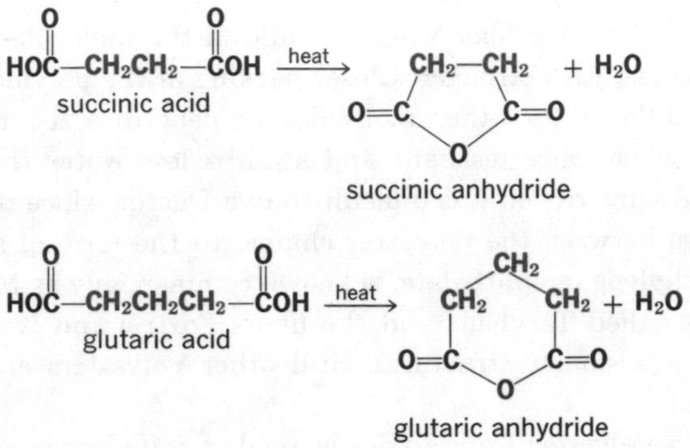

Fig. 12-8. Heating a 1,4- or a 1,5-diacid leads to a cyclic anhydride.

are free from strain. As a further example, maleic acid (an unsaturated diacid with *cis* carboxyl groups) readily forms a cyclic anhydride on heating (Fig. 12-9). Fumaric acid, an isomer with the carboxyl groups *trans,* does not.

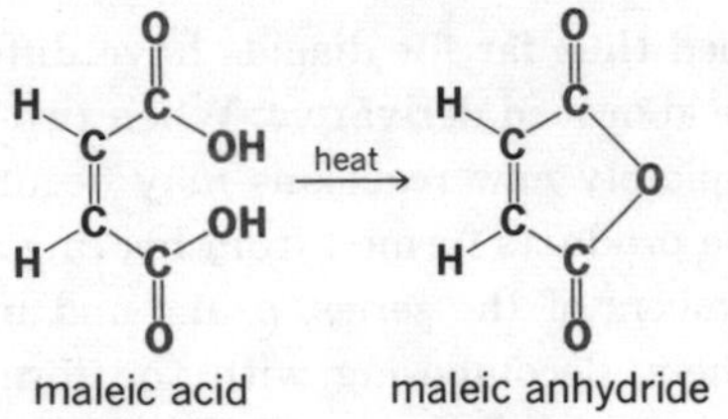

Fig. 12-9. Maleic acid readily forms an anhydride, while its isomer fumaric acid, in which the carboxyl groups are *trans* to one another, does not.

Once formed, cyclic anhydrides react like other anhydrides with alcohols, amines, and other reagents. A particularly useful reaction of cyclic anhydrides is the Friedel-Crafts reaction leading to the formation of phenyl substituted keto acids (Fig. 12-10).

Some dicarboxylic acids undergo special reactions which have chemical or industrial importance. We have already discussed the polymerization of terephthalic

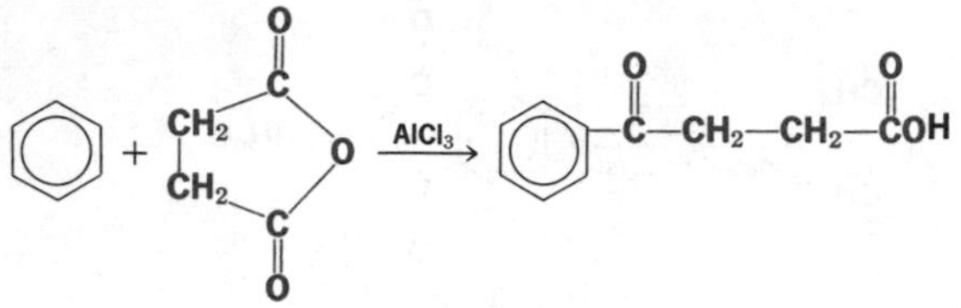

Fig. 12-10. Cyclic anhydrides make useful substrates in the Friedel-Crafts reaction.

acid (or its ester) to Dacron, and the conversion of adipic acid to Nylon will be mentioned in the next section of the chapter. Oxalic acid oxidizes easily; because it is readily obtainable in a pure and dry state it serves as a standard reagent for determining the concentration of oxidizing solutions such as potassium permanganate.

PREPARATION OF DIACIDS

In many cases, simple extensions of the methods used for monoacids are sufficient for the preparation of dicarboxylic acids; succinic acid, for example, may be obtained from ethylene by the sequence of reactions shown in Fig. 12-11. On the

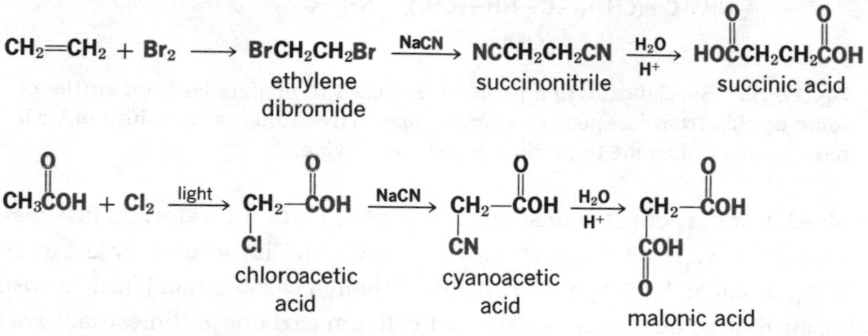

Fig. 12-11. Malonic and succinic acids may be synthesized by reactions analogous to those used for monocarboxylic acids.

other hand, some dicarboxylic acids are prepared by special processes. This is especially true of those acids used in large quantities, such as those involved in the naphthalene (Fig. 11-11) by air oxidation, and o-xylene and terephthalic acid is similarly obtained from p-xylene. Adipic acid (for Nylon) is often prepared industrially by nitric acid oxidation of cyclohexanone (Fig. 12-12).

DERIVATIVES OF CARBONIC ACID

The simplest diacid, and at the same time a juncture between organic and inorganic chemistry, is carbonic acid, H_2CO_3. This is formed when carbon dioxide

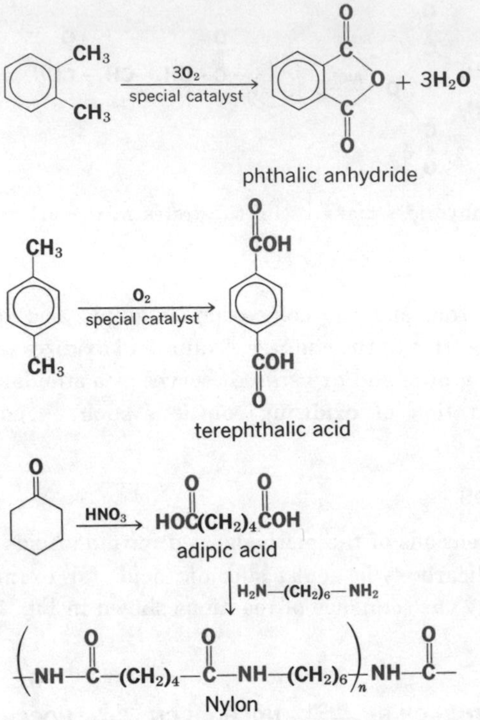

phthalic anhydride

terephthalic acid

adipic acid

Nylon

Fig. 12-12. Special oxidation processes are used to prepare large quantities of some diacids from inexpensive starting materials. Adipic acid is heated with hexamethylenediamine to produce a polymer, Nylon.

is dissolved in water, but it is unstable in the pure state. In water, its first dissociation constant is $K_{a_1} = 4.3 \times 10^{-7}$ ($pK_{a_1} = 6.37$) and its second dissociation constant is $K_{a_2} = 5.6 \times 10^{-11}$ ($pK_{a_2} = 10.25$). Although carbonic acid itself is unstable, its salts, such as sodium bicarbonate and calcium carbonate (limestone) are well-

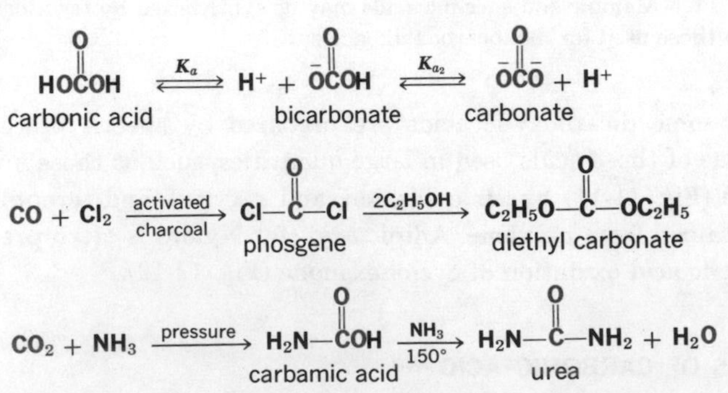

carbonic acid   bicarbonate   carbonate

phosgene   diethyl carbonate

carbamic acid   urea

Fig. 12-13. Carbonic acid is not stable but many of its derivatives are: salts (bicarbonates, carbonates), esters (diethyl carbonate), the acid chloride (phosgene), and the diamide (urea).

known (Fig. 12-13). From an organic chemical standpoint, some of its other derivatives are more interesting. These include diesters like diethyl carbonate, a useful chemical intermediate, carbonyl chloride, $COCl_2$, better known as the war gas phosgene, and urea, whose synthesis from ammonium isocyanate is usually said to have signaled the origin of organic chemistry as a separate science.

Urea is an important compound in industrial organic chemistry as well as in biochemistry. It is an end product of the biological use of proteins and thus plays an important role in nitrogen metabolism. Its greatest industrial use is as a fertilizer and as a reagent in the preparation of barbiturates and polymers. Barbiturates are formed by heating urea with the diethyl ester of malonic acid or its derivatives in which the central hydrogen atoms have been replaced by aryl or alkyl groups (Fig. 12-14). The parent compound, barbituric acid, was first synthesized from diethyl malonate and urea in 1863, but it was not until 1903 that the barbiturates were introduced into medicine. Many hundreds of derivatives of barbituric acid have been prepared since that time; the structures of some which have gained the most medical importance are presented in Fig. 12-14. All of these drugs are habit-forming and available only on prescription.

Urea resins are produced by reaction of urea with formaldehyde. These are cross-linked polymers with the individual chains joined together by methylene groups, and are hard and brittle (Fig. 12-15).

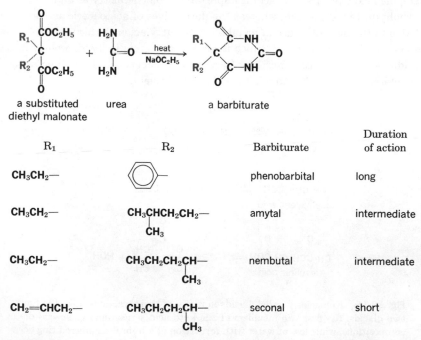

R_1	R_2	Barbiturate	Duration of action
CH_3CH_2-	⬡ (phenyl)	phenobarbital	long
CH_3CH_2-	$CH_3CHCH_2CH_2-$ $\quad\ \ CH_3$	amytal	intermediate
CH_3CH_2-	$CH_3CH_2CH_2CH-$ $\qquad\qquad CH_3$	nembutal	intermediate
$CH_2=CHCH_2-$	$CH_3CH_2CH_2CH-$ $\qquad\qquad CH_3$	seconal	short

Fig. 12-14. Barbiturates are derivatives of barbituric acid ($R_1=R_2=H$), prepared by reaction of urea with substituted diethyl malonates.

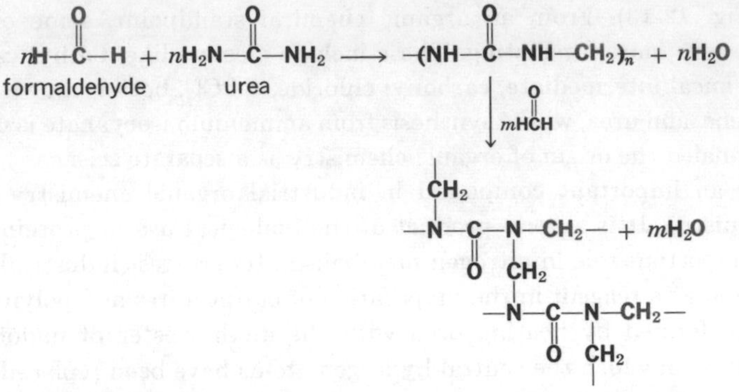

$$n\text{H}-\overset{\overset{\text{O}}{\|}}{\text{C}}-\text{H} + n\text{H}_2\text{N}-\overset{\overset{\text{O}}{\|}}{\text{C}}-\text{NH}_2 \longrightarrow -(\text{NH}-\overset{\overset{\text{O}}{\|}}{\text{C}}-\text{NH}-\text{CH}_2)_{\overline{n}} + n\text{H}_2\text{O}$$

formaldehyde   urea

Fig. 12-15. Resins are formed from the condensation of urea with formaldehyde to give a cross-linked polymer.

KETO ACIDS

Interaction of the two functional groups in compounds containing both a ketonic and a carboxylic component is similar to that found in diacids (Fig. 12-16). Pyruvic acid is much stronger than propionic acid just as oxalic acid is much more acidic than acetic, and acetoacetic acid readily loses carbon dioxide on heating just as malonic acid does. Pyruvic acid is important in biochemistry as an intermediate in carbohydrate metabolism, whereas the derivatives of acetoacetic acid are intermediates in the biosynthesis and metabolism of fatty acids. A third relatively common keto acid is levulinic acid, which is made commercially by vigorously heating an acidic solution of crude hexoses. Pyruvic, acetoacetic, and levulinic acids are often referred to as α-, β- and γ-keto acids, respectively.

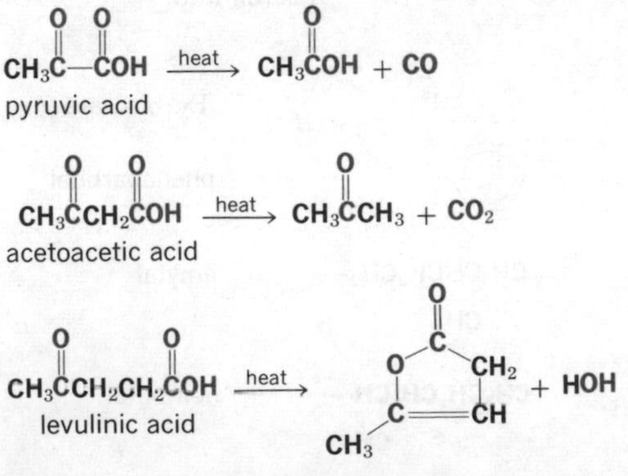

Fig. 12-16. Ketoacids parallel diacids in many of their reactions. Like the first two diacids, the first two members of the keto acid series undergo special decompositions, while loss of water with formation of a 5- or 6-membered ring occurs if possible.

HYDROXY ACIDS

Acids containing hydroxyl groups are prominent in both organic chemistry and biochemistry (Fig. 12-17). Among the most important members of this group are lactic acid, found in muscle and in sour milk, malic acid found in apples, tartaric acid found in wine, citric acid found in oranges, lemons, and other fruit. A number

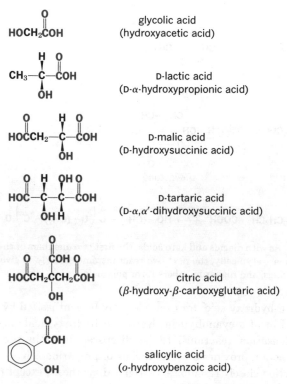

glycolic acid
(hydroxyacetic acid)

D-lactic acid
(D-α-hydroxypropionic acid)

D-malic acid
(D-hydroxysuccinic acid)

D-tartaric acid
(D-α,α'-dihydroxysuccinic acid)

citric acid
(β-hydroxy-β-carboxyglutaric acid)

salicylic acid
(o-hydroxybenzoic acid)

Fig. 12-17. Some common hydroxy acids.

of hydroxy acids (glycolic, lactic, and citric among them) are intermediates in important biosynthetic sequences.

Like keto acids and dicarboxylic acids, hydroxy acids behave differently, depending upon the distance between the hydroxyl and carboxyl groups in the molecule (Fig. 12-18). If the two groups are appropriately placed for the formation of a 5- or 6-membered ring, an internal ester, called a *lactone,* may result. β-Hydroxy acids undergo ready dehydration with the formation of unsaturated acids, and α-hydroxy acids form dimeric esters known as lactides. When the two functional groups are separated by more than four carbon atoms, intermolecular reaction takes place and a polymer may result.

Like most other difunctional compounds, keto and hydroxy acids can often be prepared by the same methods used for the preparation of the monofunctional

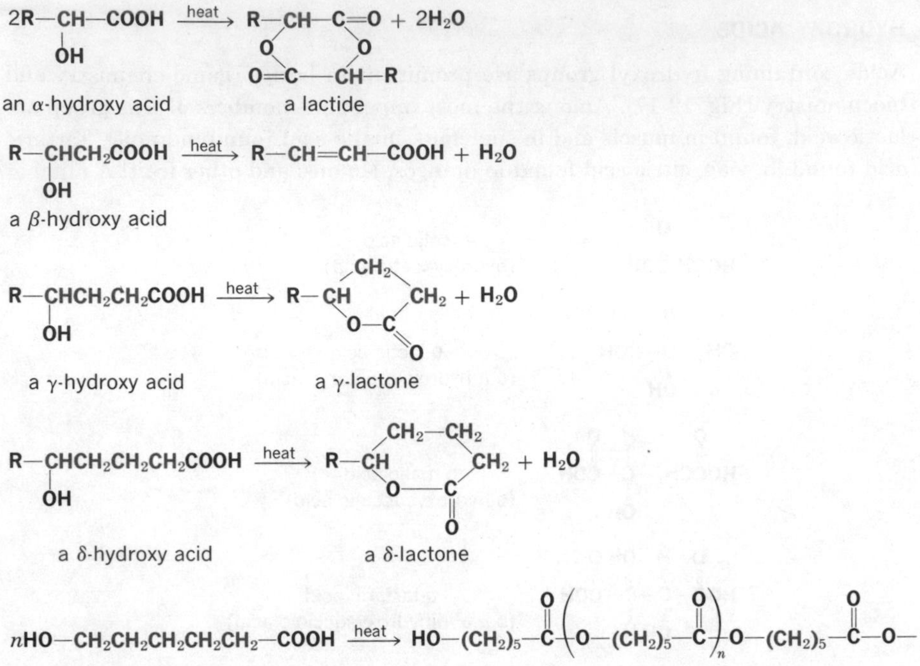

$2R-\underset{\underset{OH}{|}}{CH}-COOH \xrightarrow{heat} R-CH-C=O + 2H_2O$

an α-hydroxy acid   a lactide

$R-\underset{\underset{OH}{|}}{CH}CH_2COOH \xrightarrow{heat} R-CH=CH-COOH + H_2O$

a β-hydroxy acid

$R-\underset{\underset{OH}{|}}{CH}CH_2CH_2COOH \xrightarrow{heat} R-CH \quad + H_2O$

a γ-hydroxy acid   a γ-lactone

$R-\underset{\underset{OH}{|}}{CH}CH_2CH_2CH_2COOH \xrightarrow{heat} R-CH \quad + H_2O$

a δ-hydroxy acid   a δ-lactone

$n HO-CH_2CH_2CH_2CH_2CH_2-COOH \xrightarrow{heat} HO-(CH_2)_5-\overset{O}{C}\left(O-(CH_2)_5-\overset{O}{C}\right)_n O-(CH_2)_5-\overset{O}{C}-O-$

Fig. 12-18. As with diacids and keto acids, the first two members of the hydroxy acid series react atypically, the next two react intramolecularly to give 5- and 6-membered rings, and higher members form polymers.

compounds. An α-hydroxy acid, for example, may be synthesized by the hydrolysis of an α-haloacid or of a cyanohydrin. Keto and hydroxy acids may also be prepared by condensation reactions, to be discussed later in the chapter. The Reformatsky reaction provides a useful means of preparing β-hydroxy esters (Fig. 12-19). The reaction closely resembles a Grignard synthesis, except that zinc metal

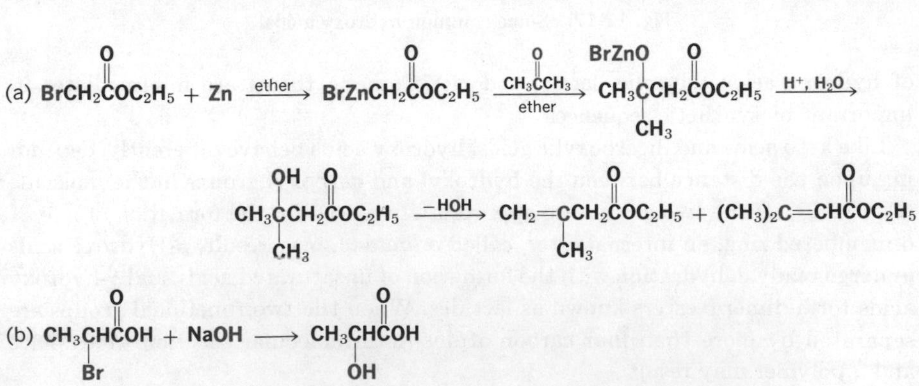

(a) $BrCH_2\overset{O}{C}OC_2H_5 + Zn \xrightarrow{ether} BrZnCH_2\overset{O}{C}OC_2H_5 \xrightarrow[ether]{CH_3\overset{O}{C}CH_3} CH_3\overset{BrZnO}{\underset{CH_3}{C}}CH_2\overset{O}{C}OC_2H_5 \xrightarrow{H^+, H_2O}$

$CH_3\underset{\underset{CH_3}{|}}{\overset{OH}{C}}CH_2\overset{O}{C}OC_2H_5 \xrightarrow{-HOH} CH_2=\underset{\underset{CH_3}{|}}{C}CH_2\overset{O}{C}OC_2H_5 + (CH_3)_2C=CH\overset{O}{C}OC_2H_5$

(b) $CH_3\underset{\underset{Br}{|}}{CH}\overset{O}{C}OH + NaOH \longrightarrow CH_3\underset{\underset{OH}{|}}{CH}\overset{O}{C}OH$

Fig. 12-19. Methods for the preparation of hydroxy acids include (a) the Reformatsky reaction, and (b) base treatment of α-bromo acids. β-Hydroxy esters are easily dehydrated.

is used instead of magnesium; the organozinc reagent is less reactive than the usual Grignard reagent and reacts selectively with the carbonyl group of the ketone rather than with both the ketone and ester groups.

ENOLATE REACTIONS

Aldehydes, ketones, esters, and other carbonyl-containing compounds undergo a number of surprising reactions at the saturated carbon adjacent to the carbonyl group. Let us call this the α-carbon for convenience and illustrate these reactions by the simple example of hydrogen-deuterium exchange. If diethyl ketone is dissolved in heavy water (D_2O) and a small amount of base is added, all the hydrogen atoms on the α-carbon atoms are replaced by deuterium atoms within a few hours at room temperature. Evidently, these α-hydrogen atoms (hydrogen atoms attached to α-carbon atoms) are slightly acidic and can be removed by base. But this appears inconsistent with the fact that, in general, carbon–hydrogen bonds are strong and difficult to break and are not acidic. Resonance theory accounts for this apparently anomalous behavior. When the α-hydrogen atom is removed from a carbonyl-containing molecule, an anion is formed. This anion is a resonance hybrid, since its negative charge can be shared by the α-carbon atom and the oxygen of the carbonyl group; because of this sharing, and particularly because one of the sharing atoms is an oxygen atom which accommodates a negative charge well, the C—H bond adjacent to a carbonyl group is more easily broken than a normal C—H bond (Fig. 12-20).

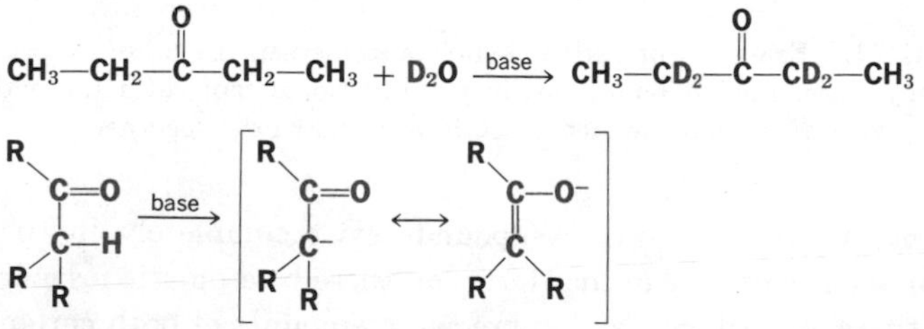

Fig. 12-20. α-Hydrogens, that is, hydrogen atoms attached to carbon atoms adjacent to carbonyl groups, are much more acidic than those in other parts of the molecule. The carbanion formed by removal of an α-hydrogen atom is greatly stabilized by the carbonyl group.

Because the α-hydrogen atoms are slightly acidic, nearly every carbonyl compound can exist, at least to a small extent, in an isomeric form in which the hydrogen atom is transferred to the carbonyl oxygen and a carbon-carbon double bond replaces the carbon-oxygen double bond. Such an isomer contains both an alkene bond and an alcohol group and is called an *enol*. Any two isomers, like a carbonyl group and its enol, which differ from each other only in the location of a fairly acidic proton, are called *tautomers;* the process by which one is converted into the other is called *tautomerization.* The establishment of an equilibrium between the carbonyl and enol forms is facilitated by acids and bases. For simple carbonyl compounds like acetone and diethyl ketone, acetaldehyde, or ethyl acetate, much less than 1 per cent enol is present at equilibrium, and for most purposes its presence can be ignored (Fig. 12-21).

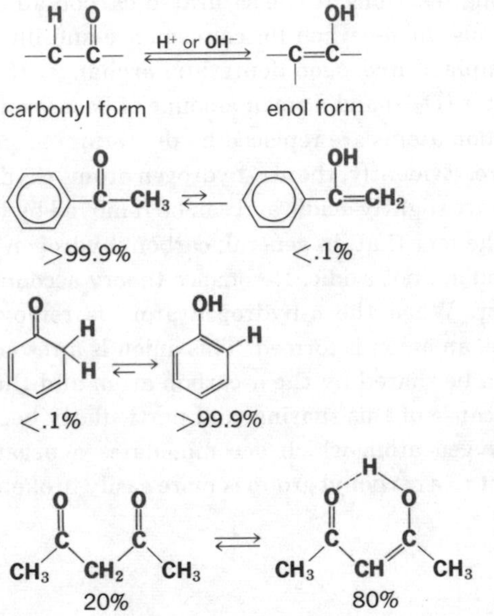

Fig. 12-21. Examples of carbonyl-enol tautomerism. In most molecules the carbonyl form predominates, but in polyfunctional molecules the enol form may, in special cases, be favored, or both forms may exist together.

At the other extreme, some compounds exist completely in the enol form. Phenol is an enol since only in that form can there be aromatic resonance. In a few molecules there is a balance, and appreciable amounts of both carbonyl and enol forms exist at equilibrium. This condition is found particularly in compounds in which two carbonyl groups are separated by a single saturated carbon atom (β-diketones and β-ketoesters); in such cases the enol double bond is stabilized because it is conjugated to the other carbonyl group, and the hydroxyl group may be stabilized by hydrogen bonding to the same carbonyl group. Both factors make the enol form of one carbonyl group more stable than it ordinarily would be, and thus increase the enol content of the molecule.

Many reactions of aldehydes, ketones, and esters which seem surprising at first glance become readily understandable in terms of reactions of the enol form or of the enolate anion formed by ionization. Acetophenone is ordinarily quite stable to the action of iodine, but reacts readily with it in the presence of sodium hydroxide.

The base promotes the formation of the enol form (by way of the even more reactive enolate ion) which is readily halogenated. This reaction is the basis of a simple visual chemical test for ketones which have an adjacent methyl group (methyl ketones).

The three acidic hydrogen atoms on the methyl group are removed one by one by the base and each enolate anion reacts with iodine. When three iodine atoms have accumulated on the same carbon atom, the molecule becomes unstable and is hydrolyzed by the base to iodoform and a carboxylic acid. The iodoform is precipitated and identified by its medicinal odor and its melting point (Fig. 12-22). This

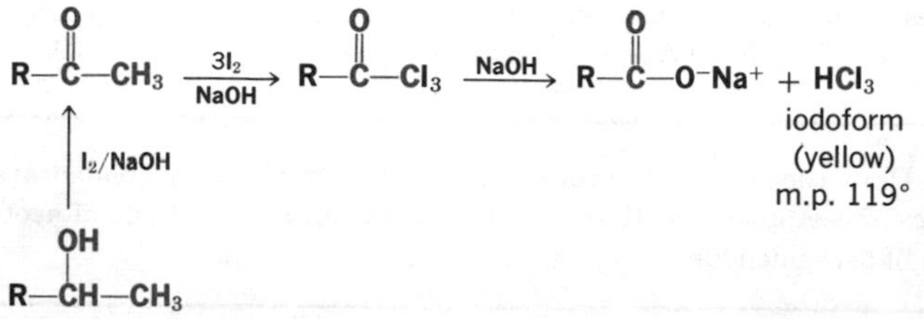

$$R-\overset{\overset{\displaystyle O}{\|}}{C}-CH_3 \xrightarrow[\text{NaOH}]{3I_2} R-\overset{\overset{\displaystyle O}{\|}}{C}-CI_3 \xrightarrow{\text{NaOH}} R-\overset{\overset{\displaystyle O}{\|}}{C}-O^-Na^+ + HCI_3$$

$$\overset{\displaystyle \uparrow}{\underset{\displaystyle I_2/\text{NaOH}}{}}$$

$$R-\overset{\overset{\displaystyle OH}{|}}{CH}-CH_3$$

iodoform
(yellow)
m.p. 119°

Fig. 12-22. The iodoform reaction is a visual chemical test for methyl ketones and methyl carbinols. Other ketones react, but do not form iodoform.

iodoform test is also positive for secondary alcohols which can be oxidized to methyl ketones, since iodine in base is a strong enough reagent to carry out this oxidation.

Prob. 12-2. What is the structure of the only aldehyde that will give a positive iodoform reaction? The only primary alcohol?

ALDOL CONDENSATION

An enolate anion is a carbanion and like other carbanions (for example, CN^-) it can form a stable adduct with a carbonyl group. Thus, if acetaldehyde is allowed to react in basic solution, the enolate ion formed from one molecule of acetaldehyde adds across the carbon-oxygen double bond of another molecule to form the hydroxy aldehyde *aldol*. Other aldehydes and ketones containing at least one α-hydrogen atom may undergo this aldol condensation reaction, so that this constitutes a convenient method for the synthesis of a number of difunctional molecules (Fig. 12-23).

Although enolate reactions are usually carried out in basic solution, they can also be effected by acid catalysts. Bromination and aldol condensation of acetone are both catalyzed by acid (Fig. 12-24). Acid catalyzes the formation of a small amount of the enol which is the reactive intermediate.

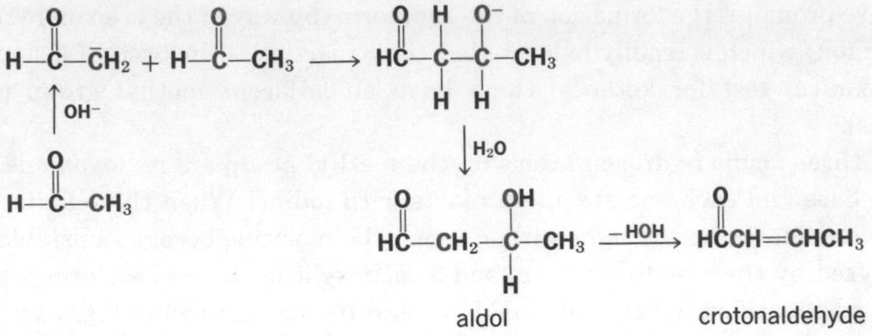

$$\text{H}-\overset{\text{O}}{\underset{}{\text{C}}}-\bar{\text{C}}\text{H}_2 + \text{H}-\overset{\text{O}}{\underset{}{\text{C}}}-\text{CH}_3 \longrightarrow \text{HC}-\overset{\text{O}}{\underset{\text{H}}{\text{C}}}-\overset{\text{H}}{\underset{\text{H}}{\text{C}}}-\text{CH}_3$$

$$\uparrow \text{OH}^-$$

$$\text{H}-\overset{\text{O}}{\underset{}{\text{C}}}-\text{CH}_3$$

$$\downarrow \text{H}_2\text{O}$$

$$\text{HC}-\text{CH}_2-\overset{\text{OH}}{\underset{\text{H}}{\text{C}}}-\text{CH}_3 \xrightarrow{-\text{HOH}} \text{HCCH}=\text{CHCH}_3$$

aldol   crotonaldehyde

Fig. 12-23. The aldol condensation reaction is general for aldehydes and ketones containing at least one α-hydrogen atom. β-Hydroxy aldehydes and ketones, like β-hydroxy esters, are easily dehydrated.

Prob. 12-3. Draw the structure (a) of the product from the aldol condensation reaction of two molecules of acetophenone, (b) of the product from one molecule of acetophenone and one molecule of benzaldehyde.

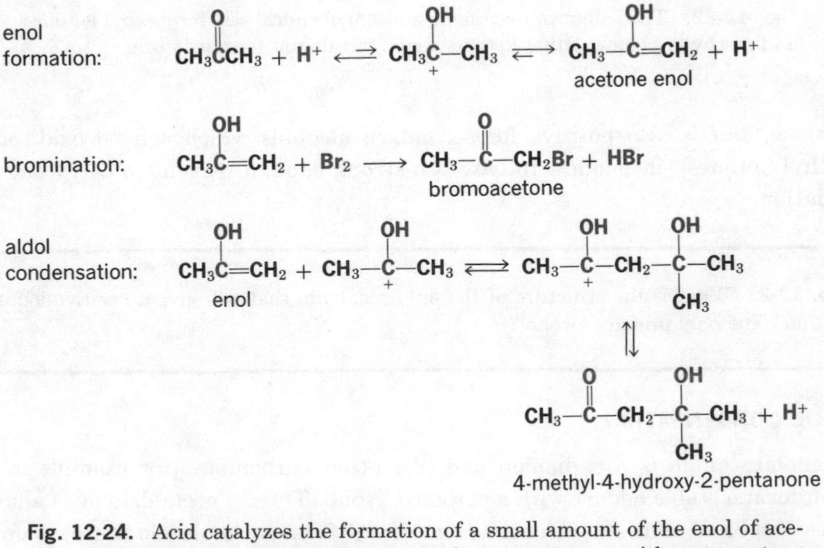

enol formation: $\text{CH}_3\overset{\text{O}}{\underset{}{\text{C}}}\text{CH}_3 + \text{H}^+ \rightleftharpoons \text{CH}_3\overset{\text{OH}}{\underset{+}{\text{C}}}-\text{CH}_3 \rightleftharpoons \text{CH}_3-\overset{\text{OH}}{\underset{}{\text{C}}}=\text{CH}_2 + \text{H}^+$
                                                                                              acetone enol

bromination: $\text{CH}_3\overset{\text{OH}}{\underset{}{\text{C}}}=\text{CH}_2 + \text{Br}_2 \longrightarrow \text{CH}_3-\overset{\text{O}}{\underset{}{\text{C}}}-\text{CH}_2\text{Br} + \text{HBr}$
                                                                bromoacetone

aldol condensation: $\text{CH}_3\overset{\text{OH}}{\underset{}{\text{C}}}=\text{CH}_2 + \text{CH}_3-\overset{\text{OH}}{\underset{+}{\text{C}}}-\text{CH}_3 \rightleftharpoons \text{CH}_3-\overset{\text{OH}}{\underset{+}{\text{C}}}-\text{CH}_2-\overset{\text{OH}}{\underset{\text{CH}_3}{\text{C}}}-\text{CH}_3$
                                enol

$$\updownarrow$$

$$\text{CH}_3-\overset{\text{O}}{\underset{}{\text{C}}}-\text{CH}_2-\overset{\text{OH}}{\underset{\text{CH}_3}{\text{C}}}-\text{CH}_3 + \text{H}^+$$

4-methyl-4-hydroxy-2-pentanone

Fig. 12-24. Acid catalyzes the formation of a small amount of the enol of acetone which may react with bromine to give bromoacetone, or with more acetone to give the hydroxy ketone aldol condensation product.

CLAISEN CONDENSATION

Esters undergo a reaction known as the Claisen condensation reaction, which is analogous to the aldol condensation. The enolate anion of an ester molecule, formed by reaction with a base like sodium ethoxide (sodium hydroxide cannot be used because it would hydrolyze the ester group), adds to the carbonyl group of another ester molecule. This initial adduct is not stable, since it contains both an

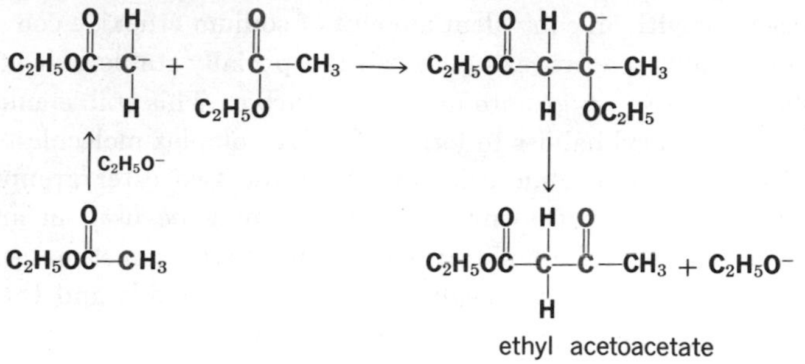

Fig. 12-25. Base-catalyzed condensation of two ester molecules is known as the *Claisen condensation reaction,* and leads to the formation of β-keto esters.

ether and an alcohol group on the same carbon atom and is rapidly transformed into a β-keto ester (Fig. 12-25). Again, a difunctional molecule has been prepared from monofunctional compounds by use of a condensation reaction.

ACETOACETIC ESTER AND MALONIC ESTER SYNTHESES

Ethyl acetoacetate (sometimes called acetoacetic ester), the β-keto ester formed by a Claisen condensation reaction of ethyl acetate, provides another good illustration of the special reactivities which may be conferred on a compound by the presence of two functional groups properly placed in the same molecule. In this molecule, the α-hydrogen atoms between the two carbonyl groups are rendered acidic by both groups (Fig. 12-26). As a consequence, ethyl acetoacetate is even more acidic than water and has a dissociation constant of about 10^{-10}. Reaction of

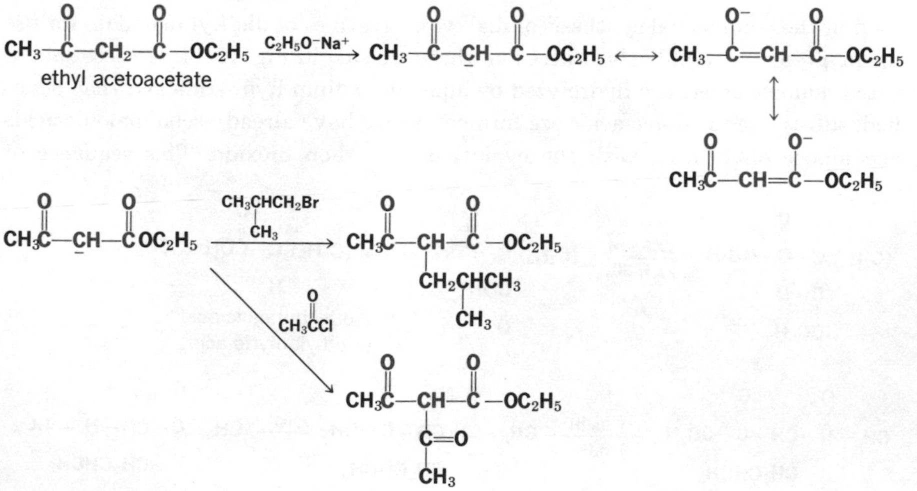

Fig. 12-26. Hydrogen atoms on a carbon atom between two carbonyl groups are acidic enough to react completely with bases. The resulting enolate ion may undergo substitution reactions with alkyl and acyl halides.

ethyl acetoacetate with an equivalent amount of sodium ethoxide converts it completely into its sodium enolate salt; this salt is especially stable, since the negative charge is shared by two oxygen atoms and one carbon. This stable anion can react with most alkyl and acyl halides to form still more complex molecules.

The diethyl ester of malonic acid, in which the two ester groups make the hydrogen atoms of the methylene group acidic, may be used in an analogous manner for the synthesis of complex diesters. The diester, sometimes simply called malonic ester, is converted to its salt with sodium ethoxide and the salt reacts with an alkyl halide. The steps may be repeated to introduce a second alkyl group, either the same or different from the first (Fig. 12-27). The reaction is extensively

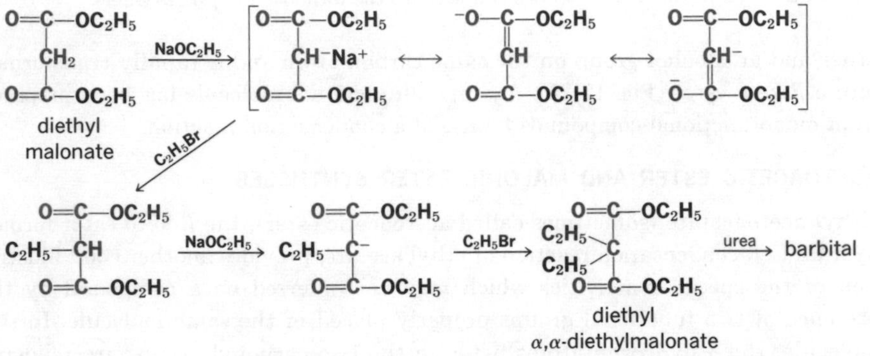

Fig. 12-27. Barbital (Veronal) is a long-acting sedative which is synthesized by dialkylation of ethyl malonate with ethyl bromide, followed by condensation with urea.

used in the commercial synthesis of dialkyl derivatives of diethyl malonate for use in the preparation of barbiturates like those we saw in Fig. 12-14. If these substituted malonic esters are hydrolyzed by aqueous sodium hydroxide and then acidified, substituted malonic acids are formed. As we have already seen malonic acids decompose on heating with the evolution of carbon dioxide. This sequence of

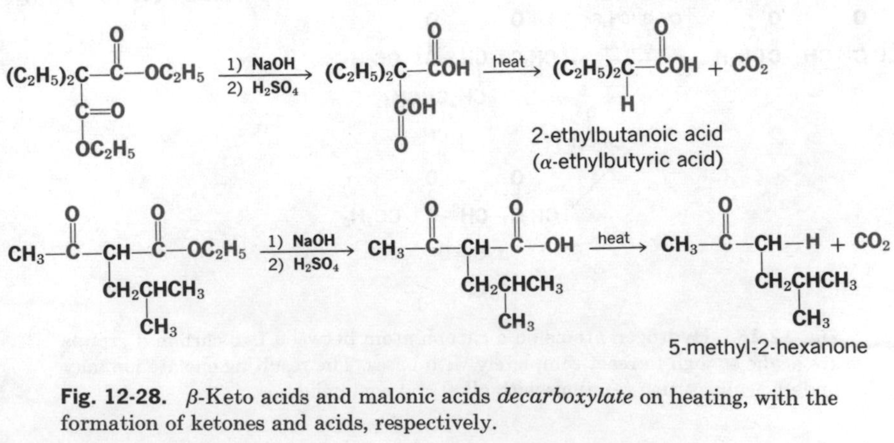

Fig. 12-28. β-Keto acids and malonic acids *decarboxylate* on heating, with the formation of ketones and acids, respectively.

reactions—substitution of diethyl malonate, hydrolysis, and decarboxylation—is known as the malonic ester synthesis and provides a convenient synthesis of carboxylic acids. The synthesis of 2-ethylbutanoic acid by this route is shown in Fig. 12-28. Similarly, substituted β-keto esters are hydrolyzed to β-keto acids which decarboxylate on heating to yield substituted ketones in a sequence known as the acetoacetic ester synthesis.

Prob. 12-4. Show how

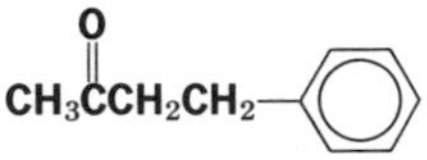

$$CH_3\overset{O}{\overset{\|}{C}}CH_2CH_2-\bigcirc$$

could be synthesized from ethyl acetate and benzyl bromide, making use of the Claisen condensation reaction, followed by alkylation, hydrolysis, and decarboxylation.

Prob. 12-5. What would you expect to be the product of each of the following reactions?

(a)

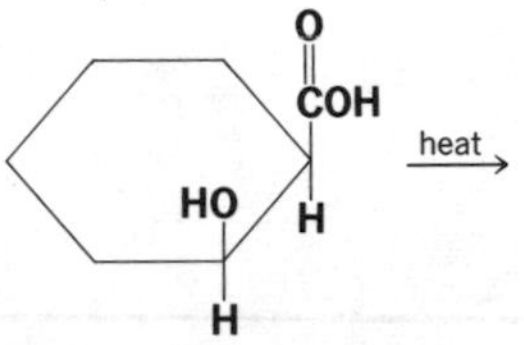

(b)

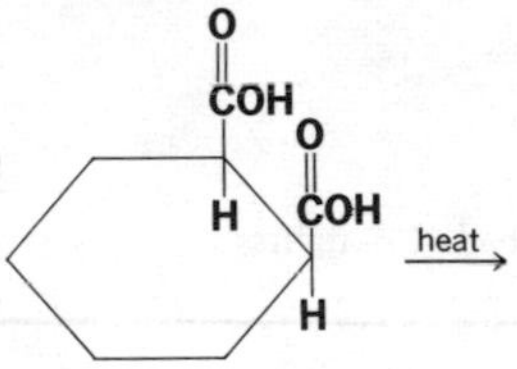

(c)

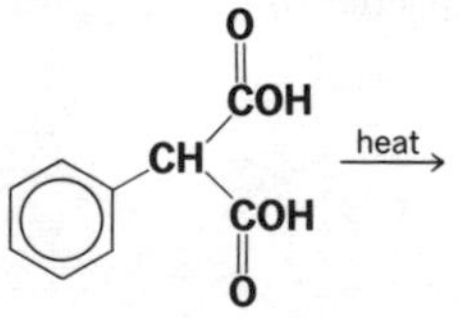

(d)

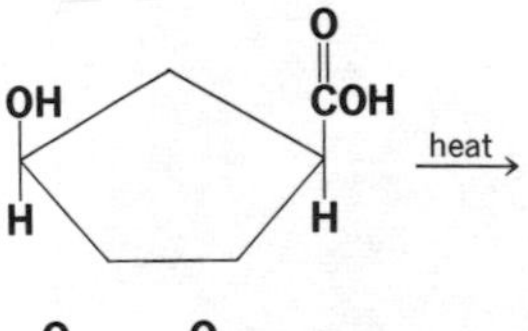

(e) $Cl\overset{O}{\overset{\|}{C}}(CH_2)_4\overset{O}{\overset{\|}{C}}Cl + H_2N(CH_2)_6NH_2 \longrightarrow$

(f)

$+ CH_3O^-Na^+ \longrightarrow$

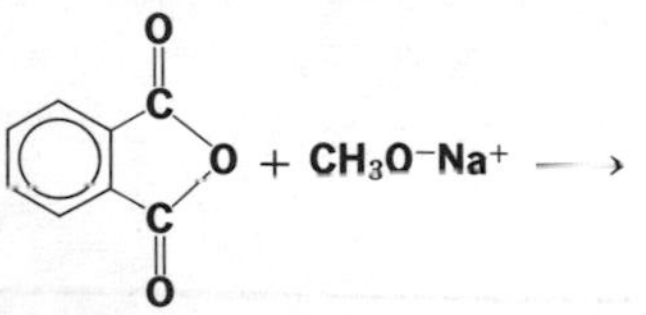

Prob. 12-6. Write equations for the following reactions.

(a) An aldol condensation reaction between two molecules of propionaldehyde.

(b) A Claisen condensation reaction between two molecules of ethyl phenylacetate.

(c) The products of the iodoform reaction on acetophenone (methyl phenyl ketone).

Prob. 12-7. Show how the following compounds could be prepared from diethyl malonate and any other needed reagents.

(a) 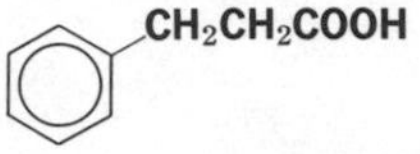 $\underset{\text{CH}_2\text{CH}_2\text{COOH}}{\bigcirc}$

(b) $(C_2H_5)_2C$ — ring structure with $\overset{O}{\underset{}{C}}$—NH, C=O, $\overset{}{\underset{O}{C}}$—NH

(c) $CH_3\overset{\displaystyle CH_2OH}{\underset{\displaystyle CH_2OH}{CH}}$

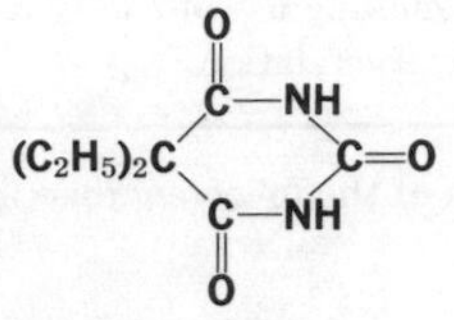

Prob. 12-8. Show how

$$n\text{-}C_6H_{13}CH_2\overset{O}{\overset{\|}{C}}CH_3$$

could be prepared from ethyl acetoacetate and any other needed reagents.

Prob. 12-9. Which of the following compounds would be expected to give a positive iodoform test?

(a) $CH_3CH_2\overset{O}{\overset{\|}{C}}CH_3$

(b) 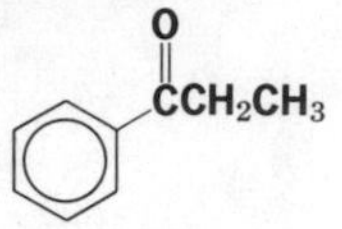 $\bigcirc\overset{O}{\overset{\|}{C}}CH_2CH_3$

(c) cyclohexane–$\overset{OH}{\underset{}{CHCH_3}}$

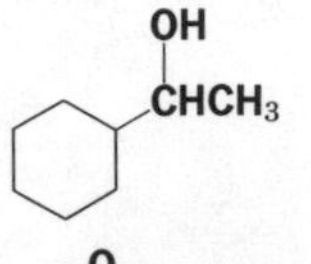

(d) $CH_3\overset{O}{\overset{\|}{C}}OH$

(e) $CH_3CH_2CH_2OH$

(f) $CH_3\overset{O}{\overset{\|}{C}}CH_2\overset{O}{\overset{\|}{C}}OCH_3$

Prob. 12-10. What are the uses or special importance of the following compounds? Draw the structures.

(a) methyl methacrylate   (d) salicylic acid

(b) adipic acid   (e) phenobarbital

(c) urea

Prob. 12-11. Give equations showing the preparation of:

(a) lactic acid from acetaldehyde   (e) diethyl carbonate from phosgene

(b) glycolic acid   (f) barbituric acid

(c) phthalic acid from *o*-xylene   (g) urea

(d) methyl methacrylate

CHAPTER

AMINO ACIDS, PEPTIDES, AND PROTEINS

As much as any other class of natural products, proteins seem inseparable from life itself. These compounds range from hemoglobin, which carries oxygen in our blood, to enzyme systems, which catalyze the digestion of our food. Many other proteins play important biological roles. Keratins are the proteins of hair and feathers, fibroin is the protein of silk, and collagen is the protein of the connective tissue of flesh, tendons, and muscle. Egg albumin, the casein in milk, and antibodies are all proteins, as are snake venoms, hormones like ACTH from the pituitary gland, and insulin.

Our knowledge of these systems is far from complete and is, in fact, just beginning to accumulate. In proteins, the organic chemist encounters what is probably the ultimate in chemical complexity—compounds of molecular weight ranging from a few thousand to several million; molecules of 10,000 and more atoms arranged in complex sequences, coiled and twisted into fantastic shapes, which have been unpredictable thus far. Until recently, it was common to refer to proteins only by descriptive names. The term "fibrous" was given to the stringy proteins like keratin, fibroin, and collagen, and the term "globular" was applied to the more nearly spherical proteins like albumin and casein.

Today, organic chemists are slowly coming to understand these complex molecules. Scientists are beginning to see how reactions and interactions of the simple groups discussed thus far can give rise to the mysterious processes of life. In this chapter, we shall summarize some of the more important aspects of protein chemistry now known.

Proteins are said to have *primary structures,* and also *secondary, tertiary,* and

Table 13-1. α-Amino Acids Produced by Heating Proteins with Strong Aqueous Acid (From Haggis, et al., *Introduction to Molecular Biology*, John Wiley and Sons, Inc., New York, 1964, pp. 40–41)

	molecular weight	alanine	glycine	valine	leucine	isoleucine	proline	phenylalanine	tyrosine	tryptophan	serine	threonine	cystine	cysteine	methionine	arginine	histidine	lysine	aspartic acid + asparagine	glutamic acid + glutamine	hydroxyproline	hydroxylysine
human insulin	6,000	1	4	4	6	2	1	3	4	0	3	3	3	0	0	1	2	1	3	7	0	0
ribonuclease	15,000	12	3	9	2	3	4	3	6	0	15	10	4	0	4	4	4	10	15	12	0	0
egg albumin	45,000	35	19	28	32	25	14	21	9	3	36	16	1	5	16	15	7	20	32	52	0	0
horse myoglobin	17,000	15	13	6	22	0	5	5	2	2	6	7	0	0	2	2	9	18	10	19	0	0
horse hemoglobin	68,000	54	48	50	75	0	22	30	11	5	35	24	0	4	4	14	36	38	51	38	0	0
human serum albumin	69,000	–	15	45	58	9	31	33	18	1	22	27	16	4	6	25	16	58	46	80	0	0
human γ-globulin	160,000	–	90	133	114	34	112	45	61	22	175	114	16	10	11	45	26	88	106	128	0	0
pepsin	34,000	–	29	21	27	28	15	13	16	4	40	28	2	2	4	2	2	2	41	28	0	0
chymotrypsinogen	24,000	16	20	21	16	9	8	5	3	7	25	22	3	3	2	4	2	13	20	12	0	0
α-casein	?	43	30	54	60	49	65	28	45	8	60	41	2	–	17	25	19	61	63	153	0	0
silk fibroin	?	334	581	31	7	8	6	20	71	0	154	13	–	–	–	6	2	5	21	15	0	0
collagen	?	107	363	29	28	15	131	15	5	0	32	19	0	0	5	49	5	31	47	77	107	7
elastin	?	58	376	118	56	26	136	29	8	–	9	10	2	–	0	6	0	3	4	22	107	0
wool keratin	?	46	87	40	86	–	83	22	26	9	95	54	49	–	5	60	7	19	54	96	0	0

protein $\xrightarrow[100°, 12 \text{ hours}]{12N \text{ HCl}}$ mixture of amino acids

even *quaternary structures.* The meanings of the latter terms will become clear presently, but let us begin by discussing the primary structures. We must first note that proteins are polymeric materials, composed of amino acid monomeric units joined in amide linkages.

NATURALLY OCCURRING AMINO ACIDS

When any common protein is boiled for several hours with strong aqueous acid, it becomes completely hydrolyzed to a mixture of as many as 20 different α-amino acids. In Table 13-1, the numbers in the columns under individual amino acids indicate how many molecules of that acid are obtained through hydrolysis of one molecule of the particular protein. Where the molecular weight of a protein is not precisely known (denoted by a question mark in the molecular weight column), the figures refer to the number of amino acid molecules calculated for a hypothetical protein of 100,000 molecular weight. The structures of the amino acids named will be shown in later figures. Many of these amino acids are found to recur in most proteins, but only about 25 amino acids have been positively identified in protein hydrolyzates.

As implied by the name, an amino acid is simply a compound containing both amino and carboxyl groups; in an α-amino acid the amino group is on the carbon atom adjacent to the carboxyl group. Thus, all α-amino acids may be considered to be derivatives of aminoacetic acid. In fact, aminoacetic acid, whose common name is *glycine,* is one of the commonest amino acids; for example, nearly half of the amino acid molecules obtained when silk is hydrolyzed are glycine. With the exception of glycine, all of the amino acids found in proteins are optically active— and all of them have the L-configuration in which the amino group is on the left (Fig. 13-1) when the principal functional group, the carboxyl group, is up and the horizontal groups extend forward. A similar convention was used for the carbohydrates.

$$
\underset{\text{neutral form}}{
\begin{array}{c}
\overset{\displaystyle O}{\overset{\displaystyle \|}{\text{COH}}}\\
H_2N-\underset{\underset{R}{|}}{\overset{\overset{}{|}}{C}}\!\rightarrow\! H
\end{array}}
\quad \rightleftarrows \quad
\underset{\text{Zwitterion form}}{
\begin{array}{c}
\overset{\displaystyle O}{\overset{\displaystyle \|}{\text{CO}^-}}\\
\overset{+}{H_3N}-\underset{\underset{R}{|}}{\overset{\overset{}{|}}{C}}\!\rightarrow\! H
\end{array}}
$$

Fig. 13-1. Nearly all amino acids found in proteins can be represented by the general formulas shown; their salt-like physical properties are in accord with their formulation as the Zwitterion form.

In many of the formulas for the amino acids and the complex compounds deriving from them, it will be necessary to recognize the L-configuration in different guises. An easy way to convert one mentally to another is to recognize that an exchange of any two groups about an asymmetric carbon atom produces a compound of the opposite configuration. Two such exchanges therefore restore the original configuration.

When amino acids were first isolated, chemists had some difficulty in reconciling their structures with their physical properties, since they are nonvolatile, crystalline, high-melting substances, which are very soluble in water, and insoluble in most organic solvents. It was eventually recognized that amino acids were better represented by a dipolar "Zwitterion" form (a name derived from the German expression for a double ion); according to this conception, the basic amino group and the acidic carboxyl group react to form a salt (Fig. 13-1). This doubly charged structure accounts for the salt-like characteristics and other physical properties of amino acids.

In presenting the structures of the 23 commonest amino acids of proteins, we shall group them into classes approximately according to the polarity of their side chains, because it now appears that polarity may be of considerable importance in determining the shapes of proteins. Figure 13-2 shows the amino acids with nonpolar (hydrocarbon) substituents; these seven amino acids have no hetero atoms other than those in the carboxyl and amino groups. They are neutral amino acids, since each contains one basic group and one acidic group. Tough, insoluble proteins like silk, wool, collagen, and elastin (found in ligaments) have a high proportion of one or more of these amino acids (see Table 13-1).

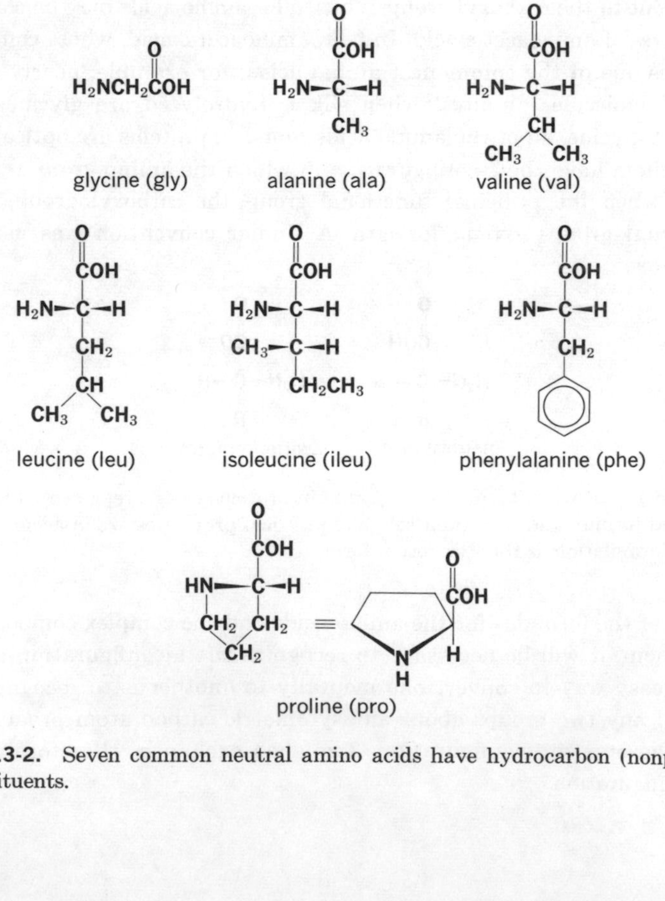

Fig. 13-2. Seven common neutral amino acids have hydrocarbon (nonpolar) substituents.

Common names are used almost exclusively for amino acids. These names are often condensed to the abbreviations indicated in parentheses—"gly" for glycine, "ala" for alanine, etc. IUPAC names could be given for the compounds, but they are not often used, because they are cumbersome.

A second group of amino acids, shown in Fig. 13-3, have polar but neutral side chains. Two of them, asparagine and glutamine, are derivatives of acidic amino

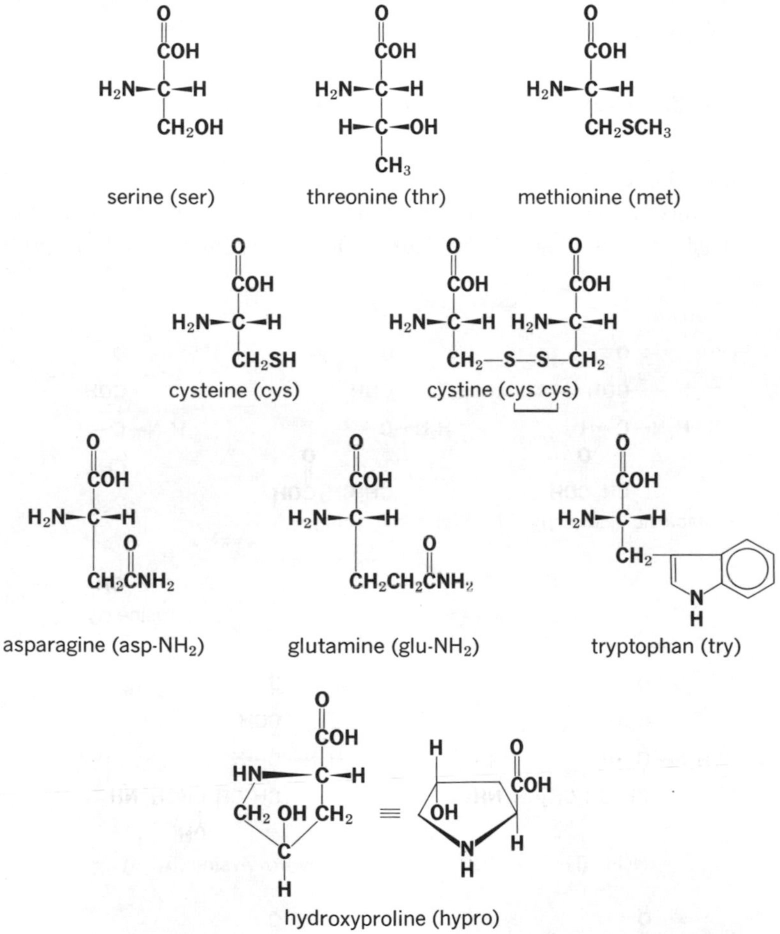

Fig. 13-3.   Nine amino acids which are polar but neutral.

acids. The presence of a large number of polar amino acids increases the water solubility of a protein. Two of these amino acids are formed from others only after they have been incorporated into a protein molecule. These are hydroxyproline, formed from proline by reaction with oxygen of the air, and cystine, similarly formed by oxidation of two molecules of cysteine. Hydroxyproline makes up a large part of the protein collagen, which is converted to the protein gelatin upon boiling. We will say more later about the important role cystine plays in determining the three-dimensional structure of proteins.

Prob. 13-1. Give the IUPAC names for serine, threonine, and cysteine. For alanine, leucine and valine.

Methionine is an important dietary constituent; it is frequently missing from the diets of poultry and must be added. An interesting observation is that the

α-hydroxy acid, CH_3SCH_2CHCOH, can apparently replace methionine in these

supplemented diets.

Finally, a very important group of six amino acids have side chains that contain acidic or basic groups (Fig. 13-4). These side chains, in addition to promoting

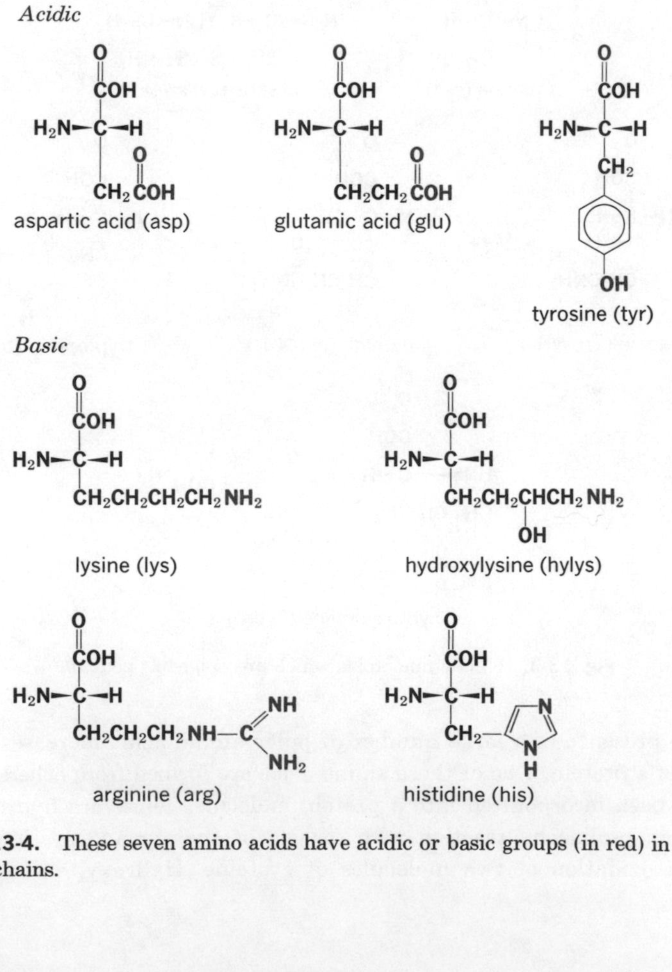

Acidic

aspartic acid (asp)   glutamic acid (glu)

tyrosine (tyr)

Basic

lysine (lys)   hydroxylysine (hylys)

arginine (arg)   histidine (his)

Fig. 13-4. These seven amino acids have acidic or basic groups (in red) in their side chains.

water-solubility of proteins, seem to have a great deal to do with the actual functioning of many proteins. They furnish many of the "active sites" in enzymes, at which catalysis of organic reactions occurs. The sodium salt of glutamic acid (monosodium glutamate) is used as a flavor-enhancing agent, sold under the tradename *Accent.*

Prob. 13-2. Show two resonance forms for the protonated form of the imidazole group

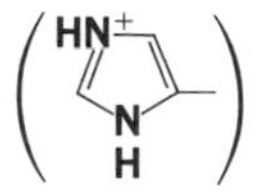

$$\left(\begin{array}{c} HN \overset{+}{} \\ \diagup\!\!\diagdown \\ N \\ H \end{array} \right)$$

of histidine and three resonance forms for the protonated form of the guanidine group

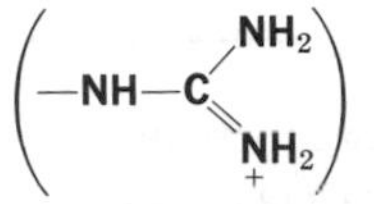

$$\left(-NH-C \overset{NH_2}{\underset{\overset{NH_2}{+}}{}} \right)$$

of arginine. Would you expect arginine or lysine to be a stronger base?

Although the 23 amino acids named are the building blocks of proteins, they are not the only amino acids that occur naturally; nevertheless, in the process of evolution these appear to have developed as the most genetically suitable. Other amino acids (including some of the 23 in the D- rather than the L- form) occur among lower plants and bacteria; microorganisms often utilize D-amino acids in antibiotics.

OTHER AMINO ACIDS

All the amino acids found in proteins are α-amino acids. However, other amino acids are also important. *p*-Aminobenzoic acid, for example, is necessary for the growth of certain microorganisms, including a number of bacteria (Fig. 13-5). *p*-Aminobenzenesulfonic acid resembles a *p*-aminobenzoic acid in structure, and it seems logical that derivatives of the sulfonic acid might compete and interfere

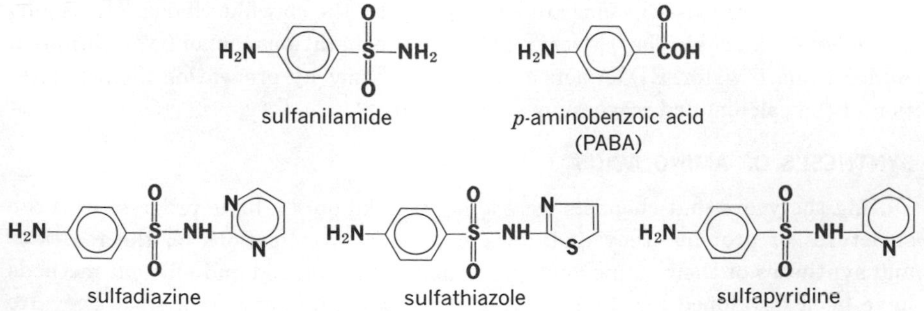

Fig. 13-5. Sulfa drugs compete with *p*-aminobenzoic acid, which is a bacterial growth factor.

with the metabolism of the carboxylic acid in the bacteria. This would block further conversions and prevent growth of the bacteria. The amide *p*-aminobenzenesulfonamide (sulfanilamide) is indeed an effective bacteriostatic agent.

When a compound is found to be an effective medicinal agent, chemists usually conduct an intensive search for closely related compounds which are even more potent. Thus, when sulfanilamide was recognized as a bacteriostatic agent, many other sulfonamides containing aromatic ring systems were tested for this capacity. Some, especially sulfadiazine, sulfathiazole, and sulfapyridine, were found to be even more effective than sulfanilamide.

Prob. 13-3. What is the name of the heterocyclic ring system of sulfadiazine?

Amino acids may have great practical importance outside of protein chemistry. Ethylenediaminetetraacetic acid (EDTA, Fig. 13-6) is an example. The particularly favorable arrangement of acidic and basic sites gives this molecule a very strong

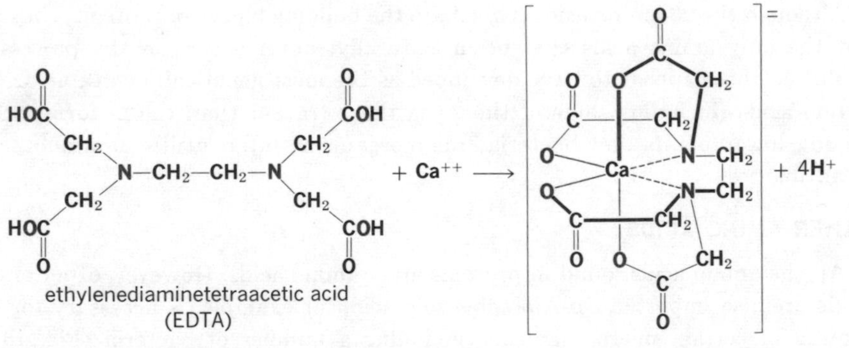

ethylenediaminetetraacetic acid
(EDTA)

Fig. 13-6. EDTA forms stable, water-soluble salts with metals which cause soaps to precipitate.

affinity for metal ions—the ions are held tightly by the clawlike chains. The resulting *chelate* (Gk.: *chele,* claw) is very stable, and the metal ions cannot be precipitated. Added to hard water, EDTA acts as a water softener by preventing the precipitation of the calcium and magnesium salts of soap.

SYNTHESES OF AMINO ACIDS

During the years that chemists were able to make only a little progress with the structures of proteins, they undertook extensive investigations on the reactions and syntheses of their amino acid constituents. Specialized and efficient methods have been developed for the synthesis of most amino acids and, since they are important in nutrition, many have been produced on an industrial scale. We shall present two general methods of preparation (Fig. 13-7), both of which are closely

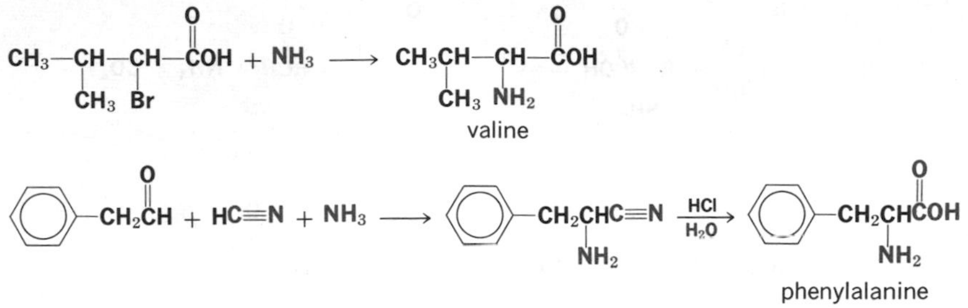

CH$_3$—CH—CH—COH + NH$_3$ ⟶ CH$_3$CH—CH—COH

CH$_3$ Br   CH$_3$ NH$_2$

valine

⬡—CH$_2$CH + HC≡N + NH$_3$ ⟶ ⬡—CH$_2$CHC≡N $\xrightarrow[H_2O]{HCl}$ ⬡—CH$_2$CHCOH

NH$_2$ NH$_2$

phenylalanine

Fig. 13-7. Two relatively general methods for the synthesis of amino acids. The reactions shown give racemic mixtures of valine and phenylalanine.

analogous to reactions studied in previous chapters. More specialized methods, each useful for the preparation of only a few amino acids, are also available.

The simplest, though not always the best, method of preparing an amine is through the reaction of an alkyl halide with ammonia. Similarly, nearly all amino acids can be prepared by reaction of an α-halo acid with ammonia, an excess of ammonia being used to favor the primary amine. The halo acids, in turn, are usually preparable by catalyzed bromination of the corresponding acid. This method of synthesis is most satisfactory for the preparation of the amino acids with hydrocarbon side chains. As might be anticipated, the rather drastic conditions of bromination and reaction with ammonia may destroy other functional groups.

A second general method of synthesis is analogous to cyanohydrin formation. In this method, an aldehyde containing one carbon atom less than the amino acid desired is treated with hydrogen cyanide in the presence of ammonia. A cyanoamine is formed which may be hydrolyzed to an amino acid. The method is relatively mild, and proves useful if the required aldehyde can be prepared. Both this method and the α-bromo acid-ammonia reaction give racemic mixtures of amino acids when the starting materials are optically inactive.

Prob. 13-4. Suggest the steps involved in the formation of the cyanoamine from the aldehyde, hydrogen cyanide, and ammonia in Fig. 13-7.

REACTIONS OF AMINO ACIDS

In general, the reactions of amino acids are those expected of the individual functional groups found in them. Of analytical importance are the reactions that serve as qualitative or quantitative tests. When amines are treated with nitrous acid, nitrogen gas evolves (see Fig. 8-15). In the Van Slyke procedure for analysis of amino acids, the nitrogen is collected and its volume measured under conditions of standard temperature and pressure. The chemist can determine the number of moles of amino acid present from the volume of gas evolved.

The ninhydrin test for amino acids (Fig. 13-8) is more complicated: Ninhydrin

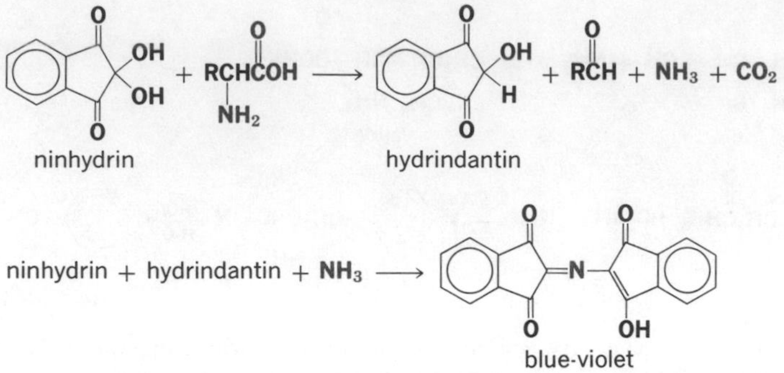

Fig. 13-8. The reaction of ninhydrin with amino acids produces a blue-violet dye which may be used as a qualitative or quantitative test for amino acids.

oxidizes an amino acid to ammonia, carbon dioxide, and an aldehyde; a molecule of ninhydrin then reacts with both the ammonia produced and a molecule of reduced ninhydrin (called hydrindantin) to create a blue dye. The intensity of the blue color can be used as a measure of the amount of amino acid present. The reaction can also be used as a simple color test for the presence of amino acids.

In combination with paper chromatography, the ninhydrin reaction can be used to *identify* amino acids. For example, a protein can be hydrolyzed with strong acid to give a mixture of the amino acids present. A small amount of this mixture is then dissolved in water and applied (spotted) to a sheet of filter paper near the lower edge (at the origin). This is the area marked + at the bottom left of the paper in Fig. 13-9. A solvent (in this case, a solution containing phenol and water) is allowed to rise by capillary action through the paper, carrying the amino acids along with it at different rates; the less polar amino acids migrate faster than the more polar ones. The separation can be increased if the paper (a chromatogram) is dried and rotated by 90°, and a second solvent mixture (here, 2-butanol, formic acid, and water) is allowed to flow across the paper; this is called a two-dimensional papergram. To locate the separated amino acids, a solution of ninhydrin in alcohol is sprayed on the dried paper. Because of reactions like that shown in Fig. 13-8, a spot appears at those places where amino acids are present.

Heating the amine salt of an acid will produce an amide. Since an amino acid contains both amine and carboxyl groups, conditions for polymerization are theoretically met. If glycine is heated strongly, for example, water may be split out between two molecules to form glycylglycine (Fig. 13-10). This amide still contains a carboxylate and an ammonium ion, and elimination of water can continue. Reaction of the amide with additional molecules of glycine forms the polymer *polyglycine*. On the other hand, the two functional groups are ideally located for reaction with each other to form diketopiperazine, which has a 6-membered ring. Both reactions occur.

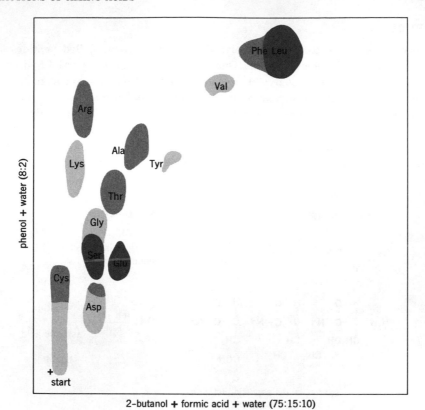

Fig. 13-9. A two-dimensional paper chromatogram of an amino-acid mixture, such as might result from the hydrolysis of a protein. (From F. Cramer, *Papier-chromatographie,* 4th ed., Verlag. Chemie, Weinheim/Bergstr., 1958.)

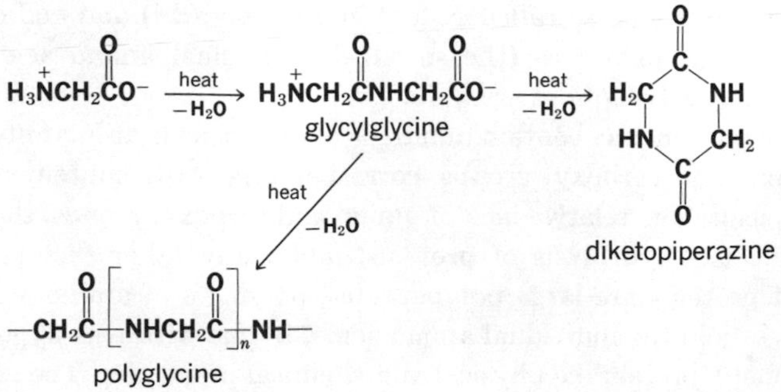

Fig. 13-10. Strong heating of glycine gives amides—polyglycine, diketopiperazine, or both—as a result of loss of water.

PEPTIDES

If proteins are only partially hydrolyzed, smaller polymers called peptides are formed along with the amino acids. One of the products of the partial hydrolysis of silk, for example, is glycylglycine, the amide formed from two glycine molecules. A peptide is a proteinlike substance, but contains many fewer amino acid units. In peptides, the amino acids are joined by amide linkages: A peptide containing two amino acid units is a dipeptide and one containing four is a tetrapeptide; those containing few or many amino acid units are oligopeptides or polypeptides, respectively (Fig. 13-11). Peptides are named by combining the names or abbreviations of

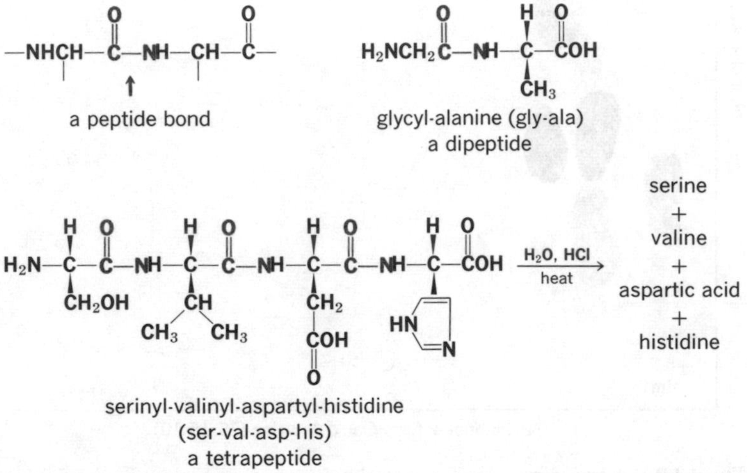

Fig. 13-11. A peptide bond is an amide bond linking two amino acids; in this figure, all peptide bonds are shown in red. Hydrolysis of a peptide gives the amino acid components.

the individual amino acids, starting (by convention) with the amino acid whose amino group is free (the so-called N-terminal amino acid) and ending with that whose carboxyl group is free (the so-called C-terminal amino acid); names of oligopeptides and polypeptides are quite complex.

Although a protein may contain hundreds of amino acids, it has only a relatively few free amino and carboxyl groups, corresponding to its content of acidic and basic amino acids. The relative lack of amino and carboxyl groups, the isolation of peptides from the hydrolysis of proteins, and many other factors have made it clear that proteins are large polypeptides, polymers of amino acids in which amide linkages join the individual amino acids. In line with this hypothesis, polyglycine has many proteinlike physical and chemical properties. The amide linkage plays such an important role in protein structure that it is often called the "peptide bond"; however, it is really no different from any other amide bond, except for the fact that it joins two amino acids.

Some idea of the enormous complexity of protein molecules emerges from considering that four hundred different *dipeptides* are possible from amide formation between any two of twenty different amino acids. Not only the amino acid content of the dipeptide is important, but also the sequence of joining the amino acids. Thus, in glycylalanine, glycine is N-terminal; the carboxyl group of glycine is joined to the amino group of alanine; in alanylglycine, by contrast, glycine is C-terminal, and the carboxyl group of alanine is joined to the amino group of glycine.

SYNTHESIS OF PEPTIDES

It is not practical to synthesize mixed dipeptides by heating a mixture of the two amino acids, since a complex mixture of products would result. Heating a mixture of glycine and alanine, for example, would produce four dipeptides; these could react further to produce diketopiperazines and polymers. To prevent this, the amino group of one of the amino acids is protected before reaction by converting it to some derivative which may be readily reconverted to the free amino acid. An example of this protection, which employs the reaction of an amino acid with phthalic anhydride and subsequent removal of the phthaloyl group, is the synthesis of glycylalanine (Fig. 13-12). The phthaloyl group from phthalic acid is useful in this reaction, since it is easily removed by hydrazine at room temperature.

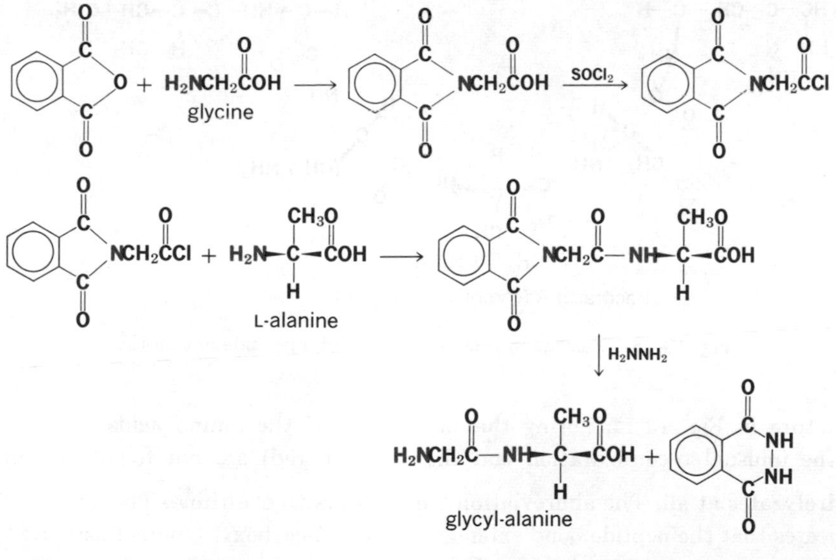

Fig. 13-12. In the synthesis of a peptide, the amino group of one amino acid must be protected to prevent the formation of numerous byproducts.

Prob. 13-5. Using a scheme similar to that of Fig. 13-12 show how you would synthesize alanylglycine.

SMALL PEPTIDES

As the length of a peptide chain increases, the number of possible isomers increases enormously. Thus, there are at least 8,000 tripeptides theoretically possible from 20 amino acids. A number of small peptides occur naturally; some antibiotics, like bacitracin, are peptides and all plant and animal cells contain peptides. Compare the complete structure of bacitracin in Fig. 13-13 with the abbreviated

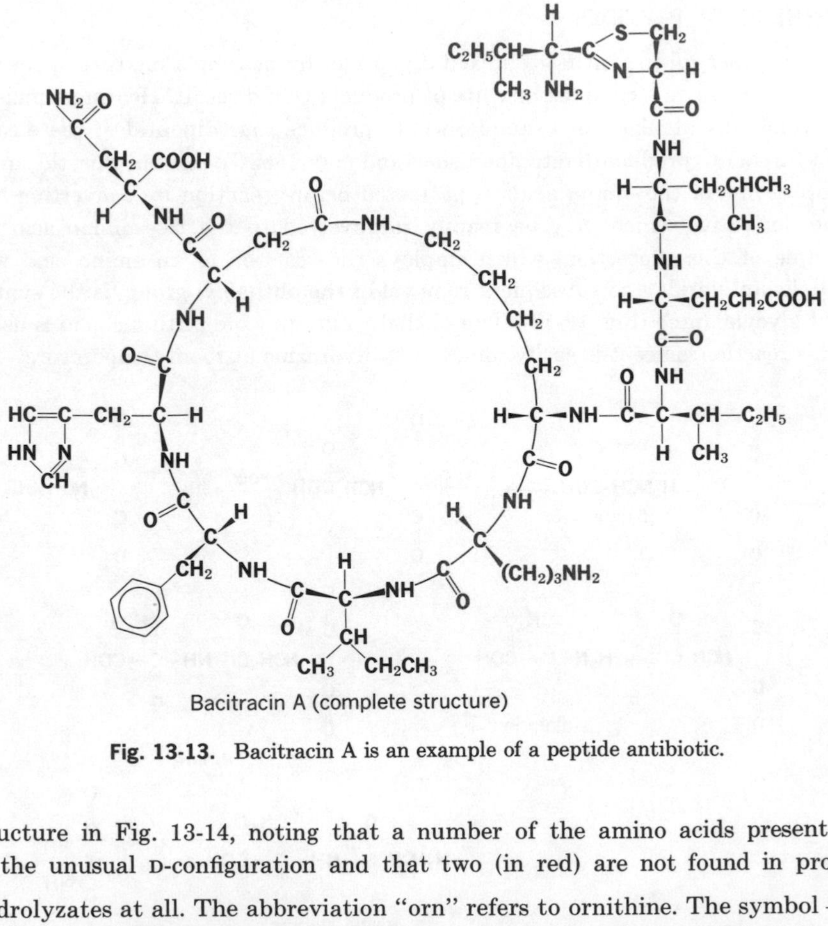

Bacitracin A (complete structure)

Fig. 13-13. Bacitracin A is an example of a peptide antibiotic.

structure in Fig. 13-14, noting that a number of the amino acids present are of the unusual D-configuration and that two (in red) are not found in protein hydrolyzates at all. The abbreviation "orn" refers to ornithine. The symbol $\xrightarrow{\beta,\varepsilon}$ indicates that the peptide bond extends from the β-carboxyl group of aspartic acid to the ε-amino group of lysine.

Two peptides of special significance are the hormones oxytocin and vasopressin (Fig. 13-15, p. 262). These were the first peptide hormones to be synthesized, a feat for which du Vigneaud of Cornell University was awarded the Nobel Prize in 1955. Both hormones illustrate, on a scale of medium complexity, some of the structural problems encountered in considering proteins.

Vasopressin is produced in minute amounts by the pituitary gland, located at

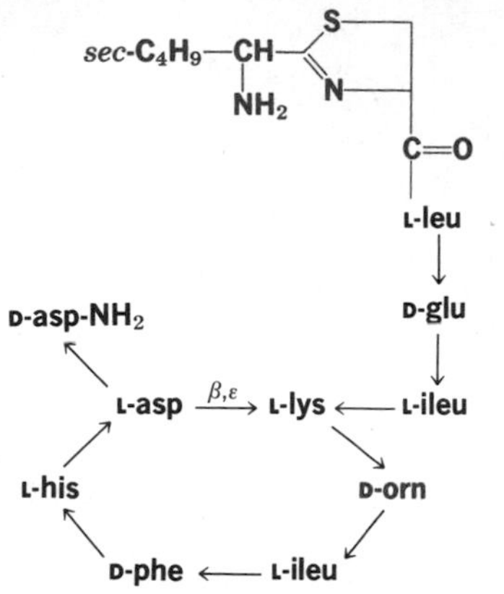

$$sec\text{-}C_4H_9\text{—}CH$$

Bacitracin A (abbreviated structure)

Fig. 13-14. Abbreviated structure of Bacitracin A. Notice the abnormal amino acids (in red).

the base of the brain. It regulates the excretion of water by the kidneys, and affects the blood pressure. Lack of vasopressin leads to a disease known as *diabetes insipidus,* in which too much urine is excreted. Vasopressin is a nonapeptide and contains in order, starting from the C-terminal end, cysteine, tyrosine, phenylalanine, glutamine, asparagine, cysteine, proline, arginine, and glycine (which is present as an amide). The resulting chainlike molecule is formed into a loop by joining the two cysteine molecules, through an S—S bond, into cystine. A condensed representation of the molecule is also shown in Fig. 13-15, in which the individual amino acids are represented by their abbreviations.

Prob. 13-6. Draw the complete structure of beef vasopressin.

The second hormone, *oxytocin,* is also a nonapeptide formed by the pituitary gland. Although it differs from vasopressin only in the replacement of two amino acids by two others, its physiological action is quite different: Instead of acting on blood pressure and kidney function, oxytocin brings about the contraction of smooth muscle, especially that of the uterus, and it is often administered at childbirth to induce delivery.

Not every amino acid change has such a dramatic effect. The formula of vasopressin given is that found in beef. Swine vasopressin has a molecule of lysine in place of arginine, yet its physiological action appears to be unchanged; either type can be administered to a human to relieve *diabetes insipidus.*

DETERMINATION OF PEPTIDE STRUCTURES

Determining the amino acid sequence in even a simple peptide can be a formidable task, and we will only briefly indicate the methods used. Suppose a new penta-

oxytocin (complete)

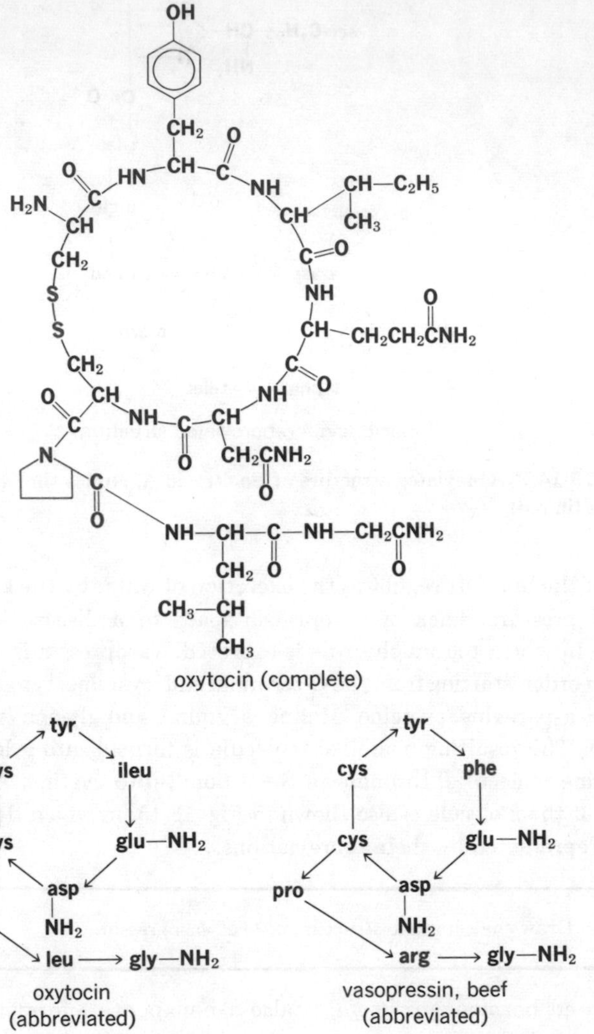

oxytocin
(abbreviated)

vasopressin, beef
(abbreviated)

Fig. 13-15. Vasopressin and oxytocin are two pituitary hormones which have been synthesized. Both contain only L-amino acids; only the two amino acids in red in vasopressin differ from those in oxytocin. Here the ring is formed by the S—S linkage in cystine. The amino acid proline plays a special role in determining the shape of proteins, a role which will be discussed later.

peptide has been isolated, and complete hydrolysis and paper chromatographic analysis shows it to be composed of one molecule each of the first 5 amino acids in Fig. 13-2, glycine, alanine, valine, leucine, and isoleucine. Such a peptide ordinarily contains a free amino group at one end and a free carboxyl group at the other.* If

* Some peptides, like bacitracin A (Figs. 13-13 and 13-14), are cyclic, being joined into a ring through peptide bonds; the determination of the structure of such a peptide is slightly more difficult.

the amino end group is marked by being converted into a derivative before hydrolysis, the N-terminal amino acid can be identified after hydrolysis because it is present as a derivative rather than as a free amino acid. For determining the N-terminal amino acid, 2,4-dinitrofluorobenzene is usually employed (Fig. 13-16). It reacts with the free amino group, giving a yellow derivative. On hydrolysis of the derived peptide, only the N-terminal amino acid is absent and is found as its dinitrophenyl derivative. The C-terminal amino acid can be established by heating the peptide with hydrazine at 100°. Hydrazine reacts under these conditions with amide carbonyl groups, yielding hydrazides, but not with free carboxyl groups. Thus, the only amino acid left is the C-terminal acid, all others having been converted to their hydrazides.

Let us suppose that these methods locate alanine as the N-terminal, and leucine as the C-terminal, amino acid. Next, the peptide is only partially hydrolyzed, to give a complex mixture of tetra-, tri-, and dipeptides, as well as individual amino acids. Although in an actual experiment studies would probably be made on all of these components, for illustration let us concentrate on the tripeptides, which can be separated from the rest of the materials by relatively straightforward methods.

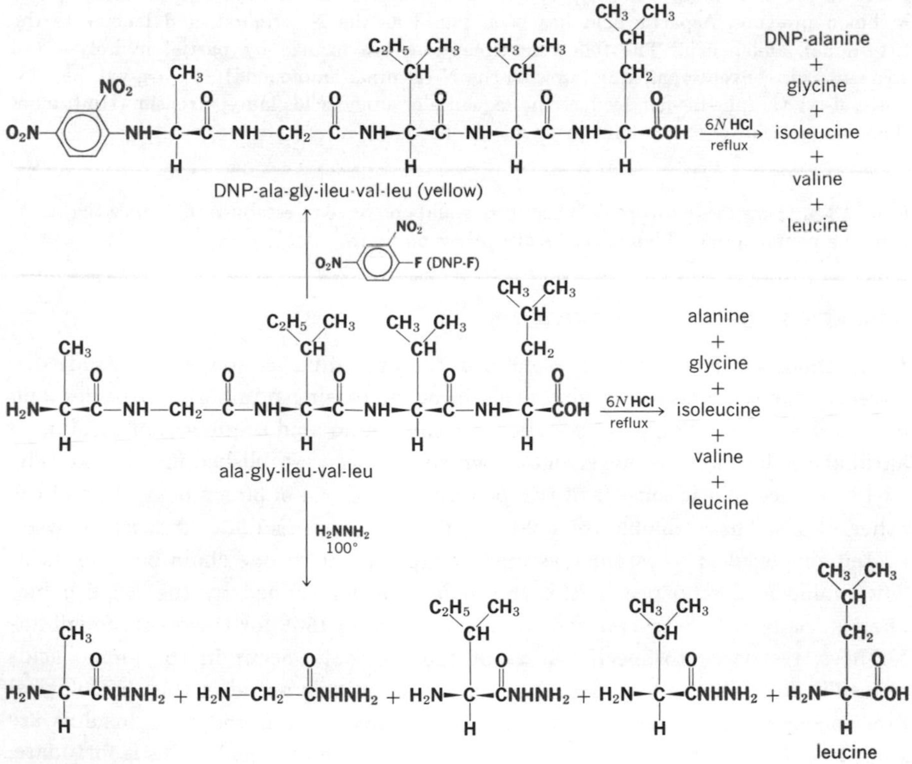

Fig. 13-16. N-Terminal amino acids in a peptide are often identified as their dinitrophenyl derivatives. C-Terminal amino acids can be found by the hydrazine reaction shown.

Up to three different tripeptides will be isolated, resulting from hydrolysis of different peptide bonds. The sequence of amino acids in any tripeptide is easily determinable, since the two end amino acids can be identified by the methods of Fig. 13-16. If the amino acid composition of the pentapeptide is known, determining the structures of any two tripeptides derived from the pentapeptide is sufficient to determine the structure of the pentapeptide. Alternatively, one can deduce the structure of the pentapeptide from that of any one tripeptide, if one knows the pentapeptide's N-terminal and C-terminal amino acids.

$$\text{ala-gly-ileu-val-leu} \xrightarrow[\text{1N HCl}]{80°} \begin{array}{l} \text{ileu-val-leu} \\ \text{gly-ileu-val} \\ \text{ala-gly-ileu} \end{array}$$

Fig. 13-17. The determination of the sequence of amino acids in any two tripeptides is sufficient to determine the sequence in a pentapeptide from which they are derived by partial hydrolysis.

Prob. 13-7. The decapeptide *hypertensin* is formed in the kidneys and promotes a rise in blood pressure. Aspartic acid has been found as the N-terminal, and leucine as the C-terminal, amino acid. The following tripeptides are formed by partial hydrolysis (all written, as is conventional, starting with the N-terminal amino acid): asp-arg-val; his-pro-phe; val-tyr-val; phe-his-leu. Deduce the sequence of amino acids in hypertensin. (Hint: more than one molecule of some amino acids may be present.)

Prob. 13-8. How many dipeptide structures would one have to establish to deduce the structure of a pentapeptide which gave the dipeptides on hydrolysis?

PRIMARY STRUCTURE OF PROTEINS

By methods similar to those presented in the preceding section, scientists are discovering the sequences of amino acids in an increasing number of peptides, and even in proteins. The primary structure (the amino acid sequence) of insulin, an antidiabetic hormone, is one structure which has been established in this way (Fig. 13-18). Notice that it consists of two peptide chains, one of 30 amino acids, and the other of 21. These chains are held together by two disulfide linkages between cysteine molecules; a cysteine-cysteine linkage also folds one chain back on itself. The amino acid sequence in this molecule was determined by the English biochemist Sanger; he was awarded the Nobel Prize in 1958 for this work. Small differences, restricted to specific areas of the molecule, occur in the amino acids of insulin from different species of animals, but these do not alter the physiological function of the molecules. (Note that beef, horse, sheep, and pork insulins are slightly different, but that whale and pork insulin are identical). This is fortunate, for diabetics who become allergic to one type of insulin may begin using insulin from another source, and thereby avoid the allergic reactions.

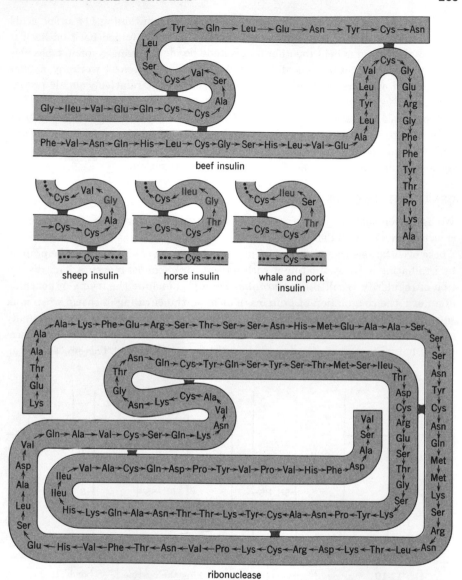

Fig. 13-18. The primary structures (amino acid sequences) of the hormone insulin and the enzyme ribonuclease. In these formulas, asparagine is abbreviated as "asn" (instead of asp-NH_2) and glutamine as "gln" (instead of glu-NH_2). Both structures are made more globular by the S-S linkages of cystine (shown in red). (From *Introduction to Molecular Biology* by G. H. Haggis, D. Michie, A. R. Muir, K. B. Roberts, and P. B. M. Walker, John Wiley and Sons, Inc., New York, 1964, p. 45.)

The primary structure of the enzyme ribonuclease, containing 114 amino acids, is now also known. It is a single-chain protein, which is folded back on itself in several places and is held together by disulfide bonds between cysteine molecules. This primary structure was determined after several years' work by a team of research workers, although ribonuclease is only a relatively small protein molecule.

A protein's primary structure is only the first thing one needs to know in order to be able to say that its complete "structure" is known; the secondary, tertiary, and even quaternary structure must also be discovered. We shall examine these terms in order, after brief mention of protein denaturation.

DENATURATION OF PROTEINS

We have seen that the primary structures of proteins are complex. Other levels of structure involve well-defined orientations of the polymers, as we shall see shortly. These orientations can be disturbed in a number of ways—by heating the protein, by irradiating it, or by treating it with solvents or chemical reagents. This disruption of regularity is called *denaturation*. Examples include the frying or poaching of an egg, the coagulation of proteins in alcohol, the curdling of casein when milk sours, and the curling or straightening of hair. Once denatured, a protein usually cannot resume its former shape. In most cases this is regrettable, but the modification of hair character is of commercial importance (Fig. 13-19). This process is usu-

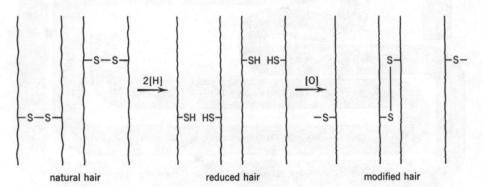

Fig. 13-19. Waving of hair involves first breaking the cystine S—S bonds, then reforming them in a new way.

ally accomplished by reduction with thioglycollic acid, which breaks the hair's cystine disulfide bonds to create cysteine sulfhydryl groups. The reduced hair is then placed on rollers or curlers, or is otherwise constrained to a desired configuration, and the mercaptan groups are reoxidized to the disulfides. Thus, the new bonds formed do not ordinarily develop between the same amino acids as those broken earlier and a new "permanent" set is achieved—until the hair grows.

SECONDARY STRUCTURE OF PROTEINS

Suppose we prepare a polymer containing 100 units of a single amino acid. This molecule might be expected to assume an almost infinite variety of shapes, being randomly tangled like a long thread. To the contrary, most such polymers automatically acquire a regular structure in which the chain is coiled into a spiral known as a *helix*. Like a spiral staircase or a screw, a helix can be either right- or left-handed; for a polymer of L-amino acids, however, the right-handed helix seems to be a little more stable.

In the so-called α-helix suggested by Linus Pauling, the spiral is held together in part by hydrogen bonds. Each bond formed ties the N—H group of one peptide linkage to the oxygen of the C=O group above it on the next turn of the helix, four amino acid units farther along the chain. In Fig. 13-20, the drawing on the right shows how hydrogen bonding (C=O···HN) stabilizes the α-helix. The medium red balls represent amino acid side chains, the black balls carbon atoms, the dark red balls nitrogen atoms, and the light red balls oxygen atoms. There are 3.6 amino acid units for each turn of the helix, and after 18 amino acid units in the chain returns exactly to its starting point. Notice that the substituent

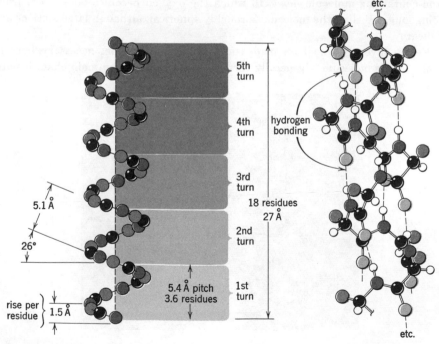

Fig. 13-20. A polypeptide coiled into an α-helix. The helix is held together by hydrogen bonds between —NH and C=O groups (shown as dotted lines in the drawing on the right). (From *Scientific American*, December 1961. Used with permission.)

groups, which distinguish the amino acids from one another, project outward from this basic core. The drawing on the left shows the five turns required to return to the start of the helix. In this drawing a carbonyl group is represented by a dark red ball, an NH group by a light ball, and the remainder of the amino acid by a black ball.

The arrangement in space of the polyamide chain to which the substituent groups are attached defines the *secondary structure* of a protein molecule. Although the helix is not the only type of secondary structure a protein may have (in silk protein, for example, pleated sheets of molecules apparently occur), it seems to be of great importance.

TERTIARY STRUCTURE

A molecule like ribonuclease cannot be completely coiled into a helix because the presence of the numerous disulfide linkages would prevent such coilage. Even if a protein molecule contains none of the cysteine required for this type of cross-linkage, however, it is seldom the long thin molecule predicted by the helical theory. The protein myoglobin is an example (Fig. 13-21). This is an oxygen-carrying protein which tints muscle tissue red; it is found in especially high concentration in birds and whales. Myoglobin contains the protein *globin,* which consists of a single chain of 153 amino acid units without any cysteine, and the iron-containing molecule *heme,* to which the oxygen becomes bound. Far from being long and slim, the molecule is roughly spherical, although large sections are helical.

Recent investigations have made some minor modifications necessary, but the shape of the molecule is generally correct. The course of the main chain is indi-

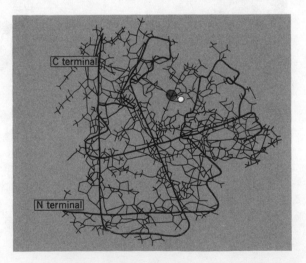

Fig. 13-21. An atomic model of sperm whale myoglobin. The polypeptide backbone is shown in black, the heme group, containing the iron atom, in red. [From J. C. Kendrew et al., *Nature,* **190,** 666 (1961).]

cated by the black cord in Fig. 13-21; the terminal amino and carboxyl groups are marked. The iron atom is represented by a red ball, and a water molecule presumed to be coordinated to it is represented by a small white one. All the other atoms are represented by Dreiding models: A carbon atom is shown as four spokes pointing to the corners of a tetrahedron, a benzene ring is shown as a hexagonal ring, and so on. The heme group is accommodated in a pocket formed by the globin chain.

The structures of myglobin and that of hemoglobin are known from X-ray studies of Kendrew and Perutz, Cambridge University, for which they won the Nobel Prize in 1963. The helices are apparently folded back and forth on one another in a complicated and not especially symmetrical way. When we speak of the *tertiary structure* of a protein, we mean this ultimate arrangement of the (mainly) helical chains.

We know some of the reasons that cause this final twisting and curving of protein molecules, but not others. One simple cause is the presence of the amino acid proline. Look again at the structure of the helix (Fig. 13-20) and notice how the structure is held together by hydrogen bonds. Next look at the structure of proline shown in the lower left-hand corner of the oxytocin molecule in Fig. 13-15. It is the only amino acid that has its side chain attached to the nitrogen atom, so that the crucial N—H bond needed for hydrogen bonding is missing. A helix appears to bend where a proline molecule occurs; myoglobin for example, contains four molecules of proline, each at a corner. There are other subtler causes of bending—the attraction or repulsion of charged amino acids, for example. Undoubtedly other important reasons will be discovered as investigations proceed.

In a protein involving perhaps thousands of functional groups, is it profitable to adopt an organic-chemical outlook and to hope to understand its properties in terms of the simple reactions of the individual functional groups? Not only is this profitable, it is essential, for each protein ultimately owes its physiological activity to these reactions. And, despite a protein's complexity, straightforward chemical reactions can often be performed on it. Many students have noticed the yellow color that develops when nitric acid comes into contact with the skin. This color arises from nitration of the aromatic rings present in proteins, giving rise to yellow nitro-aromatics. Subtler and more deliberate chemical transformations are being used to explore the active sites of enzymes. If a protein is treated with nitrous acid, for example, the free amino group in the side chain of lysine is removed and replaced by a hydroxyl group. If lysine is actively involved in the functioning of an enzyme, this change may inactivate it. Analogously, the hydroxyl groups in serine or threonine can be esterified and a variety of other transformations readily imagined.

One final point may be made about the structure of myoglobin, which may prove to be true for most other globular (semispherical) proteins. A detailed study of myoglobin's structure discloses that the amino acids with hydrocarbon (nonpolar) side chains lie mainly on the *inside* of the structure, whereas the polar and ionic amino acid units lie mainly on the surface of the molecule and make it soluble in water. One then sees something like a small hydrocarbon sphere with ionic groups on the surface, somewhat resembling the picture of an emulsion of oil in water (Fig. 11-22). The molecule of heme, together with the iron atom which carries oxygen to the cells, is partially buried within the hydrocarbon part of the globin molecule.

QUATERNARY STRUCTURE

With all of this, there is still a fourth important level of structural complexity of proteins—the quaternary structure; protein subunits can be joined together into still larger molecules. Hemoglobin, which carries oxygen in the red cells of the blood, affords an excellent example of the importance of quaternary structure. It is composed of two pairs of two different proteins, each about the size and shape of the myoglobin molecule and each containing a molecule of heme. In Fig. 13-22, the drawings follow the representation scheme used in three-dimensional models built by M. F. Perutz and his co-workers. The irregular blocks represent electron density patterns at various levels in the hemoglobin molecule. The four subunits are arranged tetrahedrally: Two identical *alpha* chains (light blocks) and two identical *beta* chains (dark blocks). The letter N in the top view identifies the amino ends of the two alpha chains; the letter C identifies the carboxyl ends. Each chain enfolds a heme group (red disk), the iron-containing structure that binds oxygen to the molecule. The four subunits are held together by polar and ionic forces but not, apparently, by covalent bonds.

It is remarkable that, despite the similarity in physiological function and in size and shape (as revealed by X-ray analysis) between myoglobin and the two types of hemoglobin subunits, only 24 out of 152 amino acid units appear in the same place in all three chains. Nature has apparently devised quite different ways to accomplish the same task!

Fig. 13-22. The hemoglobin molecule as deduced from X-ray diffraction studies is shown from above (left) and side (right). (From M. F. Perutz, *Scientific American,* November, 1964, p. 65. Used with permission.)

Prob. 13-9. A hexapeptide (A) was treated with 2,4-dinitrofluorobenzene, then hydrolyzed to give *glycine,* L-*valine,* L-*serine* and two moles of L-*alanine*. When A was heated with hydrazine at 100°, the only free amino acid isolated was alanine. Partial hydrolysis of the hexapeptide gave two tripeptides. One of these, B, was completely hydrolyzed to give L-alanine, L-serine, and L-*phenylalanine;* on heating with hydrazine, it gave L-serine. The second tripeptide, C, gave L-serine, L-alanine, and glycine on complete hydrolysis. Give structures for the compound in italics. What is the structure of A?

Prob. 13-10. Draw all stereoisomers of the following compound:

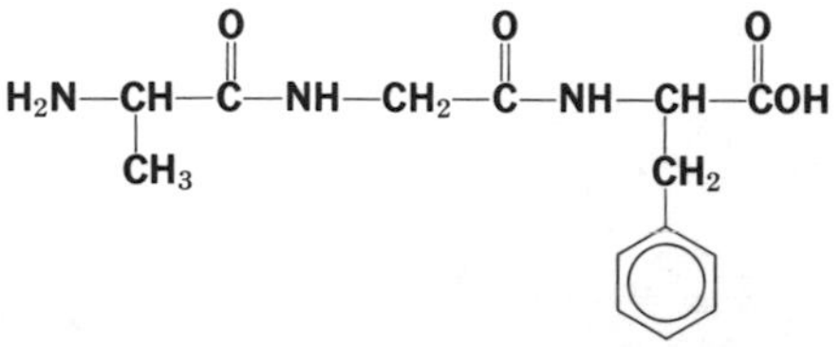

$$\underset{\underset{CH_3}{|}}{H_2N-CH}-\overset{\overset{O}{\|}}{C}-NH-CH_2-\overset{\overset{O}{\|}}{C}-NH-\underset{\underset{CH_2}{|}}{CH}-\overset{\overset{O}{\|}}{C}OH$$

Prob. 13-11. Indicate by equations all the steps necessary for the preparation of the tripeptide glycyl-alanyl-valine.

Prob. 13-12. Explain what is meant by the following terms. Illustrate where possible by a formula or equation.

(a) dipeptide

(b) basic amino acid

(c) polypeptide

(d) denatured protein

(e) Van Slyke determination

CHAPTER

14

BIOCHEMICAL REACTIONS AND METABOLISM

Substantially all of the chemical reactions discussed in the foregoing chapters occur in living systems. Esters are formed and hydrolyzed, aldehydes are oxidized to acids and reduced to alcohols, and double bonds are hydrated or otherwise transformed. In contrast to the often drastic conditions and potent chemicals used in the laboratory for these reactions, biological systems employ only the physiological conditions of aqueous solutions and body temperatures. In this chapter we shall briefly explore some of the pathways living systems use to carry out standard organic reactions.

ENZYMES AND COENZYMES

Organic reactions which require drastic conditions in the laboratory proceed rapidly in biological systems because of the extremely potent catalysis of enzymes, the protein molecules that increase the speed with which reactions occur. α-Chymotrypsin, a protein whose molecular weight is about 25,000, can serve as a general example of an enzyme. Produced in the pancreas and secreted into the small intestine, chymotrypsin brings about the hydrolysis of amide linkages in proteins under nearly neutral conditions, whereas the same process requires hot concentrated hydrochloric acid in the laboratory. The enzyme accomplishes this by replacing the slow, direct reaction between an amide and water with two or more rapid reactions in the living organism. A simple, though crude, analogy within the realm of organic laboratory reactions may be seen in the catalysis by sulfuric acid of the reaction between two moles of an alcohol to give a dialkyl ether. The uncat-

alyzed reaction is immeasurably slow, but the acid brings about the rapid formation of a reactive carbonium ion intermediate.

Several characteristics of enzymes should be emphasized. In the first place they
are usually effective in extremely small amounts; in some cases a single enzyme
molecule can catalyze the reaction of 3,000,000 molecules of a substance per
minute. Secondly, the enzyme, like any true catalyst, is not used up in the reaction, nor does it change the position of equilibrium. It accelerates a reaction but
cannot force one to proceed that is energetically unfavorable.

Finally, enzymes are remarkably specific in their catalysis. α-Chymotrypsin, for
example, does not catalyze the hydrolysis of all amide linkages, but only those
involving the carbonyl group of the amino acids L-tyrosine, L-phenylalanine,
L-tryptophan, or L-methionine. The enzyme trypsin, on the other hand, will
hydrolyze only amide linkages whose carbonyl groups are derived from L-lysine or
L-arginine. Similar or greater specificity is shown by many other enzymes.

Prob. 14-1. Which of the following peptide bonds should hydrolyze more rapidly in the
presence of chymotrypsin? Of-trypsin? Indicate the expected products.

   (a) gly · tyr · phe   (c) gly · ala · lys
   (b) try · arg · leu   (d) val · thr · met

Over a thousand different enzymes are known, and many more are discovered
each year. The International Union for Biochemistry has proposed a systematic
classification of enzymes according to the general types of reactions which they
catalyze (Fig. 14-1). α-Chymotrypsin, it may be seen, belongs to the third class,
hydrolases.

In carrying out their functions, enzymes are frequently assisted by much smaller
organic molecules called coenzymes. Coenzymes usually serve as counterfoils to the
organic substrate undergoing reaction. Thus, if the substrate is to be oxidized, the
coenzyme provides the oxidant and is itself reduced; if phosphate is released by
the substrate it is stored on the coenzyme, and so on. Structures of some of the
coenzymes which will be cited in this chapter are shown in Fig. 14-2 (p. 276).

For the most part, the actual functional groups of the coenzymes are small parts
of the molecules, indicated in red in Fig. 14-2. The adenosine di- and triphosphates
(ADP, ATP) serve as sources and repositories of phosphoric acid, as will be discussed later. The positively charged form of nicotinamide adenine dinucleotide
(NAD^+)* is an oxidizing agent, while coenzyme A (CoA) is acylated on its mercapto
group, from which the acyl group can be transferred elsewhere. Both NAD
and CoA contain vitamins as part of their structures: NAD contains nicotinamide
and CoA contains pantothenic acid. The necessity for these vitamins in the diet is
probably explained by their role in the coenzymes shown.

It is interesting that the structures are quite similar at their nonreactive ends.

---

* This coenzyme was formerly called diphosphonucleotide (DPN^+ in its oxidized form).

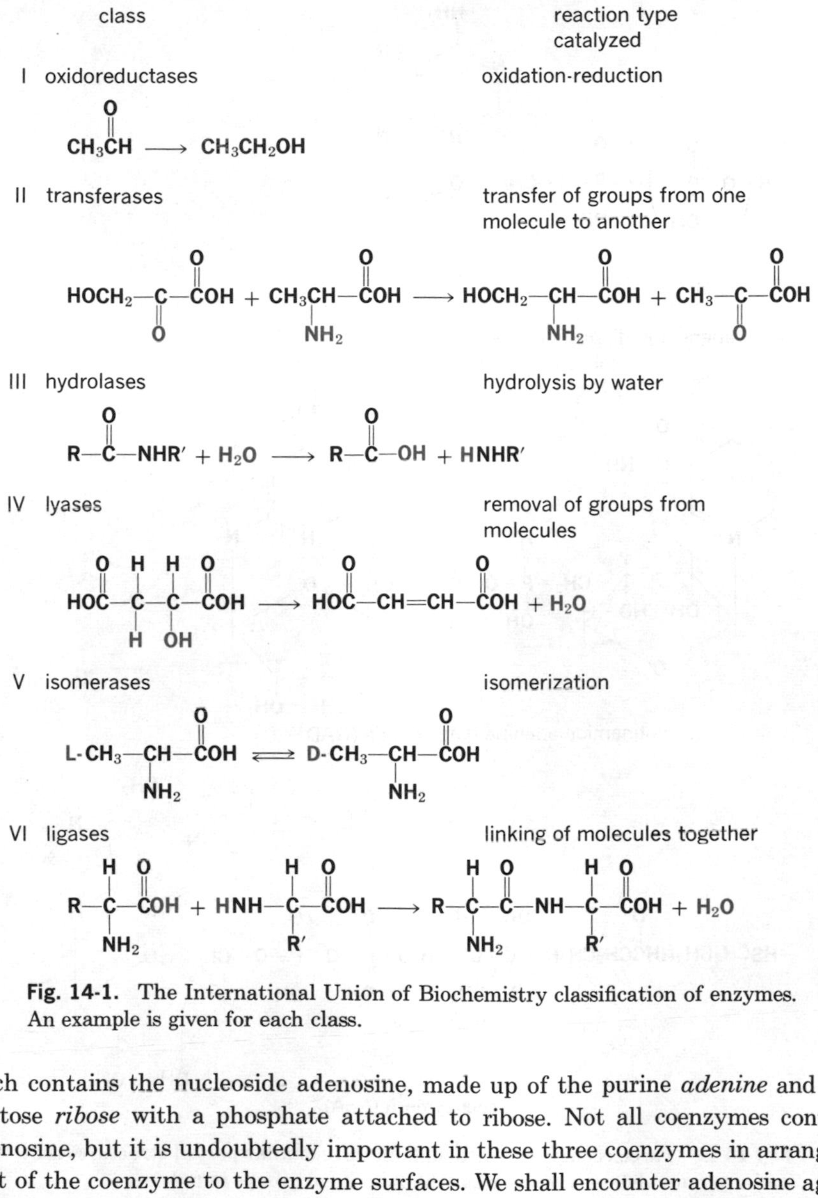

class	reaction type catalyzed

I oxidoreductases   oxidation-reduction

$$CH_3\overset{O}{\overset{\|}{C}}H \longrightarrow CH_3CH_2OH$$

II transferases   transfer of groups from one molecule to another

$$HOCH_2-\overset{O}{\overset{\|}{C}}-\overset{O}{\overset{\|}{C}}OH + CH_3\overset{}{\underset{NH_2}{C}}H-\overset{O}{\overset{\|}{C}}OH \longrightarrow HOCH_2-\overset{}{\underset{NH_2}{C}}H-\overset{O}{\overset{\|}{C}}OH + CH_3-\overset{O}{\overset{\|}{C}}-\overset{O}{\overset{\|}{C}}OH$$

III hydrolases   hydrolysis by water

$$R-\overset{O}{\overset{\|}{C}}-NHR' + H_2O \longrightarrow R-\overset{O}{\overset{\|}{C}}-OH + HNHR'$$

IV lyases   removal of groups from molecules

$$HO\overset{O}{\overset{\|}{C}}-\overset{H}{\underset{H}{C}}-\overset{H}{\underset{OH}{C}}-\overset{O}{\overset{\|}{C}}OH \longrightarrow HO\overset{O}{\overset{\|}{C}}-CH{=}CH-\overset{O}{\overset{\|}{C}}OH + H_2O$$

V isomerases   isomerization

$$L\text{-}CH_3-\overset{}{\underset{NH_2}{C}}H-\overset{O}{\overset{\|}{C}}OH \rightleftharpoons D\text{-}CH_3-\overset{}{\underset{NH_2}{C}}H-\overset{O}{\overset{\|}{C}}OH$$

VI ligases   linking of molecules together

$$R-\overset{H}{\underset{NH_2}{C}}-\overset{O}{\overset{\|}{C}}OH + HNH-\overset{H}{\underset{R'}{C}}-\overset{O}{\overset{\|}{C}}OH \longrightarrow R-\overset{H}{\underset{NH_2}{C}}-\overset{O}{\overset{\|}{C}}-NH-\overset{H}{\underset{R'}{C}}-\overset{O}{\overset{\|}{C}}OH + H_2O$$

Fig. 14-1. The International Union of Biochemistry classification of enzymes. An example is given for each class.

Each contains the nucleoside adenosine, made up of the purine *adenine* and the pentose *ribose* with a phosphate attached to ribose. Not all coenzymes contain adenosine, but it is undoubtedly important in these three coenzymes in arranging a fit of the coenzyme to the enzyme surfaces. We shall encounter adenosine again in the next chapter when we discuss nucleic acids.

METABOLISM OF CARBOHYDRATES

Since carbohydrates remain the major source of energy for most peoples of the world, let us begin our discussion of biological transformations with the steps in the metabolism of glucose in the body. This process takes place largely in the liver and releases energy (690 kcal per mole of glucose) (Fig. 14-3). Many steps are

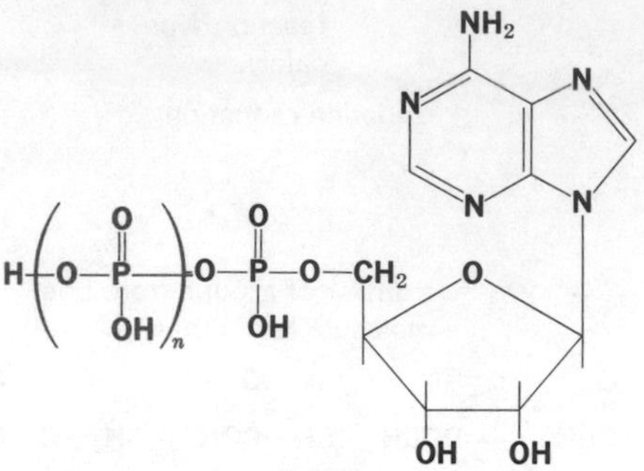

adenosine diphosphate (ADP): $n = 1$
triphosphate (ATP): $n = 2$

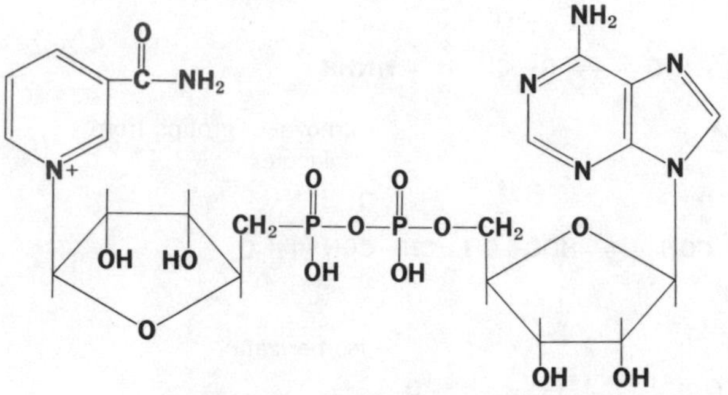

nicotinamide adenine dinucleotide (NAD$^+$)

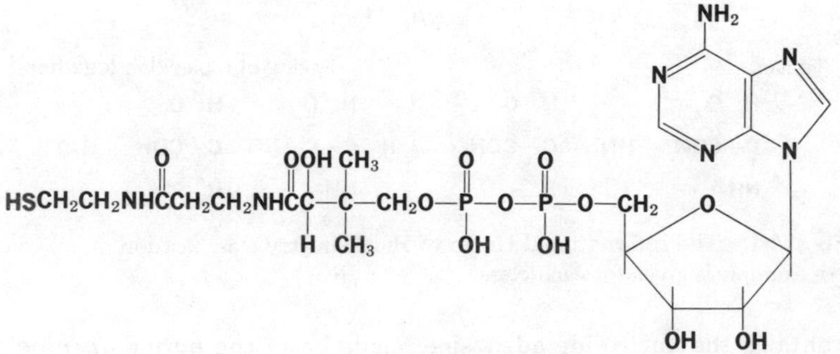

coenzyme A (CoA)

Fig. 14-2. Three coenzymes. Although all have similar partial structures they undergo quite different reactions at the functional groups in red.

involved, each catalyzed by an enzyme, yet the organic reactions involved are not essentially different from those we have already discussed.

Most of the carbohydrates used nutritionally are consumed in the form of starch or sucrose, and the digestive tract contains specific enzymes for the hydrolysis of these di- and polysaccharides. For simplicity, let us assume that pure glucose has been eaten and follow its metabolism. In the first step, the glucose is converted to

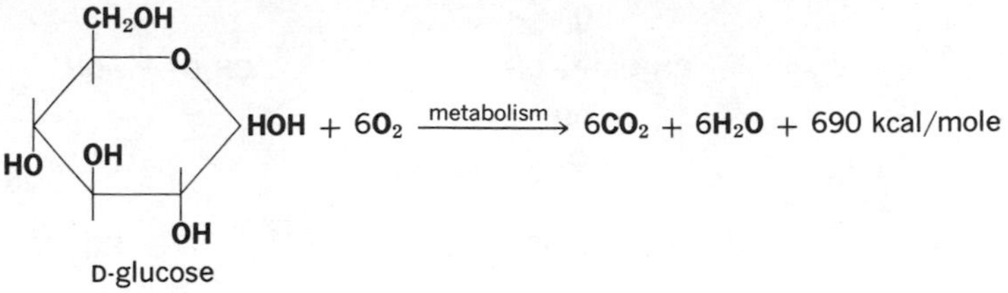

$$\text{D-glucose} \quad \text{HOH} + 6O_2 \xrightarrow{\text{metabolism}} 6CO_2 + 6H_2O + 690 \text{ kcal/mole}$$

Fig. 14-3. Total metabolic oxidation of glucose provides a large amount of energy.

its 6-phosphate ester (Fig. 14-4). The biological esterifying agent is a derivative of phosphoric acid anhydride, just as acetic anhydride is used for the preparation of acetate esters in the laboratory; the specific reagent used biologically is adenosine triphosphate (Fig. 14-2). The enzyme *hexokinase* catalyzes this reaction, and since its function is to transfer the phosphate group from one molecule to another, it is classified as a transferase (Class II of Fig. 14-1).

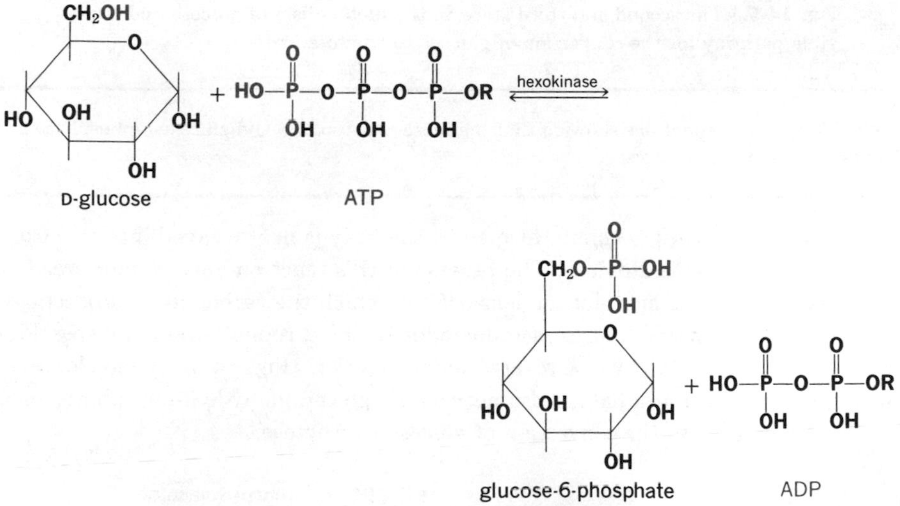

Fig. 14-4. Glucose metabolism begins with the formation of glucose-6-phosphate. The complete structure of ATP is found in Fig. 14-2.

Next, glucose-6-phosphate is isomerized to fructose-6-phosphate by the enzyme phosphoglucoisomerase (an isomerase, Class V) and the latter is esterified a second time by adenosine triphosphate. Although isomerization of glucose to fructose appears complex, it can be accomplished in the laboratory (Fig. 14-5). If the aldehyde group in glucose is converted to its enol, the resulting compound is the enol (more accurately, the enediol) of both glucose and fructose—and also of mannose. Ketonization of this enol may then form fructose.

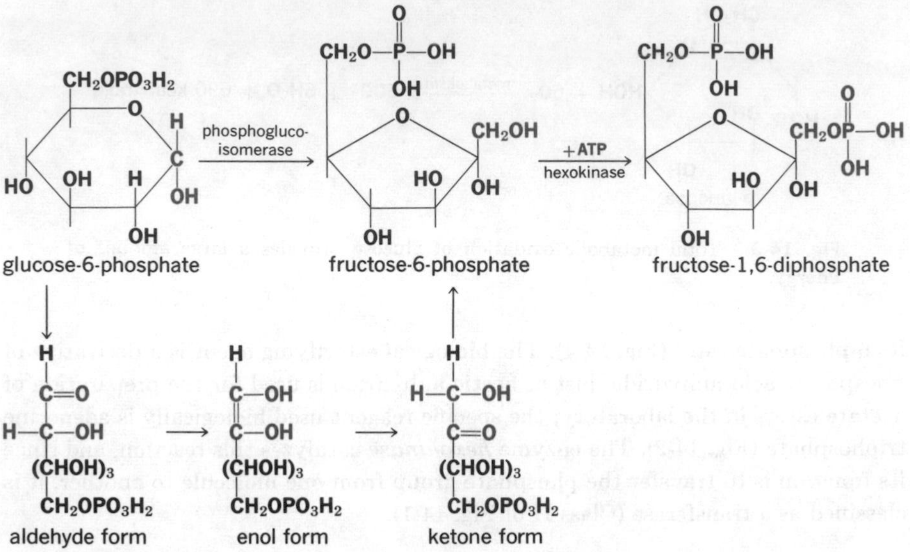

Fig. 14-5. The second and third steps in the metabolism of glucose and a possible pathway for the conversion of glucose to fructose.

Prob. 14-2. Write equations showing that mannose-6-phosphate and glucose-6-phosphate are the same in their enol forms.

The fructose-1,6-diphosphate formed in this way is next cleaved into two fragments by the enzyme aldolase. The reverse of this reaction may be more readily recognized, since it is an aldol condensation in which the carbon atom adjacent to the carbonyl group in dihydroxyacetone adds to the carbonyl group of glyceraldehyde. The cleavage is then a reverse aldol reaction (Fig. 14-6). After cleavage, dihydroxyacetone phosphate is isomerized to glyceraldehyde-3-phosphate, in a reaction analogous to the conversion of glucose to fructose.

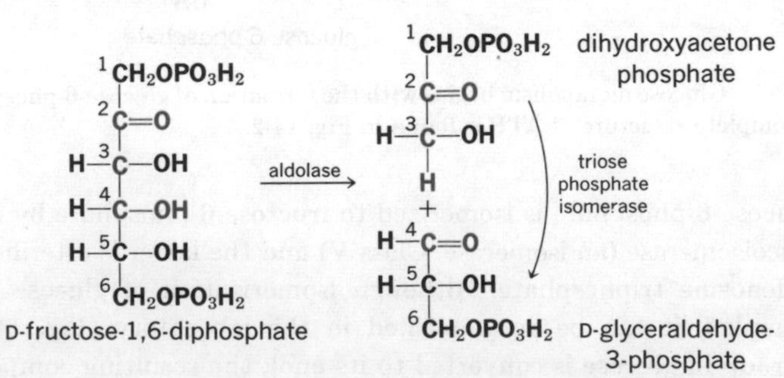

Fig. 14-6. Fructose is cleaved by a reverse aldol condensation, and the upper cleavage fragment (dihydroxyacetone phosphate) is isomerized into a second mole of glyceraldehyde-3-phosphate.

Up to this point, the reactions in the metabolism of glucose have involved only ester formation, tautomerization, or reverse aldol condensations, all of which require only acidic or basic catalysis and no oxidation or reduction reactions. In the next step, glyceraldehyde-3-phosphate must be oxidized to glyceric acid 1,3-diphosphate. Obviously, an oxidizing agent is needed, and the one provided by nature is nicotinamide adenine dinucleotide, NAD$^+$ (Fig. 14-7, see also Fig. 14-2).

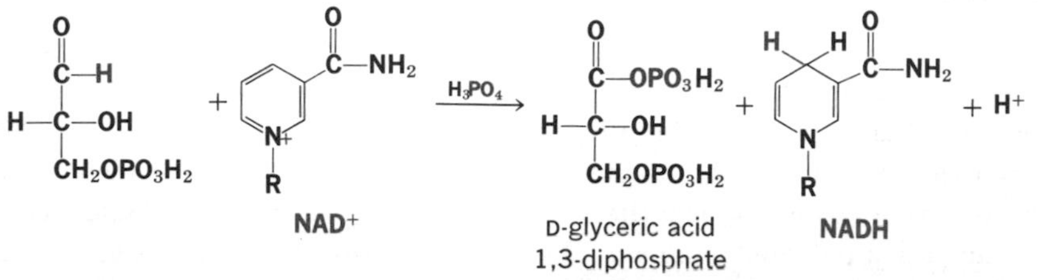

Fig. 14-7. Oxidation of glyceraldehyde-3-phosphate to glyceric acid-1,3-diphosphate involves the reduction of NAD$^+$; complete structure of NAD$^+$ is found in Fig. 14-2.

Although no exact analogy to this reaction has been presented in this book, the oxidation of aldehydes to acids was discussed in Chapter 9; more exact laboratory analogies are also known.

After this oxidation reaction, the metabolism of glucose continues with a series of phosphorylations and tautomerizations. The 1-phosphate group of glyceric acid 1,3-diphosphate is transferred back to ADP with the help of the enzyme phosphoglyceryl kinase, regenerating the ATP needed in the first step of glucose metabolism. Next, the phosphate group is transferred from the 3- to the 2- position, so that subsequent loss of water forms the phosphate ester of an enol (Fig. 14-8).

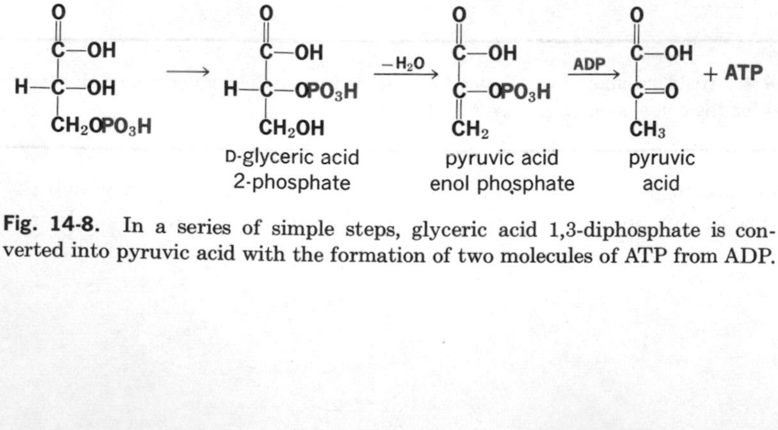

Fig. 14-8. In a series of simple steps, glyceric acid 1,3-diphosphate is converted into pyruvic acid with the formation of two molecules of ATP from ADP.

Prob. 14-3. Show by a simple balanced equation that the conversion of glucose to pyruvic acid represents an oxidation.

Transfer of this phosphate to ADP leads to the important metabolic intermediate pyruvic acid.

ANAEROBIC GLUCOSE METABOLISM

Thus far, glucose metabolism is the same, no matter whether the process takes place in human muscle tissue, in the liver, or in a bottle of wine fermenting in the cellar of a French chateau. The subsequent steps diverge; the conversion of glucose to pyruvic acid is an oxidation, but in an anaerobic process (that which occurs in the absence of air) no oxygen, the ultimate oxidizing agent, is available, and, as a consequence, a reduction step must be coupled to the oxidation to keep things in balance. In muscle tissue, an anaerobic process takes place and the pyruvic acid is reduced to lactic acid (Fig. 14-9). The reducing agent is the same NADH formed in the previous oxidation step; so a small amount of NAD^+ can catalyze the metabolism of a great deal of glucose in the muscle by being oxidized and reduced many times.

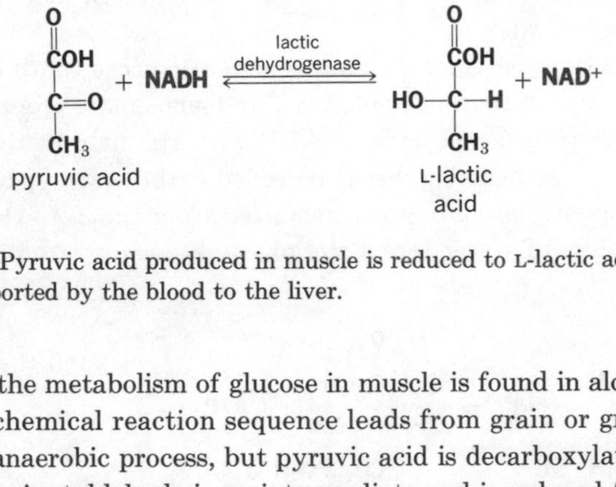

Fig. 14-9. Pyruvic acid produced in muscle is reduced to L-lactic acid, which is then transported by the blood to the liver.

A variant on the metabolism of glucose in muscle is found in alcoholic fermentation. Here the chemical reaction sequence leads from grain or grapes to ethanol. This is also an anaerobic process, but pyruvic acid is decarboxylated before reduction (Fig. 14-10). Acetaldehyde is an intermediate and is reduced to ethanol. Again the reduction is brought about by NADH, so that oxidation and reduction are kept in balance.

Prob. 14-4. Write summarizing balanced equations (a) for the conversion of glucose to lactic acid, (b) for the conversion of glucose to ethanol.

An important aspect of carbohydrate metabolism is the way in which the body makes use of this process to maintain life. In the first place, many of the reactions

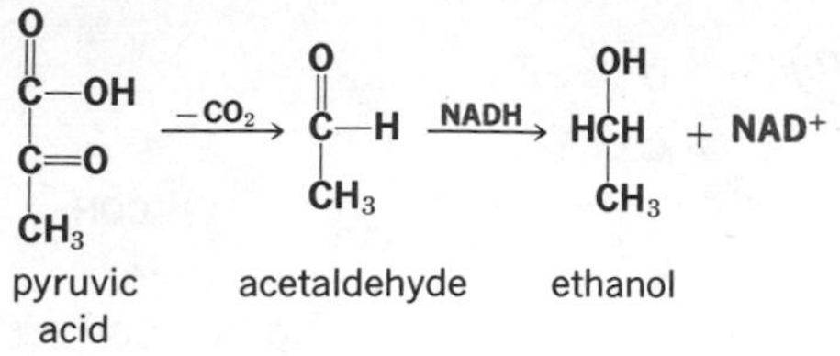

Fig. 14-10. In fermentation of glucose, pyruvic acid is decarboxylated and the acetaldehyde produced is reduced to ethanol.

shown are exothermic—heat is given off and body temperature is maintained; somewhat more than half of the available energy appears in this form. Energy is also stored for use in other chemical processes that require it. To see how this is accomplished, notice the important role played by ATP. Each molecule of glucose metabolized requires two molecules of ATP, both of which are involved in the formation of fructose diphosphate. These esterification reactions occur easily and completely because ATP is an anhydride. In later steps ATP is reformed from ADP; a careful analysis of the reactions will show that, in all, twice as much ATP is formed as is consumed. Thus, part of the energy released in the metabolism of glucose is stored by converting the less reactive ADP to the more reactive ATP. A crude analogy might be given. If we heated a tube and the heat were going to waste, we might store some of the energy by using the heat to convert acetic acid to acetic anhydride. If we wanted to get the heat back, we could add the anhydride to water; or, we could be more sophisticated and use the anhydride to carry out some chemical reaction for which the acid alone would not be reactive enough. So it is in biological systems. Energy is stored in ATP and used to carry out reactions that would not occur with a less reactive species.

AEROBIC GLUCOSE METABOLISM

In the presence of oxygen, quite a different fate befalls pyruvic acid. Although the formation of this acid represents a net oxidation from glucose, only 57 kcal of heat is liberated in the process. Thus, the major exothermic steps in the conversion of glucose to carbon dioxide and water lie beyond pyruvic acid. The principal sequence of reactions by which this is effected is known as the *Krebs cycle* (Fig. 14-11). The process is a complicated one, and the details of the enzymes and coenzymes involved will not be included here. Instead, we shall emphasize some of the chemical reactions.

The key compound entering the Krebs cycle is acetylcoenzyme A, with the acetyl group attached to the mercapto group of coenzyme A (Fig. 14-2). It is formed from pyruvic acid by loss of carbon dioxide; it is also, we shall see, a metabolic product of fats and some amino acids. The Krebs cycle therefore plays a central role in the metabolism of all three major types of nutrients. Most of the steps in the cycle have simple analogies among the laboratory reactions seen in earlier chapters.

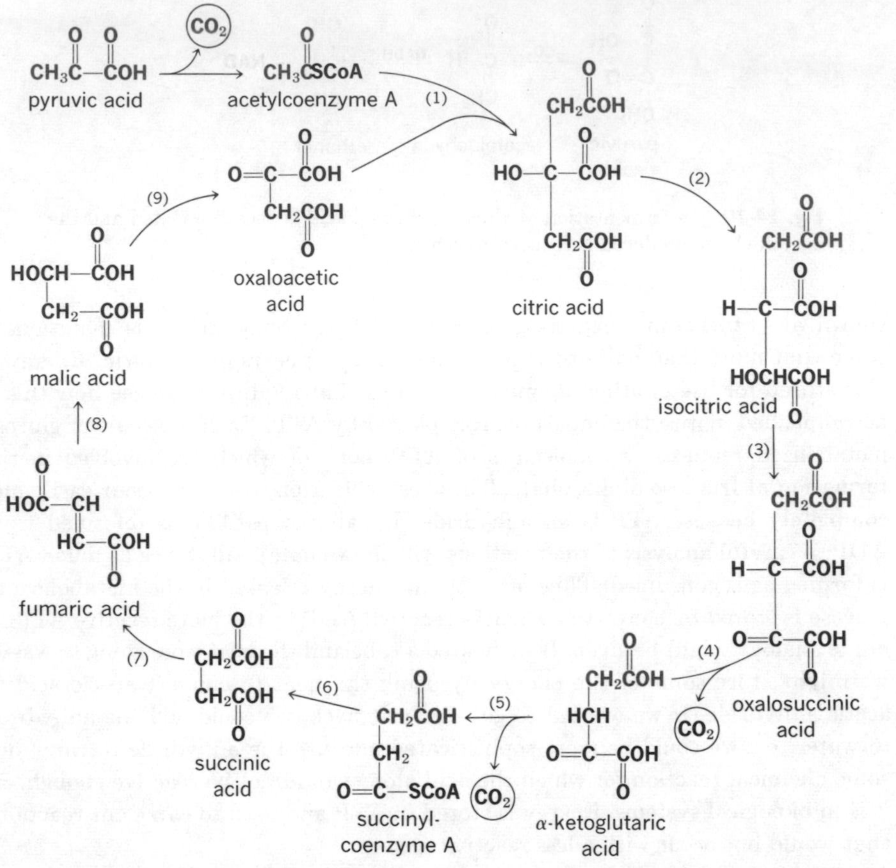

pyruvic acid   acetylcoenzyme A   (1)

oxaloacetic acid

citric acid

isocitric acid

malic acid

(9)   (8)   (2)   (3)

fumaric acid

succinic acid

(7)   (6)   (5)   (4)

succinyl-coenzyme A

α-ketoglutaric acid

oxalosuccinic acid

Fig. 14-11. The Krebs cycle for the conversion of pyruvic acid (via acetyl-coenzyme A) to carbon dioxide. The three molecules of carbon dioxide produced are circled. Notice that the first time through the cycle two carbon dioxide molecules arise from carbon atoms already in the cycle. The complete structure of coenzyme A is found in Fig. 14-2.

Step 1 is a condensation reaction between the acidic α-hydrogens of acetyl-coenzyme A and the carbonyl group of oxaloacetic acid. Step 2 is an isomerization, the details of which are not completely understood. Step 3 is an oxidation in which NAD^+ is involved. The loss of carbon dioxide in step 4 is the decarboxylation of a β-keto acid as discussed in Chapter 12 for substituted acetoacetic acids. Step 5, in which the final molecule of carbon dioxide evolves, is actually a complex series of steps, the same series as is involved in the conversion of pyruvic acid to acetyl-coenzyme A.

Prob. 14-5. Write a balanced equation for step (3) of the Krebs cycle in Fig. 14-11. Use NAD^+ as oxidizing agent.

Although citric acid is a symmetrical molecule, the enzyme which catalyzes its conversion to isocitric acid operates asymmetrically and the original pyruvic acid carbon atoms are distinguishable from those of oxaloacetic acid. However, after hydrolysis to succinic acid (step 6) it is no longer possible to keep track of the individual carbon atoms because of the high degree of symmetry of the molecule. As a consequence, the malic acid formed after oxidation and hydration could have its hydroxyl group as shown, or the bottom methylene group might be substituted by hydroxyl instead. If we began the cycle with pyruvic acid in which all three carbon atoms were labeled with isotopic carbon, the first molecule of carbon dioxide eliminated, which had evolved in the formation of acetylcoenzyme A, would be isotopically labeled. But the second two molecules of carbon dioxide, as circled on the diagram, arise from carbons already in the cycle and would not be labeled. On a second turn of the cycle one of the two carbon dioxide molecules evolved would be labeled.

METABOLISM OF LIPIDS

In higher animals, including man, lipids enter the body through the mouth and pass to the stomach, where they are little affected by the acidic environment. Once in the alkaline conditions of the small intestine, however, the triglycerides are largely hydrolyzed with the help of enzymes known as *lipases*. From the intestines, the hydrolyzed lipids enter the bloodstream and are transported to organs for further metabolism. Passage through the intestinal walls is a complex process, and far from completely understood. In part, the fatty acids themselves are involved, in part the mono-, di- and tri-glycerides. Some of these molecules pass directly into the bloodstream, some arrive there through the lymphatic system.

Once in the bloodstream, the fatty acids are reesterified with glycerol and the triglycerides complexed with blood protein, and transported either to storage sites for deposition as "depot fat" or to body organs, largely the liver, for metabolism. Depot fat is itself available for transport to the liver, and lipids are generally transferred back and forth among the various sites. In the liver, the triglycerides are rehydrolyzed to fatty acids and oxidized, ultimately to carbon dioxide and water. A large amount of energy is released in this oxidation, considerably more per unit of weight than in the metabolism of glucose (Fig. 14-12).

$$\underset{\text{palmitic acid}}{CH_3(CH_2)_{14}\overset{\displaystyle O}{\overset{\|}{C}}OH} + 23O_2 \longrightarrow 16CO_2 + 16H_2O + 2338 \text{ kcal/mol}$$

Fig. 14-12. Fatty acids are oxidized in the body to carbon dioxide and water. A great deal of energy is released, considerably more per gram than from oxidation of carbohydrates.

Prob. 14-6. Compare the relative amounts of energy to be derived from complete combustion of one gram of fat (taking palmitic acid, Fig. 14-12, as a model) and one gram of carbohydrate (taking glucose as a model).

As with glucose, a large number of steps are involved in this conversion. From many observations it has long been recognized that fatty acids are broken down (and synthesized) in units of two carbon atoms. For instance, almost without exception, the fatty acids found in fats of higher plants and animals contain even numbers of carbon atoms. Another important observation was that of Knoop who, in 1904, prepared fatty acids in which one of the hydrogens of the terminal methyl group had been replaced by a phenyl group. When these fatty acids were fed to dogs, the side chains were metabolized, but the aromatic ring was resistant to metabolism and was excreted unchanged. When the aliphatic chain had an even number of carbon atoms, phenylacetic acid was the excretion product, while benzoic acid was formed from fatty acids with an odd number of carbon atoms in

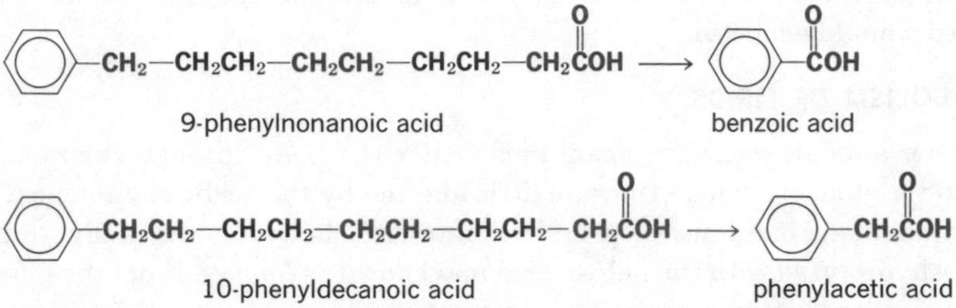

9-phenylnonanoic acid   benzoic acid

10-phenyldecanoic acid   phenylacetic acid

Fig. 14-13. When phenyl substituted fatty acids are metabolized, the end product is benzoic or phenylacetic acid, depending on whether the side chain has an odd or an even number of carbon atoms.

the side chain (Fig. 14-13). Both observations are consistent with the view that two-carbon units are important in lipid metabolism.

The multistep pathway by which fatty acids are broken down in two-carbon units is now rather well understood. The acid is first converted into a thioester derivative of coenzyme A (Fig. 14-14). The resulting ester is oxidized to give an α,β-un-

palmitic acid

Fig. 14-14. In fatty acid metabolism, the acid is esterified with an SH group of coenzyme A, and then oxidized to a conjugated unsaturated derivative. All steps are catalyzed by enzymes.

saturated thioester, which is then hydrated to form a β-hydroxythioester (Fig. 14-15). Oxidation of this alcohol to a ketone (NAD^+ is the oxidizing agent) is followed by a reverse Claisen condensation reaction in which a β-ketoester is hydrolyzed to acetylcoenzyme A and a new fatty acid thioester two carbon atoms shorter than the original (Fig. 14-16). With this new thioester, the whole sequence

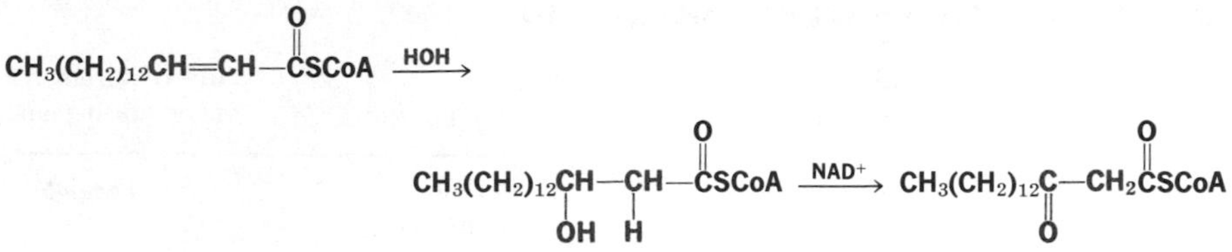

$$CH_3(CH_2)_{12}CH{=}CH{-}\overset{\overset{O}{\|}}{C}SCoA \xrightarrow{\text{HOH}}$$

$$CH_3(CH_2)_{12}\underset{\underset{OH}{|}}{C}H{-}\underset{\underset{H}{|}}{C}H{-}\overset{\overset{O}{\|}}{C}SCoA \xrightarrow{\text{NAD}^+} CH_3(CH_2)_{12}\overset{\overset{O}{\|}}{C}{-}CH_2\overset{\overset{O}{\|}}{C}SCoA$$

Fig. 14-15. The unsaturated thioester is hydrated and oxidized to a β-ketothioester.

of reactions (dehydrogenation, hydration, oxidation, and reverse Claisen condensation) begins again. From palmitic acid, for example, eight units of acetylcoenzyme A can be formed by repetition of these steps.

The two-carbon fragments of acetylcoenzyme A find a variety of biological uses. They may enter the Krebs cycle and be converted into carbon dioxide, thus providing energy; they may be carboxylated to pyruvic acid and ultimately to glu-

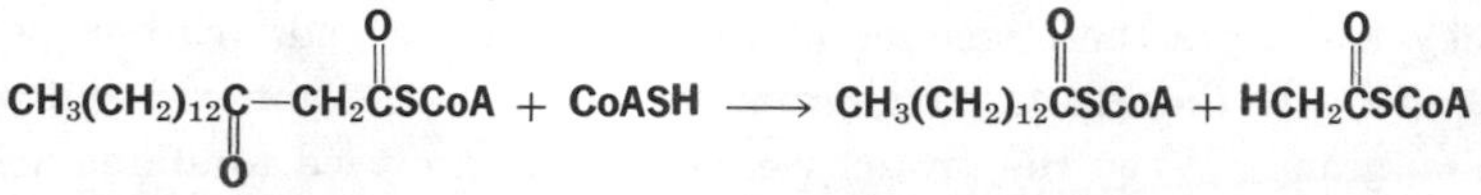

$$CH_3(CH_2)_{12}\overset{\overset{O}{\|}}{C}{-}CH_2\overset{\overset{O}{\|}}{C}SCoA + CoASH \longrightarrow CH_3(CH_2)_{12}\overset{\overset{O}{\|}}{C}SCoA + HCH_2\overset{\overset{O}{\|}}{C}SCoA$$

Fig. 14-16. A 2-carbon fragment is split off by a reverse Claisen condensation, yielding acetylcoenzyme A and the thioester of a new fatty acid.

cose; or, they may serve as building blocks for the biological synthesis of amino acids and a host of other naturally occurring substances, some of which will be discussed in the next chapter.

Prob. 14-7. A recent best-selling book on reducing extols the virtues of losing weight by restricting the intake of carbohydrates while eating as much fat as desired. Does this seem reasonable? (Hint: Consider Prob. 14-6 and Figs. 14-11 and 14-16.)

Prob. 14-8. In the metabolic disease diabetes, acetoacetic acid, β-hydroxybutyric acid, and acetone accumulate in the patient. These are all presumably formed from acetoacetylcoenzyme A, itself formed by the reverse of the reaction of Fig. 14-16,

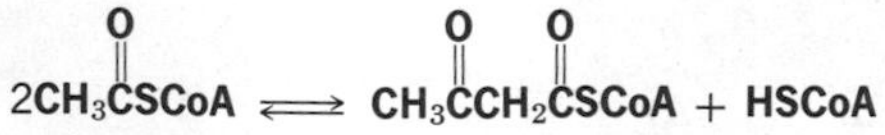

$$2CH_3\overset{\overset{O}{\|}}{C}SCoA \rightleftharpoons CH_3\overset{\overset{O}{\|}}{C}CH_2\overset{\overset{O}{\|}}{C}SCoA + HSCoA$$

Give equations based on analogies from Fig. 14-11 for the conversion of acetoacetic acid to β-hydroxybutyric acid and acetone.

METABOLISM OF AMINO ACIDS

Proteins, the structural matter of flesh, skin, muscles, and nerves, constitute the third member of the triumvirate of nutritive sources in animal metabolism. Of the

Table 14-1. Eight Amino Acids Indispensable in the Human Diet

amino acid	daily requirement for an adult man	amino acid	daily requirement for an adult man
lysine	0.8 g. per day	valine	0.8 g. per day
tryptophan	1.1	methionine	0.25
phenylalanine	1.1	leucine	1.1
threonine	0.7	isoleucine	0.5

approximately 21 amino acids found in the proteins of the human body, most can be synthesized by enzymatic processes, starting from carbohydrates or lipids and an inorganic nitrogen source. Eight, the so-called indispensable or essential amino acids, must be obtained from proteins which are taken in and digested (Table 14-1).

The initial step in the metabolism of proteins is hydrolysis, first to peptides, then to amino acids. The actions of α-chymotrypsin and trypsin were mentioned at the beginning of this chapter: These enzymes, called proteinases, degrade the proteins to peptides. At that point another set of enzymes, the peptidases, take over; they hydrolyze these smaller molecules from the ends (carboxypeptidase from the end with the free carboxyl group, aminopeptidase from the end with the free amino group). When the proteins have been hydrolyzed to amino acids and small peptides, they are absorbed into the bloodstream and carried to the tissues, where they are used in various ways.

Because of the great diversity of structure among the amino acids, we cannot generalize as much about their metabolic pathways as we can about the pathways for carbohydrates and lipids. One important route involves the oxidation and loss of ammonia with the formation of α-keto acids. In the amino acid alanine this process leads to pyruvic acid and then through the Krebs cycle to glucose or fatty acids. Other important constituents of the Krebs cycle, for instance oxaloacetic acid and α-ketoglutaric acid, are also formed directly from the amino acids aspartic acid and glutamic acid by this pathway. Moreover, it is possible to interconvert amino acids by means of the corresponding α-keto acids, as shown in Fig. 14-17.

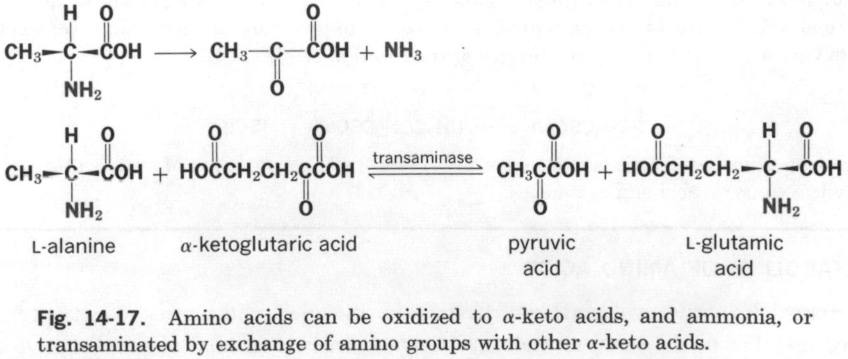

Fig. 14-17. Amino acids can be oxidized to α-keto acids, and ammonia, or transaminated by exchange of amino groups with other α-keto acids.

Thus there is a direct link between carbohydrate and protein metabolism, just as there is between carbohydrate and lipid metabolism.

Prob. 14-9. Show by a balanced equation the interconversion of the amino acids L-glutamic acid and L-aspartic acids with their α-keto acid analogs.

As an example of the metabolism of a more complex amino acid, let us consider some of the products to which phenylalanine is transformed in the body. In the first place phenylalanine may be oxidized in the liver to the amino acid tyrosine,* and thence to 3,4-dihydroxyphenylalanine (DOPA). The latter, in turn, may yield the hormone adrenaline (Fig. 14-18). The skin pigment melanin may also be produced from DOPA, as well as numerous other products.

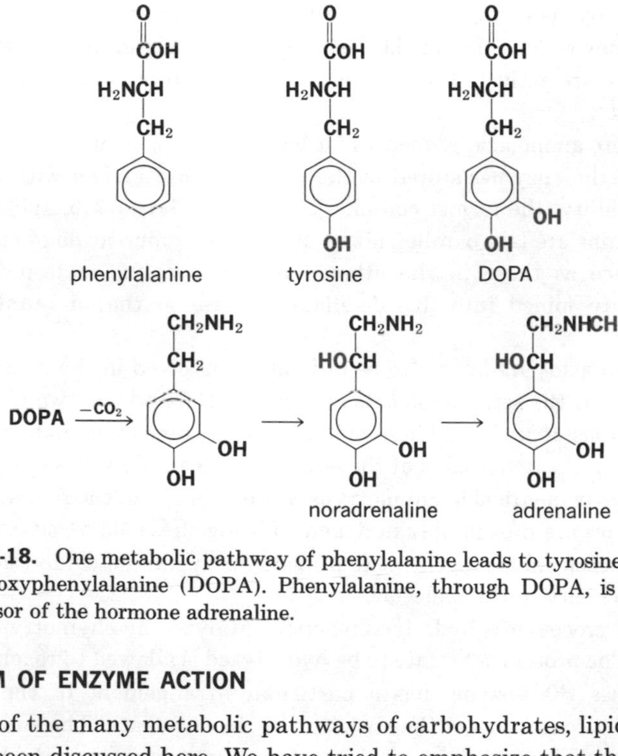

phenylalanine   tyrosine   DOPA

DOPA $\xrightarrow{-CO_2}$ noradrenaline   adrenaline

Fig. 14-18. One metabolic pathway of phenylalanine leads to tyrosine and 3,4-dihydroxyphenylalanine (DOPA). Phenylalanine, through DOPA, is also the precursor of the hormone adrenaline.

MECHANISM OF ENZYME ACTION

Only a few of the many metabolic pathways of carbohydrates, lipids, and amino acids have been discussed here. We have tried to emphasize that this metabolism

---

* Persons afflicted with the disease phenylketonuria lack the enzyme necessary to catalyze this conversion. Other metabolic pathways for phenylalanine become of increased importance, and large quantities of the end products of these paths, phenylpyruvic acid, phenyllactic acid, and phenylacetic acid, accumulate. Among other effects these chemicals cause brain damage. It is estimated that 1% of all mentally retarded persons in the United States may suffer from this disease. Control is possible with diets which include only proteins which are low in phenylalanine.

generally involves simple organic chemical reactions which relate to the general functional group reactions presented in previous chapters. Before proceeding to discuss the biosynthesis of other complex organic molecules, we will briefly describe some aspects of the catalysis mechanisms of enzymes, since these molecules play so decisive a role in biological organic chemistry. Unfortunately, the precise way in which any enzyme carries out its catalytic function is far from clear. However, organic chemists learn more each year, and it now seems likely that an enzyme contains a binding site, where the substrate (an organic compound) is confined while the desired reaction is carried out on it; this active site is usually found in only one region of the enzyme. Accessibility to the site, which has rather closely defined geometry, is allowed only to those molecules whose geometry matches that of the site. This accounts for enzyme specificity.

More is known about α-chymotrypsin and trypsin than most other enzymes. In the form in which these enzymes are originally prepared and stored in the pancreas, they are inactive as catalysts; this is a fortunate circumstance, because if they were active, they would catalyze the destruction of the gland that forms them. After secretion, they are activated in the intestine by hydrolysis of a few of their own peptide bonds.

The complete amino acid sequences for both trypsinogen and chymotrypsinogen (the forms of the enzymes stored in the pancreas) are known with a reasonable degree of certainty; the former contains 229, and the latter 246, amino acid units. If the two chains are laid parallel, about 40% of the amino acids of one will fall at the same place as those in the other. The ten cysteine molecules of chymotrypsinogen are joined into five disulfide bridges, so that a number of loops are formed.

Three amino acids are known to be intimately involved in the catalytic activity of chymotrypsin: the serine molecule at location 195 and the two histidine molecules at positions 40 and 57. These molecules and their immediate neighbors are said to make up the *active sites* of the enzyme. The amino acid sequences in these regions are nearly identical in chymotrypsin and in trypsin; the remaining portions of the molecules are presumably designed to bring these active sites into the correct three-dimensional arrangement to provide for maximum catalytic activity and to impart specificity to the molecule.

The overall process in a hydrolysis reaction catalyzed by chymotrypsin is simple (Fig. 14-19). The protein substrate to be hydrolyzed is allowed to reach the enzyme surface because the enzyme has a particular arrangement of the amino acid sequence which complements the structure of the substrate. The substrate fits on the surface almost like a key in a lock, so that its amide group to be hydrolyzed is brought close to the serine hydroxyl group of the enzyme. Aided in some manner by the two histidine side chains, the carbonyl group of the protein is transferred to the serine hydroxyl and the protein is cleaved, allowing the part of the molecule containing the free amino group to leave the enzyme surface. Chymotrypsin esters corresponding to this intermediate stage can be isolated under certain circumstances, so that the two parts of the enzymatic process can be studied separately. Hydrolysis

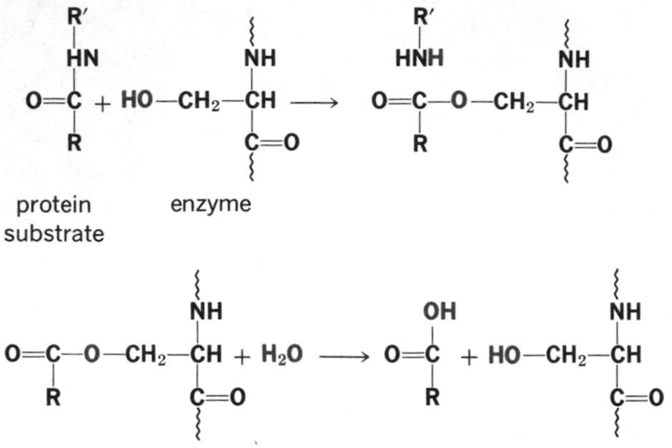

Fig. 14-19. A representation of the steps involved in hydrolysis of a peptide bond by chymotrypsin. Specificity is provided by the general shape of the enzyme, which binds certain groups but not others.

is completed by what amounts to the reverse of these steps, with water reacting with the acyl-serine linkage. In this sequence, the serine side chain is regenerated and the enzyme is made ready for another protein substrate molecule. Repetition of these steps leads to the hydrolysis of a large number of peptide bonds by a single molecule of chymotrypsin.

Prob. 14-10. Indicate briefly how carbohydrate (aerobic), protein, and lipid metabolisms are interrelated. Cite two key compounds which are important to more than one pathway.

Prob. 14-11. What is the ultimate fate of pyruvic acid in aerobic carbohydrate metabolism? In anaerobic metabolism in muscle? In fermentation?

Prob. 14-12. Give structural formulas for the compounds listed below. Indicate how each is involved in the metabolism of lipids, carbohydrates, proteins, or none of these classes of compounds.

(a) α-ketoglutaric acid   (d) lactic acid
(b) pyruvic acid   (e) acetoacetic acid
(c) citric acid   (f) acetylsalicylic acid

CHAPTER

BIOSYNTHESIS AND THE CHEMISTRY OF NATURAL PRODUCTS

Over the centuries, thousands of organic compounds have been isolated from natural sources in more-or-less pure form. Many of these compounds, usually called natural products, have been used as medicines, dating back to the salicylates extracted from willow leaves or to earlier herbal medicines. Such folk remedies have yielded many useful drugs. For example, doctors in India have known for many years that chewing the leaves of the *Rauwolfia serpentina* plant brings on a state of euphoria. Recent investigation has revealed that these leaves contain reserpine, a compound now marketed as a tranquilizer and widely used in the treatment of mental diseases.

Other natural products have been used for their pleasurable or hallucinatory effects—for example, alcohol, opium, and mescaline. And, still others are violent poisons, like strychnine, often used to kill rats, or the hemlock extract coniine used by the ancient Greeks to kill Socrates.

One thing about many of these natural products should be emphasized: To have commercial importance, they must normally be produced in reasonably large quantities by a plant or animal; they are not mere transient metabolic intermediates like many of the compounds mentioned in the last chapter, but end products of synthetic or metabolic pathways. A reasonable question would be, why does an organism go to the trouble to synthesize a complex molecule like actinomycin D or morphine? (See Fig. 15-16 and Fig. 15-19.) Strangely enough, most of the products which we shall be discussing have no known physiological function within the

291

plant or animal from which they are isolated. A few may play a protective role—penicillin, for example, may protect the fungus which produces it from bacterial infection. However, some other antibiotics actually poison the very organisms that produce them. Others appear simply to be offshoots of the main life processes, blind alleys which might once have been main metabolic highways. This is a subject about which there has been a great deal of speculation, but the economic and medicinal importance of the compounds has made them the objects of an enormous amount of chemical and biochemical research.

CLASSIFICATION OF NATURAL PRODUCTS

Natural products have a fantastic range of organic structures, but they can be organized into a number of classes according to their ultimate uses or because of similarities in their chemical structure. *Alkaloids* are nitrogen-containing plant products; most of them are basic and can be extracted by acids. Strychnine, morphine, and quinine are representative members of this potent class. *Steroids* are a class of compounds containing the tetracyclic steroid skeleton seen first in Fig. 2-13. They are usually found in the ether extracts of plant and animal tissue, along with fats and other lipids. When this extract is saponified, the fats and oils are hydrolyzed, but the steroids are *nonsaponifiable* and remain soluble in ether. Cholesterol is the most abundant steroid in animal systems; many important hormones, including cortisone, and vitamin D are also steroids. *Terpenes* are plant products that bear a particular structural relationship to one another. Camphor and menthol belong to this class of compounds.

Antibiotics, on the other hand, are classified on the basis of their use. Various definitions are used, but the most commonly accepted one describes an antibiotic as a compound produced by one microorganism which is toxic to another microorganism. Since this is a wholly biological definition, it implies nothing about the chemical nature of the compounds. Indeed, antibiotics constitute no well-defined class of chemically related substances, but instead possess exceedingly varied structures. Many other natural products also do not fall into any typical class.

Rather than simply listing formulas for different types of natural products in this chapter, we shall show a relationship among groups of these products, based on the biosynthetic pathways by which they are formed (biogenesis), or on their relationships to the lipids, amino acids, and carbohydrates which make up the primary building blocks of living systems.

BIOSYNTHESIS OF FATTY ACIDS FROM ACETATE

We saw in Chapter 14 that fatty acids are degraded metabolically by the successive chopping off of two-carbon fragments after β-oxidation. Fatty acids are built up by an essentially reverse process (Fig. 15-1). Feeding sodium acetate, isotopically labeled with ^{14}C in the carboxyl group, to a variety of living systems produces fatty acids with even numbers of carbon atoms. The isotope is incorporated with high efficiency and is distributed in the carboxyl group and the other odd-numbered carbon atoms (C-3, C-5, etc).

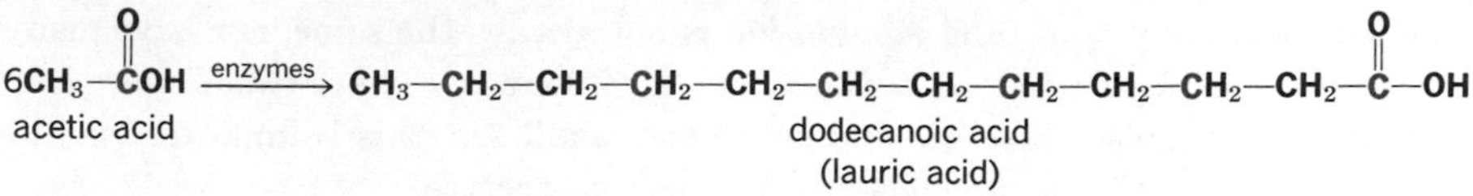

$$6CH_3-\overset{\overset{\text{O}}{\|}}{C}OH \xrightarrow{\text{enzymes}} CH_3-CH_2-CH_2-CH_2-CH_2-CH_2-CH_2-CH_2-CH_2-CH_2-CH_2-\overset{\overset{\text{O}}{\|}}{C}-OH$$

acetic acid   dodecanoic acid
(lauric acid)

Fig. 15-1. Experiments with isotopically labeled acetate show that fatty acids can be synthesized directly from this substrate.

The biosynthesis does not proceed by exactly the same steps as the metabolism, however. The crucial difference lies in the very first step of the biosynthetic pathway, which is the last step of metabolism. In the metabolic pathway, this step involves the cleavage of a β-ketoester derivative to acetylcoenzyme A. This step is theoretically reversible, but the equilibrium lies so far on the side of cleavage that the same reaction cannot be used to synthesize fatty acids. Energy must somehow be supplied to the system to overcome this unfavorable equilibrium.

One important source of energy in biological systems is ATP (adenosine triphosphate, Fig. 14-2). In the last chapter we discussed how energy released in the metabolism of carbohydrates was stored in this molecule for eventual use. One such use is in the biosynthesis of fatty acids; in this process, acetylcoenzyme A reacts with carbon dioxide and ATP to form malonylcoenzyme A (Fig. 15-2). During the process, ATP is converted to ADP and phosphoric acid. Malonylcoenzyme A will then condense under the catalytic influence of an enzyme to give a β-ketoester *plus carbon dioxide,* whose elimination provides the driving force for the reaction.

Subsequent steps in the biosynthesis of a fatty acid are substantially the reverse of those of its metabolism. Thus, the β-keto acid is reduced to a β-hydroxy acid, water is eliminated, and the resulting double bond is reduced. The steps are then repeated with another molecule of malonylcoenzyme A. The exact sequence of

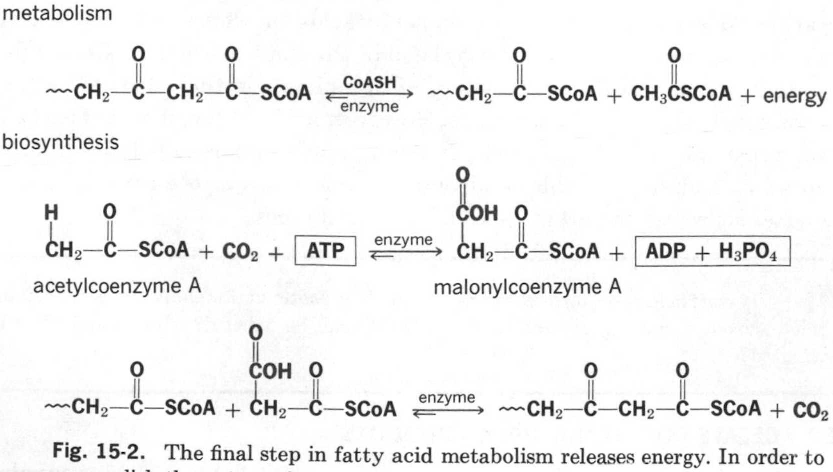

metabolism

$$\sim CH_2-\overset{\overset{\text{O}}{\|}}{C}-CH_2-\overset{\overset{\text{O}}{\|}}{C}-SCoA \underset{\text{enzyme}}{\overset{\text{CoASH}}{\rightleftharpoons}} \sim CH_2-\overset{\overset{\text{O}}{\|}}{C}-SCoA + CH_3\overset{\overset{\text{O}}{\|}}{C}SCoA + \text{energy}$$

biosynthesis

$$\overset{\text{H}}{\underset{}{CH_2}}-\overset{\overset{\text{O}}{\|}}{C}-SCoA + CO_2 + \boxed{ATP} \underset{\text{enzyme}}{\rightleftharpoons} \overset{\overset{\text{COH}}{}}{CH_2}-\overset{\overset{\text{O}}{\|}}{C}-SCoA + \boxed{ADP + H_3PO_4}$$

acetylcoenzyme A   malonylcoenzyme A

$$\sim CH_2-\overset{\overset{\text{O}}{\|}}{C}-SCoA + \overset{\overset{\text{COH}}{}}{CH_2}-\overset{\overset{\text{O}}{\|}}{C}-SCoA \underset{\text{enzyme}}{\rightleftharpoons} \sim CH_2-\overset{\overset{\text{O}}{\|}}{C}-CH_2-\overset{\overset{\text{O}}{\|}}{C}-SCoA + CO_2$$

Fig. 15-2. The final step in fatty acid metabolism releases energy. In order to accomplish the reverse, fatty acid biosynthesis, this energy must be supplied by ATP, which aids in the formation of malonylcoenzyme A.

condensation, reduction, and elimination is not always the same, nor have many steps been completely defined; it is possible, for instance, to have two or more condensations take place before reduction. As we shall see, this is important in the synthesis of many other products originating from acetate.

Of the pathways available for formation of lipids containing unsaturated fatty acids in animals, the simplest pathway involves introducing a double bond by direct oxidation (dehydrogenation) of the chain of a saturated fatty acid; this reaction has no laboratory analogy. It is interesting that a double bond introduced in this way in animals is always at least six carbon atoms from the methyl end of the chain, reflecting, presumably, a structural demand of one of the enzymes involved. Unsaturated acids of the oleic and palmitoleic acid family are formed in this way (Fig. 15-3).

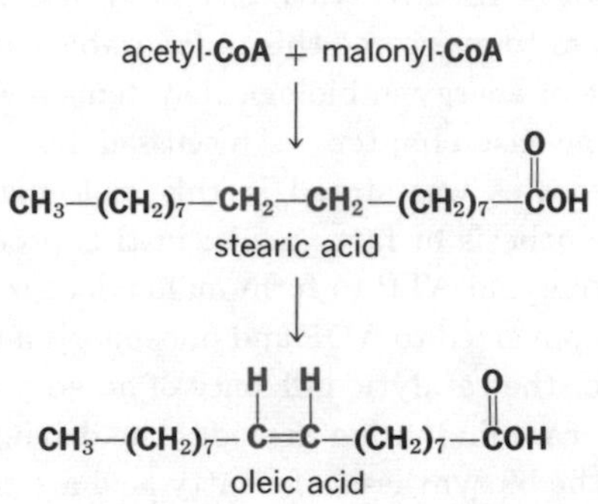

acetyl-**CoA** + malonyl-**CoA**

↓

$$CH_3-(CH_2)_7-CH_2-CH_2-(CH_2)_7-\overset{\overset{\displaystyle O}{\|}}{C}OH$$
stearic acid

↓

$$CH_3-(CH_2)_7-\overset{\overset{\displaystyle H}{|}}{C}=\overset{\overset{\displaystyle H}{|}}{C}-(CH_2)_7-\overset{\overset{\displaystyle O}{\|}}{C}OH$$
oleic acid

Fig. 15-3. Saturated fatty acids like stearic acid, derived from acetate and malonate units, can be dehydrogenated directly in animals to unsaturated acids like oleic acid. However, linoleic and linolenic acids must come from animals' diets.

Unsaturated acids like linoleic or linolenic acids in which the double bond is fewer than six carbons from the methyl end of the chain are biologically synthesized only in plants; they must be taken in by animals in their diets since they cannot be synthesized in animal tissues. However, acids of the oleic, linoleic, and linolenic types can all be further dehydrogenated by animals to polyunsaturated acids in which additional double bonds are introduced nearer the carboxyl group. These latter acids play important roles in cell membranes.

Prob. 15-1. If oleic acid were formed in the presence of acetic and malonic acids containing ^{14}C-labeled carboxyl groups, should C-10 of oleic acid be labeled? How could this be demonstrated?

OTHER ACETATE-DERIVED NATURAL PRODUCTS

If certain molds are allowed to grow in the presence of labeled acetate, a number of products in addition to fatty acids are found to contain radioactivity. 6-Methyl-salicyclic acid, for instance, contains a high level of activity. Degradative studies have shown that the label is distributed in a way that is consistent with the biosynthetic scheme shown, in which four molecules of acetylcoenzyme A (or their equivalent, malonylcoenzyme A) condense into the triketo thioester shown. Such a molecule would cyclize easily, and subsequent reduction, elimination of water, and enolization would lead to the observed product, although the exact sequence of these latter reactions is not known. Many other natural products arise by similar, though more involved, cyclizations. Juglone, a quinone, probably is produced from five molecules of acetate by the sequence shown in Fig. 15-4.

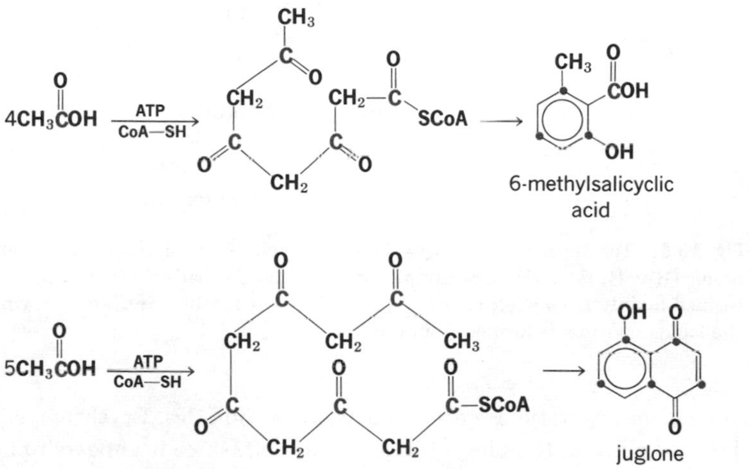

Fig. 15-4. Many phenolic natural products, including salicyclic acid derivatives and juglone, are derived from acetate units by cyclization.

Prob. 15-2. Suggest which carbon atoms of the fungal product curvulinic acid

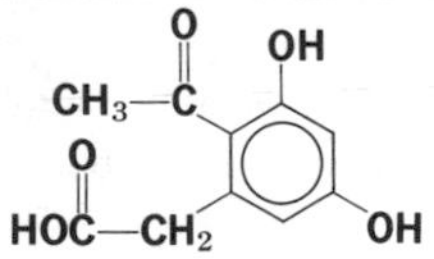

would be expected to be derived from the carboxyl group of acetate.

Acetate is also the precursor of more complicated aliphatic, heterocyclic, and aromatic-aliphatic natural products. The *tetracyclines* are examples of the latter class (Fig. 15-5). These are broad spectrum antibiotics which are active against a large number of bacteria. In addition to the parent compound, *aureomycin* and *terramycin* are tetracycline antibiotics. The basic skeleton of these antibiotics is formed from acetate units. *Erythromycin* is a representative of the important class of *macrolide antibiotics,* a group in which all members contain large lactone rings.

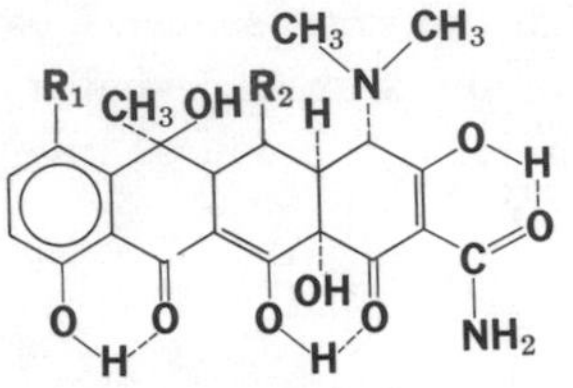

Fig. 15-5. Tetracycline (R$_1$=R$_2$=H), aureomycin (R$_1$=Cl, R$_2$=H), and terramycin (R$_1$=H, R$_2$=OH) are examples of widely used broad-spectrum antibiotics formed mainly from acetate. Erythromycin is a macrolide antibiotic in which the lactone portion is formed from propionate.

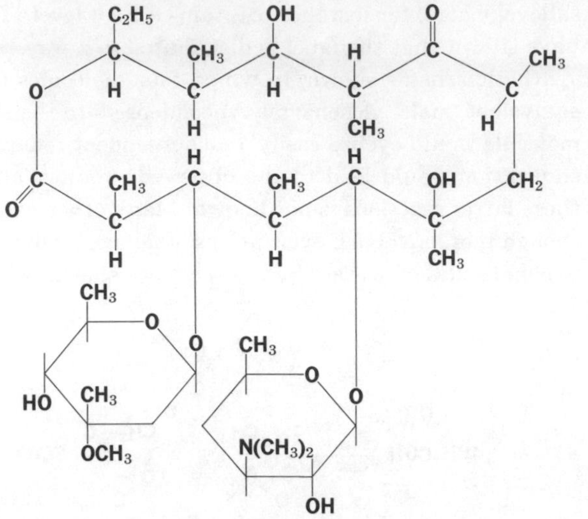

Magnamycin and nystatin are other macrolide antibiotics. Erythromycin is especially interesting from the biosynthetic standpoint, since it appears to be formed by the combination of propionate units (or the equivalent methylmalonate units,

$$\overset{O}{\overset{\|}{HOCCH}}(CH_3)\overset{O}{\overset{\|}{CSCoA}})$$ rather than acetate units. This accounts for the large number of C—CH$_3$ units present in the molecule.

Prob. 15-3. How many stereoisomers are possible for tetracycline, aureomycin, terramycin, and erythromycin? Hint: How many asymmetric carbon atoms are in each molecule?

TERPENES

Three acetate units can be combined biosynthetically in a nonlinear way to form the important biosynthetic intermediate *mevalonic acid* (Fig. 15-6). To form this compound, the third acetate undergoes what is essentially an aldol or Claisen condensation and condenses at the ketone group of acetoacetate; subsequent reduction leads to mevalonic acid. We shall see presently how mevalonic acid is related to biosynthesis of the class of compounds known as *terpenes,* but first we must define that class.

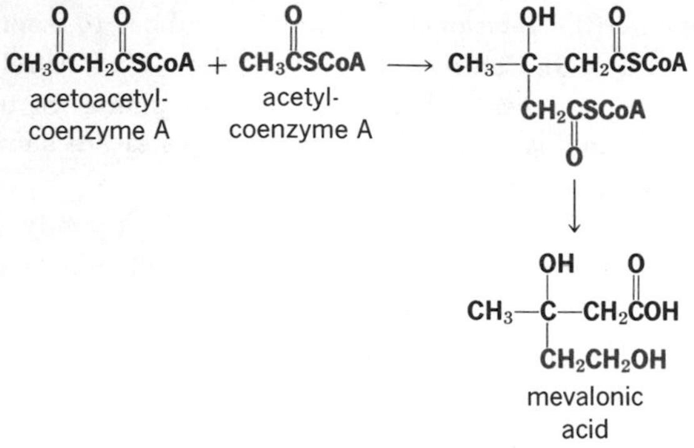

Fig. 15-6. Mevalonic acid, a biological precursor of terpenes and steroids, is formed from three acetate units.

For a long time organic chemists had realized that many naturally occurring substances could be considered to be formed by appropriate combination of the five-

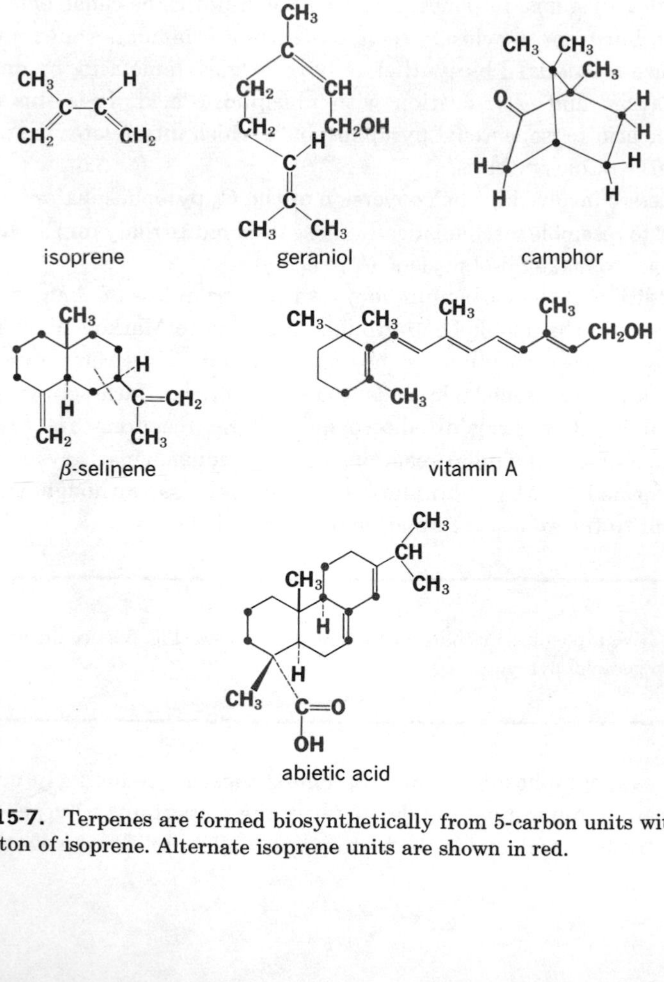

isoprene geraniol camphor

β-selinene vitamin A

abietic acid

Fig. 15-7. Terpenes are formed biosynthetically from 5-carbon units with the skeleton of isoprene. Alternate isoprene units are shown in red.

carbon unit isoprene (the relationship of natural rubber to isoprene has already been discussed in Fig. 4-8). Compounds with the most obvious relationship to isoprene are known as terpenes and occur widely in plants. Structures of a few terpenes were found in Fig. 3-2, other typical terpenes are shown in Fig. 15-7, together with their relationship to isoprene.

Terpenes are classified as monoterpenes if they can be formally derived from two isoprene units, diterpenes if they can be derived from four isoprene units, etc. Geraniol, from geraniums, and the well-known camphor are monoterpenes (C_{10}); β-selinene, from oil of celery, is a sesquiterpene (C_{15}, sesqui = 1½); vitamin A and abietic acid are diterpenes (C_{20}). Lanosterol, which we shall encounter in Fig. 15-10, is a triterpene (C_{30}).

Prob. 15-4. Identify the isoprene units in limonene and bornene (Fig. 3-2).

In biological systems, terpenes are now known not to be constructed from isoprene itself, but from the closely related 5-carbon fragments shown in Fig. 15-8. These in turn are derived biosynthetically from mevalonic acid, by dehydration, decarboxylation, and esterification with phosphoric acid. It is this conversion of mevalonic acid to isopentenyl pyrophosphate which interrelates the acetate and isoprene paths of biosynthesis.

The processes involved in the conversion of the C_5 pyrophosphates into terpenes are thought to resemble mechanistically those used industrially for the dimerization of isobutylene to make diisobutylene (Fig. 3-21).

Thus, addition of the carbonium ion, resulting from loss of the pyrophosphate group adjacent to the double bond, would, according to Markownikoff's rule, lead to the stable tertiary carbonium ion shown; this would yield geraniol pyrophosphate after loss of a proton. Repetition leads to a sesquiterpene, farnesol pyrophosphate, and a third addition leads to diterpenes. These reactions are catalyzed by enzymes, of course, but similar reactions occur in nonenzymatic systems. Natural rubber is formed by the continuation of this process, although the enzymes involved lead to the exclusive formation of *cis* double bonds.

Prob. 15-5. Give a possible mechanism by which limonene (Fig. 3-2) could be formed biologically from geraniol pyrophosphate.

Two farnesyl pyrophosphates may be joined together reductively head-to-head through their pyrophosphate ends to form the important triterpene squalene, found in shark's liver oil, and in the human liver and scalp. For purposes which will

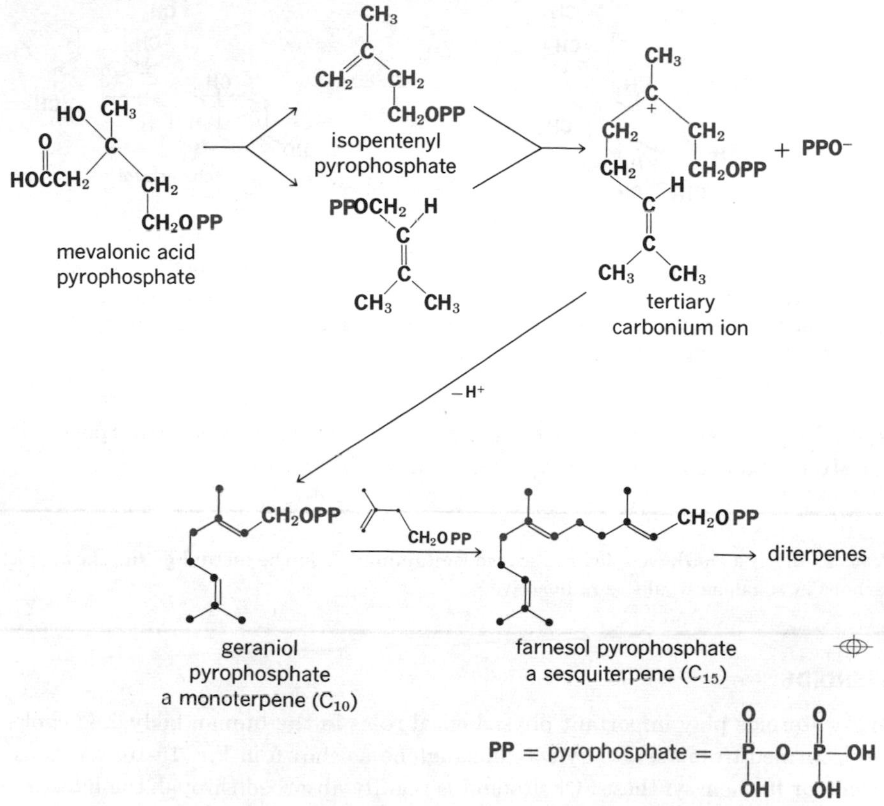

Fig. 15-8. The stepwise addition of C_5 isopentenyl fragments leads to the building up of terpene skeletons. In the compounds shown, the double bonds are *trans*. Similar steps with enzymes that give *cis* isomers lead to natural rubber.

become apparent shortly, the farnesyl molecules are written in a slightly different way in Fig. 15-9. Triterpenes, of which many are known, seem to be formed this way rather than by linear polymerization as might have been expected. Squalene

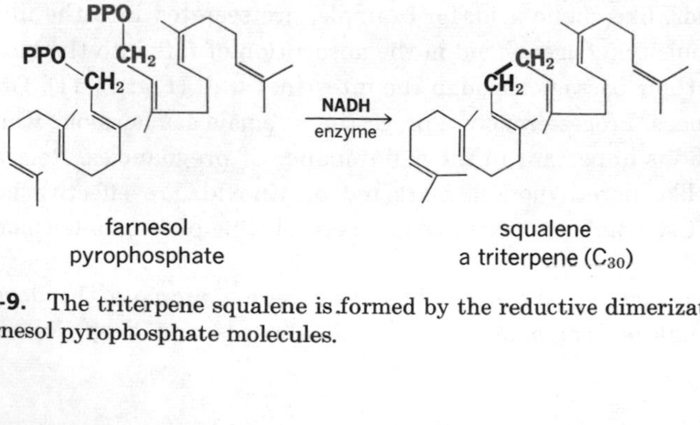

farnesol pyrophosphate

squalene a triterpene (C_{30})

Fig. 15-9. The triterpene squalene is formed by the reductive dimerization of two farnesol pyrophosphate molecules.

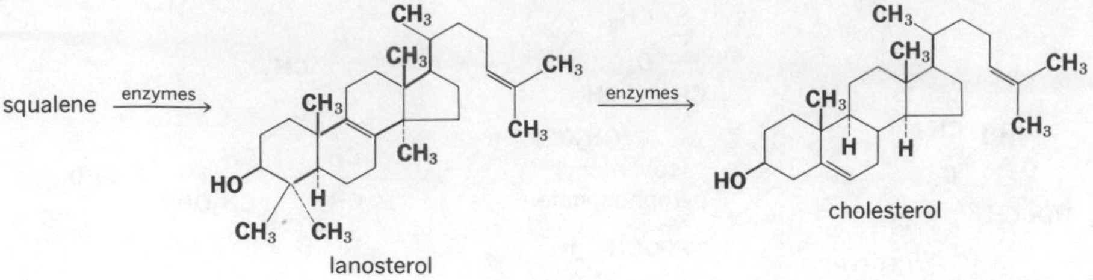

Fig. 15-10. Squalene is a precursor of lanosterol (a triterpene) and cholesterol. In the formation of lanosterol from squalene, the tetracyclic ring system has resulted from the formation of the bonds in red and the two methyl groups in red have changed their positions by one carbon each.

is further converted by cyclization reactions into tetracyclic triterpenes like lanosterol and eventually into steroids, as shown in Fig. 15-10.

Prob. 15-6. If a shark were fed acetic acid containing ^{14}C in the methyl group, show which carbons in squalene would be radioactive.

STEROIDS

Many steroids play important physiological roles in the human body, and cholesterol, formed from acetate by way of squalene as shown in Fig. 15-10, serves as a precursor in their synthesis. Cholesterol is readily absorbed through the intestines, so that any consumed in food is added to the body's supply. However, this is not the sole source of cholesterol in the body: Since we know the metabolic relationship between fats and squalene, it is easy to consider a relationship between fat intake and cholesterol levels in the blood. When too much cholesterol is present in the system, it begins to precipitate from solution. Crystalline cholesterol precipitates in the gall bladder as gall stones, while cholesterol precipitated in the veins and arteries constricts the flow of blood and leads to high blood pressure and related medical symptoms.

The body converts cholesterol, in turn, into a great number of other steroids. The bile acids, like cholic acid, for example, are secreted into the intestines and, acting as emulsifying agents, aid in the absorption of fats into the bloodstream by assisting in their passage through the intestinal wall (Fig. 15-11). Other steroids act as hormones. Progesterone is a progestin, a female sex hormone which represses ovulation and is important in the maintenance of pregnancies. Related synthetic compounds like norethynodrel, marketed as Enovid, are effective in preventing conception. Estradiol is an example of a second type of female hormone, called an estrogen.

Male sex hormones, androgens like testosterone promote the development of secondary male sexual characteristics like beards and deep voices as well as

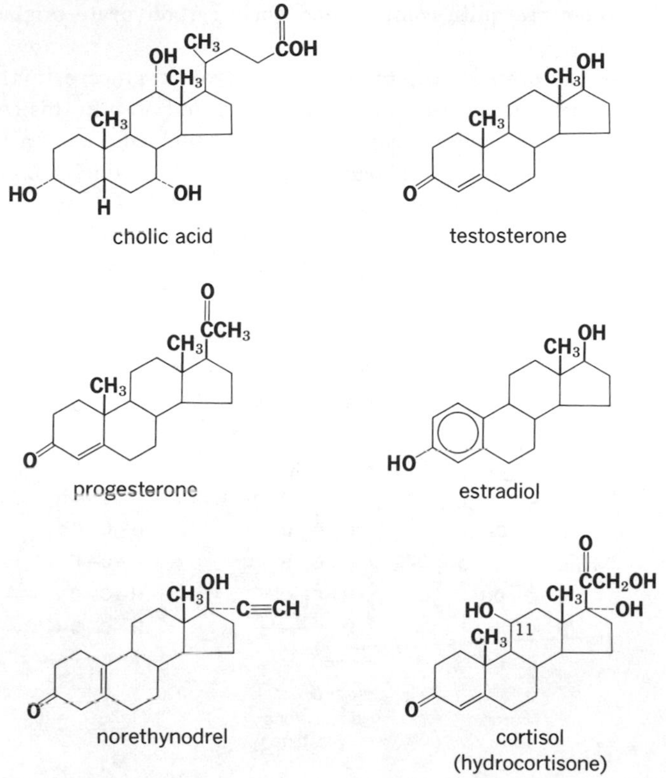

cholic acid

testosterone

progesterone

estradiol

norethynodrel

cortisol
(hydrocortisone)

Fig. 15-11. Typical examples of the bile acid, male and female sex hormone, and corticosteroid families.

fertility. A further series of hormones, the corticosteroids, are produced in the adrenal cortex and have important roles in the regulation of a great many body functions. One of these hormones, cortisol, the principal hormone of the adrenal glands, is closely related to cortisone; the latter compound is known for its medical uses in treating skin diseases and arthritis. Cortisone differs from cortisol (hydrocortisone) only in having a keto group instead of a hydroxyl group at C-11.

Prob. 15-7. Draw the structure of cortisone and show which carbons would be radioactive if acetic acid with ^{14}C in the methyl group were converted biologically into cortisone.

NATURAL PRODUCTS FROM CARBOHYDRATES

A second large group of naturally occurring compounds is that formed from carbohydrate precursors. Some of these are relatively simple compounds and their relationship to sugars is obvious; ascorbic acid (vitamin C) belongs to this group

(Fig. 15-12). Others are quite complex and their carbohydrate origins are more obscure.

Ascorbic acid has been shown to be formed from D-glucose in the livers of a number of animals and also in some plants. The first step in this conversion is the oxidation of the C-6 primary hydroxyl group of D-glucose to a carboxyl group and its cyclization to a lactone, D-glucurono-γ-lactone. The aldehyde group is next reduced to an alcohol, and the synthesis is completed by oxidation, involving the loss of two hydrogen atoms. Notice that C-1 of glucose (red carbon atom) has become C-6 of ascorbic acid. When the formula of the compound is written with the principal functional group at the top (C=O) the bottom hydroxyl group of ascorbic acid is on the left, so that it is designated L-ascorbic acid (see Fig. 15-12). The enzymes required for the individual steps of these transformations have not yet been completely isolated and characterized.

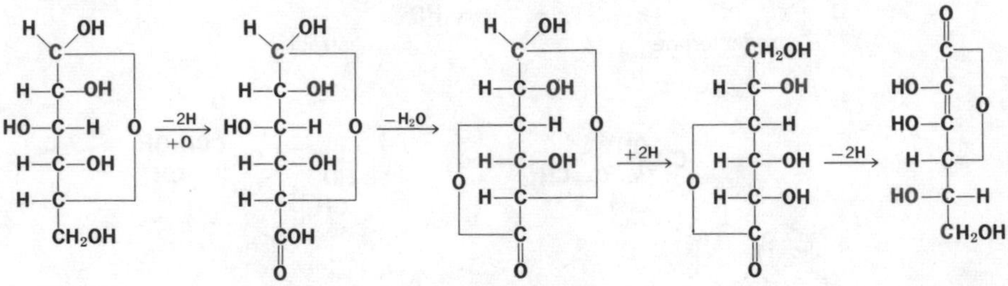

Fig. 15-12.   The biological conversion of D-glucose to L-ascorbic acid.

Prob. 15-8.   L-Ascorbic acid can also be formed by a series of reactions similar to those of Fig. 15-12, but starting from D-galactose. Write this reaction sequence.

Prob. 15-9.   To what hexose is the unnamed compound of Fig. 15-12 most closely related?

Another naturally occurring group of compounds obviously related to the hexoses are the inositols, 1,2,3,4,5,6-hexahydroxycyclohexanes. Of the several isomers of this structure, *myo*-inositol is the most widely distributed in nature. It has been shown to be formed in some plants from D-glucose by a series of steps in which the 6-membered chain remains intact and C-1 of glucose becomes the carbon shown in red in *myo*-inositol (Fig. 15-13). Intermediates are known to be glucose-6-phosphate and a *myo*-inositol phosphate.

An ever-increasing number of medically important antibiotics of carbohydrate origin are being used, and studies on their biogenesis are currently proceeding in several laboratories. The best known of these antibiotics are *streptomycin* and the three members of the deoxystreptamine class, *neomycin, paromomycin,* and

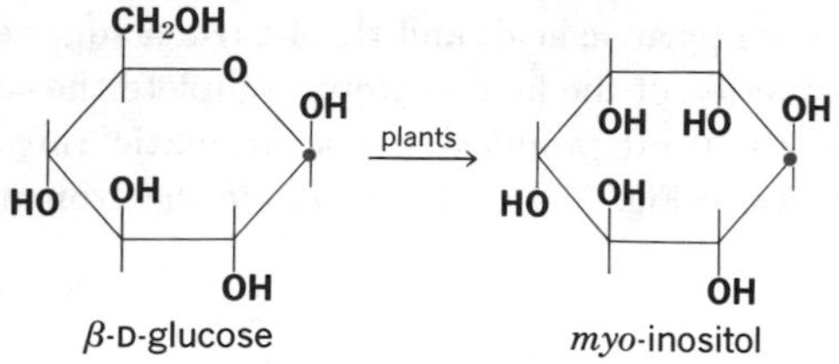

Fig. 15-13. D-Glucose can be converted to *myo*-inositol without breakdown of the carbon chain.

kanamycin. Structures of streptomycin and neomycin were shown in Fig. 10-17; paromomycin and kanamycin are related to neomycin. Though all the steps are not yet clear, these antibiotics are apparently synthesized in microorganisms from simple carbohydrates.

SHIKIMIC ACID

Surprisingly, carbohydrates are also an important source of many naturally occurring aromatic compounds, including the aromatic amino acids. The crucial intermediate in this conversion is the cyclic compound shikimic acid (Fig. 15-14). This acid contains seven carbon atoms and is formed by an aldol condensation reaction and cyclization from two separate metabolic products of glucose, pyruvic acid enol

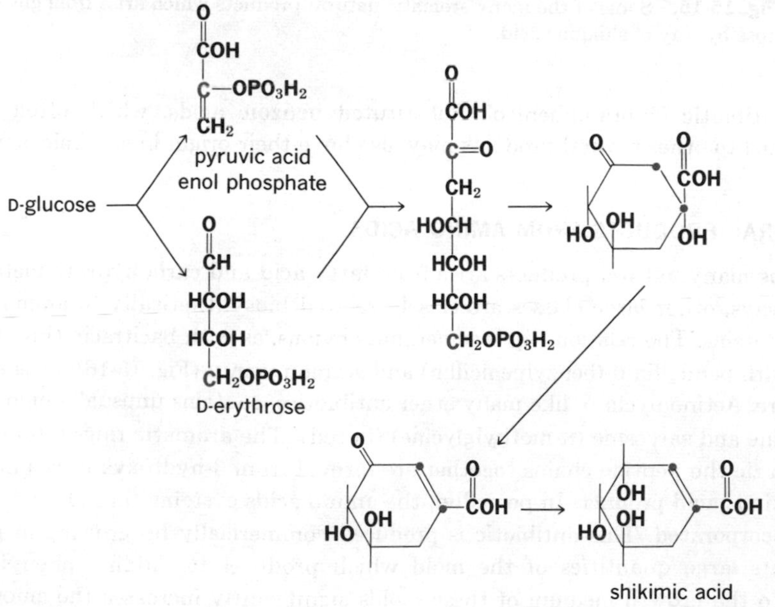

Fig. 15-14. In the biological synthesis of aromatic amino acids from carbohydrates, shikimic acid plays a central role. Its three- and four-carbon precursors are formed from glucose by separate metabolic pathways.

phosphate (phosphoenol pyruvic acid) and the 4-carbon sugar erythrose. Elimination of water and reduction of the ketone group complete the conversion.

Some of the many natural products whose aromatic rings are derived from shikimic acid are shown in Fig. 15-15. These include the aromatic amino acids and

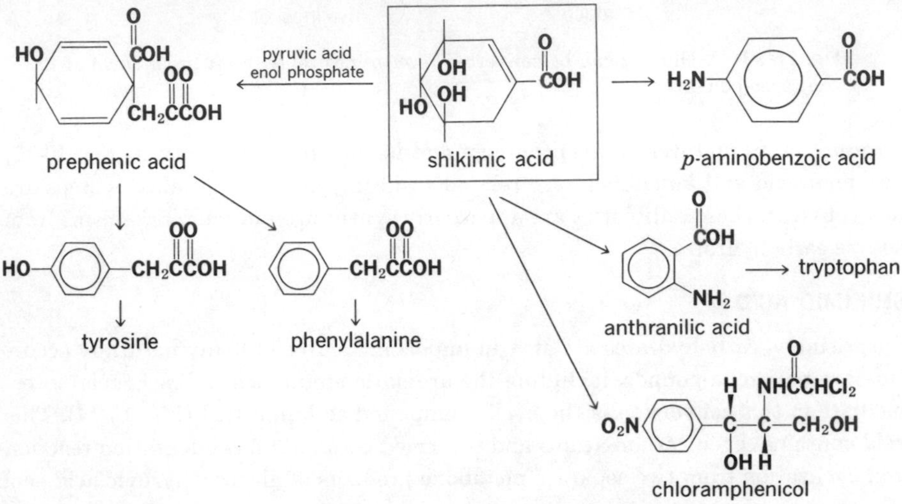

Fig. 15-15. Some of the many aromatic natural products which arise from glucose by way of shikimic acid.

the antibiotic chloramphenicol. Substituted benzoic acids, which often occur attached to other natural products may also have their origin in shikimic acid.

NATURAL PRODUCTS FROM AMINO ACIDS

Just as many natural products arise from fatty acid and carbohydrate metabolic pathways, other large classes are closely related biosynthetically to amino acids and proteins. The relationship is sometimes obvious, as with bacitracin (Fig. 13-13) and with penicillin G (benzylpenicillin) and actinomycin D (Fig. 15-16); oftener it is obscure. Actinomycin D, like many other antibiotics, contains unusual amino acids, D-valine and sarcosine (N-methylglycine) (in red). The aromatic rings (also in red) which tie the peptide chains together are formed from 3-hydroxyanthranilic acid, a shikimic acid product. In penicillin, the amino acids cysteine (in red) and valine are incorporated. This antibiotic is produced commercially by growing in gigantic vats large quantities of the mold which produces it. Adding phenylacetic acid to the growth medium of these molds significantly increases the amount of penicillin G produced. Other penicillins, in which the benzyl group of the phenylacetic acid has been replaced by other groups, are also known, but penicillin G is the most important commercially.

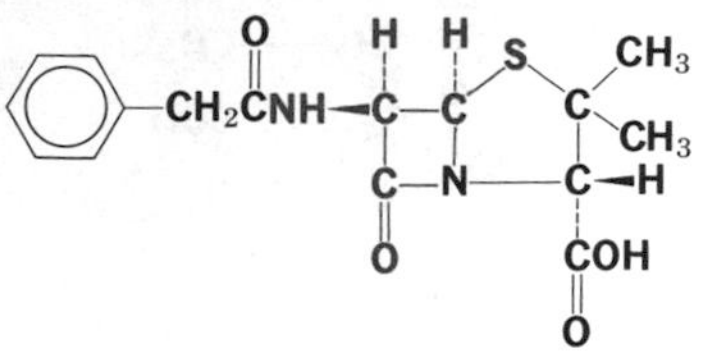

penicillin G

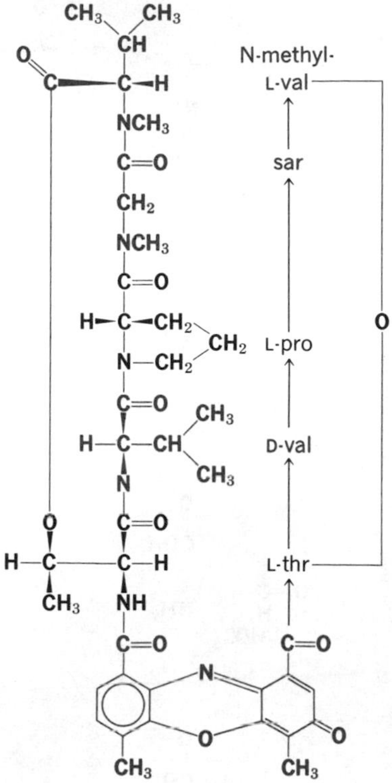

actinomycin D

Fig. 15-16. Some natural products, like the antibiotics penicillin G (benzyl-penicillin) and actinomycin D, resemble peptides and proteins, and are clearly derived from common amino acids.

ALKALOIDS

Many naturally occurring substances, especially alkaloids, hardly reveal their amino acid precursors at first glance. Nicotine is a typical example. This alkaloid contains both pyridine and pyrrolidine rings, and is found in tobacco. It is synthesized in the plant by a complex series of reactions beginning with two amino acids, tryptophan, which gives rise to the pyridine ring, and glutamic acid, which is converted to the pyrrolidine ring by the steps indicated (Fig. 15-17).

Many other alkaloids are derived, at least in part, from amino acids. Although the exact details by which these compounds are synthesized in plants are far from completely understood, the scheme outlined for the examples in Figs. 15-18 and 15-19 is probably close to that which actually takes place; in any event, the scheme has been extremely useful in predicting the structures of new alkaloids. It makes use of two known reactions of amino acids: their conversion into amines by loss of carbon dioxide, and their degradation into aldehydes by oxidation and loss of ammonia. The resulting aldehyde and amine combine, often spontaneously even

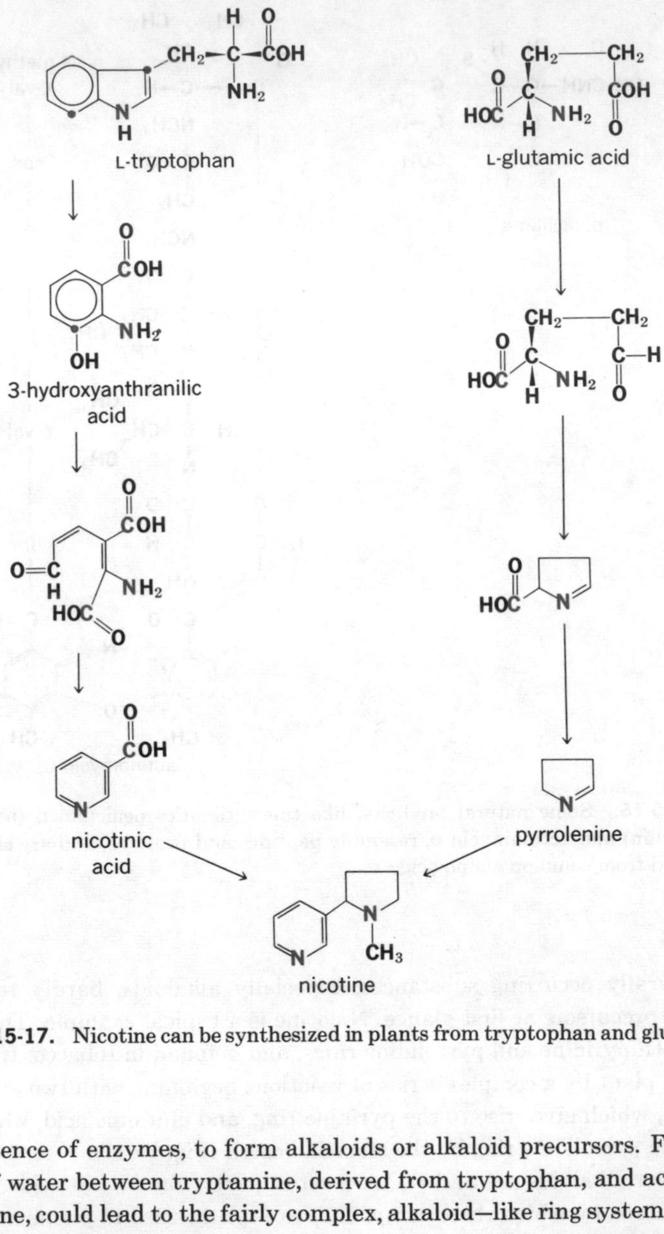

Fig. 15-17. Nicotine can be synthesized in plants from tryptophan and glutamic acid.

in the absence of enzymes, to form alkaloids or alkaloid precursors. For instance, the loss of water between tryptamine, derived from tryptophan, and acetaldehyde, from alanine, could lead to the fairly complex, alkaloid—like ring system of harmane (Fig. 15-18).

Most of the enormous diversity of structure among alkaloids arises by subsequent reactions after this basically simple type of condensation. If we start with the aldehyde and amine derived from dihydroxyphenylalanine, cyclization involving the loss of a mole of water leads directly to the alkaloid *norlaudanosoline*. Ring closure without incorporation of additional carbon atoms can occur in several dif-

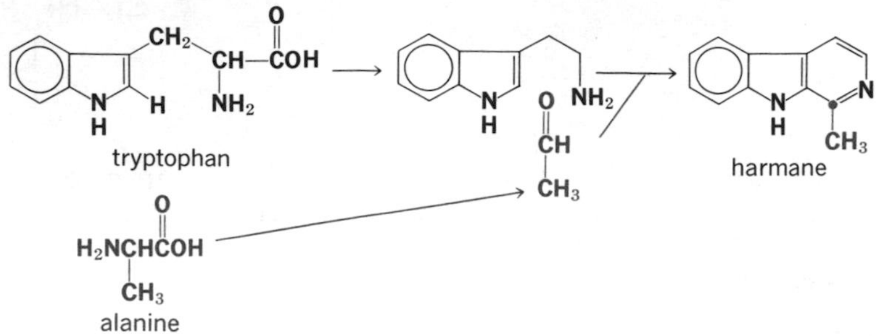

Fig. 15-18. Many alkaloids, like harmane, appear to be formed by condensations between amines and aldehydes related to amino acids.

ferent ways: One of the ways leads to *morphine* (Fig. 15-19), others lead to less well-known alkaloids. Despite the vast superficial differences in structure among alkaloids, many seem to arise by analogous biosynthetic pathways.

References to alkaloids pervade history and literature. One alkaloid of particular

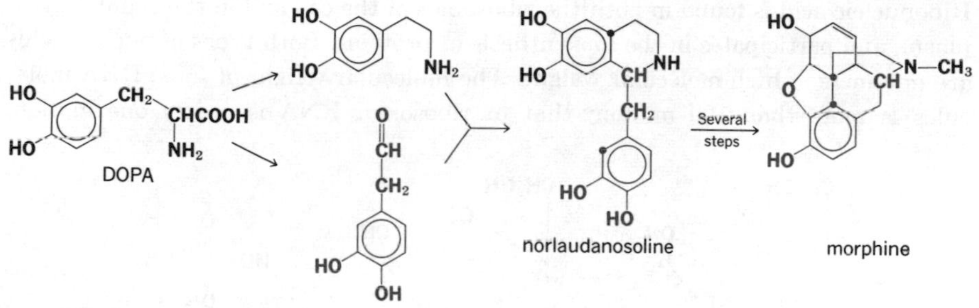

Fig. 15-19. Morphine is among the alkaloids which may be formed from the amine and aldehyde related to dihydroxyphenylalanine. The atoms marked with heavy dots should aid the reader in visualizing the cyclizations involved.

historical significance is *coniine,* for it is this compound which led to the death of Socrates in 399 B.C., *Cocaine,* with the peculiar bicyclic ring structure shown in Fig. 15-20, is a narcotic which Sherlock Holmes found relaxing ("Quick, Watson, the needle!"). *Quinine,* extracted from the bark of an East Indian tree, is used in the treatment of malaria.

Prob. 15-10. Many alkaloids contain heterocyclic ring systems like those discussed in Chapter 8. Identify the heterocyclic rings outlined in red in the structures of Fig. 15-20.

NUCLEIC ACIDS

We shall complete our discussion of naturally occurring organic molecules with a few words about the chemistry of nucleic acids. These important compounds are

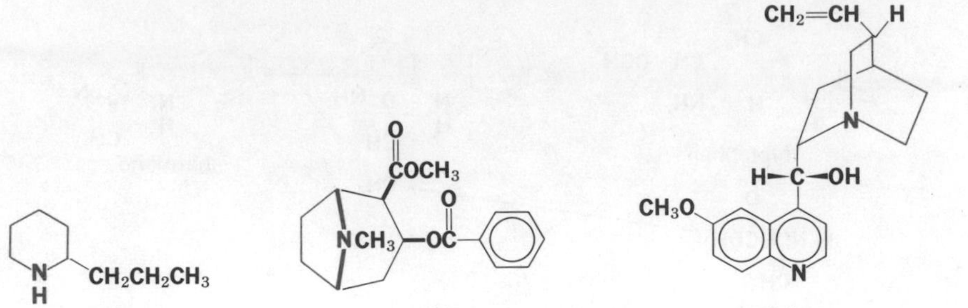

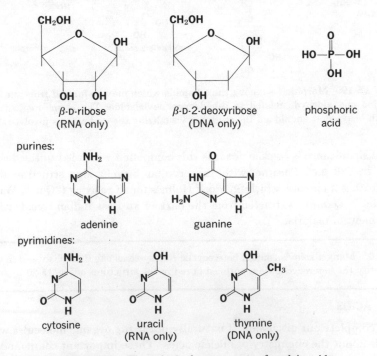

Fig. 15-20. Three alkaloids of historical, literary, and medicinal importance, respectively.

involved in some of the most fundamental life processes, including the biosynthesis of proteins and the transmittal of information from one generation to the next through the genes. Two types of nucleic acids are common: *DNA* (*deoxyribonucleic acid*) and *RNA* (*ribonucleic acid*). Deoxyribonucleic acid is found in the chromosomes of the cell nucleus and is responsible for the transfer of genetic information. Ribonucleic acid is found in both the ribosomes of the cell and in the cellular cytoplasm, and participates in the biosynthesis of proteins. Both types of nucleic acids are polymers of high molecular weight. The molecular weight of some DNA molecules is more than 100 million; that of ribosomal RNA is nearly one million,

Fig. 15-21. The principal components of nucleic acids.

whereas that of cytoplasmic or "soluble" RNA is lower: between 20,000 and 30,000.

As is suggested by their names, the two types of nucleic acids differ from each other in their carbohydrate components. Ribose is the monosaccharide of RNA, deoxyribose (lacking the C-2 hydroxyl group) that of DNA. In addition to these two sugars, the nucleic acids contain phosphoric acid and certain heterocyclic bases, as shown in Fig. 15-21. The four principal bases of DNA are the purines adenine and guanine and the pyrimidines cytosine and thymine. The four bases of RNA include three of these—adenine, guanine and cytosine, together with the pyrimidine uracil in place of thymine.

In nucleic acids, ribose and deoxyribose are attached in their β-furanoside forms to nitrogen atoms of the bases, at N-1 of the pyrimidines and at N-9 of the purines. Simple compounds of this type can be isolated and are called nucleosides. Some examples of nucleosides are 1-(β-ribofuranosyl)-uracil, called uridine, and 9-(β-deoxyribofuranosyl)-adenine, called deoxyadenosine.

Nucleosides are joined together in nucleic acids by phosphate bonds from the C-5 hydroxyl group of one sugar molecule to the C-3 hydroxyl group of another. Thus, partial formulas for DNA and RNA look like those of Figs. 15-22 and 15-23 respectively, where names of the nucleoside components are also indicated.

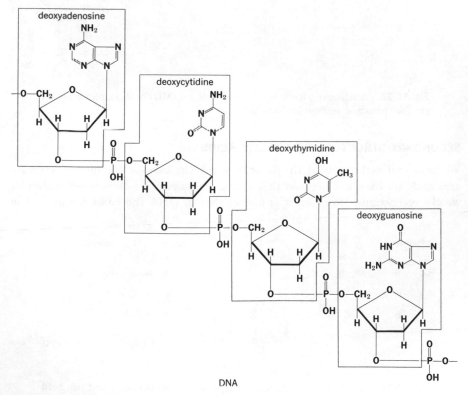

DNA

Fig. 15-22. A schematic formula of deoxyribonucleic acid (DNA) showing (in boxes) the four principal nucleosides found.

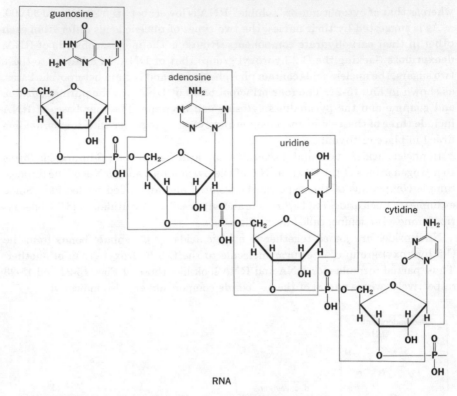

Fig. 15-23. A schematic formula of ribonucleic acid (RNA) showing (in boxes) the four principal nucleosides found.

SECONDARY STRUCTURE OF NUCLEIC ACIDS

We have said nothing about the order in which the bases of the nucleic acids are arranged; we have not because this is not yet known for these high molecular weight compounds. However, it is known that in DNA the bases are present in

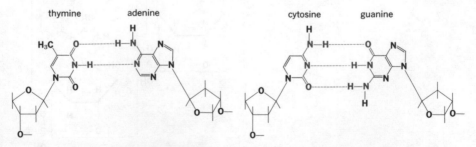

Fig. 15-24. Thymine and adenine fit together along the edge and are held together by hydrogen bonding. Cytosine and guanine similarly complement one another.

purine-pyrimidine pairs, the amount of thymine always equaling the amount of adenine and the amount of cytosine equaling the amount of guanine. Models show that these pairs are nearly perfect complements, and that the bases are held in proximity to each other by strong hydrogen bonding of the groups shown in red (Fig. 15-24).

It is now recognized that a DNA molecule is a double-stranded helix, in which one strand is the exact complement of the other in terms of base sequence (Fig. 15-25). Thus, if one strand had the sequence cytosine-adenine-thymine, the other strand of the same helix would have the sequence guanine-thymine-adenine at the same point. The two strands are held together throughout their entire length by the hydrogen bonds between complementary pairs of bases. This is known as the Watson-Crick model for nucleic acids, after the scientists (Nobel Prize, 1962) who first proposed it.

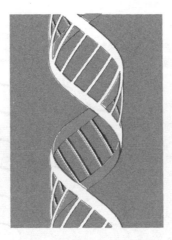

Fig. 15-25. DNA is a double-stranded helix held together by hydrogen bonding, in which each strand is the complement of the other, in terms of base sequence. (Taken from Wagner and Mitchell, *Genetics and Metabolism,* 2nd ed., John Wiley and Sons, Inc., New York, 1964, p. 93.)

BIOSYNTHESIS OF PROTEINS

Ribonucleic acid, as noted, controls the biosynthesis of proteins (Fig. 15-26, p. 312). An amino acid to be incorporated into a protein is first activated by reaction with adenosine triphosphate, then transferred to the end of a molecule of soluble RNA (transfer RNA), where it forms an ester bond with the C-2 or C-3 hydroxyl group of ribose. The soluble RNA molecule, with its attached amino acid, then binds itself to the much larger template RNA (messenger RNA) fixed to the ribosomes. The amino acids thus activated and held in place on the ribosome are polymerized enzymatically.

The apparent mechanism by which the sequence of amino acids in a protein is regulated is intriguing. As noted, a separate transfer RNA molecule is required for each amino acid. Hence, a code must exist for locating the individual transfer RNA

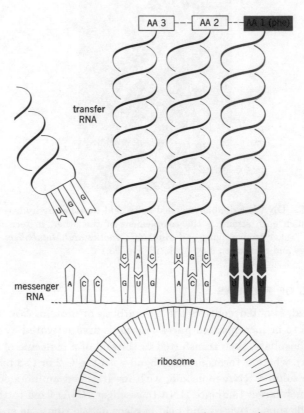

Fig. 15-26. The determination of the amino acid sequence in a protein occurs at the ribosomes after an activated amino acid has been attached to a transfer RNA molecule. (Taken from P. Karlson, *Introduction to Modern Biochemistry*, 2nd ed., Academic Press, Inc., New York, 1965, p. 134.

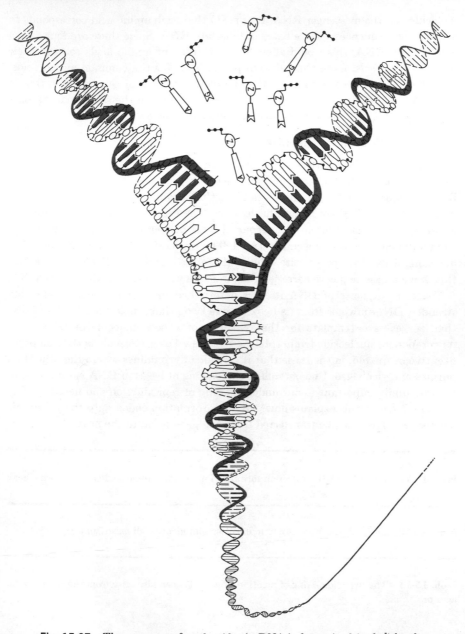

Fig. 15-27. The sequence of nucleosides in DNA is determined (coded) by the pairing of its bases with those of one strand of a double-stranded helix. (Taken from P. Karlson, *Introduction to Modern Biochemistry,* 2nd ed., Academic Press, Inc., New York, 1956, p. 130.)

molecules on the messenger RNA. It appears that each amino acid corresponds to a particular sequence of three bases in template RNA. Since there are four different bases in RNA, this would allow $4^3 = 64$ different amino acids to have their own code symbols, more than enough possibilities for the common amino acids. The information needed to store the complete amino acid sequence for the 51 amino acids in beef insulin could, for example, be coded in the sequential arrangement of 153 (51×3) of these bases along an RNA chain.

BIOSYNTHESIS OF DNA AND RNA

How is template RNA formed? How is the sequence of bases determined which, in turn, establishes the sequence of amino acids in proteins? Template (messenger) RNA is transferred to the ribosomes from the chromosomes, where it is formed from the triphosphates of its four nucleosides. The exact sequence of nucleosides in messenger RNA is apparently determined by a primer DNA molecule unwound from a double strand into a single strand. The nucleosides line up along the DNA molecule, where they polymerize. The newly formed messenger RNA molecule will thus have a base sequence corresponding in some way to that of the primer DNA.

The base sequence of DNA itself is determined in a similar manner. Doubly stranded DNA unwinds from its helix to give two primer molecules. Each of these then serves as a template for the synthesis of a new molecule of DNA from its component nucleoside triphosphates. The new DNA molecule is then an exact negative of the old, in the sense that it contains pyrimidines where the other had purines and vice versa. Understanding the pairing of bases in DNA is thus seen to be profoundly important to our understanding of reproduction and heredity (Fig. 15-27). Knowing this explains how genetic information coded onto the polymeric backbone of DNA can be transferred from one generation to the next.

Prob. 15-11. Draw Haworth projection formulas for α-D-glucuronic acid and L-ascorbic acid.

Prob. 15-12. Draw all the stereoisomeric inositols and identify all *meso* isomers.

Prob. 15-13. The pyrrolidine ring of nicotine (Fig. 15-17) can also arise from the basic amino acid ornithine,

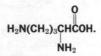

Suggest a reasonable biosynthetic pathway for the conversion of ornithine to pyrrolenine.

Prob. 15-14. What would be reasonable biological sources of the two heterocyclic rings of the alkaloid anabasine? See Prob. 15-13.

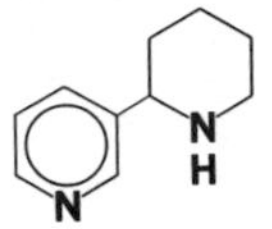

anabasine

Prob. 15-15. Lysergic acid is believed to be synthesized biologically from tryptophan (via tryptamine) and isopentenyl pyrophosphate. Identify these fragments in lysergic acid. Draw the structure of lysergic acid diethyl amide (LSD).

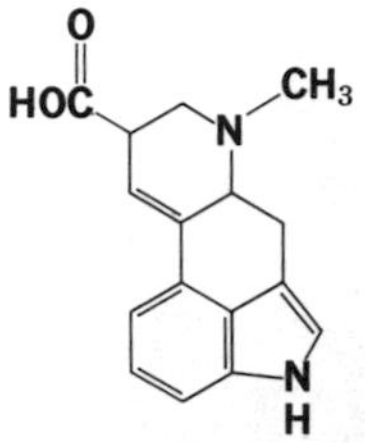

lysergic
acid

CHAPTER

16

COLOR AND DYES

The production of dyes and the fermentation of sugar most closely link modern and ancient science. Thus, a study of the color of organic compounds has historical as well as practical significance. The nails and fingers of Egyptian mummies, for example, are often found stained with *henna,* a dye used even today to color the hair. Other dyes—for example, *indigo* and *alizarin*—evoke thoughts of medieval rites and mysteries.

LIGHT ABSORPTION AND COLOR

Color usually is caused, among organic as well as inorganic molecules, by the *absorption* of light.* White light contains all colors, from violet and blue through green and yellow to red and purple. This can be demonstrated by the familiar experiment of passing white light through a prism (or a raindrop), which disperses the light into a rainbow. If a beam of white light falls upon an organic compound that does not absorb any color, the compound will appear white if the light is reflected, or colorless if the light is transmitted through the compound. Conversely, the compound will appear black if it absorbs all the light. However, if some of the colors are absorbed while others are not, the reflected or transmitted light will no longer contain the color or colors absorbed and the material will appear to be colored. It is important to recognize that the color observed and the color absorbed are not the same; the observed color is a mixture of all colors *except* the ones absorbed. Indigo, for example, is a deep blue dye because it absorbs yellow light, and a mixture of all colors except yellow appears blue. In general, a

---

* Color may also arise from the *emission* of light, as in the flame test for sodium, in which the sodium atoms give off a brilliant yellow light. This is rarely useful for organic compounds.

bright yellow dye absorbs blue light (4,000–5,000 Å) and a magenta dye absorbs green light (5,000–6,000 Å).

Visible light makes up only a small portion of the known radiation in the electromagnetic spectrum. It is simply the light in the region of the spectrum where the human eye is sensitive; this includes radiation of wave length between 4,000 and 7,600 Å. Ultraviolet light lies in a similar region, but the human eye is not sensitive to its wavelengths. This is indicated in Fig. 16-1, where the wavelengths of visible light are correlated with their colors.

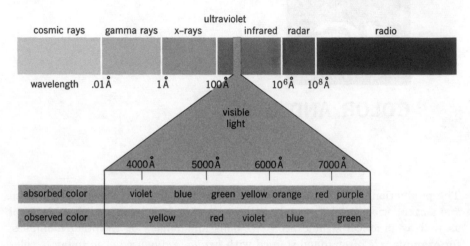

Fig. 16-1. Visible light comprises only a tiny fraction of the spectrum of electromagnetic radiation. An observed color is the one seen when the color on the line above is absorbed from white light.

Notice that short wavelengths correspond to blue and violet light, and long wavelengths, to red and purple light. Light of wavelengths slightly shorter than the visible ones is called ultraviolet light; that of wavelengths slightly longer than the visible ones is called infrared. The shorter the wavelength of radiation, the more energy it contains. This can be seen from the fact that cosmic, gamma, and x-rays are powerfully destructive, ultraviolet and visible light are less energetic but still cause sunburn, and radio waves are harmless.

ELECTRONIC EXCITATIONS. CONJUGATED SYSTEMS

When ultraviolet or visible light is absorbed by an atom or molecule, an electron is *excited,* that is, it is raised to an orbital of higher energy than the one it ordinarily occupies. The process is most easily illustrated for an atom. A helium atom contains two electrons in its $1s$ orbital. It could absorb radiation which would excite one of these electrons into the $2s$ orbital. The amount of energy required to do this is, however, very large, and visible light does not have sufficient energy to accomplish it; thus, helium is colorless.

All organic compounds absorb ultraviolet radiation; this can be detected on instruments sensitive to ultraviolet light. However, visible light contains so much less energy than ultraviolet light that only molecules containing electrons that are very easily excited will appear to be colored. In organic compounds, π electrons are rather easily excited; the most easily excited are those in molecules containing a number of adjacent π electrons in conjugated unsaturated centers (Fig. 16-2).

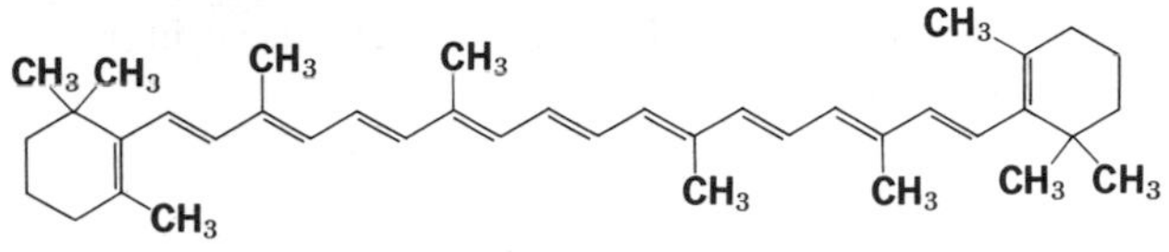

β-carotene
orange

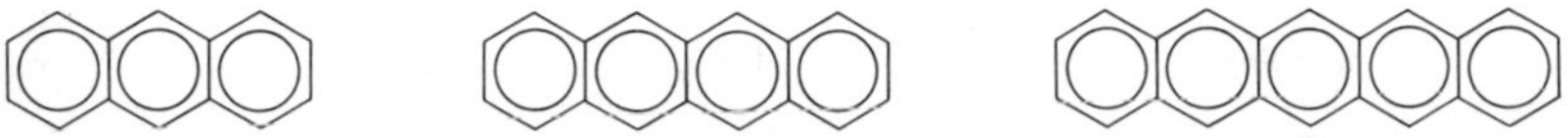

anthracene
colorless

naphthacene
yellow

pentacene
blue

Fig. 16-2. Compounds containing an extended conjugated system of π electrons are colored.

Ethylene absorbs light of wavelength far into the ultraviolet part of the spectrum, at 1,800 Å. Butadiene, with two conjugated double bonds, absorbs at 2,170 Å, a wavelength closer to the visible zone than that absorbed by ethylene. 1,3,5-Hexatriene absorbs still closer to the visible regions, at 2,580 Å. All three compounds are colorless; however, as the number of conjugated double bonds increases, the position of absorption falls nearer the visible region, and with enough conjugation, the molecules are colored. The pigment β-carotene contains eleven conjugated double bonds and is the dye mainly responsible for the color of carrots. It absorbs light of wavelength 4,510 Å. Although the light absorbed is blue, carrots are, of course, orange.

Benzene absorbs light at 2550 Å and is therefore colorless, as are naphthalene and anthracene. As the number of fused rings increases, the position of absorption approaches the visible region, so that naphthacene, with four linearly fused rings, is yellow (absorbs blue light) and pentacene, with five, is blue (absorbs orange light). We have already seen that graphite is a sheet of benzene rings fused in all directions; it is black, absorbing all colors almost completely.

Prob. 16-1. Would you predict that compound A would more likely appear to be red or green? Why? What about B?

A

B

CHROMOPHORES

Other organic groups besides those with carbon-carbon double bonds and benzene rings are also rich in easily excited π electrons, and are important light absorbing units. Such groups are called chromophores, from the Greek words *chroma* and *phoros* meaning color-bearing. The nitro and carbonyl groups, and the azo and quinone groups, are powerful chromophores (Fig. 16-3). Picric acid (Fig. 6-21), with three nitro groups, is yellow. Rhodomycinone, the quinone of rhodomycin (Fig. 6-27), is red, and azobenzene is orange-red.

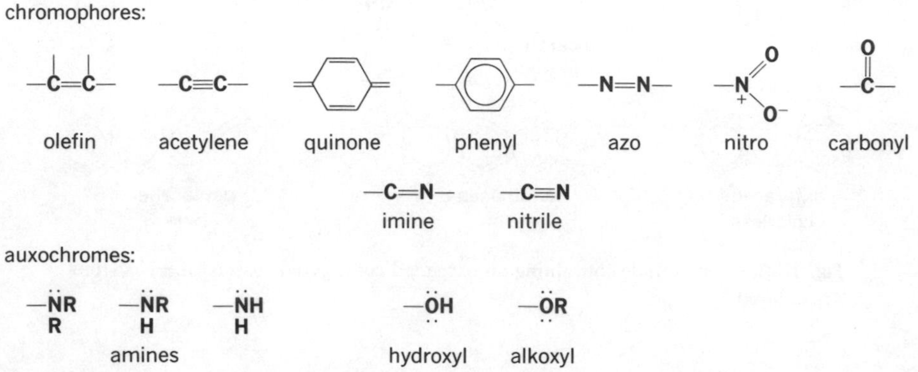

chromophores:

olefin   acetylene   quinone   phenyl   azo   nitro   carbonyl

—C=N—   —C≡N
imine   nitrile

auxochromes:

amines   hydroxyl   alkoxyl

Fig. 16-3. Chromophores contain multiple bonds (π electrons), auxochromes contain unbonded p electrons. Most organic dyes contain both types of groups.

Additional organic groups are not themselves chromophores, but augment the color of chromophores when present in the same molecule. Such groups are called auxochromes, from the Greek words *auxanein* and *chroma* meaning increasing color. A dye of deep color usually contains one or more conjugated chromophores, together with some auxochromes. The amino and hydroxyl groups are especially good auxochromes.

ABSORBANCE

One other noteworthy measure of the absorption of light is the absorbance, or absorbing power, of a molecule. This quantity, usually expressed in terms of the molar absorbance or molar extinction coefficient, determines how much of a dye needs to be applied to obtain a desired depth of color. Two compounds may absorb light at the same wavelength, but one may be twice as efficient in absorption, so that only half the concentration is necessary to give the same intensity of color.

A number of considerations are significant in determining the molar absorbance of a compound. One of the most important is the length of the conjugated system. Notice that in β-carotene (see Fig. 16-2) all of the double bonds are *trans*, so that if all of them are coplanar the molecule is extended to its maximum length. However, if the central double bond is converted to the *cis* configuration, the molecule is bent back into a large U shape in which the chromophoric system is of shorter length; the molar absorbance of this *cis* isomer is only 80% that of the all-*trans* isomer.

Prob. 16-2. Show the structure of the isomer of β-carotene in which the central double bond has the *cis* configuration.

A compound's absorption of light is generally tabulated graphically by plotting absorbance against the wavelength of light absorbed. Figure 16-4 shows a typical

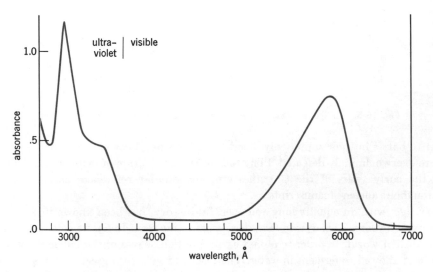

Fig. 16-4. The visible absorption spectrum of indigo. Indigo absorbs light strongly in the yellow part of the spectrum, making it a brilliant blue dye. (From W. R. Brode, E. G. Pearson, and G. M. Wyman, *J. Am. Chem. Soc.,* **76,** 1034 (1954).)

plot for indigo, which absorbs rather sharply in the yellow portion of the visible spectrum. Such a relatively sharp absorption gives rise to a bright dye. A broader absorption might give nearly the same color, but the dye would be duller and less brilliant.

NATURAL DYES

Until the middle of the last century, dyes were all naturally occurring materials and the art of dyeing was a complicated and mysterious process handed down from generation to generation. *Alizarin,* a red dye from the roots of the madder plant, has been used since before recorded history (Fig. 16-5). Alexander the Great probably used alizarin to simulate blood stains on the clothes of his army in a famous battle with the Persians. The Persian soldiers, seeing the Greeks stagger

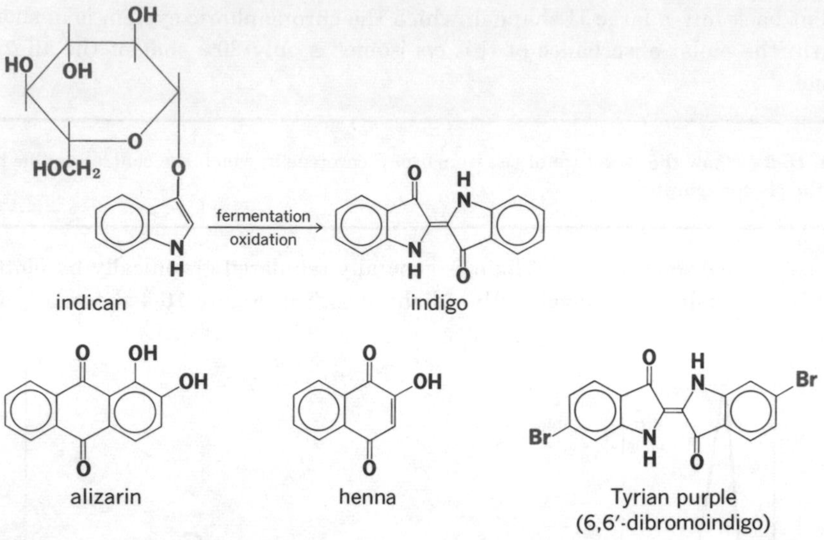

Fig. 16-5. Indigo, alizarin, Tyrian purple, and henna are all ancient dyes.

out to battle in their supposedly bloodstained clothes, became overconfident and were overwhelmingly defeated. Pliny tells of the cultivation of madder near Rome in the early years of the Christian era, and similar references can be found throughout ancient manuscripts.

Indigo, with an equally long and eventful history, has been known in Asia for over 4,000 years. This dye, in fact, derives its name from India, its chief source in the ancient world. In order to obtain natural indigo, leaves of the indigo plant are cut and allowed to ferment in water. The resultant yellowish green liquid is drawn off into vats where it is exposed to air, traditionally by beating the surface of the mixture with bamboo sticks. The color of the solution gradually deepens, and eventually the blue indigo develops. The sludge is removed, heated to prevent further fermentation, and formed into cakes of indigo for commerce. As may be deduced from this process, the blue dye itself does not exist in the plant. The naturally occurring precursor of indigo is a β-D-glucoside, *indican,* which is stable in the plant. In the fermentation process, the glucose splits off; indigo then forms by air oxidation during the beating process.

Tyrian purple, a dibromo derivative of indigo, was the most valuable of all ancient dyes. It was extracted in minute amounts from the glands of certain snails harvested off the coast of Asia Minor. Legend has it that the dye was discovered by Hercules when his sheep dog bit into a snail and the dog's jaws were stained purple. Because of its great scarcity and expense,* Tyrian purple was long reserved for royalty. Even today, one commonly hears that a prince is "born to the purple."

---

* In order to obtain 1.4 gm of the dye with which to determine its structure, the organic chemist Friedlander had to extract 12,000 snails.

Prob. 16-3. Identify the chromophoric and auxochromic groups in the dyes indigo and alizarin (Fig. 16-5).

SYNTHETIC DYES

The first synthetic dye was discovered accidentally by the English chemist William Perkin in 1856. At the time he was eighteen years old and was trying to synthesize quinine by a procedure now known to have been impossible. Perkin recognized the importance of his discovery rather quickly, and resigned his university position to manufacture the dyestuff. Other synthetic dyes followed soon after, many of them far superior to natural dyes, and severe economic repercussions ensued for large parts of the world where plants containing natural dyes were grown commercially. Investigations were soon carried out on the structures and syntheses of indigo, alizarin, and other natural dyestuffs. Friedlander showed, for example, that Tyrian purple was identical with indigo, except that in the former dye each of the benzene rings contained one bromine atom *para* to the carbonyl group. The occurrence of these two similar dyes in such different sources is remarkable.

Since 1850, tens of thousands of dyes have been synthesized. Well over a thousand are commercially available at the present time, so we will mention only a few of the general types of dyes in use. The largest group in commercial importance are the *azo dyes,* which are prepared from diazonium salts, discussed in Figs. 8-13 and 8-14. These dyes are derivatives of azobenzene, and the first azo dye synthesized, aniline yellow (1863), is simply prepared by treating benzenediazonium salts (from aniline and nitrous acid) with aniline (Fig. 16-6). Orange II, prepared in a

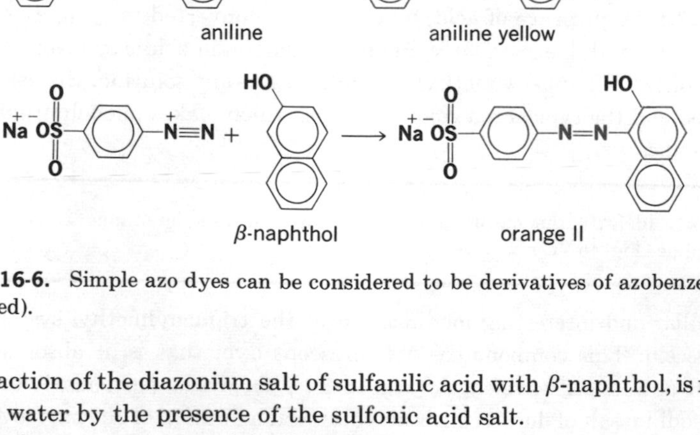

aniline   aniline yellow

β-naphthol   orange II

Fig. 16-6. Simple azo dyes can be considered to be derivatives of azobenzene (in red).

similar reaction of the diazonium salt of sulfanilic acid with β-naphthol, is rendered soluble in water by the presence of the sulfonic acid salt.

Another important group of dyes are derivatives of triphenylmethane and are called *triphenylmethyl dyes* (Fig. 16-7). These are especially useful as indicators. Triphenylmethyl alcohol is a colorless solid; however, its derivatives which have

colorless   red

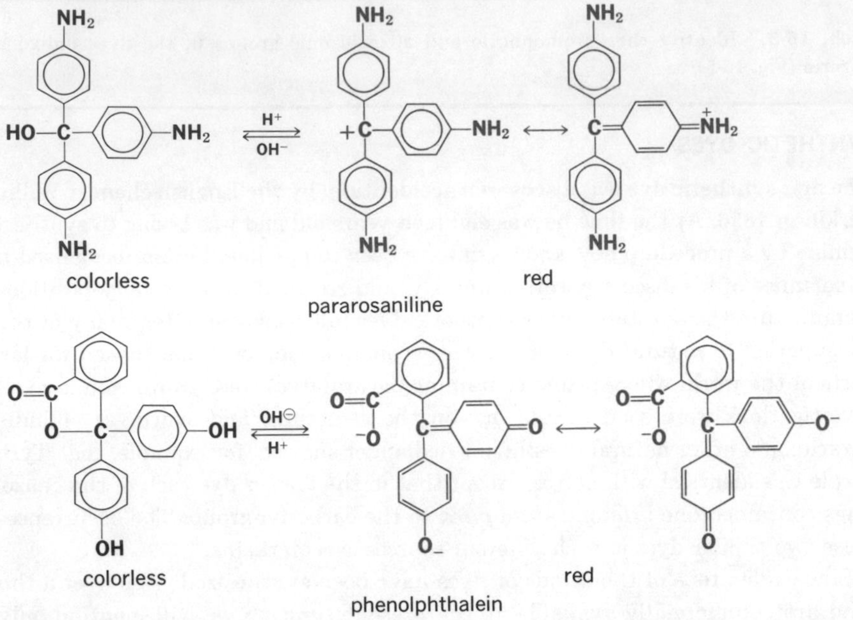

pararosaniline

colorless   red

phenolphthalein

Fig. 16-7. The triphenylmethyl system (in red) gives rise to highly colored dyes when the central carbon is trigonal. When the central carbon is tetrahedral, compounds are colorless.

trigonal central carbon atoms (sp^2 carbons) have a highly conjugated system extending over all three benzene rings and are colored. Pararosaniline is a simple example in which the triphenylmethyl system is substituted with three auxochromic amino groups. Pararosaniline base is a derivative of triphenylmethyl alcohol and is colorless. In the presence of acid, however, it is converted to a highly conjugated salt which is a red dye. Similarly, phenolphthalein, in acidic solution, is a lactone of a derivative of triphenylmethyl alcohol. In alkaline solution, the ester group is eliminated and the typical red color develops, which makes phenolphthalein a very popular indicator.

Prob. 16-4. Identify the chromophores and auxochromes in orange II (Fig. 16-6) and pararosaniline (Fig. 16-7).

A familiar and interesting modification of the triphenylmethyl system is found in fluorescein. This compound is a fluorescent dye; that is, it absorbs light and reemits it at a longer wavelength (Fig. 16-8). This gives a particularly brilliant dye and the sodium salt of fluorescein is detectable at a dilution of one part in 40,000,000. Fliers carry it as a marker in case of forced landings over water. It has also been used to follow underground rivers, to locate the source of the Amazon, and to find leaks in sewer lines.

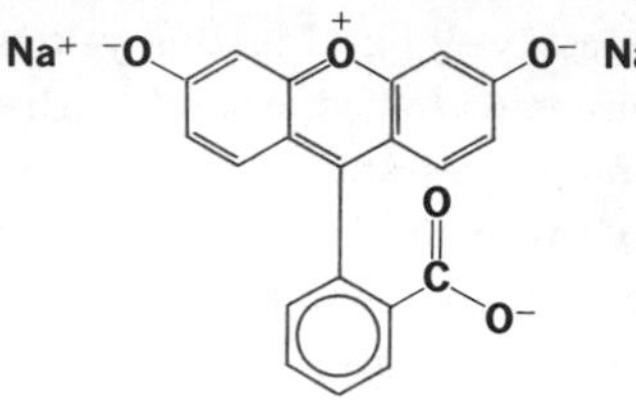

fluorescein

Fig. 16-8. A fluorescent dye.

Prob. 16-5. Fluorescein is prepared from phthalic anhydride and resorcinol (*m*-dihydroxybenzene). Identify these two starting materials in fluorescein.

Among other classes of dyes are the beautiful, yellow *flavanthrone* and the deep blue *copper phthalocyanine* (Fig. 16-9). The latter is structurally related to the green plant pigment chlorophyll and the blood pigment heme. Flavanthrone is rather unstable to sunlight, but phthalocyanines are among the most stable dyes known. They are even unaffected by boiling acids or bases, and for that reason are often used as pigments for painting chemical laboratories.

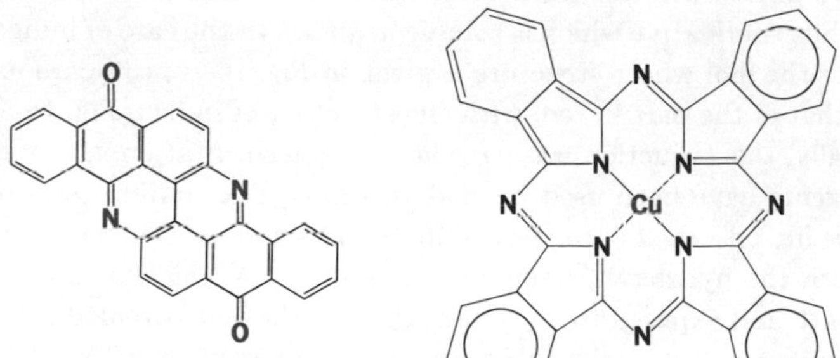

flavanthrone

copper
phthalocyanine

Fig. 16-9. Representatives of other dye classes.

APPLICATION OF DYES TO CLOTH

Color alone does not make an organic compound a useful dye; methods must be found to get the dye on the fabric and to insure that it will neither wash out nor fade. The protein fibers wool and silk are easiest to dye, because they contain acidic and basic groups which form salts with basic or acidic dyes; by this process, the dye is firmly attached to the fiber, and the fabric can usually be dyed merely by dipping the fabric into a solution of the dye. Dyes suitable for this purpose are called *direct dyes;* acidic direct dyes, like Martius yellow (Fig. 16-10), are used for wool, and basic direct dyes are used for paper and leather. The two nitro groups of Martius yellow act as chromophores and, at the same time, render the phenolic hydroxyl group acidic enough to make it a moderately strong acid. The molecule then forms a salt with free amino groups in proteins. Other direct dyes contain sulfonic acid groups like that found in orange II.

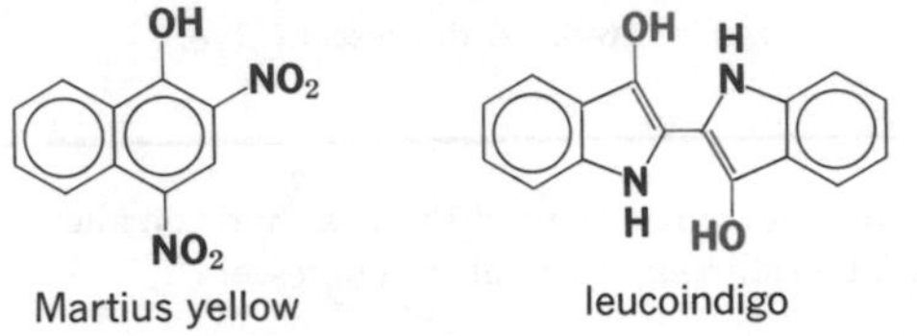

Martius yellow   leucoindigo

Fig. 16-10. Martius yellow is a simple acidic direct dye for silk and wool. Leucoindigo is the reduced alkali soluble form of indigo used in vat dyeing.

Although there are some direct dyes for cotton, other methods of applying dyes are more common, since cellulose molecules have no acidic or basic sites and do not readily absorb dyes. The process known as *vat dyeing* is common for cottons, and this method has been used since antiquity for the application of indigo. In vat dyeing, the dye is first reduced to a colorless leuco (from the Greek word *leukos,* meaning white) derivative which is soluble in alkali. In the case of indigo, this leuco derivative is the diol whose structure is given in Fig. 16-10; compare its structure, especially that of the part in red, with the structure of indigo, Fig. 16-5.

Historically, this reduction was carried out by fermentation, although chemical reducing agents have been used in modern times. The sodium salts of the leuco dyes are readily adsorbed onto the cellulose fibers and are held there by hydrogen bonding with the hydroxyl groups of the cellulose. When the fabric is removed from the bath and exposed to oxygen in the air, the salt is reoxidized to the dye, which precipitates on the fabric. Vat dyes are ordinarily very "fast," that is, they do not wash out easily, so that the term "vat dyed" often refers to any fast dye, whether or not it has been applied by this process of reduction and oxidation. Most vat dyes are quinones or related compounds which are reduced to hydroquinones and subsequently reoxidized; after azo dyes, anthraquinone vat dyes are the most important commercially.

A third method of fixing the dyes to the fiber is the process known as *mordant dyeing* (from the Latin *mordere* meaning to bite). In this process a metal ion, usually aluminum, is used to form an insoluble precipitate as a link between the fiber and the dye on the fiber (Fig. 16-11). A number of organic molecules have the ability to form strong complexes, called *chelates* (pronounced "kee-late," from the Greek word *chele,* meaning claw) with metal ions. One complex example is the copper phthalocyanine of Fig. 16-9, in which the copper ion is so tightly complexed with the four nitrogen atoms that it cannot be removed even by boiling with base.

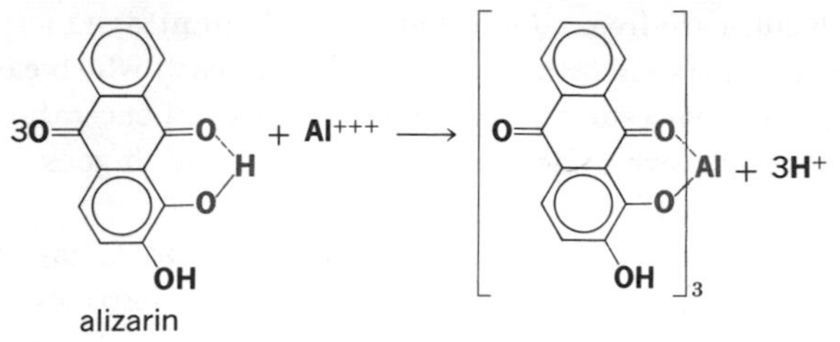

Fig. 16-11. Alizarin forms chelates with metal ions; this property is employed in mordant dyeing.

A simpler example is the water-softening agent EDTA (ethylenediaminetetraacetic acid, see Fig. 13-6). This molecule acts like a claw, complexing so tightly with calcium and magnesium ions that it prevents their precipitation with soap. EDTA can even extract calcium from bones.

In mordant dyeing, the cloth is soaked in a solution of a metal salt before a solution of the dye is applied; the metal ions form a chelate with the dye, and attach it firmly to the fiber. Alizarin has been applied in this way for thousands of years (see Fig. 16-11). Traditionally, the aluminum was supplied in the form of alum, aluminum ammonium sulfate, or aluminum potassium sulfate. The colors developed by mordant dyeing are sensitive to the nature of the metal used, and iron is particularly detrimental to the development of the best alizarin color. Because iron is a common impurity in aluminum, it became especially important to the ancient dyers to obtain aluminum free of this element. Fortunately, the alums crystallize in beautiful, large, pure crystals, and by repeated crystallizations alum could be freed of iron. Thus, alum was perhaps the only really pure compound known to the ancients.

Finally, a number of dyes can be synthesized directly on the fiber, where they precipitate and remain fast. This method is particularly useful for azo dyes. The relatively small, soluble diazonium salts and phenols or amines can be individually absorbed by the fiber while the larger azo product might not be. Other types of dyes can also be prepared by this method.

Synthesis of dyes directly on cloth is especially important in printing designs on a fabric. In one method a pattern is printed on the cloth with a paste containing the naphthol part of a dye. The cloth is then dipped in a bath containing a diazotized amine. A dye is produced only at the sites containing the naphthol, and precipitates as formed.

The dyeing of synthetic fibers presents special problems and was initially very difficult. Dacron affords a good example of the difficulties encountered. In the first place, Dacron has no acidic or basic sites and no hydroxyl groups for hydrogen bonding, so its affinity for dye molecules is low. In addition to this difficulty, the individual Dacron molecules pack together very tightly, so that there is little room for dye molecules to penetrate.

To avoid these problems dyeing may be carried out at high temperatures, so that the Dacron molecules are freer to move about and admit dye molecules. Alternatively, certain chemicals may be added to the dyeing bath which cause the fiber to swell and thus create spaces in the fiber for the dyes to penetrate. Each new synthetic fiber presents its own difficulties, and much research goes into determining the best method of dyeing it.

In absorbing electromagnetic radiation, a molecule may engage in other activities besides the production of color. It can, for instance, participate in a chemical reaction, which may sometimes be of great nuisance value; for example, they are primarily responsible for the fading of dyes.

Actually, the absorption of light gives rise to energy-rich molecules which can and often do undergo interesting and unusual reactions, but these reactions constitute the study of photochemistry, which is subject matter for another course in organic chemistry and the material for another book.

Prob. 16-6. Suggest how one could make the dye methyl orange in the laboratory. This dye is an indicator; show a form which would account for its change of color in acid.

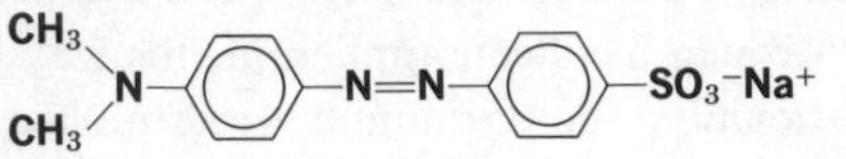

Prob. 16-7. In acid, fluorescein is nearly colorless. Draw a form which would explain this color shift.

ANSWERS TO PROBLEMS—CHAPTER 1

1-1. The carbon dioxide formed is $224/22,400 = 0.01$ mole, containing 0.01 gram atoms of carbon. The water formed is $0.36/18 = 0.02$ mole, containing 0.04 gram atoms of hydrogen. Therefore, methane contains 4 hydrogen atoms for each carbon atom and is CH_4.

1-2. 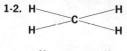 rectangular; 3 dichloromethanes.

 pyramidal (square base); 2 dichloromethanes

Both tetrahedral and square planar structures predict only one tri- and one tetrachloromethane.

1-3. (a) ionic   (c) intermediate
      (b) covalent   (d) covalent

1-4. Oxygen $1s^2 2s^2 2p_x^2 2p_y^1 2p_z^1$
      Neon $1s^2 2s^2 2p_x^2 2p_y^2 2p_z^2$

1-5.

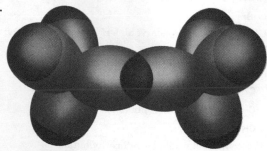

329

1-6. CH$_3$—CCl$_3$
1,1,1-trichloroethane

ClCH$_2$—CCl$_3$
1,1,1,2-tetrachloroethane

Cl$_2$CH—CCl$_3$
1,1,1,2,2-pentachloroethane

(or simply pentachloroethane, since there is only one isomer)

ClCH$_2$—CHCl$_2$
1,1,2-trichloroethane

Cl$_2$CH—CHCl$_2$
1,1,2,2-tetrachloroethane

Cl$_3$C—CCl$_3$
hexachloroethane

1-7. CH$_3$—CH$_2$—CH$_2$Cl

CH$_3$—CH—CH$_3$
|
Cl

CH$_3$—CH$_2$—CHCl$_2$

1-chloropropane   2-chloropropane   1,1-dichloropropane

CH$_3$—CH—CH$_2$Cl
|
Cl

ClCH$_2$—CH$_2$—CH$_2$Cl

CH$_3$—C—CH$_3$ with Cl above and Cl below

1,2-dichloropropane   1,3-dichloropropane   2,2-dichloropropane

1-8.

The first structure is the most stable, since the large methyl groups are as far away from one another as possible. In the other two structures, the methyl groups bump into one another.

1-9. CH$_3$—CH$_2$—CH$_2$—CH$_2$—CH$_2$—CH$_3$

CH$_3$—CH$_2$—CH$_2$—CH—CH$_3$
                                    |
                                    CH$_3$

CH$_3$
|
CH$_3$—C—CH$_2$—CH$_3$
|
CH$_3$

CH$_3$—CH$_2$—CH—CH$_2$—CH$_3$
                      |
                      CH$_3$

CH$_3$—CH—CH—CH$_3$
          | |
          CH$_3$ CH$_3$

1-10. (a) CH$_3$—CH—CH—CH$_2$—CH$_2$—CH$_3$
                      | |
                      CH$_3$ CH$_3$

(b) CH$_3$—CH$_2$—CH$_2$—CH—CH$_2$—CH$_2$—CH$_3$
                                  |
                                  CH$_3$—CH—CH$_3$

(c) CH$_3$—CH$_2$—CH$_2$—Ⓒ—CH—CH$_2$—CH$_3$ with CH$_2$—CH$_2$—CH$_3$ above, and CH$_3$ CH$_3$ CH$_2$—CH$_3$ below

(d) CH$_3$—CH—CH$_3$
              |
              Cl

(e) CH$_3$—CH$_2$—CH—CH$_2$—CH—CH$_2$—CH$_2$—CH$_3$
                    | |
                    Br   I

All methyl groups are primary; all CH$_2$ groups are secondary; all CH groups are tertiary; the central (circled) carbon is quaternary.

1-11. (a) Numbered from the wrong end:

CH$_3$
|
CH$_3$—CH$_2$—C—CH$_3$ 2,2-dimethylbutane
|
CH$_3$

Another wrong name for this compound would be 2-dimethylbutane

(b) Longest chain not chosen:

$$CH_3—CH—CH_2—CH_2—CH_2—CH_3 \quad \text{4-methyloctane}$$
$$\quad\quad\;\; CH_2—CH_2—CH_3$$

(c) Longest chain not chosen:

$$CH_3—CH_2—CH—CH_2—CH_2—CH_2—CH_3 \quad \text{3-ethylheptane}$$
$$\quad\quad\quad\quad\; CH_2—CH_3$$

(d) Numbered from wrong end:

$$CH_3CH(CH_2)_6CH_2F \quad \text{1,8-difluorononane}$$
$$\quad\;\; F$$

1-12. $CH_3—CH_2—CH_2—CH_2—CH_2—CH_2—CH_3$ $CH_3—CH_2—CH_2—CH_2—CH—CH_3$
heptane CH_3

$CH_3—CH_2—CH_2—CH—CH_2—CH_3$ 2-methylhexane
$\quad\quad\quad\quad\quad\; CH_3$
3-methylhexane

$CH_3—CH_2—CH—CH—CH_3$ $CH_3—CH_2—CH_2—C—CH_3$ $CH_3—CH—C—CH_3$
$\quad\quad\quad CH_3\; CH_3$ CH_3 $CH_3\; CH_3$
2,3-dimethylpentane   2,2-dimethylpentane   2,2,3-trimethylbutane

$CH_3—CH_2—C—CH_2—CH_3$ $H_3C—CH—CH_2—CH—CH_3$ $CH_3—CH_2—CH—CH_2—CH_3$
$\quad\quad\quad\; CH_3$ $CH_3\quad\quad CH_3$ $CH_2—CH_3$
3,3-dimethylpentane   2,4-dimethylpentane   3-ethylpentane

1-13. (a) Same   If in doubt, name each by the IUPAC System. Correctly named, identi-
       (b) Different   cal compounds will have the same name.
       (c) Same

1-14. (a) $2C_6H_{14} + 19O_2 \longrightarrow 12CO_2 + 14H_2O$

      (b) $(CH_3)_4C + 12Cl_2 \longrightarrow (CCl_3)_4C + 12HCl$

ANSWERS TO PROBLEMS—CHAPTER 2

2-1.

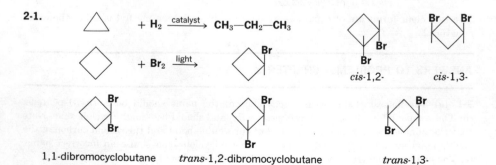

1,1-dibromocyclobutane   *trans*-1,2-dibromocyclobutane   *trans*-1,3-

2-2. In a planar cyclopentane molecule all atoms would be exactly eclipsed. This unfavorable arrangement is relieved by puckering.

2-3. In *trans*-decalin, each ring constitutes a pair of the more stable equatorial substituents for the other. In *cis*-decalin, one substituent is axial, the other equatorial.

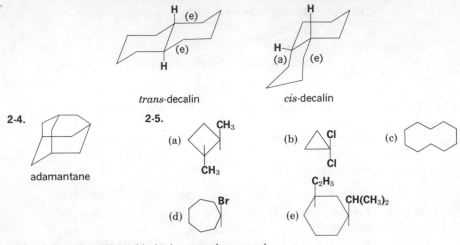

2-6. (a) Cyclopropyl bromide (or bromocyclopropane)
(b) *trans*-1,2-Dibromocyclopentane
(c) *trans*-1-*n*-Propyl-3-isopropylcyclohexane

2-7.

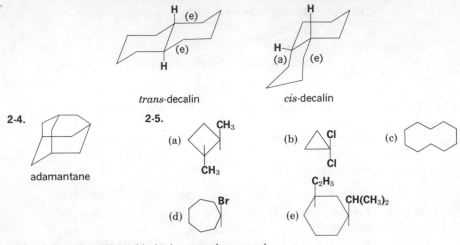

The first structure is the more stable, because both methyl groups are in the stable equatorial position.

cis-1,4-dimethylcyclohexane

The two chair forms are of equal energy because, in each, one methyl is axial, the other equatorial.

ANSWERS TO PROBLEMS—CHAPTER 3

3-1. (a) The longest chain has not been chosen; the name should be 2-ethyl-1-pentene.
(b) The compound has been numbered incorrectly, and should be 3-methylcyclohexene. Note that the numbering must start at one end of the double bond and the second carbon of the double bond must be numbered 2, and so 2-methylcyclohexene is also an incorrect name.
(c) The chain is numbered from the wrong end; the name should be 2-methyl-2-butene.

3-2.

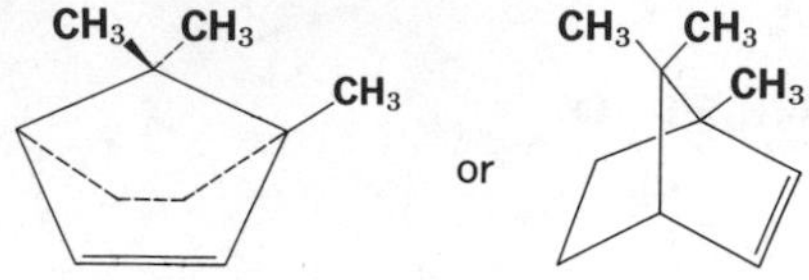

or

3-3. Niagara Falls, just outside Buffalo, produces inexpensive electrical power for the electric furnaces required in the production of calcium carbide.

3-4. In a *cis* double bond,

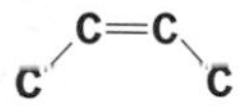

a six-membered ring can easily be completed by the addition of two more carbon atoms. In a *trans* double bond,

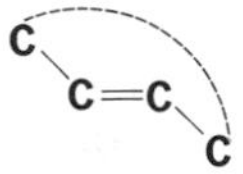

two atoms are not sufficient. The smallest ring which can accommodate a *trans* double bond is cyclooctene.

3-5. $CH_3—CH_2—CH_2—CH=CH_2$

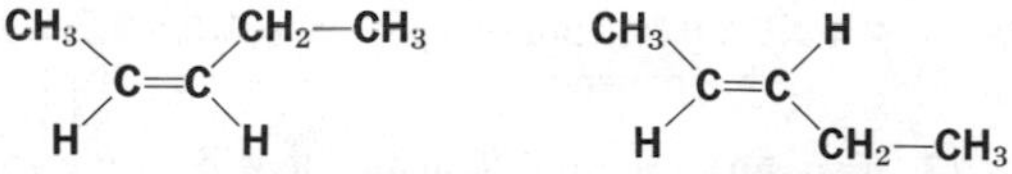

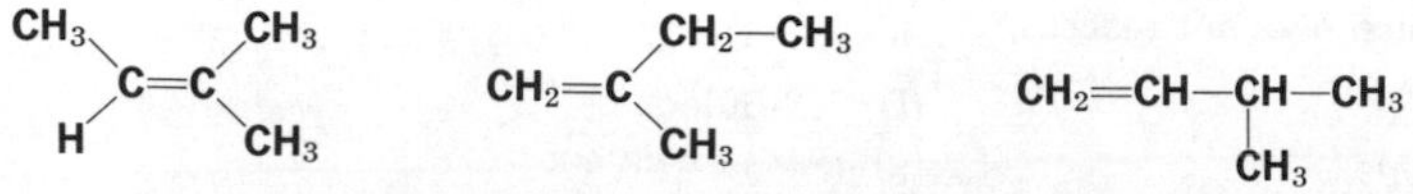

3-6. A triple bond is linear $C—C\equiv C—C$, and two more carbons are not enough to complete the ring without a large amount of bending of the angles. Cyclooctyne is known.

3-7. Addition to a double bond is always begun by a Lewis *acid*. Only chloride ion (Cl^-) is present, so that the addition can be completed by Cl^- but must be started by Br_2.

3-8. The product would be

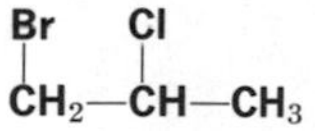

The Lewis acid (Br_2) adds, in accordance with Markownikoff's rule, to give

$$BrCH_2\overset{+}{CH}—CH_3$$

3-9. A better statement of Markownikoff's rule is that the acid adds in the way which forms the more stable carbonium ion. Addition to the carbon with the more hydrogens would place two positive charges adjacent to one another. Addition in the opposite direction would place them farther apart. The second carbonium ion is the more stable.

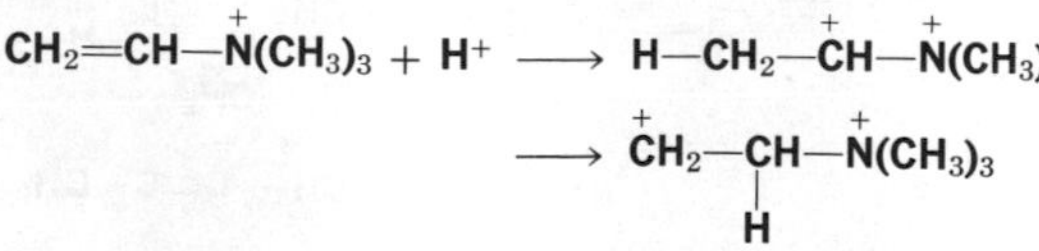

$$CH_2=CH—\overset{+}{N}(CH_3)_3 + H^+ \longrightarrow H—CH_2—\overset{+}{CH}—\overset{+}{N}(CH_3)_3$$

3-10. (c) An excess of acetylene. This will minimize the formation of 1,1-dichloroethane.

3-11.

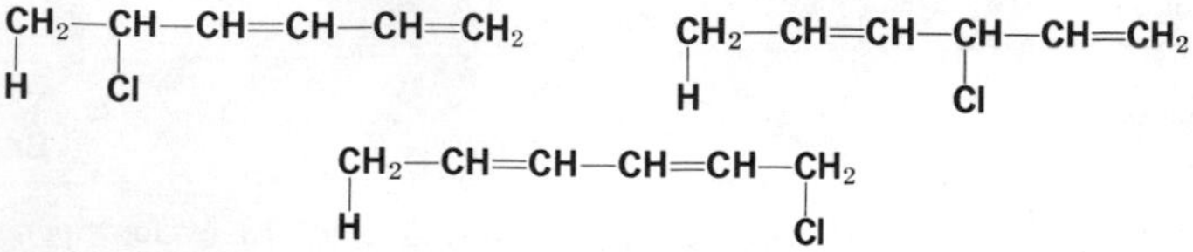

3-12.

$$CH_3-\underset{\underset{CH_3}{|}}{\overset{\overset{CH_3}{|}}{C}}-CH_2-\underset{\underset{CH_3}{|}}{\overset{\overset{CH_3}{|}}{C}}-CH_2-\underset{\underset{CH_3}{|}}{C}=CH_2 \xrightarrow{H^+} RCH_2-\underset{\underset{CH_3}{|}}{\overset{\oplus}{C}}-CH_3$$

2,4,4,6,6-pentamethyl-1-heptene

$$CH_3-\underset{\underset{CH_3}{|}}{\overset{\overset{CH_3}{|}}{C}}-CH_2-\underset{\underset{CH_3}{|}}{\overset{\overset{CH_3}{|}}{C}}-CH=\underset{\underset{CH_3}{|}}{C}-CH_3$$

2,4,4,6,6-pentamethyl-2-heptene

H⁺

CH₂=C—CH₃ with CH₃

$$R-CH_2-\underset{\underset{CH_3}{|}}{\overset{\overset{CH_3}{|}}{C}}-CH_2-\underset{\underset{\oplus}{}}{\overset{\overset{CH_3}{|}}{C}}-CH_3 \text{ with } CH_3$$

−H⁺

−H⁺

$$R-CH_2-\underset{\underset{CH_3}{|}}{\overset{\overset{CH_3}{|}}{C}}-CH=\underset{}{C}-CH_3 \text{ with } CH_3$$

2,4,4,6,6,8,8-heptamethyl-2-nonene

$$R-CH_2-\underset{\underset{CH_3}{|}}{\overset{\overset{CH_3}{|}}{C}}-CH_2-\underset{}{C}=CH_2 \text{ with } CH_3$$

2,4,4,6,6,8,8-heptamethyl-1-nonene

3-13. Test with bromine. The alkene will decolorize this, so that *n*-hexane can be identified as the bottle which does not react.

3-14. (a) 1-Butene
(b) 2-Butyne
(c) 3-Ethyl-2-pentene
(d) Cyclohexene
(e) 2,3-Dimethyl-1,3-butadiene
(f) 1,3-Butadiyne
(g) *trans*-2-Pentene
(h) *cis*-1,2-Dibromoethene
(i) 3-Methylcyclopentene
(j) 1-Methyl-1,4-cyclohexadiene

3-15. (a)
$$\underset{H}{\overset{CH_3}{\diagdown}}C=C\underset{CH_3}{\overset{H}{\diagup}}$$

(b) HC≡C—(CH₂)₄—CH₃

(c) CH₃—CH=C—CH₂—CH₂—CH₂—CH₃
with CH(CH₃)₂

(d) CH₂—CH
    CH₂—CH

(e) CH₂, CH, CH, C(CH₃)(CH₃) ring with CH₂, CH₂, CH₂

(f) CH₂=CH—CH₂—CH₂—CH=CH₂

(g) CH₂ ring structure with CH₂—CH₂, H, CH₂, CH₂, C—H

(h) CH₃—C≡C—CH₂—CH₂—C≡C—CH₃

3-16. (a) conjugated   (c) conjugated
(b) unconjugated   (d) unconjugated

CH₂CH=CH—CH—CH₂—CH₃
with Br and Br

Br (cyclohexene ring with Br)

3-17. The normal bond angles in ethylene are 122° (see Fig. 3-9). In cyclopropene they would have to be close to 60°. The strain makes cyclopropene highly reactive.

3-18.

trans-trans   cis-trans   cis-cis

3-19. (a)

(b) $CH_3-CBr_2-CBr_2-CH_3$ (c)

ANSWERS TO PROBLEMS—CHAPTER 4

4-1. $RO \cdot + RSH \longrightarrow RS \cdot + ROH$

                   (A)   (B)

$RS \cdot + CH_2=CH-CH_3 \longrightarrow RS-CH_2-\overset{\cdot}{C}H-CH_3$

                             (C)

$RS-CH_2-\overset{\cdot}{C}H-CH_3 + RSH \longrightarrow RS-CH_2-CH_2-CH_3 + RS \cdot$

$2RS-CH_2-\overset{\cdot}{C}H-CH_3 \longrightarrow (RS-CH_2-\underset{\underset{CH_3}{|}}{CH})_2$

$2RS \cdot \longrightarrow RS-SR$

4-2. (a) $ROOR \longrightarrow 2RO \cdot$

    (b) $RO \cdot + CH_2=CHCl \longrightarrow RO-CH_2-\overset{\cdot}{C}HCl$

    (c) $ROCH_2\overset{\cdot}{C}HCl + CH_2=CCl_2 \longrightarrow ROCH_2CHClCH_2\overset{\cdot}{C}Cl_2 \longrightarrow$ etc.

    (d) $ROCH_2\sim\sim CH_2\overset{\cdot}{C}HCl + RO \cdot \longrightarrow ROCH_2\sim\sim CH_2\underset{\underset{OR}{|}}{C}HCl$

In step (b) the reaction could be initiated by reaction with vinylidene chloride rather than vinyl chloride.

4-3. $CH_3CH_2CH_2CH_2Br$

4-4.

Acid	Radical	Base
Cl^+	$Cl \cdot$	Cl^-
H_3C^+	$H_3C \cdot$	H_3C^-
H^+	$H \cdot$	H^-
HO^+	$HO \cdot$	HO^-
Br^+	$Br \cdot$	Br^-
HS^+	$HS \cdot$	HS^-

4-5. $\cdot \overset{..}{N} \overset{..}{O} :$ Nitric oxide is a free radical itself. It combines with other free radicals and terminates any polymerization before it gets started.

ANSWERS TO PROBLEMS—CHAPTER 5

5-1. Referring to the resonance structures for naphthalene in Fig. 5-6, we see that the 9,10-bond is double in one structure and single in the other two. It is consequently ⅓ double, ⅔ single, or 1⅓ bond. The 1,9–bond is also 1⅓.

5-2.

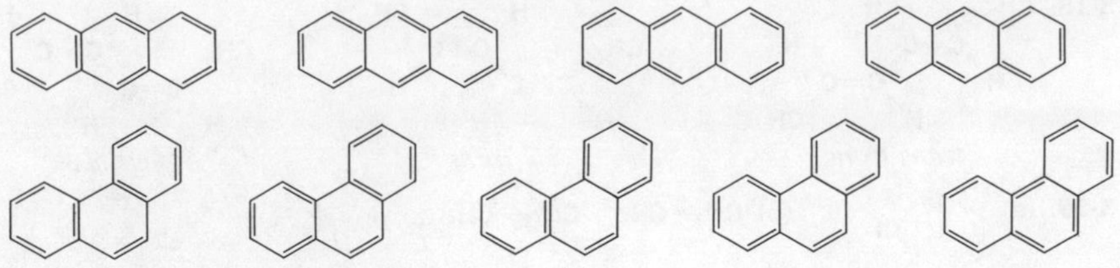

5-3. If the double bonds in naphthalene were normal, there would be five of them (as in any of the resonance structures of Fig. 5-6). Five normal double bonds would release $5 \times 28.6 = 143.0$ kcal of heat upon hydrogenation. Naphthalene releases only 82.0 kcal of heat. Therefore, the resonance energy of benzene is $143.0 - 82.0 = 61.0$ kcal. Notice that the resonance energy of naphthalene is not quite twice as large as that of benzene, although it contains two benzene rings. Evidently, the necessity of the two central carbon atoms to take part in both rings accounts for this. In biphenyl

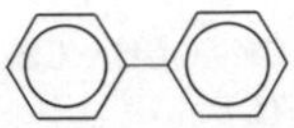

the rings are independent and the resonance energy is more nearly twice that of benzene.

5-4.

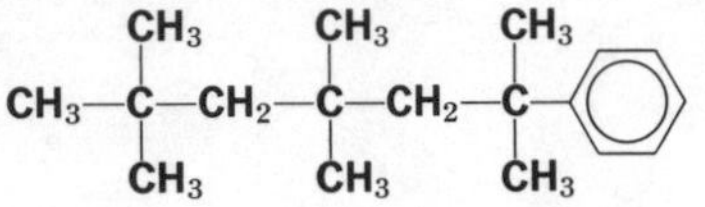

5-5.

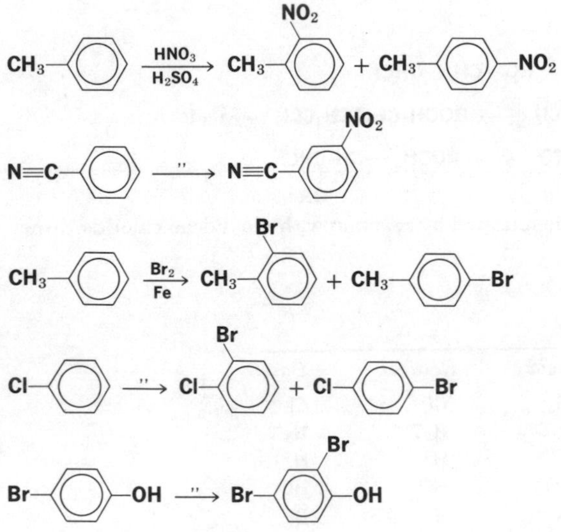

5-6.

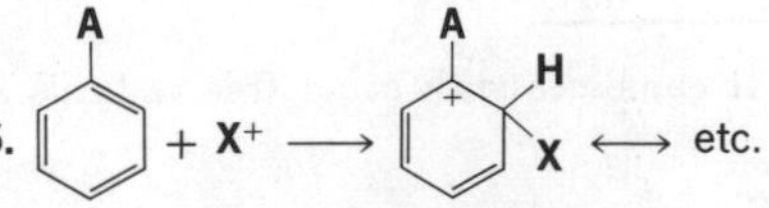

5-7. Ten double bonds contain 20 electrons. The $(4n + 2)$ rule ($n =$ any integer) predicts that 18 electrons ($n = 4$) and 22 electrons ($n = 5$) will be aromatic, while 20 electrons will be nonaromatic. Fifteen double bonds obey the rule $(4n + 2) = 30$ if $n = 7$. This compound has been prepared, but shows few aromatic properties.

$C_{30}H_{30}$

5-8.  has only 4 π electrons and so does not obey $4n + 2$ rule;  has 8 π electrons.

5-9. (a)  (d)  (g)

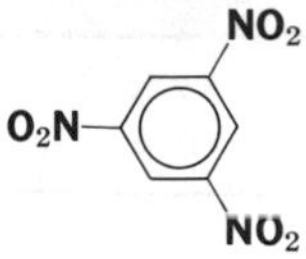

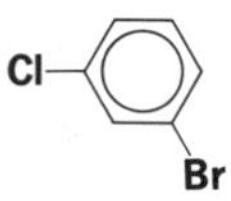

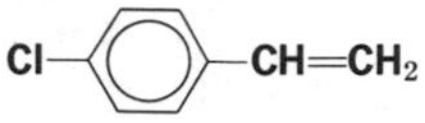

(b) (e) (h)

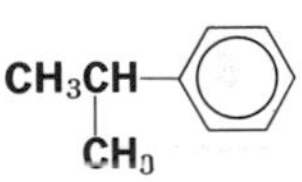

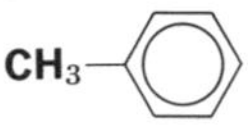

(c) (f)

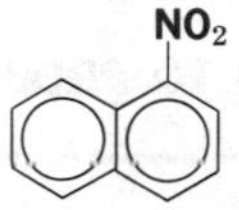

5-10. (a) *p*-Bromochlorobenzene or *p*-chlorobromobenzene (d) Anthracene
(b) *o*-Dinitrobenzene (e) Ethylbenzene
(c) *p*-Iodotoluene (f) 2-Phenyl-1-chloroethane

5-11. (a) 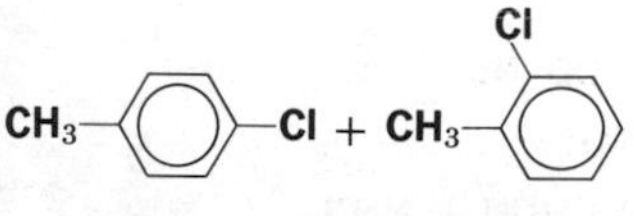 (b) 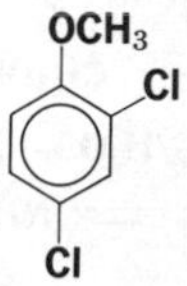 (c)

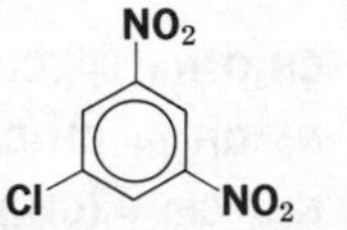

(d)

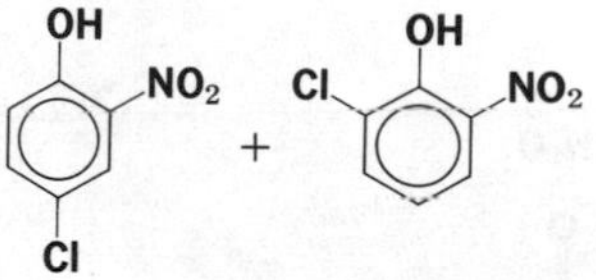

5-12. (a) Review Fig. 5-11.

(b)

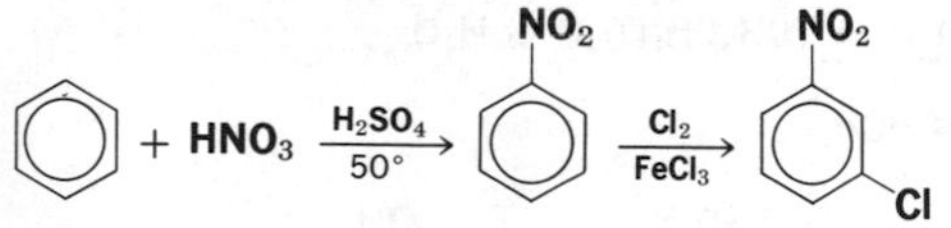

(c) 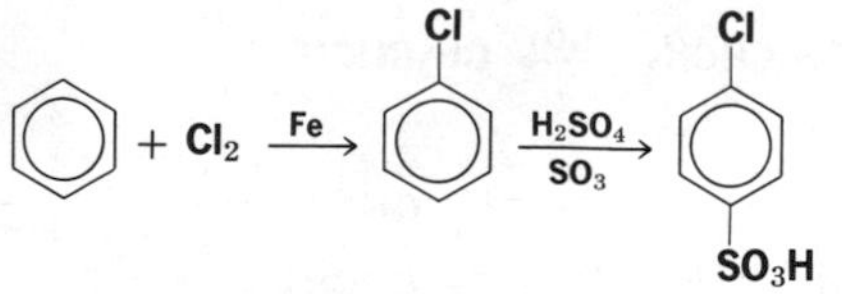
(plus *o*-isomer)

5-13.

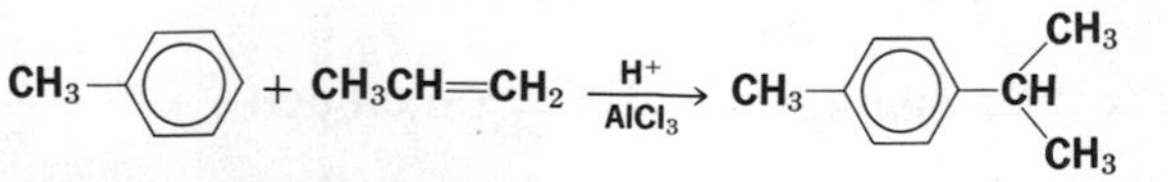

Some *o*-isomer would also be formed and would have to be separated.

5-14.

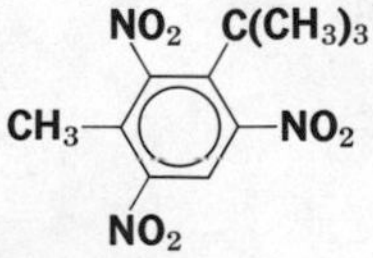

5-15. → The positions indicated by arrows are activated by *both* CH$_3$ groups (either *ortho* to one and *para* to the other or *ortho* to both). This is not the case with the other two isomers where any one position is activated by only *one* CH$_3$ group.

ANSWERS TO PROBLEMS—CHAPTER 6

6-1. (a) 2-propanol   (c) 1-cyclohexyl-3-buten-2-ol
       (b) 3-methyl-1-butanol   (d) 2-phenyl-1-ethanol *or* 2-phenylethanol

6-2. $CH_3(CH_2)_3CH_2OH + Na \longrightarrow$ gas evolved; $CH_3(CH_2)_3CH{=}CH_2 + Br_2 \longrightarrow$ colorless
                                                        red
       $CH_3(CH_2)_4CH_3 + Na$ or $Br_2 \longrightarrow$ no reaction

6-3. primary: 3-methyl-1-pentanol, 3-methyl-1-butanol, 2-phenylethanol;
       secondary: *trans*-4-methylcyclohexanol, 3-phenyl-2-butanol, 4-penten-2-ol, 2-propanol,
                1-cyclohexyl-3-buten-2-ol.

6-4. $CH_3O^-Na^+ + (CH_3)_3COH \rightleftharpoons CH_3OH + (CH_3)_3CO^-Na^+$

       $Na^+OH^- + CH_3CH_2SH \rightleftharpoons H_2O + CH_3CH_2S^-Na^+$

       $NH_4^+Cl^- + (CH_3)_2CHO^-Na^+ \rightleftharpoons NH_3 + (CH_3)_2CHOH + NaCl$

6-5. $CH_3CH_2OH + \overset{\displaystyle O}{P}(OH)_3 \rightleftharpoons CH_3CH_2O\overset{\displaystyle O}{P}(OH)_2 + H_2O$

       $CH_3CH_2OH + CH_3CH_2O\overset{\displaystyle O}{P}(OH)_2 \rightleftharpoons (CH_3CH_2O)_2\overset{\displaystyle O}{P}OH + H_2O$

       $CH_3CH_2OH + (CH_3CH_2O)_2\overset{\displaystyle O}{P}OH \rightleftharpoons (CH_3CH_2O)_3\overset{\displaystyle O}{P} + H_2O$

6-6. $HOCH_2CH_2CH_3 \xrightarrow[130°]{H_2SO_4} CH_2{=}CHCH_3$

       $CH_2{=}CHCH_3 + HO{-}\overset{\displaystyle O}{\underset{\displaystyle O}{S}}{-}OH \longrightarrow CH_3\overset{OSO_3H}{\underset{|}{C}}HCH_3 \xrightarrow{H_2O} CH_3\overset{OH}{\underset{|}{C}}HCH_3$

6-7. $CH_3C{\equiv}CH + H_2 \xrightarrow{Pt} CH_3CH{=}CH_2 \xrightarrow{H_2SO_4} \xrightarrow{H_2O} CH_3\overset{OH}{\underset{|}{C}}HCH_3$
                    1 mole

       $CH_3CH_2CH{=}CH_2 \xrightarrow{H_2SO_4} \xrightarrow{H_2O} CH_3CH_2\overset{OH}{\underset{|}{C}}HCH_3 \xrightarrow{KMnO_4} CH_3CH_2\overset{\displaystyle O}{C}CH_3$

6-8. In BH_3, there are insufficient electrons to give boron a share in eight electrons;
It is therefore a Lewis acid, seeking a pair of electrons to complete its octet.

                                                  H
                                               H:B
                                               H

6-9. $R{-}S{-}O{-}H \rightleftharpoons R{-}S{-}O^- + H^+$

       $R{-}\overset{\displaystyle O}{\underset{\displaystyle O}{S}}{-}O{-}H \rightleftharpoons R{-}\overset{\displaystyle O}{\underset{\displaystyle O}{S}}{-}O^- \longleftrightarrow R{-}\overset{O^-}{\underset{\displaystyle O}{S}}{=}O + H^+$

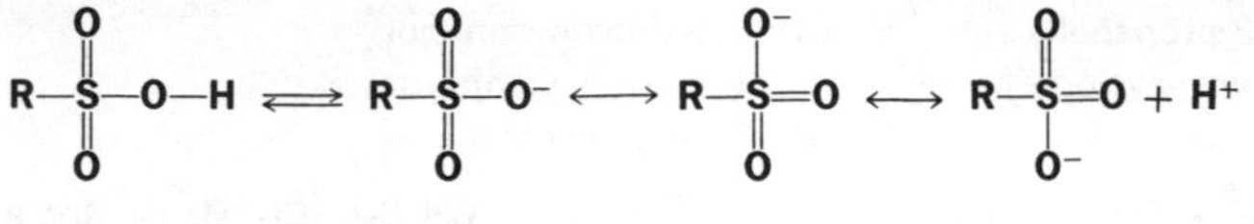

$$R\overset{\overset{O}{\|}}{\underset{\underset{O}{\|}}{S}}\text{—O—H} \rightleftharpoons R\overset{\overset{O}{\|}}{\underset{\underset{O}{\|}}{S}}\text{—O}^- \longleftrightarrow R\overset{\overset{O^-}{\|}}{\underset{\underset{O}{\|}}{S}}\text{=O} \longleftrightarrow R\overset{\overset{O}{\|}}{\underset{\underset{O^-}{\|}}{S}}\text{=O} + H^+$$

6-10.

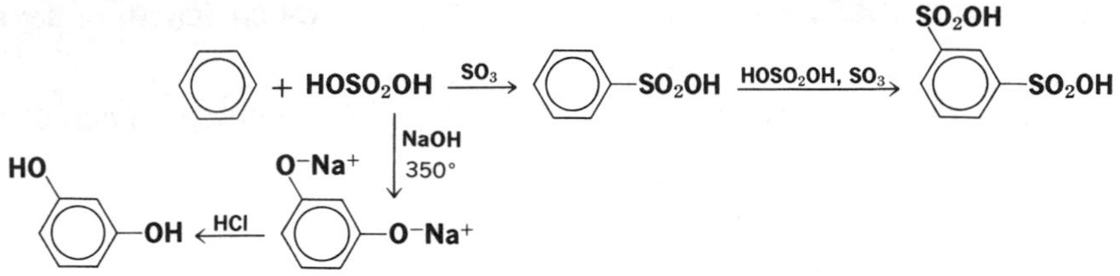

6-11. 3 $\left[\begin{array}{c} \text{catechol} \longrightarrow \text{o-benzoquinone} + 2H^+ \end{array}\right]$

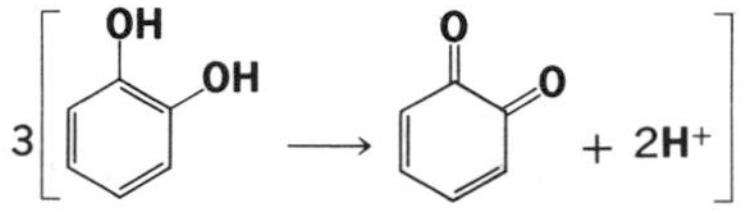

$$2[CrO_3 + 6H^+ \longrightarrow Cr^{+++} + 3H_2O]$$

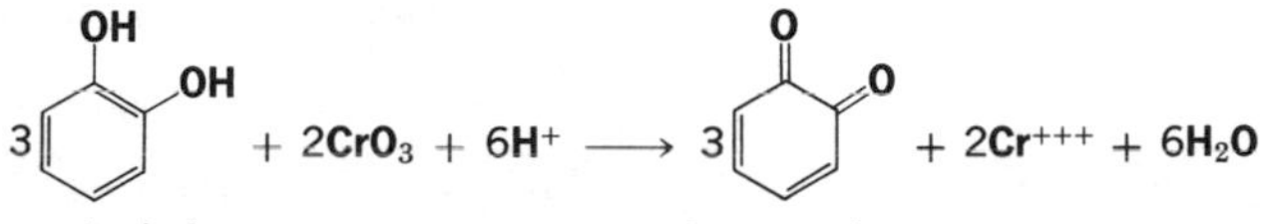

3 catechol + 2CrO₃ + 6H⁺ ⟶ 3 o-benzoquinone + 2Cr⁺⁺⁺ + 6H₂O

catechol   o-benzoquinone

No structure maintaining the tetravalence of every carbon atom can be drawn for the quinone derived from resorcinol.

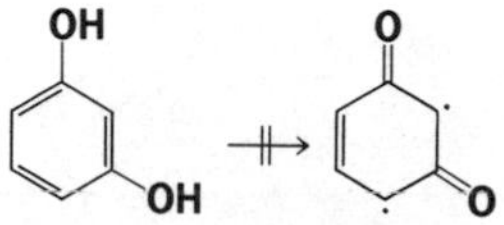

resorcinol

6-12. $CH_3CH_2CH_2OH + CH_3CH_2OH \xrightarrow[140°]{H_2SO_4}$

$$CH_3CH_2CH_2OCH_2CH_2CH_3 + CH_3CH_2OCH_2CH_2CH_3 + CH_3CH_2OCH_2CH_3$$

6-13. (a) 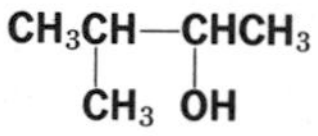 $CH_3CH\text{—}CHCH_3$ with CH_3 and OH

(b)

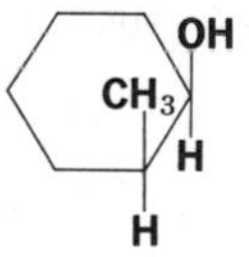

(c)

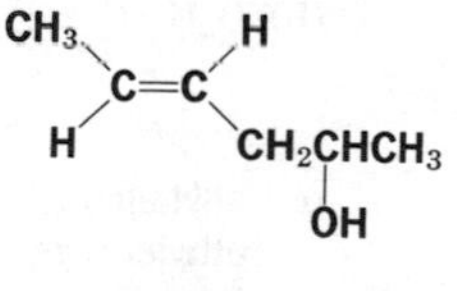

(d) 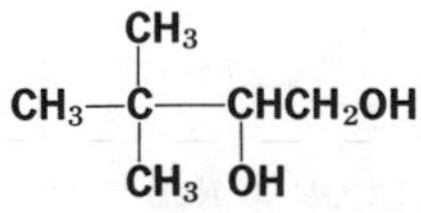 $CH_3\text{—}\overset{CH_3}{\underset{CH_3}{C}}\text{—}CHCH_2OH$ with OH

(e) 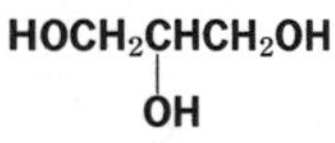 $HOCH_2CHCH_2OH$ with OH

(f)

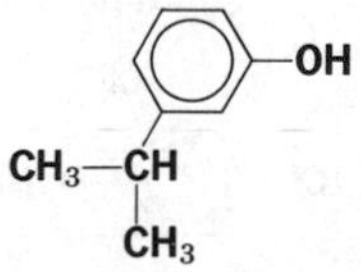

(g)

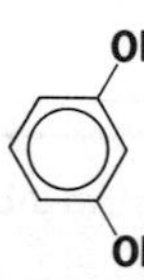

(h)

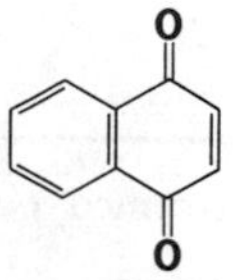

(i) 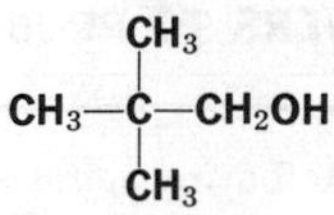 $CH_3\text{—}\overset{CH_3}{\underset{CH_3}{C}}\text{—}CH_2OH$

(j) 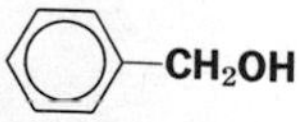 —CH₂OH

(k) 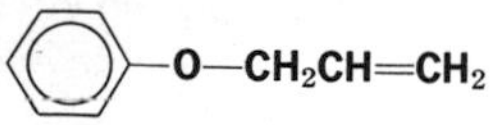 —O—CH₂CH=CH₂

(l)

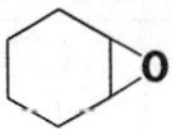

6-14. (a) 2-methyl-2-propanol   (d) 3,5-dibromophenol
       (b) *trans*-2-phenylcyclopropanol   (e) 1-methylcyclopentanol
       (c) 2-butanol   (f) 2-cyclohexenol

6-15. (a) $\xrightarrow{H_2SO_4}$ $\xrightarrow{H_2O}$ $CH_3CH_2CHCH_3$ (d) $\xrightarrow[100°]{H_2SO_4}$ $CH_3CH{=}CHCH_3$ (+ some
                                 | 1-butene)
                               OH

       (b) $\xrightarrow{BH_3}$ $\xrightarrow{H_2O_2}$ $CH_3CH_2CH_2CH_2OH$ (e) $\xrightarrow[140°]{H_2SO_4,\ H_2O}$ $CH_3CH_2CH_2CH_2OCH_2CH_2CH_2CH_3$

       (c) $\xrightarrow[NaOH]{HOCl}$ $CH_3CH_2CH{-}CH_2$
                                       \O/

6-16. (a) Fig. 6-23. (b) Fig. 6-30. (c) Fig. 6-19. (d) Fig. 6-23.

6-17. $(CH_3)_3C{-}\bigcirc{-}OH$ + $(CH_3)_3C{-}\bigcirc{-}OH$ $\xrightarrow[ether]{NaOH,\ H_2O}$

$(CH_3)_3C{-}\bigcirc{-}OH$
(ether solution)

$(CH_3)_3C{-}\bigcirc{-}O^-Na^+$
(NaOH solution)
  | HCl, H₂O
$(CH_3)_3C{-}\bigcirc{-}OH$
ppt.

6-18. (a) $\bigcirc$ + **Br₂** ⟶ colorless; $\bigcirc{CH_3}{OH}$ + HCl $\xrightarrow{ZnCl_2}$ immediate second layer
                  red

       (b) $O_2N{-}\bigcirc{-}OH$ + **NaHCO₃** $\xrightarrow{H_2O}$ soluble; $\bigcirc{-}OH$ + Na ⟶ gas evolved
            (NO₂ groups)

       (c) allyl alcohol: water-soluble, + **Br₂** test
           ethylene glycol: water-soluble, − **Br₂** test
           2-hexene: water-insoluble.

6-19. $Cl{-}\bigcirc{-}O^-Na^+$ + $BrCH_2\overset{O}{C}OH$ ⟶ $Cl{-}\bigcirc{-}OCH_2\overset{O}{C}OH$ + NaBr

---

ANSWERS TO PROBLEMS—CHAPTER 7

7-1. A foot, a spiral staircase, and a one-armed paperhanger. Symmetrical objects are identical with their mirror image.

7-2. $[\alpha]_D^{25} = \dfrac{(+0.24) \times (1000)}{1 \times 20} = +12.0°$ (2.0, in ethanol)

7-3. This problem can best be answered using models.

7-4. Each reaction of a Br⁻ ion with a D-2-bromobutane molecule converts a D-isomer into an L-isomer. Eventually, there will be a 50-50 mixture of D- and L-2-bromobutanes.

7-5.

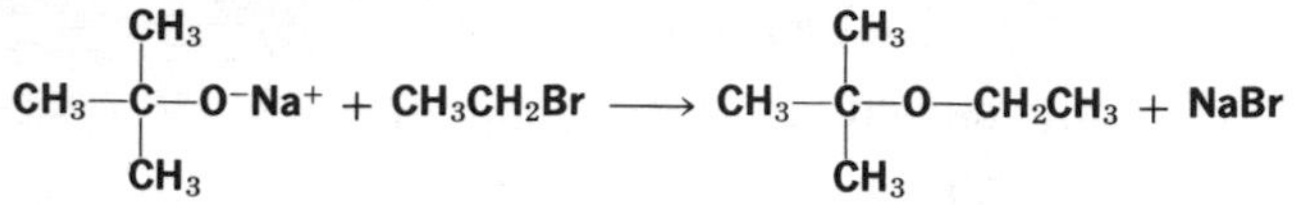

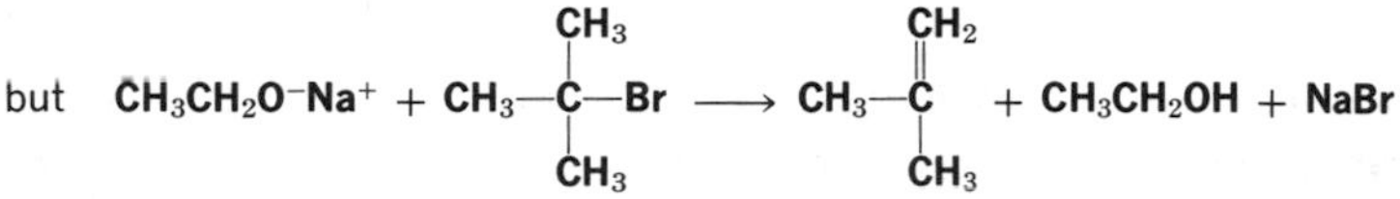

$$CH_3\text{---}\underset{\underset{CH_3}{|}}{\overset{\overset{CH_3}{|}}{C}}\text{---}O^-Na^+ + CH_3CH_2Br \longrightarrow CH_3\text{---}\underset{\underset{CH_3}{|}}{\overset{\overset{CH_3}{|}}{C}}\text{---}O\text{---}CH_2CH_3 + NaBr$$

but $CH_3CH_2O^-Na^+ + CH_3\text{---}\underset{\underset{CH_3}{|}}{\overset{\overset{CH_3}{|}}{C}}\text{---}Br \longrightarrow CH_3\text{---}\underset{\underset{CH_3}{|}}{\overset{\overset{CH_2}{||}}{C}} + CH_3CH_2OH + NaBr$

7-6. $CH_3CH_2CH_2Br + CH_3CH_2O^-Na^+ \longrightarrow CH_3CH_2CH_2OCH_2CH_3 + CH_3CH=CH_2 + CH_3CH_2OH$

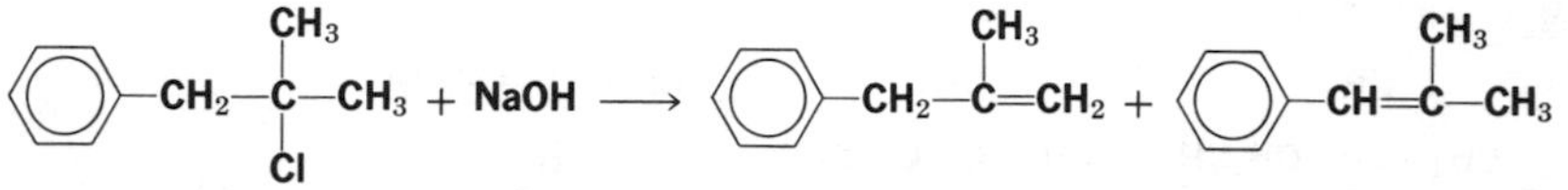

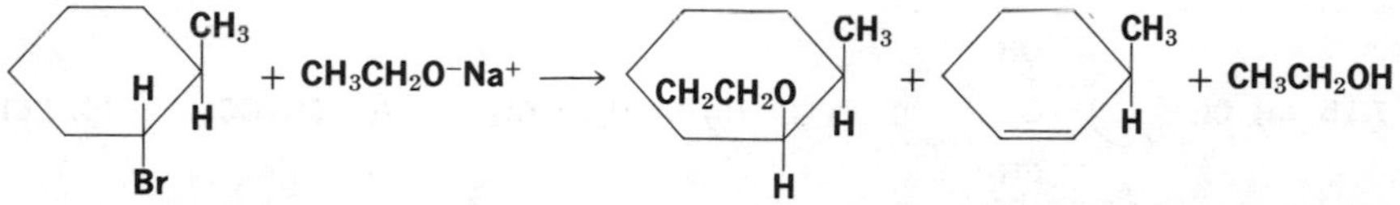

7-7. Carbon tetrachloride reacts vigorously with magnesium in a Grignard reaction. This reaction would make the fire still more vigorous.

7-8.

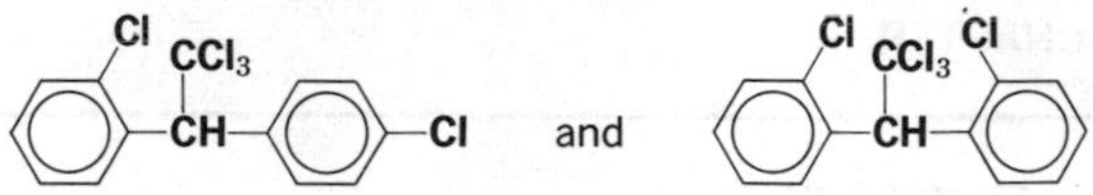

and

7-9. (b), (d), (e), (f), (h), (i). The planes of symmetry of the inactive compounds are shown in red.

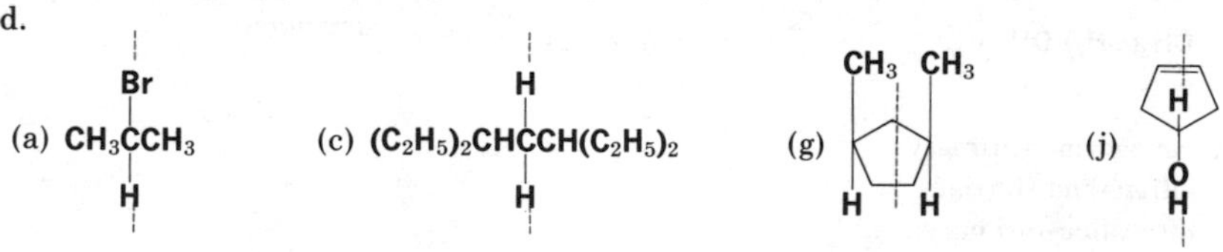

(a) $CH_3\overset{\overset{Br}{|}}{\underset{\underset{H}{|}}{C}}CH_3$ (c) $(C_2H_5)_2CH\overset{\overset{H}{|}}{\underset{\underset{H}{|}}{C}}CH(C_2H_5)_2$ (g)   (j)

7-10. Optically active—(c); optically inactive—(a), (b), (d), (e).

7-11. (a) $CH_3\text{---}\underset{\underset{OH}{|}}{\overset{\overset{H}{|}}{C}}\text{---}CH_2CH_3 + CH_2=CHCH_2CH_3 + CH_3CH=CHCH_3$ (b) $CH_3\text{---}\underset{}{\overset{\overset{CH_3}{|}}{C}}=CH_2$

cis and trans

(c)   (d)

(e)

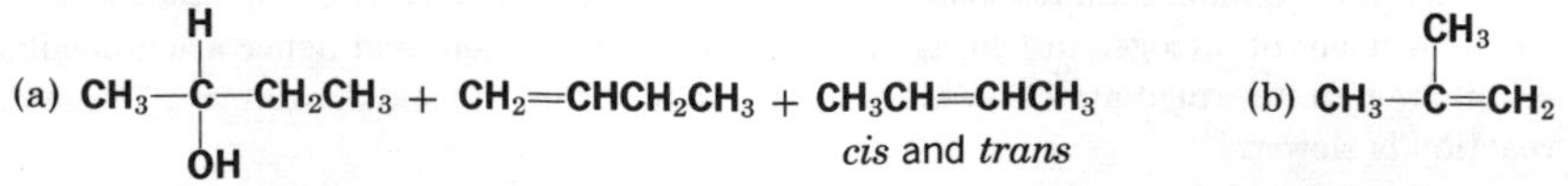

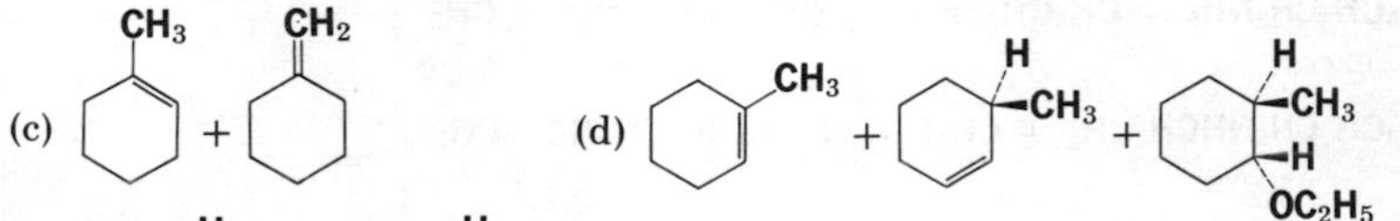

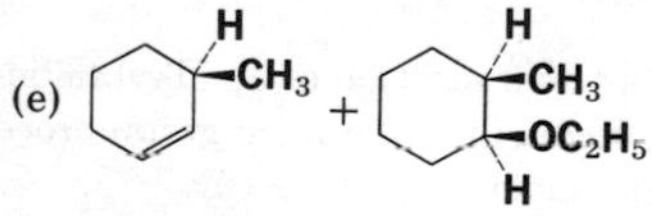

7-12. (a) ⬡—MgBr ⟶ ⬡   (c) (NO$_2$-substituted)⬡—Br + O$_2$N—⬡—Br

    (b) Fig. 7-17.   (d) Fig. 7-16.

7-13. CH$_3$—CH—C$_3$H$_7$ CH$_3$—CH—CH=CH$_2$ (cyclopropane structure CH$_3$, H, H, CH$_3$)
           | |
           C$_2$H$_5$ C$_2$H$_5$

7-14.

CH$_3$ H
  | |
CH$_3$—CH—C—CH$_3$
        |
        Br
      A

CH$_3$ OH
  | |
CH$_3$—CH—C—CH$_3$
        |
        H
      C

CH$_3$
  |
CH$_3$—CH—CH=CH$_2$
        E

CH$_3$
  |
CH$_2$=C—CH$_2$CH$_3$
       G

CH$_3$
  |
CH$_3$—CH—CH$_2$CH$_3$
      B

CH$_3$
  |
CH$_3$—C=CHCH$_3$
     D

CH$_3$
  |
CH$_3$—C—CH$_2$CH$_3$
    |
    Br
   F

7-15. (a) Cl—⬡—C(OH)(CH$_3$)—⬡—Cl   (b) ClCH$_2$C(CH$_3$)=CH$_2$ (c) Cl$_3$CCCl$_3$ (d) CCl$_3$CH(OH)(OH)

ANSWERS TO PROBLEMS—CHAPTER 8

8-1. CH$_3$(CH$_2$)$_5$NH$_2$
      +   ⟶(dilute HCl)⟶
CH$_3$(CH$_2$)$_5$OH

CH$_3$(CH$_2$)$_5$OH
insoluble   ⟶(NaOH)⟶ CH$_3$(CH$_2$)$_5$NH$_2$
                           insoluble

CH$_3$(CH$_2$)$_5$NH$_3^+$Cl$^-$
soluble

8-2. benzedrine—primary
     adrenaline—tertiary
     mescaline—primary

8-3. less readily.
In hydrogen bromide, aniline exists as the anilinium ion, C$_6$H$_5$NH$_3^+$. In this cationic form, the p-electrons of nitrogen are engaged in bonding to hydrogen, and hence are unavailable for stabilizing an intermediate carbonium ion resulting from attack of bromine. Therefore, the reaction is slower.

8-4. CH$_3$CH$_2$CH$_2$NH$_2$ + CH$_3$CH$_2$Br ⟶ CH$_3$CH$_2$CH$_2$NHCH$_2$CH$_3$
     excess

    CH$_3$CH$_2$CH$_2$NHCH$_2$CH$_3$ + CH$_3$I ⟶ CH$_3$CH$_2$CH$_2$NCH$_2$CH$_3$
         excess |
                                                 CH$_3$

8-5. Reduction of a nitrile gives a pure primary amine, while reaction of an alkyl halide with ammonia gives secondary and tertiary amines as well. Reduction of a nitro group proceeds in excellent yield, while reaction of an aryl halide with ammonia does not occur.

8-6. + **HONO₂** $\xrightarrow{H_2SO_4}$, then Fig. 8-17.

8-7. (a) CH₃CH₂C=CH₂ with CH₃

(b) CH₂=CH—CH—CH₂—N with CH₃ and CH₃

8-8. (a) dimethylamine
(b) diphenylamine
(c) methyldiethylamine (or diethylmethylamine)
(d) diethyldimethylammonium hydroxide (or dimethyldiethylammonium hydroxide)
(e) N-ethyl-*p*-bromoaniline

8-9.

8-10. —NH₂ $\xrightarrow[0°]{HONO}$ N₂; —NH₂ $\xrightarrow[0°]{HONO}$ no N₂ $\xrightarrow{heat}$ N₂

—NHCH₃ $\xrightarrow[0°]{HONO}$ yellow oil $\xrightarrow{heat}$ no N₂

8-11. (a) —NH₂ $\xrightarrow[0°]{HONO}$ —N₂⁺ $\xrightarrow[heat]{H_2O}$ —OH

(b) —NH₂ $\xrightarrow[excess]{CH_3Cl}$ —N(CH₃)₃ Cl⁻

(c) —NH₂ $\xrightarrow[0°]{HONO}$ —N₂⁺ $\xrightarrow{Cu_2Cl_2}$ —Cl

8-12. (a)

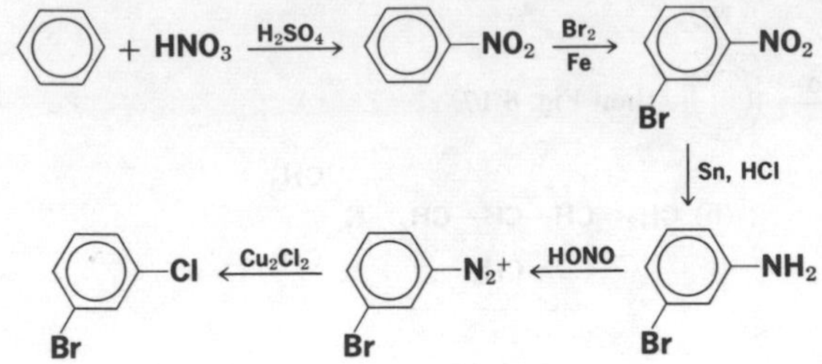

(b)

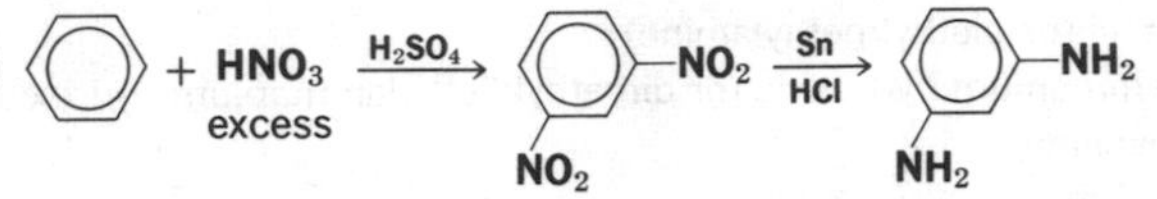

8-13. $CH_2{=}CH_2 \xrightarrow[OH^-]{HOCl} \overset{\displaystyle O}{CH_2{-}CH_2} \xrightarrow[H_2O]{(CH_3)_3N} HO{-}CH_2{-}CH_2{-}\overset{+}{N}(CH_3)_3{}^-OH$

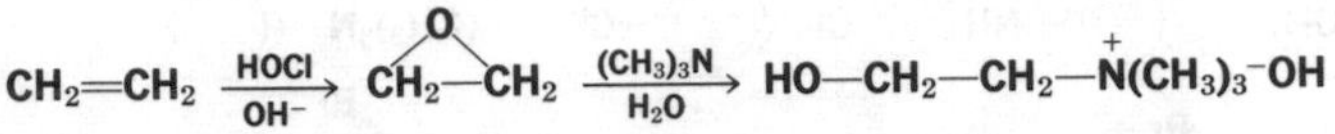

8-14. (a) 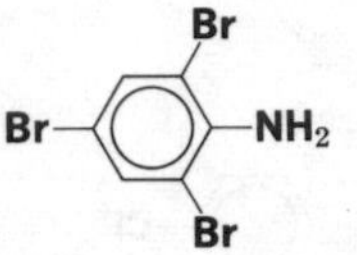   (b)

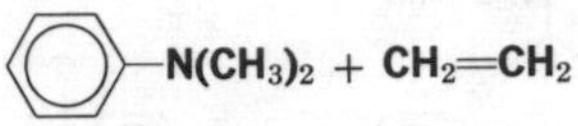

8-15. It resembles choline in having a quarternary ammonium ion, and hence can compete with choline and inhibit nerve impulse transmission.

ANSWERS TO PROBLEMS—CHAPTER 9

9-1. (a) 2-pentanone (methyl n-propyl ketone)
    (b) 2-methylpropanal (isobutyraldehyde)
    (c) 1-(p-chlorophenyl)-ethanone (methyl p-chlorophenyl ketone)
    (d) 2-propanone (acetone; dimethyl ketone; propanone)

9-2. (a) 2-hydroxypropanal   (c) 2,4-pentanedione
    (b) 3-penten-2-one   (d) 3-chlorophenylmethanal

9-3. (a) 2,2,2-trichloroethanal (or trichloroethanal)
    (b) 2,3,4,5,6-pentahydroxyhexanal
    (c) *trans*-3-phenyl-2-propenal
    (d) *trans*-2-isopropyl-5-methylcyclohexanone

9-4. $CH_3CH_2CH{=}CH_2 \xrightarrow{H_2SO_4} \xrightarrow{H_2O} CH_3CH_2\overset{\displaystyle OH}{\underset{}{C}}HCH_3 \xrightarrow{CrO_3} CH_3CH_2\overset{\displaystyle O}{\underset{}{C}}CH_3$

$CH_3CH{=}CHCH_3 \xrightarrow{H_2SO_4} \xrightarrow{H_2O}$

9-5. $CH_3CH_2\underset{\underset{\displaystyle CH_3}{|}}{C}{=}CHCH_2CH_3$

9-6.

9-7. $\overset{O}{\overset{\|}{CH_3CCH_2CH_3}}$ + $\overset{O}{\overset{\|}{H_2NNHCNH_2}}$ ⟶ $\overset{O}{CH_3C=NNH\overset{\|}{C}NH_2}$
$\underset{CH_2CH_3}{}$

9-8. $CH_3{-}\overset{}{C}{=}O$ + $BrMg{-}CH_2CH_2CH_3$
$\underset{CH_2CH_3}{}$

$CH_3C{=}O$ + $BrMg{-}CH_2CH_3$ ⟶ $CH_3{-}\overset{OMgBr}{\underset{CH_2CH_3}{C}}{-}CH_2CH_2CH_3$
$\underset{CH_2CH_2CH_3}{}$

$CH_3CH_2\overset{}{C}{=}O$ + $BrMg{-}CH_3$
$\underset{CH_2CH_2CH_3}{}$

$\downarrow H_2O$

$CH_3{-}\overset{OH}{\underset{CH_2CH_3}{C}}{-}CH_2CH_2CH_3$

9-9. (a) $\overset{O}{\overset{\|}{CH_3CCH_2CH_3}}$ + $H_2NNH{-}$$-NO_2$ ⟶ yellow ppt

  　　+ Tollen's reagent ⟶ no reaction

  $\overset{O}{\overset{\|}{CH_3(CH_2)_4CH}}$ + Tollen's reagent ⟶ silver mirror

  $CH_3(CH_2)_6CH_3$ + $H_2NNH{-}$$-NO_2$ or Tollen's reagent ⟶ no reaction

(b) $-CH_2OH$ + HCl $\xrightarrow{ZnCl_2}$ second layer

  $\overset{O}{\overset{\|}{CH_3(CH_2)_6CH}}$ + Tollen's reagent ⟶ silver mirror

  $\overset{O}{\overset{\|}{CH_3C}}$ + HCl $\xrightarrow{ZnCl_2}$ no reaction

  　　+ Tollen's reagent ⟶ no reaction

9-10. (a) $\overset{O}{\overset{\|}{CH_3CH_2CH_2CCH_2CH_2CH_3}}$　　　(b) $\overset{O}{\overset{\|}{CH_3CH_2CH}}$　　(c) $=O$

(d) 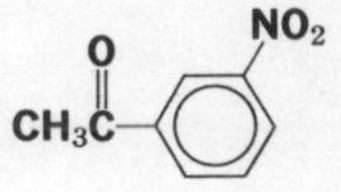 $CH_3\overset{O}{\overset{\|}{C}}$ —⬡—NO_2

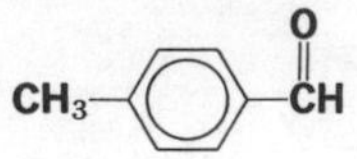

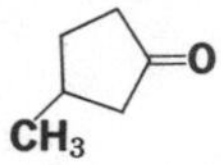

(g) $CH_3CH_2CH_2CH=CHCH$

(j) ⬡—$\overset{CH_3}{\underset{|}{C}}$=NNHC—$NH_2$ (with $\overset{O}{\overset{\|}{}}$ on C)

(e) CH_3—⬡—$\overset{O}{\overset{\|}{C}}H$

(h) $CH_3\overset{O}{\overset{\|}{C}}CH_2CH=CH_2$

(f) cyclopentanone ring with $=O$ and CH_3

(i) 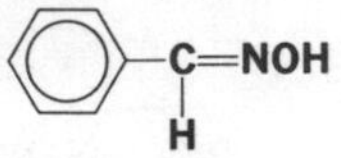 ⬡—$\overset{}{\underset{H}{C}}$=NOH

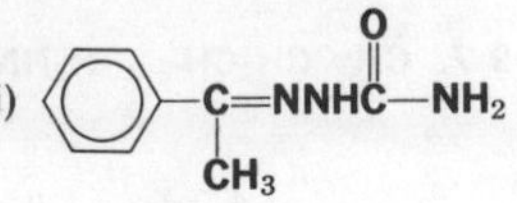

9-11. (a) 3-pentanone (c) diphenylmethanone (e) 2,2-dimethyl-3-butenal
  (b) pentanal (d) cyclopentanone

9-12. (a) $C_6H_5CH_2OH$ (c) $C_6H_5CH=NOH$ (e) C_6H_5COOH
  (b) $(C_6H_5)_2CHOH$ (d) $C_6H_5CH_2OH$ (f) $C_6H_5CH(SCH_3)_2$

9-13. (a) $H_2C=\overset{CH_3}{\underset{|}{C}}-CH_3$ (c) $CH_3-\overset{CH_3}{\underset{|}{C}}=CHCH_2CH_2CH=CHCH_2CH_3$

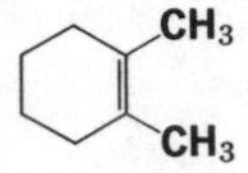

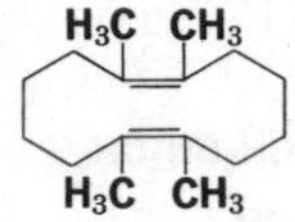

  (b) cyclohexene with two CH_3 or   cyclic structure with H_3C CH_3 / H_3C CH_3

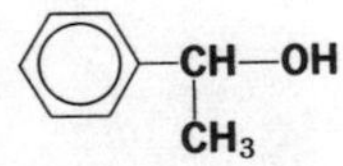

9-14. (a) CH_4 (d) $CH_3CH_2\overset{OH}{\underset{CH_3}{\overset{|}{C}}}CH_3$

  (b) $CH_3\overset{O}{\overset{\|}{C}}OH$

  (c) ⬡—$\overset{}{\underset{CH_3}{CH}}$—OH (e) CH_4

  (f) CH_3CH_2OH

9-15. (a) 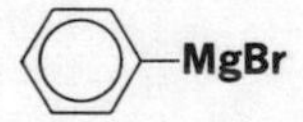 ⬡—$MgBr$ + $H_2C=O$ ⟶ $\xrightarrow{H_2O}$

  (b) $CH_3\overset{O}{\overset{\|}{C}}H$ + CH_3MgBr ⟶ $\xrightarrow{H_2O}$

  (c) $CH_3CH_2CH_2CH_2CH_2CH_2Br$ $\xrightarrow{Mg}$ $\xrightarrow{H_2O}$

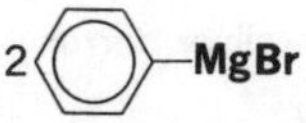

  (d) 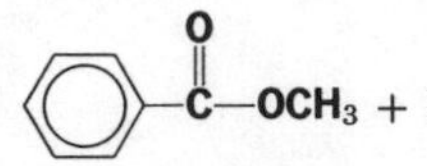 ⬡—$\overset{O}{\overset{\|}{C}}$—$OCH_3$ + 2 ⬡—$MgBr$ ⟶ $\xrightarrow{H_2O}$

9-16. (a) 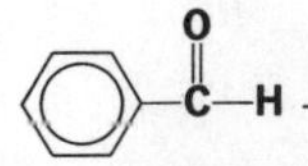 ⬡—$\overset{O}{\overset{\|}{C}}$—H + Tollen's reagent ⟶ silver mirror

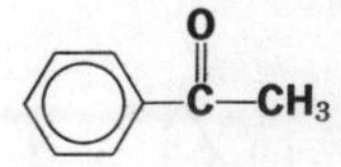

  ⬡—$\overset{O}{\overset{\|}{C}}$—$CH_3$ + Tollen's reagent ⟶ no reaction

(b) 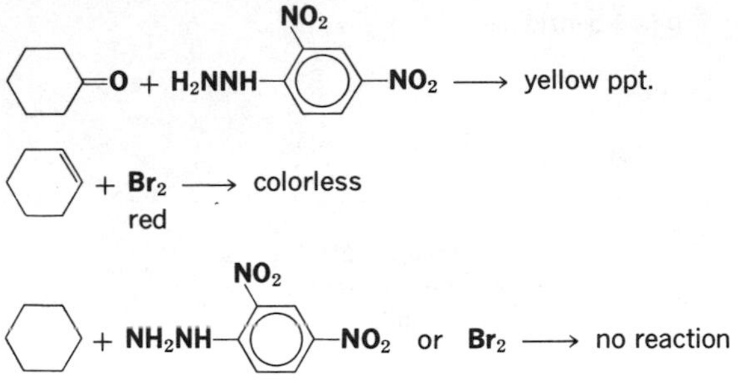 [cyclohexanone] $=O$ + H_2NNH—[2,4-dinitrophenyl with NO_2 and NO_2] $\longrightarrow$ yellow ppt.

[cyclohexene] + Br_2 $\longrightarrow$ colorless
red

[cyclohexane] + NH_2NH—[2,4-dinitrophenyl with NO_2 and NO_2] or Br_2 $\longrightarrow$ no reaction

(c) 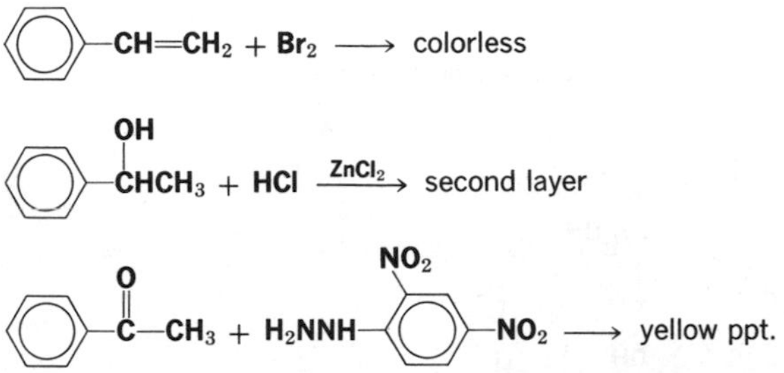 [phenyl]—$CH{=}CH_2$ + Br_2 $\longrightarrow$ colorless

[phenyl]—$\overset{OH}{\underset{}{C}}HCH_3$ + HCl $\xrightarrow{ZnCl_2}$ second layer

[phenyl]—$\overset{O}{\overset{\|}{C}}$—$CH_3$ + H_2NNH—[2,4-dinitrophenyl with NO_2 and NO_2] $\longrightarrow$ yellow ppt.

ANSWERS TO PROBLEMS—CHAPTER 10

10-1. (a)

```
    CHO              CHO
 H—C—OH          HO—C—H
HO—C—H            H—C—OH
HO—C—H            H—C—OH
   CH₂OH             CH₂OH
L-(+)-arabinose   D-(−)-arabinose
```

(b)

```
    CHO              CHO
 H—C—OH          HO—C—H
HO—C—H            H—C—OH
 H—C—OH          HO—C—H
   CH₂OH             CH₂OH
 D-(+)-xylose     L-(−)-xylose
```

(c)

```
    CHO              CHO
HO—C—H            H—C—OH
HO—C—H            H—C—OH
HO—C—H            H—C—OH
   CH₂OH             CH₂OH
 L-(+)-ribose     D-(−)-ribose
```

(d)

```
    CHO              CHO
 H—C—OH          HO—C—H
 H—C—OH          HO—C—H
HO—C—H            H—C—OH
   CH₂OH             CH₂OH
 L-(+)-lyxose     D-(−)-lyxose
```

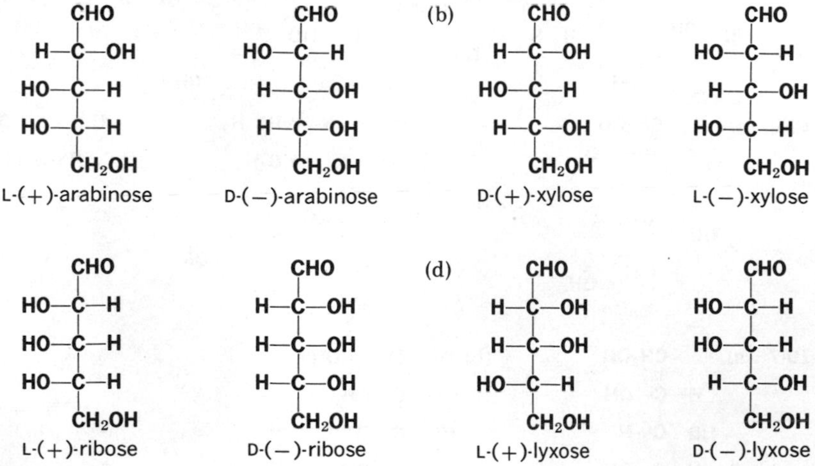

Mirror images are indicated. Each compound is a diastereomer of every other one except its mirror image.

10-2.   racemic mixture   D-(−)-benzidine

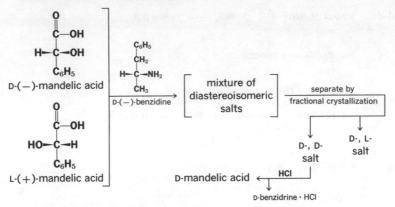

10-3. *n*-Propyl 2-amino-4-nitrophenyl ether.

10-4.

lactose

10-5. Since the sugars are nonreducing, the two glucose molecules must be joined through the hemiacetal linkages. If the disaccharide is hydrolyzed only by emulsin, both acetal linkages must be β. If by emulsin and maltase, one must be α, the other β.

10-6. (a)   CH$_2$OH   (b) CH=N—NHC$_6$H$_5$ (d)

                           C=N—NHC$_6$H$_5$

                                                   $\overset{\displaystyle S}{\underset{\displaystyle \parallel}{}}$

        —OCH$_3$ (c)   R—O—C—S$^-$Na$^+$

10-7. (a)   CH$_2$OH   (b)   CH=NOH

           H—C—OH   H—C—OH

       HO—C—H   HO—C—H

           H—C—OH   H—C—OH

           H—C—OH   H—C—OH

            CH$_2$OH   CH$_2$OH

(c)

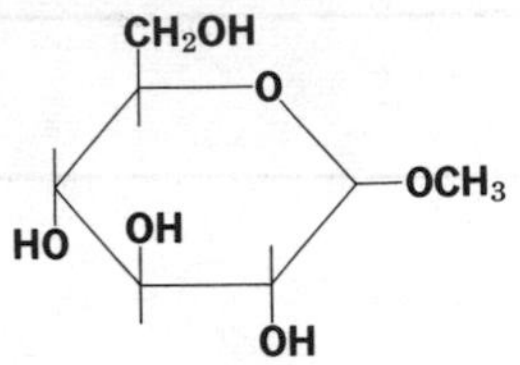

methyl α- and
β-D-glucosides

(d)

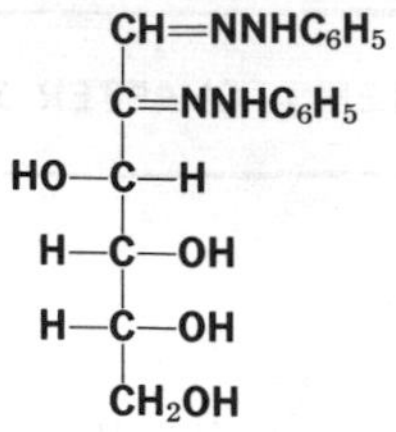

$$CH=NNHC_6H_5$$
$$C=NNHC_6H_5$$
$$HO-C-H$$
$$H-C-OH$$
$$H-C-OH$$
$$CH_2OH$$

10-8.

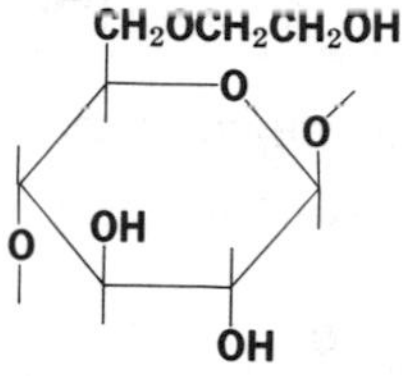

10-9.

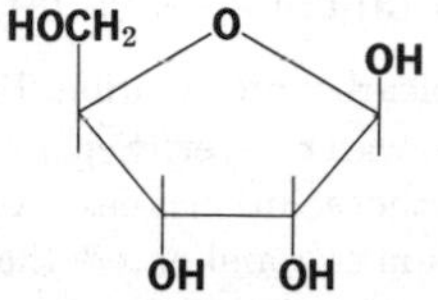

D-(−)-ribose
β-furanose form

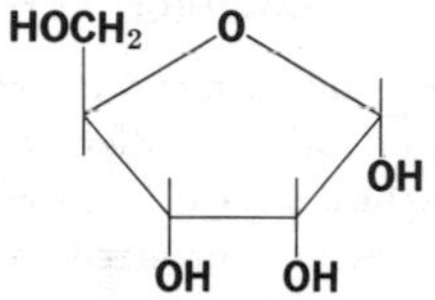

D-(−)-ribose
α-furanose form

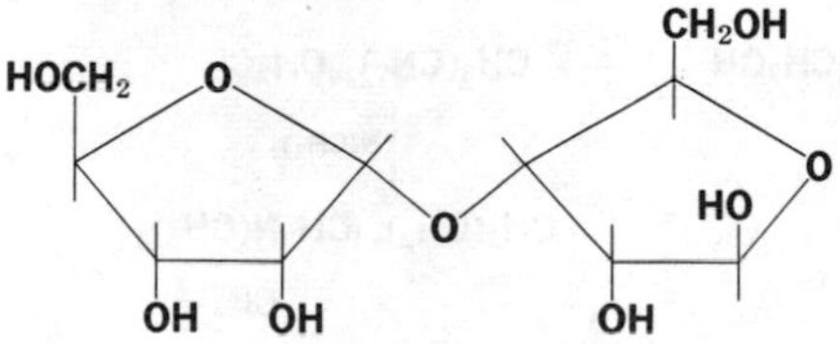

a reducing disaccharide

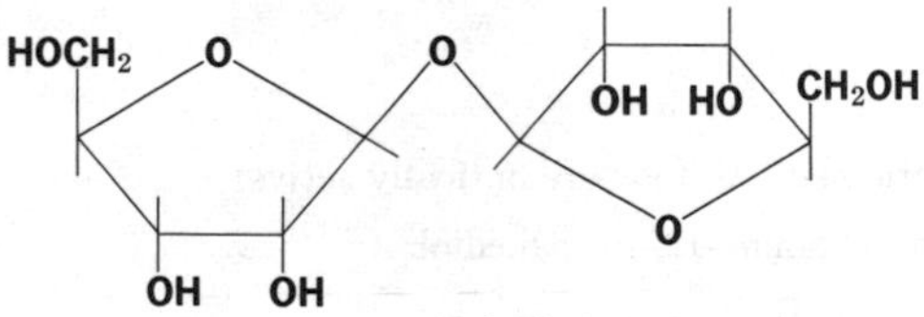

a nonreducing
disaccharide

10-10. (a) $2^2 = 4$ isomers (b) $2^2 = 4$ isomers (c) $2^5 = 32$ isomers (in the aldehyde form)
(d) $2^3 = 8$ isomers

10-11. Four isomers are possible: DL-*cis* and DL-*trans*.

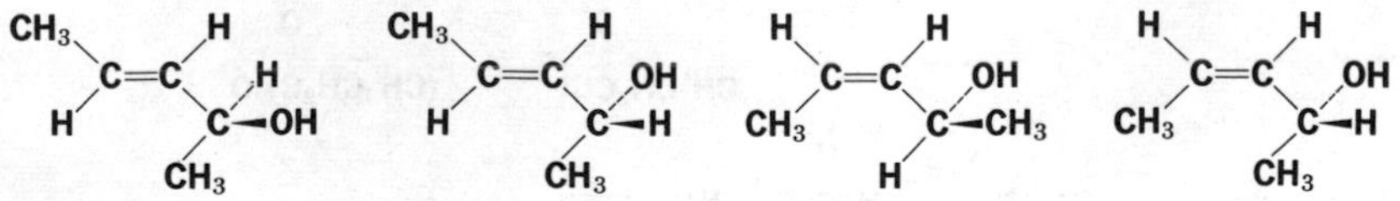

10-12. (a) I, II and III; (b) II and IV; (c) I, II, and IV; (d) II.

ANSWERS TO PROBLEMS—CHAPTER 11

11-1. Both stronger.

11-2. (a) CH_3CHCH_2COH (with O double bond, and CH_3 substituent)   (b) CH_3- (aromatic ring with CH_3) $-COH$ (O double bond)   (c) $CH_3CH_2CH_2CHCOH$ (O double bond, CH_3 substituent)

11-3. (a) $(CH_3)_2C{=}CH_2$ (b) $CH_3(CH_2)_4CH{=}C{-}C_2H_5$ (with C_2H_5 substituent)   (c) $CH_3CH{=}CHCH_3$

11-4. Since a Grignard reagent immediately reacts with the hydrogen of an alcohol, it would immediately destroy itself with its own hydroxyl group.

11-5. (a) $CH_3CH_2CH_2COCH_3$ (b) $CH_3COCH_2(CH_2)_6CH_3$ (c) $CH_3COCH_2CH_2CH(CH_3)_2$ (all with O double bonds)

11-6. Dissolve the mixture in ether and extract with sodium bicarbonate solution. Benzoic acid will react to form the sodium salt and dissolve in the water layer. Separation of the layers and acidification will give the pure acid. The remaining ether solution is next extracted with sodium hydroxide solution. Cresol is converted to its sodium salt and enters the water layer. Separation of layers and acidification gives pure cresol. Evaporation of the ether leaves pure *p*-xylene

11-7. $CH_3(CH_2)_{14}COH$ $\xrightarrow{LiAlH_4}$ $CH_3(CH_2)_{14}CH_2OH$ $\xrightarrow[ZnCl_2]{HCl}$ $CH_3(CH_2)_{14}CH_2Cl$

$\downarrow$ PCl$_3$ $\downarrow$ N(CH$_3$)$_3$

$CH_3(CH_2)_{14}\overset{+}{CH_2}N(CH_3)_3$

Cl^-

$CH_3(CH_2)_{14}CCl$ (O double bond)

$\downarrow$ (HOCH$_2$)$_4$C

$CH_3(CH_2)_{14}COCH_2C(CH_2OH)_3$ (O double bond)

11-8. Four isomers, two pairs of enantiomers. All four are optically active.

11-9. N-Dichloroacetyl-1-*p*-nitrophenyl-2-amino-1,3-propanediol.

11-10. (a) $(C_6H_5C)_2O + CH_3NH_2 \longrightarrow C_6H_5CNHCH_3$ (O double bonds)

(b) $CH_3CH_2COC_2H_5 + H_2O \xrightarrow{H^+} CH_3CH_2COH \xrightarrow{NaOH} CH_3CH_2CO^-Na^+$ (O double bonds)

$\downarrow$ PCl$_3$

CH_3CH_2CCl (O double bond) $(CH_3CH_2C)_2O$ (O double bond)

11-11. Na^+ $:\overset{-}{C}:::N:$ $H:\overset{H}{\underset{H}{C}}:C:::N:$

11-12. (a) CH₃(CH₂)₃CHCOH
              |
              CH₃

(d) O₂N—⟨benzene⟩—CNH₂

(g) CH₃CH₂CO⁻K⁺

(b) CH₃CH₂COC₂H₅

(e) [CH₃(CH₂)₁₄C]₂O

(h) CH₃CH₂COCH(CH₃)₂

(c) CH₃(CH₂)₃CBr

(f) C₆H₅COCH₂
    C₆H₅COCH
    C₆H₅COCH₂

11-13. (a) 2-Bromopropanoic acid
(b) 2-Methylbutanoic acid
(c) *n*-Propyl acetate
(d) *m*-Nitrobenzoyl chloride
(e) N,N-Dimethylisobutyramide

11-14. (a) HCl, C₂H₅OH   (b) LiAlH₄; then H⁺, H₂O   (c) 2C₆H₅MgBr; then H⁺, H₂O
(d) H⁺, H₂O   (e) KMnO₄

11-15. (a) Sodium bicarbonate solution will identify the acid. The ketone will give a precipitate with 2,4-dinitrophenylhydrazine solution.
(b) Only the alkene will decolorize bromine solution. The alcohol will liberate hydrogen when treated with sodium.

11-16. With sodium hydroxide the reaction goes to completion; with hydrochloric acid an equilibrium is established.

11-17. The presence of the hydroxyl group makes the acid salt too soluble in water.

11-18. CH₃(CH₂)₁₄COH $\xrightarrow{\text{Prob. 11-7}}$ CH₃(CH₂)₁₄CH₂Br $\xrightarrow{\text{NaCN}}$ CH₃(CH₂)₁₄CH₂CN
                                        ↓ H⁺, H₂O
                                 CH₃(CH₂)₁₄CH₂COH

11-19. (a) Br₂/Fe   (b) KMnO₄   (c) KMnO₄; then HNO₃, H₂SO₄.

ANSWERS TO PROBLEMS—CHAPTER 12

12-1.

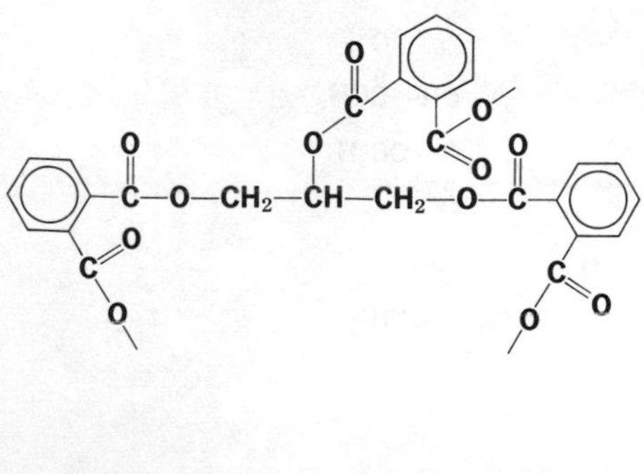

12-2. (a) $CH_3\overset{\displaystyle O}{\overset{\|}{C}}H$ 　　(b) CH_3CH_2OH

12-3. (a) 〔Ph〕$\overset{\displaystyle O}{\overset{\|}{C}}-CH_2-\overset{\displaystyle OH}{\underset{\displaystyle CH_3}{\overset{\displaystyle |}{\underset{|}{C}}}}-$〔Ph〕　　(b) 〔Ph〕$\overset{\displaystyle O}{\overset{\|}{C}}-CH_2-\overset{\displaystyle OH}{\overset{|}{C}}H-$〔Ph〕

12-4. $2CH_3\overset{\displaystyle O}{\overset{\|}{C}}-OC_2H_5 \xrightarrow{Na^+\bar{O}C_2H_5} CH_3\overset{\displaystyle O}{\overset{\|}{C}}-\bar{C}H-\overset{\displaystyle O}{\overset{\|}{C}}-OEt \xrightarrow{\text{〔Ph〕}-CH_2Br} CH_3\overset{\displaystyle O}{\overset{\|}{C}}-\underset{\underset{\text{〔Ph〕}}{\overset{\displaystyle |}{CH_2}}}{\overset{\displaystyle |}{CH}}-\overset{\displaystyle O}{\overset{\|}{C}}-OEt$

$\downarrow$ 1) NaOH   2) H^+

$CH_3\overset{\displaystyle O}{\overset{\|}{C}}CH_2CH_2-\text{〔Ph〕} \xleftarrow{heat} CH_3\overset{\displaystyle O}{\overset{\|}{C}}\underset{\underset{\text{〔Ph〕}}{\overset{\displaystyle |}{CH_2}}}{\overset{\displaystyle |}{CH}}-\overset{\displaystyle O}{\overset{\|}{C}}-OH$

12-5. (a) 〔cyclohexenyl〕$\overset{\displaystyle O}{\overset{\|}{C}}OH$　　(d) 〔bicyclic anhydride structure〕

(b) 〔cyclohexane anhydride structure〕　　(e) $-(C(CH_2)_4\overset{\displaystyle O}{\overset{\|}{C}}-\overset{\displaystyle H}{\overset{|}{N}}(CH_2)_6\overset{\displaystyle H}{\overset{|}{N}})_{\overline{n}}$ (Nylon)

(c) 〔Ph〕$-CH_2\overset{\displaystyle O}{\overset{\|}{C}}OH$　　(f) 〔Ph with $\overset{\displaystyle O}{\overset{\|}{C}}-O^-Na^+$ and OCH_3〕

12-6. (a) $2CH_3CH_2\overset{\displaystyle O}{\overset{\|}{C}}H \xrightarrow{NaOH} CH_3\underset{\underset{CH_3}{\overset{\displaystyle |}{CHOH}}}{\overset{\displaystyle |}{CH}}CHCH_2CH_3$

(b) 2 〔Ph〕$-CH_2\overset{\displaystyle O}{\overset{\|}{C}}-OC_2H_5 \xrightarrow{C_2H_5ONa}$ 〔Ph〕$-\underset{\underset{\displaystyle O}{\overset{\displaystyle |}{\overset{\|}{C}-OC_2H_5}}}{\overset{\displaystyle |}{CH}}-\overset{\displaystyle O}{\overset{\|}{C}}CH_2-$〔Ph〕

(c) 〔Ph〕$-\overset{\displaystyle O}{\overset{\|}{C}}-CH_3 \xrightarrow[I_2]{NaOH}$ 〔Ph〕$-\overset{\displaystyle O}{\overset{\|}{C}}-O^-Na^+ + CHI_3$

12-7. (a)

$$CH_2 \begin{matrix} \overset{O}{\underset{\|}{C}}-OC_2H_5 \\ \overset{}{\underset{\overset{\|}{O}}{C}}-OC_2H_5 \end{matrix} \xrightarrow[\text{2)} \langle \text{O} \rangle -CH_2Br]{\text{1)} C_2H_5O^-Na^+} \langle \text{O} \rangle -CH_2CH \begin{matrix} \overset{O}{\underset{\|}{C}}-OC_2H_5 \\ \overset{}{\underset{\overset{\|}{O}}{C}}-OC_2H_5 \end{matrix}$$

$$\xrightarrow[\text{2) H}_2SO_4]{\text{1) NaOH}}$$

$$\langle \text{O} \rangle -CH_2CH_2\overset{O}{\underset{\|}{C}}OH \xleftarrow{\text{heat}} \langle \text{O} \rangle -CH_2CH \begin{matrix} \overset{O}{\underset{\|}{C}}-OH \\ \overset{}{\underset{\overset{\|}{O}}{C}}-OH \end{matrix}$$

(b)

$$CH_2 \begin{matrix} \overset{O}{\underset{\|}{C}}OC_2H_5 \\ \overset{}{\underset{\overset{\|}{O}}{C}}OC_2H_5 \end{matrix} \xrightarrow[\substack{\text{2) C}_2H_5Br \\ \text{3) repeat 1) and 2)}}]{\text{1) C}_2H_5O^-Na^+} (C_2H_5)_2C \begin{matrix} \overset{O}{\underset{\|}{C}}OC_2H_5 \\ \overset{}{\underset{\overset{\|}{O}}{C}}OC_2H_5 \end{matrix} \xrightarrow[C_2H_5O^-Na^+]{H_2N-\overset{O}{\underset{\|}{C}}-NH_2} (C_2H_5)_2C \begin{matrix} \overset{O}{\underset{\|}{C}}-\underset{|}{N} \overset{H}{} \\ \\ \underset{\overset{\|}{O}}{C}-\underset{|}{N} \underset{H}{} \end{matrix} C=O$$

(c)

$$CH_2 \begin{matrix} \overset{O}{\underset{\|}{C}}OC_2H_5 \\ \overset{}{\underset{\overset{\|}{O}}{C}}OC_2H_5 \end{matrix} \xrightarrow[\text{2) CH}_3Br]{\text{1) C}_2H_5O^-Na^+} CH_3-CH \begin{matrix} \overset{O}{\underset{\|}{C}}-OC_2H_5 \\ \overset{}{\underset{\overset{\|}{O}}{C}}-OC_2H_5 \end{matrix} \xrightarrow{LiAlH_4} CH_3CH \begin{matrix} CH_2OH \\ \\ CH_2OH \end{matrix}$$

12-8. $CH_3\overset{O}{\underset{\|}{C}}CH_2\overset{O}{\underset{\|}{C}}OC_2H_5 \xrightarrow{C_2H_5O^-Na^+} CH_3\overset{O}{\underset{\|}{C}}\overset{-}{C}H\overset{O}{\underset{\|}{C}}OC_2H_5 \xrightarrow{n\text{-C}_6H_{13}Br} CH_3\overset{O}{\underset{\|}{C}}-\underset{\underset{C_6H_{13}}{|}}{C}H\overset{O}{\underset{\|}{C}}OC_2H_5$

$$\xrightarrow[\text{2) H}_2SO_4]{\text{1) NaOH}}$$

$$CH_3\overset{O}{\underset{\|}{C}}(CH_2)_6CH_3 \xleftarrow{\text{heat}} CH_3\overset{O}{\underset{\|}{C}}\overset{O}{\underset{\underset{C_6H_{13}}{|}}{C}}H\overset{O}{\underset{\|}{C}}OH$$

12-9. (a) (c) (f)

12-10. (a) $CH_2{=}\underset{\underset{CH_3}{|}}{C}-\overset{O}{\underset{\|}{C}}OCH_3$

monomer used in
making Plexiglass (Lucite)

(b) $HO\overset{O}{\underset{\|}{C}}-(CH_2)_4-\overset{O}{\underset{\|}{C}}OH$

monomer used in
making Nylon

(c) $H_2N \overset{\overset{O}{\underset{\|}{C}}}{} NH_2$

used to fertilize plants
and to make urea-formaldehyde
resins, barbiturates, etc.

(d)

$\langle \text{O} \rangle \begin{matrix} \overset{O}{\underset{\|}{C}}-OH \\ OH \end{matrix}$

used in making aspirin
and other analgesics

(e)

$$CH_3CH_2 \underset{\langle \text{O} \rangle}{} \overset{C}{} \begin{matrix} \overset{O}{\underset{\|}{C}}-\underset{|}{N} \overset{H}{} \\ \\ \underset{\overset{\|}{O}}{C}-\underset{|}{N} \underset{H}{} \end{matrix} C=O$$

a barbiturate

12-11. (a) $CH_3\overset{O}{\overset{\|}{C}}H \xrightarrow{HCN} CH_3\overset{OH}{\overset{|}{C}}HCN \xrightarrow[H_2O]{HCl} CH_3\overset{HO}{\overset{|}{C}}H\overset{O}{\overset{\|}{C}}OH$

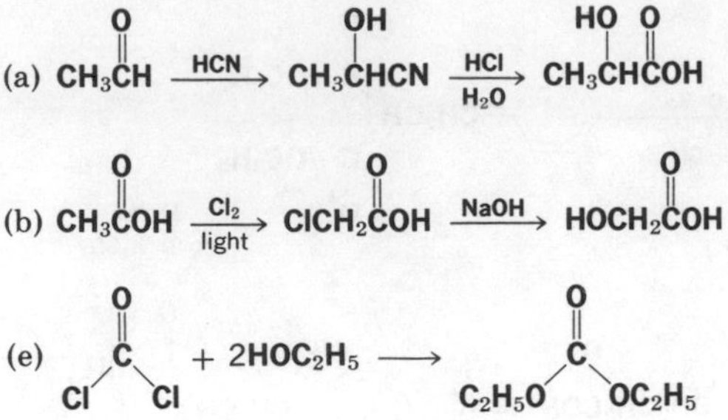

(c) Fig. 12-12.

(d) Fig. 12-4.

(f) Fig. 12-14.

(g) Fig. 12-13.

(b) $CH_3\overset{O}{\overset{\|}{C}}OH \xrightarrow[light]{Cl_2} ClCH_2\overset{O}{\overset{\|}{C}}OH \xrightarrow{NaOH} HOCH_2\overset{O}{\overset{\|}{C}}OH$

(e)

$$\underset{Cl\quad\quad Cl}{\overset{O}{\overset{\|}{C}}} + 2HOC_2H_5 \longrightarrow \underset{C_2H_5O\quad\quad OC_2H_5}{\overset{O}{\overset{\|}{C}}}$$

ANSWERS TO PROBLEMS—CHAPTER 13

13-1. serine: 2-amino-3-hydroxypropanoic acid
threonine: 2-amino-3-hydroxybutanoic acid
cysteine: 2 amino-3-mercaptopropanoic acid
alanine: 2-aminopropanoic acid
leucine: 2-amino-4-methylpentanoic acid
valine: 2-amino-3-methylbutanoic acid

13-2.

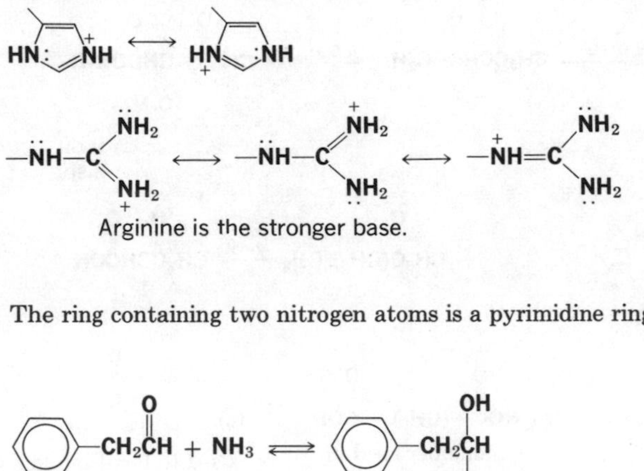

Arginine is the stronger base.

13-3. The ring containing two nitrogen atoms is a pyrimidine ring (see Fig. 8-21).

13-4.

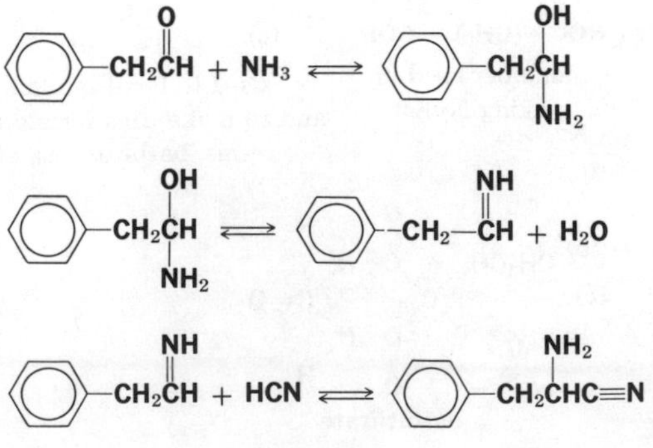

13-5. (a)

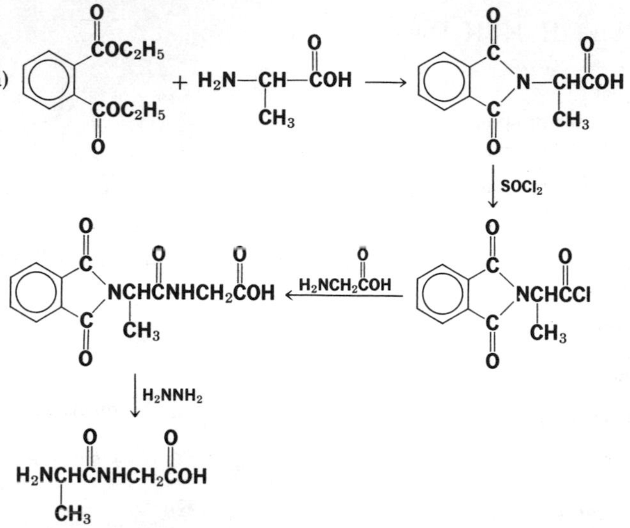

$$COC_2H_5 + H_2N-CH-COH \longrightarrow$$

$$CH_3$$

$$\downarrow SOCl_2$$

H₂NCH₂COH ←

$$CH_3$$

$$\downarrow H_2NNH_2$$

$$H_2NCHCNHCH_2COH$$
$$CH_3$$

alanyl-glycine

13-6.

OH

CH₂

tyr

phe

glu

asp

cyS

cyS

pro

gly

arg

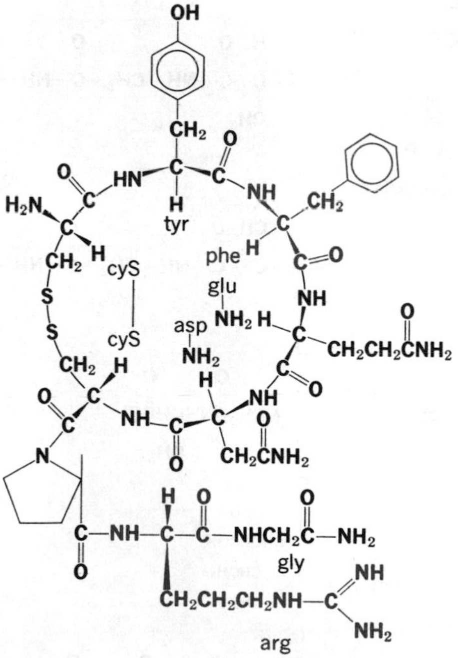

vasopressin, beef
(complete)

The two amino acids in red differ from those in oxytocin.

13.7. asp-[ ]-[ ]-[ ]-[ ]-[ ]-[ ]-[ ]-[ ]-[ ]-leu

asp-arg-val

val-tyr-val

his-pro-phe

phe-his-leu

asp-arg-val-tyr-val-his-pro-phe-his-leu

13-8. four.

13-9. See Fig. 13-2 for the structures of glycine, L-valine, L-alanine, and L-phenylalanine, and Fig. 13-3 for that of L-serine.

A $\xrightarrow{\text{2,4-DNPF}}$ DNP—A $\xrightarrow{\text{H}^+}$ gly + val + ser + 2ala

A $\xrightarrow[100°]{\text{H}_2\text{NNH}_2}$ ala

so,   [ ]-[ ]-[ ]-[ ]-[ ]-ala   so,   phe-ala-ser-[ ]-[ ]-ala

A $\xrightarrow[\text{mild}]{\text{H}^+}$ B + C   C $\xrightarrow{\text{H}^+}$ ser + ala + gly

B $\xrightarrow{\text{H}^+}$ ala + ser + phe (not found in first   so,
reaction sequence)

B $\xrightarrow{\text{H}_2\text{NNH}_2}$ ser

A is phe-ala-ser-gly-val-ala

13-10.

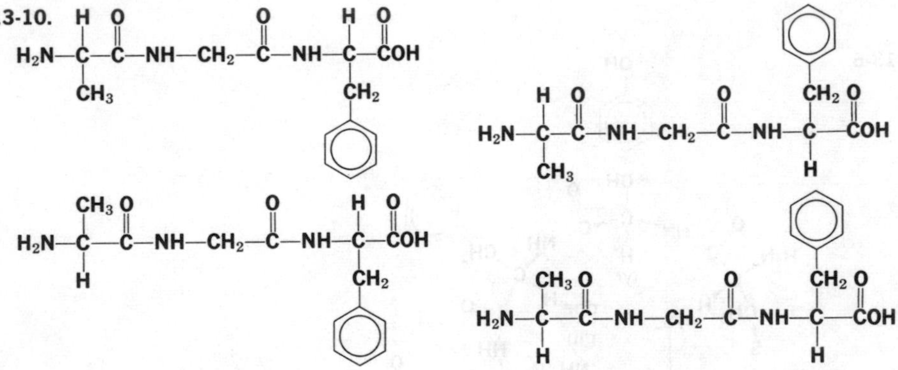

13-11.

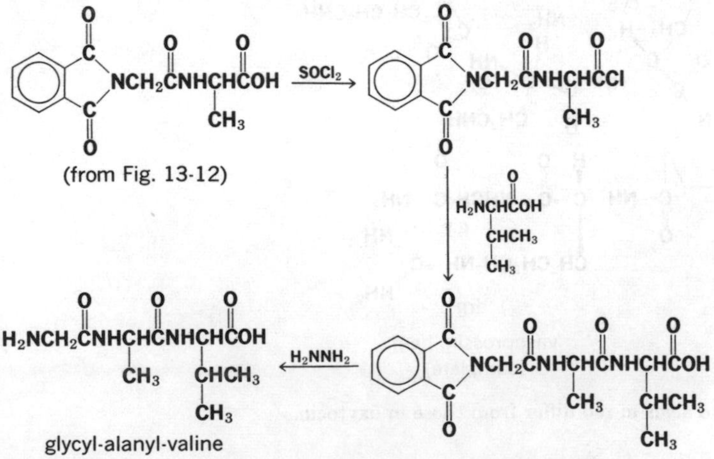

(from Fig. 13-12)

glycyl-alanyl-valine

13-12. These terms have all been discussed in this chapter. They can be located most easily by looking them up in the index.

ANSWERS TO PROBLEMS—CHAPTER 14

14-1. (a) Chymotrypsin: gly-tyr + phe   (b) Chymotrypsin: try + arg-leu
        trypsin: no catalysis   trypsin: try-arg + leu
    (c) and (d) no catalysis by either enzyme

14-2.

$$
\begin{array}{ccc}
\text{H} & \text{H} & \text{H} \\
\text{C}{=}\text{O} & \text{C}{-}\text{OH} & \text{C}{=}\text{O} \\
\text{H}{-}\text{OH} & \text{C}{-}\text{OH} & \text{HO}{-}\text{H} \\
\text{HO}{-}\text{H} \rightleftarrows & \rightleftarrows \text{HO}{-}\text{H} \\
\text{H}{-}\text{OH} & & \text{H}{-}\text{OH} \\
\text{H}{-}\text{OH} & & \text{H}{-}\text{OH} \\
\text{CH}_2\text{OPO}_3\text{H} & & \text{CH}_2\text{OPO}_3\text{H} \\
\text{glucose-6-phosphate} & & \text{mannose-6-phosphate}
\end{array}
$$

Glucose and mannose differ only in their configuration at carbon-2. In the enol the stereochemistry at this center is lost.

14-3. $C_6H_{12}O_6 + O_2 \longrightarrow 2C_3H_4O_3 + 2H_2O$
      glucose   pyruvic
                       acid

14-4. (a) $C_6H_{12}O_6 \longrightarrow 2C_3H_6O_3$ (b) $C_6H_{12}O_6 \longrightarrow 2C_2H_6O + 2CO_2$

14-5.

$$
\begin{array}{c}
\overset{\text{O}}{\underset{\|}{}}\\
\text{CH}_2\text{COH} \\
\overset{\text{O}}{\underset{\|}{}}\\
\text{CHCOH} + \text{NAD}^+ \rightleftarrows \\
\text{HOCCOH} \\
\underset{\|}{\text{O}}
\end{array}
\qquad
\begin{array}{c}
\overset{\text{O}}{\underset{\|}{}}\\
\text{CH}_2\text{COH} \\
\overset{\text{O}}{\underset{\|}{}}\\
\text{CHCOH} + \text{NADH} + \text{H}^+ \\
\text{O}{=}\text{CCOH} \\
\underset{\|}{\text{O}}
\end{array}
$$

14-6. The molecular weight of palmitic acid ($C_{16}H_{32}O_2$) is 256. Since 2,338 kcal/mol of energy is liberated in the combustion, $2,338/256 = 9.13$ kcal/g is liberated. For glucose, molecular weight 180, $690/180 = 3.83$ kcal/g.

14-7. Not very. Fats produce many more calories per gram than carbohydrates. Moreover, since all metabolic reactions discussed are reversible, fats can be converted into carbohydrates in the body *via* the key intermediates acetylcoenzyme A and pyruvic acid.

14-8.
$$\text{CH}_3\overset{\text{O}}{\underset{\|}{\text{C}}}\text{CH}_2\overset{\text{O}}{\underset{\|}{\text{C}}}\text{OH} \longrightarrow \text{CH}_3\overset{\text{O}}{\underset{\|}{\text{C}}}\text{CH}_3 + \text{CO}_2$$
            like Step 4 of Fig. 14-11.

$$\text{CH}_3\overset{\text{O}}{\underset{\|}{\text{C}}}\text{CH}_2\overset{\text{O}}{\underset{\|}{\text{C}}}\text{OH} + \text{NADH} \longrightarrow \text{CH}_3\overset{\text{OH}}{\underset{|}{\text{C}}}\text{HCH}_2\overset{\text{O}}{\underset{\|}{\text{C}}}\text{OH} + \text{H}^+ + \text{NAD}^+$$
           like the reverse of Steps 3 and 9 of Fig. 14-11.

14-9. HOCCH₂CCOH + HOCCH₂CH₂CCOH ⇌ HOCCH₂CCOH + HOCCH₂CH₂CCOH

(with structural notations: O, HO above first; NH₂ below first; O, OO above second; O, OO above third; O, HO above fourth; NH₂ below fourth)

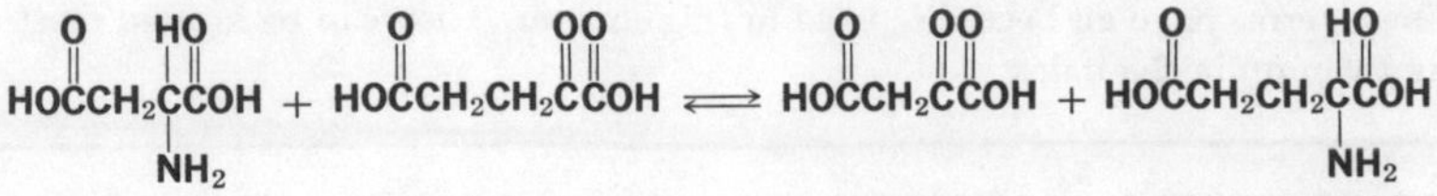

L-aspartic acid   α-ketoglutaric acid   oxaloacetic acid   L-glutamic acid

14-10. All three classes of compounds can be converted to pyruvic acid or acetic acid. The latter two compounds can be interconverted and are part of the Krebs cycle. The Krebs cycle also includes oxaloacetic acid and α-ketoglutaric acid, which can be formed directly from aspartic and glutamic amino acids.

14-11. aerobic metabolism: carbon dioxide
anaerobic (muscle): lactic acid
anaerobic (fermentation): ethanol, carbon dioxide

14-12. (a) 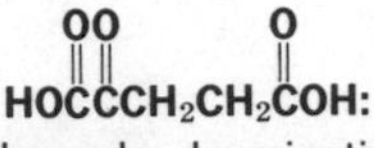 HOCCCH₂CH₂COH:
Krebs cycle; deamination of glutamic acid.

(b) 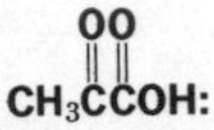 CH₃CCOH:
carbohydrate metabolism;
Krebs cycle; deamination of alanine.

(c) 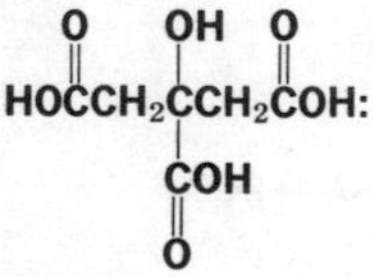 HOCCH₂CCH₂COH:
(with COH below, O below)
Krebs cycle

(d) 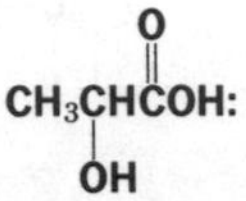 CH₃CHCOH:
(OH below)
carbohydrate metabolism;
from pyruvic acid.

(e) 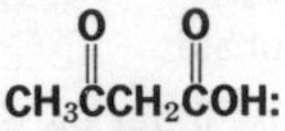 CH₃CCH₂COH:
lipid metabolism.

(f) 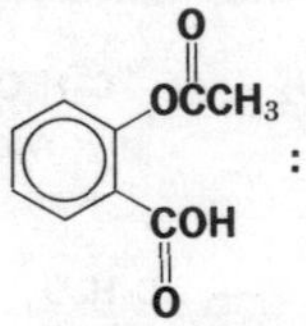 (benzene ring with OCCH₃ and COH substituents) :
aspirin. Not directly involved
in primary metabolism.

ANSWERS TO PROBLEMS—CHAPTER 15

15-1. CH₃—COH + CH₂(COH)₂

CH₃–CH₂–CH₂–CH₂–CH₂–CH₂–CH₂–CH₂–(CH)=CH–CH₂–CH₂–CH₂–CH₂–CH₂–CH₂–CH₂–COH

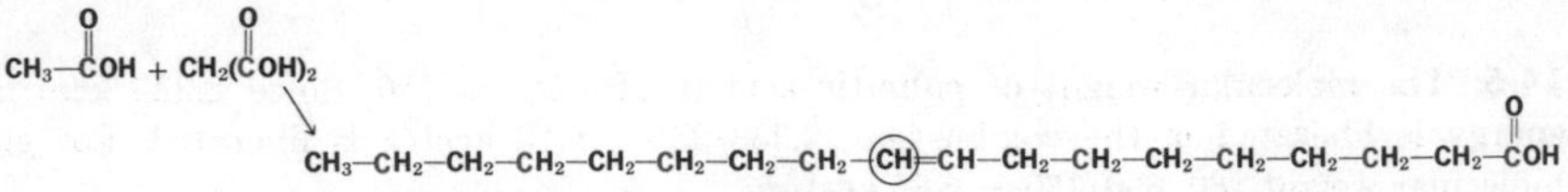

C-10 (circled) is unlabeled. This could be shown by the following sequence.

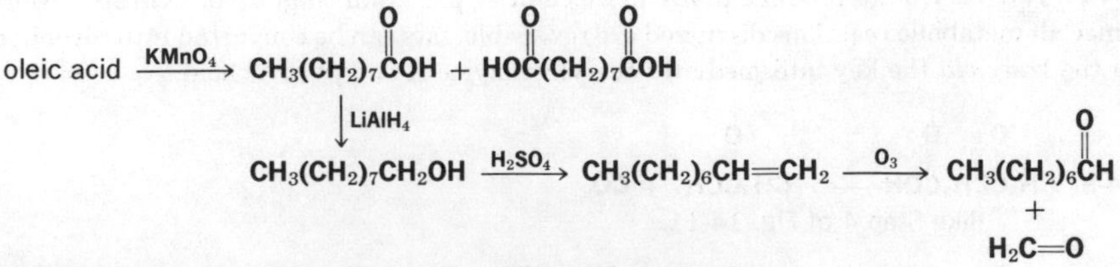

oleic acid $\xrightarrow{KMnO_4}$ CH₃(CH₂)₇COH + HOC(CH₂)₇COH

$\downarrow$ LiAlH₄

CH₃(CH₂)₇CH₂OH $\xrightarrow{H_2SO_4}$ CH₃(CH₂)₆CH=CH₂ $\xrightarrow{O_3}$ CH₃(CH₂)₆CH
+
H₂C=O

The formaldehyde could be isolated and tested for the presence of radioactivity. It would be found to be nonradioactive.

15-2. $CH_3\overset{O}{\underset{}{C}}OH \longrightarrow$ (structures) $\longrightarrow$ (aromatic structure)

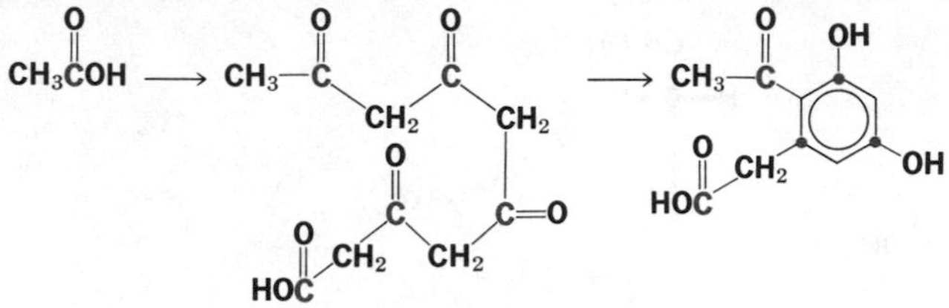

15-3. Tetracycline and aureomycin—5 asymmetric centers $= 2^5 = 32$ possible stereoisomers.
Terramycin: $2^6 = 64$ possible stereoisomers
Erythromycin: 10 asymmetric centers in the lactone ring plus 8 in the sugars, so
$2^{18} = 262,144$ possible stereoisomers.

15-4. (structures) **15-5.** (structures) $\xrightarrow{-OPP^-}$ (structure) $\longrightarrow$ (structure) $\xrightarrow{-H^+}$ (structure)

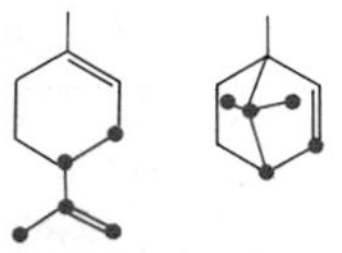

15-6. $CH_3-\overset{O}{\underset{}{C}}OH \longrightarrow$ (structure) $OPP \longrightarrow$ (structures)

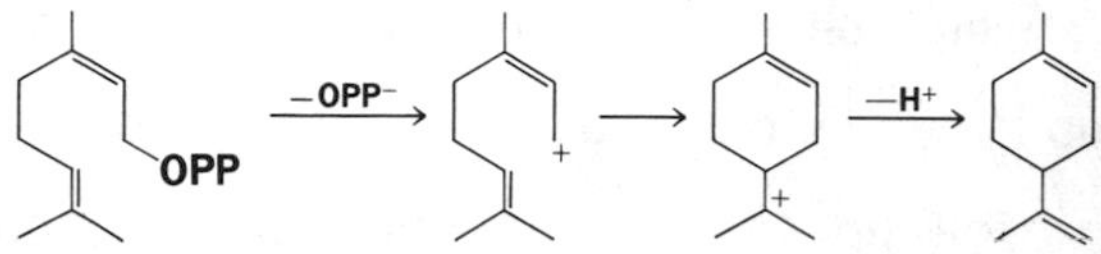

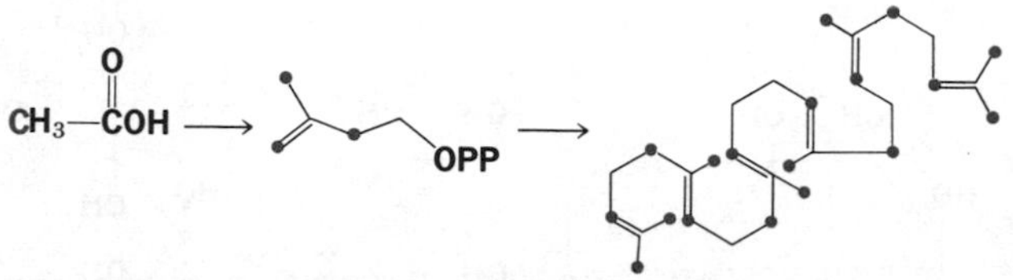

15-7. $CH_3-\overset{O}{\underset{}{C}}OH \longrightarrow$ (structure)

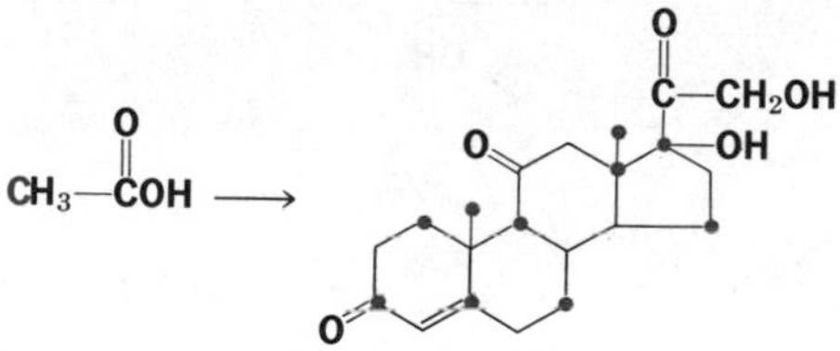

cortisone

15-8.

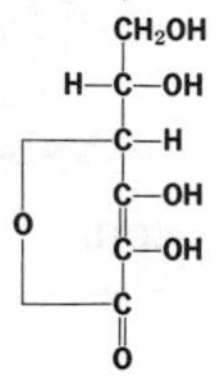

D-galactose $\longrightarrow$ D-galacturonic acid $\xrightarrow{-H_2O}$ (structure) $\longrightarrow$ (structure)

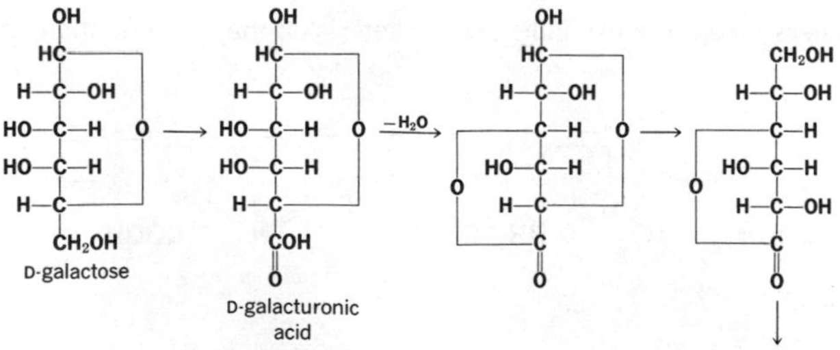

L-ascorbic acid

15-9. If the molecule is turned upside down, it will be shown to be an oxidation product of L-gulose.

15-10. Coniine—piperidine. Cocaine—pyrrolidine. Quinine—quinoline and piperidine.

15-11.

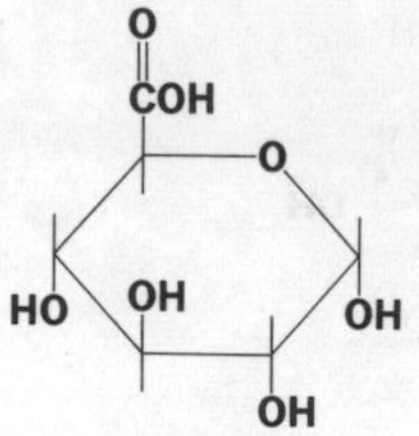

α-D-glucuronic acid 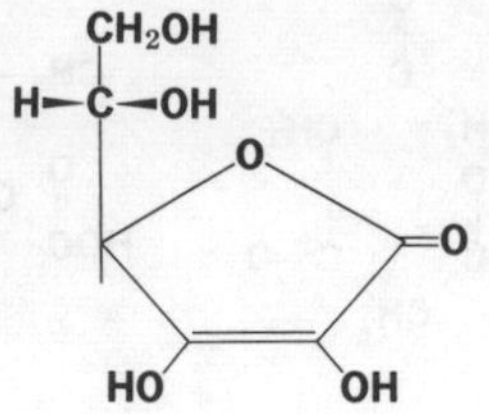   L-ascorbic acid

15-12.

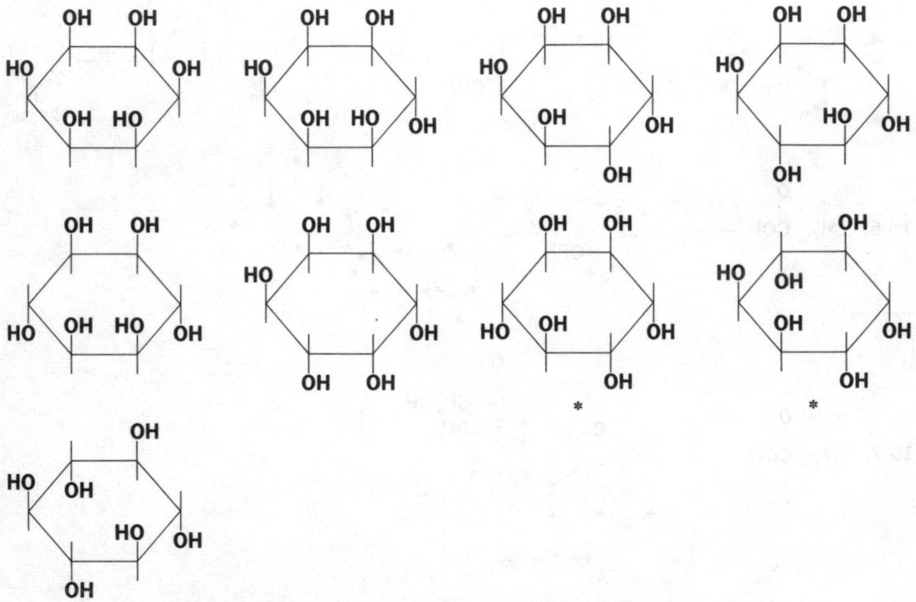

All are *meso* isomers except the two indicated by asterisks; they are enantiomers.

15-13.

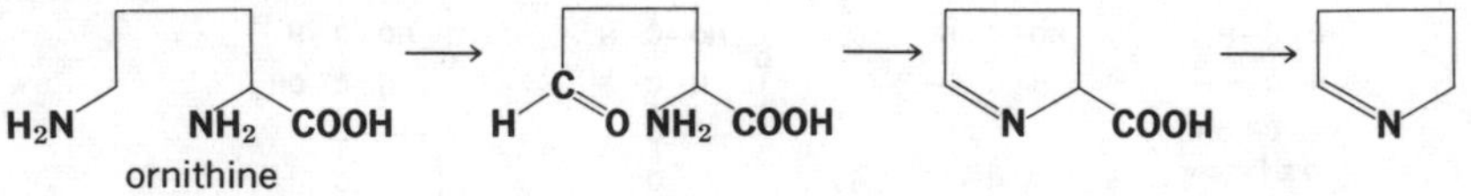

ornithine

15-14.

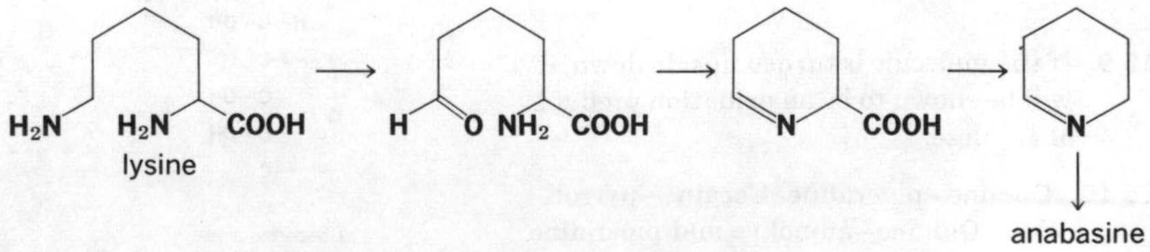

lysine

anabasine

15-15.

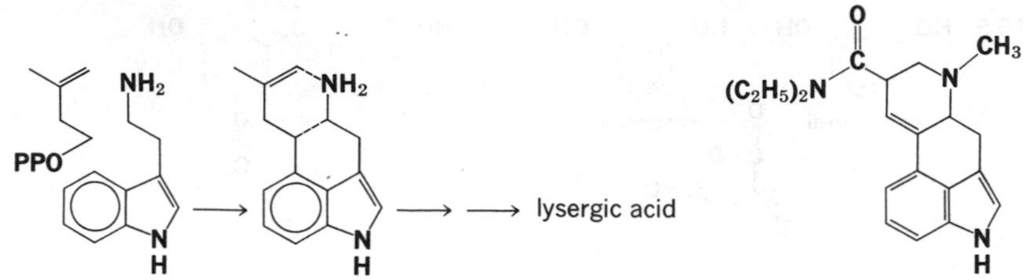

→ → → lysergic acid

LSD

ANSWERS TO PROBLEMS—CHAPTER 16

16-1. Compound A, with 6 fused rings, should absorb light of longer wave length than pentacene (Fig. 16-2), which absorbs orange light. It would be reasonable then (see Fig. 16-1) for A to absorb red to purple light, and so to appear green.

Compound B would be colorless, since it has 3 fused rings (anthracene) at the left end and 2 (naphthalene) at the right end. These are separated by a nonaromatic ring, which interrupts the conjugation.

16-2.

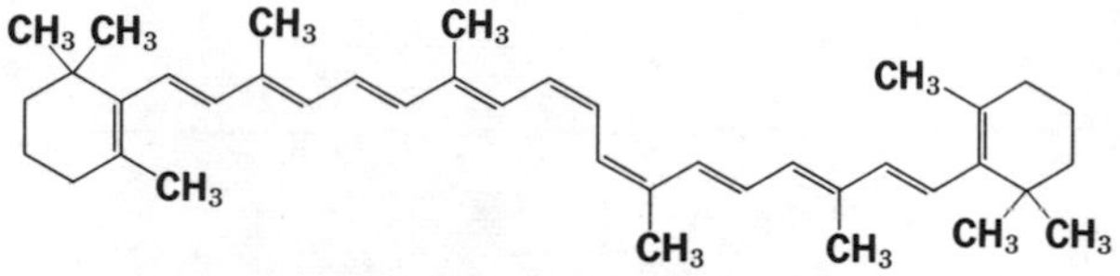

16-3. indigo: chromophores are , $-\overset{\text{O}}{\underset{}{\text{C}}}-$, and $\text{C}=\text{C}$ groups and

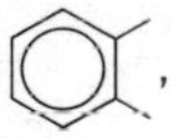

auxochromes are $-\overset{}{\underset{\text{H}}{\text{N}}}-$ groups.

alizarin: chromophores are 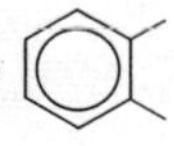 and 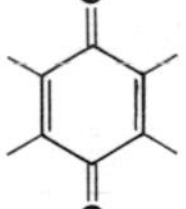 groups, and

auxochromes are —**OH** groups.

16-4. orange II: chromophores are  , 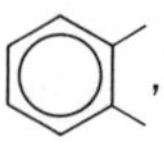 , and —N≡N— groups.

the auxochrome is the **HO**— group.

pararosaniline: chromophores are 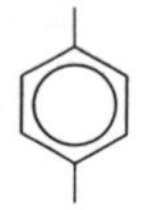 and 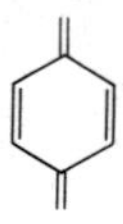 groups.

auxochromes are —**NH₂** groups.

16-5.

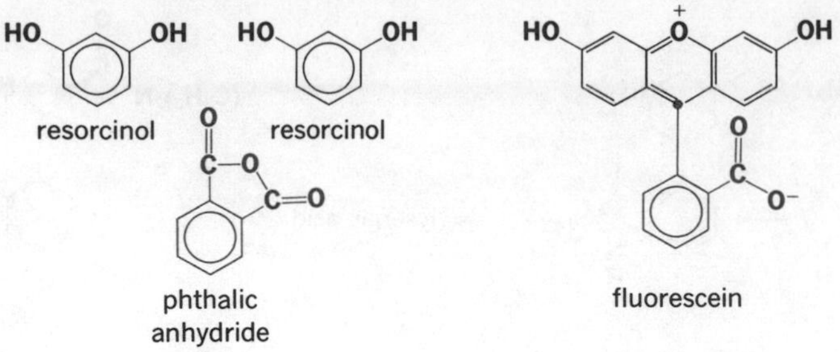

resorcinol

resorcinol

phthalic
anhydride

fluorescein

16-6.

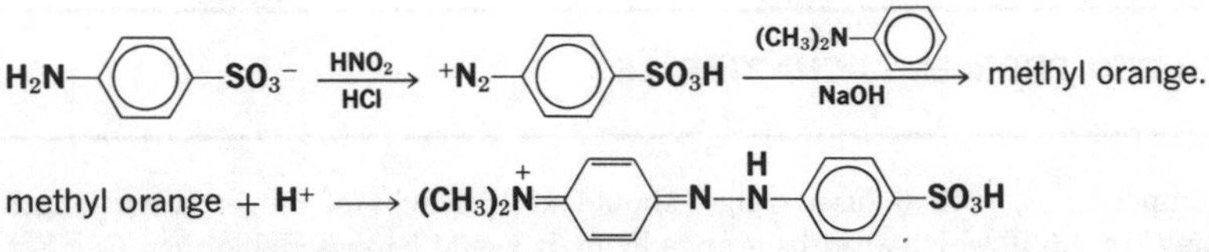

$$H_2N—\langle\rangle—SO_3^- \xrightarrow[HCl]{HNO_2} {}^+N_2—\langle\rangle—SO_3H \xrightarrow[NaOH]{(CH_3)_2N—\langle\rangle} \text{methyl orange.}$$

$$\text{methyl orange} + H^+ \longrightarrow (CH_3)_2\overset{+}{N}=\langle\rangle=N—\overset{H}{N}—\langle\rangle—SO_3H$$

16-7.

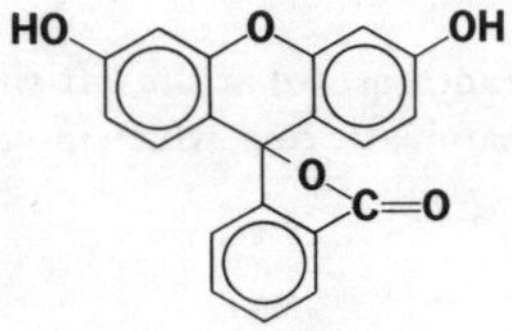

APPENDIX

SELF-CORRECTING STUDY GUIDE
FOR
IUPAC NOMENCLATURE

Summary of IUPAC* Nomenclature

Names of alkanes		Suffixes for functional groups		Names of substituent groups	
CH_4	methane	alkane	*-ane*	CH_3-	methyl-
CH_3CH_3	ethane	alkene	*-ene*	CH_3CH_2-	ethyl-
$CH_3CH_2CH_3$	propane	alkyne	*-yne*	$CH_3CH_2CH_2-$	*n*-propyl-
$CH_3(CH_2)_2CH_3$	butane	alcohol	*-ol*	CH_3-CH-	isopropyl-
$CH_3(CH_2)_3CH_3$	pentane	thiol	*-thiol*	$\quad CH_3$	
$CH_3(CH_2)_4CH_3$	hexane	aldehyde	*-al*		
$CH_3(CH_2)_5CH_3$	heptane	ketone	*-one*	⬡	phenyl-
$CH_3(CH_2)_6CH_3$	octane	acid	*-oic acid*		
$CH_3(CH_2)_7CH_3$	nonane				
$CH_3(CH_2)_8CH_3$	decane	**Prefixes for substituent groups**		**General formula**	
		F-	fluoro-	Alkanes	C_nH_{2n+2}
		Cl-	chloro-	Cycloalkane	C_nH_{2n}
		Br-	bromo-	Alkenes	C_nH_{2n}
		I-	iodo-	Alkynes	C_nH_{2n-2}
		H_2N-	amino-		
		O_2N-	nitro-		
		RO-	alkoxy-		

* IUPAC = International Union of Pure and Applied Chemistry.

QUESTIONS

---

1. Name each of the following hydrocarbons by the IUPAC system:

    (a) CH_4 (b) $CH_3CH_2CH_2CH_2CH_3$ (c) $CH_3CH_2CH_3$ (d) $CH_3(CH_2)_5CH_3$

---

2. Draw the structure of each of the following:

    (a) ethane   (c) butane

    (b) octane   (d) decane

---

3. Name each of the following groups:

    (a) CH_3CH_2-   (b) $CH_3CH_2CH_2$-

Draw the structure of each of the following groups:

    (c) methyl   (d) isopropyl

---

4. Among alkanes the longest continuous chain is considered to be the parent. Find and name this chain in the following compounds.

    (a) CH_3CH—$CHCH_2CH_3$ (b) $(CH_3)_2CHCHCH_2CH_2CH_3$ (c) $CH_3CH_2CHCH_3$

            CH_3 CH_3 $CH_2CH_2CH_3$ CH_2CH_3

---

5. Draw the structures for:

    (a) 3-isopropylheptane   (b) 2,3-dimethylbutane   (c) 2,2-dimethyl-3-ethyloctane

---

6. The chain is numbered from the end which gives the substituent the lower numbers. Name the following compounds:

                               CH_3 CH_2CH_3 CH_3

    (a) $CH_3CH_2CHCH_3$ (b) CH_3CHCH—$CHCH_3$ (c) $CH_3CH_2CHCH_2CHCH_3$

              CH_3 $CH_2CH_2CH_3$ CH_2CH_3

---

7. Name each of the following compounds by the IUPAC system:

           CH_3 CH_3 CH_2CH_3

    (a) $CH_3CHCHCHCH_3$ (b) $CH_3CCH_2CHCHCH_3$

           CH_3 CH_2CHCH_3 CH_3 CH_2CH_3

                    CH_3

---

8. Halogen atoms are treated as substituent groups —F(fluoro), Cl(chloro), Br(bromo), and I(iodo). Give structures for the following:

    (a) 2-bromopropane   (b) 2-methyl-2-bromooctane   (c) 1-chloro-2-bromobutane

---

9. The cyclic compounds are given a parent name corresponding to the number of carbons in their ring with a prefix *cyclo-*. Draw the structures of:

    (a) cyclobutane   (c) cyclopentane

    (b) cyclopropane   (d) cyclohexane

CORRECT ANSWERS FOR PREVIOUS PAGE

1.
   (a) methane   (b) pentane   (c) propane   (d) heptane

2.
   (a) CH_3CH_3 (c) $CH_3CH_2CH_2CH_3$

   (b) $CH_3CH_2CH_2CH_2CH_2CH_2CH_2CH_3$ (d) $CH_3(CH_2)_8CH_3$

3.
   (a) ethyl   (b) *n*-propyl   (c) CH_3-   (d) CH_3—$\underset{\underset{CH_3}{|}}{CH}$—

4.
   (a) pentane   (b) hexane   (c) pentane

5.
   (a) $CH_3CH_2\underset{\underset{CH_3CHCH_3}{|}}{CH}CH_2CH_2CH_2CH_3$ (b) $CH_3\underset{\underset{CH_3}{|}}{CH}$—$\underset{\underset{CH_3}{|}}{CH}CH_3$ (c) $(CH_3)_3CCH\underset{\underset{CH_2CH_3}{|}}{}CH_2CH_2CH_2CH_2CH_3$

6.
   (a) 2-methylbutane   (b) 3,4,5-trimethyloctane   (c) 4-ethyl-2-methylhexane

7.
   (a) 2,3,4,6-tetramethylheptane   (b) 2,2,5-trimethyl-4-ethylheptane

8.
   (a) $CH_3\underset{\underset{Br}{|}}{CH}CH_3$ (b) $(CH_3)_2\underset{\underset{Br}{|}}{C}(CH_2)_5CH_3$ (c) $CH_3CH_2\underset{\underset{Br}{|}}{CH}CH_2Cl$

9.
   (a) $\underset{CH_2-CH_2}{CH_2-CH_2}$ (b) cyclopropane   (c) cyclopentane   (d) cyclohexane

QUESTIONS

---

10. In cyclic systems the numbering is begun at the position which gives the substituents their smallest numbers. Give the structures of:

    (a) 1,1-dimethylcyclohexane   (c) 1,3-dimethylcyclobutane

    (b) 1-bromo-2-isopropyl-4-chlorocyclooctane   (d) 1,1-diethylcyclopropane

---

11. Name by the IUPAC system:

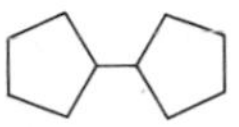

12. In cyclic systems containing two substituents, the two may be on the same side of the ring (designated *cis*) or they may be on opposite sides of the ring (*trans*); thus

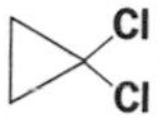

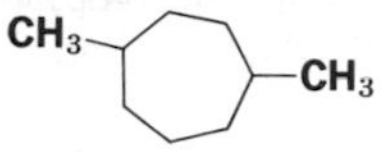

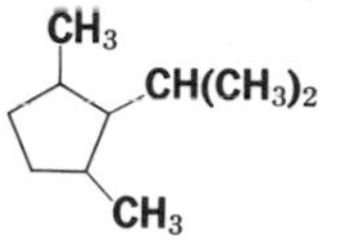

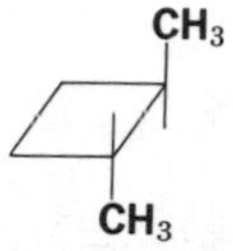

is *trans*-1,2-dimethylcyclobutane. Draw the structures of:

    (a) *cis*-1,2-dimethylcyclobutane   (b) *trans*-1,3-dimethylcyclobutane

---

13. The IUPAC ending for a double bond is -ene and for a triple bond is -yne. Give the IUPAC names for the following:

    (a) $CH_2＝CH_2$ (b) $CH_3CH＝CH_2$ (c) $HC≡CH$ (d) $CH_3C≡CH$

---

14. In compounds containing functional groups, the root name will be that of the longest continuous chain containing the principle functional group. Give the root names of the following:

$$CH_2CH_2CH_3$$

    (a) $CH_3CH_2CH_2CHCH_2CH_2CH_3$ (b) $HC≡CCH$

              $CH＝CH_2$ CH_3CHCH_3

---

15. Draw the structures from the name:

    (a) 3-methyl-1-butene   (c) 4,4-dimethyl-1-pentene

    (b) 2,3-dimethyl-2-butene   (d) 3-ethyl-4-methyl-2-hexene

---

16. Give the IUPAC names for:

    (a) $CH_3CH＝CHCH_3$ (c) $CH_3CH＝CCH_2CH_3$

                 CH_3 CH_3

    (b) $CH_2＝CHCH_2CHCH_3$ (d) $CH_3CH_2CH＝CCH_2CH_3$

                                        CH_3

ANSWERS

10.

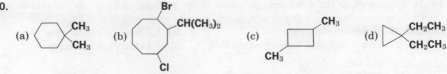

11.

(a) 1,1-dichlorocyclopropane   (c) 1,3-dimethyl-2-isopropylcyclopentane

(b) 1,4-dimethylcycloheptane   (d) cyclopentylcyclopentane

12.

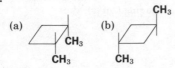

13.

(a) ethene   (c) ethyne

(b) propene or 1-propene   (d) propyne or 1-propyne

14.

(a) hexene   (b) hexyne

15.

(a) $(CH_3)_2CHCH{=}CH_2$ (c) $CH_2{=}CHCH_2C(CH_3)_3$

(b) $(CH_3)_2C{=}C(CH_3)_2$ (d) $CH_3CH_2\underset{\underset{CH_3}{|}}{\overset{\overset{CH_2CH_3}{|}}{C}}HC{=}CHCH_3$

16.

(a) 2-butene   (c) 3-methyl-2-pentene

(b) 4-methyl-1-pentene   (d) 3-methyl-3-hexene

QUESTIONS

17. Draw the structures of:
    (a) 3-isopropyl-2-hexene
    (b) 5-ethyl-3-heptyne
    (c) 3,3-dimethyl-1-pentyne

---

18. The following compounds are named (or numbered) incorrectly. Correct each name and state the rule covering the correction.

       $\overset{\text{CH}_2\text{CH}_3}{|}$ $\overset{\text{CH}_3}{|}$

(a) $CH_3CHCH=CHCH_3$ (b) $CH_3C\equiv CCHCH(CH_3)_2$

    1   4-ethyl-2-pentene   2,3-dimethyl-4-hexyne
    2   3-methyl-4-hexene

---

19. Give the IUPAC names for:
    (a) $CH_3CH_2CH_2C\equiv CCH_3$ (c) $CH_3CHC\equiv CCH_3$ (d) $CH_3CH_2CH_2CHCH_2CH_2CH_3$

    (b) $CH_3CHCH_2C\equiv CCH_2CH_3$ $\overset{|}{CH_3}$ $\overset{|}{C\equiv CH}$
        $\overset{|}{CH_3}$

---

20. In cyclic compounds containing a functional group the numbering is begun at the position of the functional group. Give the structures of:
    (a) 1-methylcyclohexene   (c) 3-methylcyclohexene
    (b) 1,3-dimethylcyclohexane   (d) cyclooctyne

---

21. Name each of the following by the IUPAC system:

(a)   (b)   (c)

---

22. Name by the IUPAC system:

(a)   (b)   (c)   (d)

---

23. In alkenes the substituents on a double bond may be arranged on the same side (*cis*) or on opposite sides (*trans*). Draw structures of the following:
    (a) 2,3-dichloro-*cis*-2-butene   (c) 2-bromo-3-chloro-*trans*-2-butene
    (b) 2,3-dibromo-*trans*-2-pentene   (d) *cis*-3-hexene

ANSWERS

17.

(a) 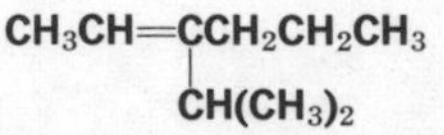 $CH_3CH{=}CCH_2CH_2CH_3$
　　　　$|$
　　　$CH(CH_3)_2$

(b) 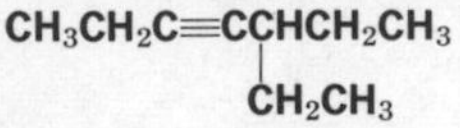 $CH_3CH_2C{\equiv}CCHCH_2CH_3$
　　　　　　　　$|$
　　　　　　CH_2CH_3

(c) 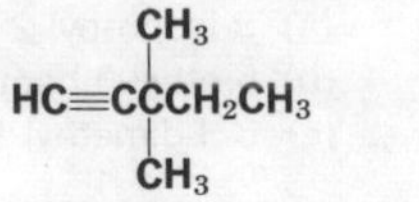 $HC{\equiv}CCCH_2CH_3$ with CH_3 above and CH_3 below the third carbon

18.

(a) 4-methyl-2-hexene
　　1 The longest chain is the parent.
　　2 The lowest number is given to the functionality which determines the parent name.
(b) 4,5-dimethyl-2-hexyne same reason as *2* above

19.

(a) 2-hexyne　　　　　　　(c) 4-methyl-2-pentyne
(b) 6-methyl-3-heptyne　　　(d) 3-*n*-propyl-1-hexyne

20.

(a) 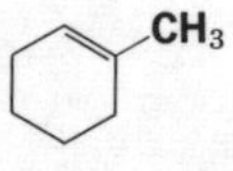 　(b) 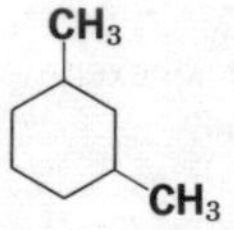 　(c) 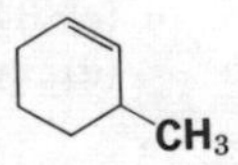 　(d)

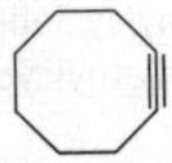

21.

(a) 1,2-dimethylcyclopentene　　(c) *trans*-3,4-dimethylcyclobutene
(b) 5-methylcyclooctyne

22.

(a) 1,1-diiodocyclopropane　　　(c) 4-methylcyclohexene
(b) 1,2-dimethylcycloheptane　　(d) 1-bromo-1-chlorocyclopentane

23.

(a) 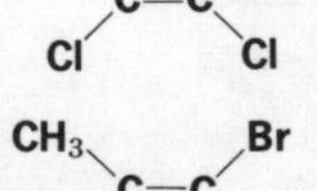 $\begin{array}{c}CH_3\\ \end{array}C{=}C\begin{array}{c}CH_3\\ \end{array}$ with Cl and Cl below

(b) $\begin{array}{c}CH_3\\ \end{array}C{=}C\begin{array}{c}Br\\ \end{array}$ with Br and CH_2CH_3 below

(c) $\begin{array}{c}CH_3\\ \end{array}C{=}C\begin{array}{c}Cl\\ \end{array}$ with Br and CH_3 below

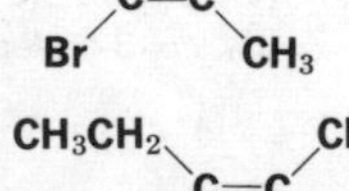

(d) 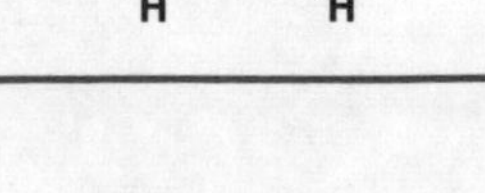 $\begin{array}{c}CH_3CH_2\\ \end{array}C{=}C\begin{array}{c}CH_2CH_3\\ \end{array}$ with H and H below

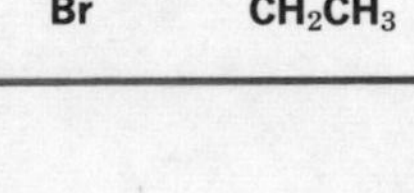

QUESTIONS

24. In compounds containing two functional groups, each must receive a number and the ending will be diene (two double bonds), triene (three double bonds), etc. Draw the structures for:

(a) 1,3-butadiene   (c) 1,4-pentadiyne

(b) 2-methyl-2,4-hexadiene   (d) 3-ethyl-1,4,7-octatriene

25. Give the IUPAC names for the following:

(a) $CH_3CH{=}CHCH{=}CH_2$ (c) $HC{\equiv}C\overset{\displaystyle CH_3}{C}HC{\equiv}CH$

(b) $CH_2{=}\overset{\displaystyle CH_2CH_3}{\underset{\displaystyle CH{=}CHCH_3}{C}}{-}CHCH_2CH_3$ (d) $HC{\equiv}CCHCH_2CH_2CH_3$
$\qquad\qquad\qquad\qquad\qquad\qquad C{\equiv}CH$

26. If a molecule contains both a double and a triple bond, both endings are used, the -ene preceding the -yne. Give the structures of:

(a) 1-butene-3-yne   (b) 1-cyclononen-5-yne   (c) 2-methyl-3-ethyl-2-octen-4-yne

27. The double bond receives the lower number in a molecule containing both a double and a triple bond. Name each of the following:

(a) $CH_3CH{=}CHCH_2C{\equiv}CH$ (c) $HC{\equiv}C\overset{\displaystyle CH_2CH_3}{\underset{\displaystyle CH_2CH_3}{C}}HC{=}CHCH_3$

(b) $CH_3\overset{}{\underset{\displaystyle CH_3}{C}}HC{\equiv}CCH{=}CHCH_3$ (d) $CH_3CH_2CH{=}\overset{}{\underset{\displaystyle CH_3}{C}}CC{\equiv}CH$

28. Derivatives of aromatic hydrocarbons are named by numbering and identifying each substituent on the parent hydrocarbon. Give the structures of:

(a) 4-nitrobromobenzene   (b) 1,3,5-trimethylbenzene   (c) 4-chlorobenzenesulfonic acid

29. Complex compounds containing both aromatic and aliphatic hydrocarbon units are usually named as derivatives of the aliphatic hydrocarbon. Name the following:

ANSWERS

24.

(a) $CH_2{=}CHCH{=}CH_2$

(c) $HC{\equiv}CCH_2C{\equiv}CH$

(b) $CH_3C{=}CH{-}CH{=}CHCH_3$
        CH_3

(d) $CH_2{=}CHCHCH{=}CHCH_2CH{=}CH_2$
                CH_2CH_3

25.

(a) 1,3-pentadiene

(c) 3-methyl-1,4-pentadiyne

(b) 2,3-diethyl-1,4-hexadiene

(d) 3-*n*-propyl-1,4-pentadiyne

26.

(a) $CH_2{=}CH{-}C{\equiv}CH$

(b)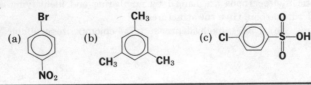

(c) CH_3
$CH_3C{=}C{-}C{\equiv}CCH_2CH_2CH_3$
        CH_2CH_3

27.

(a) 2-hexen-5-yne

(c) 3,4-diethyl-2-hexen-5-yne

(b) 6-methyl-2-hepten-4-yne

(d) 4-methyl-3-hexen-5-yne

28.

(a) [structure: benzene ring with Br at top and NO_2 at bottom]

(b) [structure: benzene ring with CH_3, CH_3, CH_3]

(c) Cl—[benzene ring]—$\overset{\displaystyle O}{\underset{\displaystyle O}{S}}$—OH

29.

(a) 2-phenyl-4-bromopentane

(c) 1-(4-chlorophenyl)-heptane

(b) 2-(1-naphthyl)-butane

QUESTIONS

30. The IUPAC ending for the alcohol group (OH) is -ol. Give the structures of:
   (a) ethanol   (c) 1-butanol
   (b) cyclopentanol   (d) 2-methyl-2-propanol

31. Give the IUPAC name for:
   (a) CH_3CHCH_3 (c) $(CH_3)_2CHCH_2OH$ (d) $CH_3CH_2CHCH_2CH_3$
          | |
          OH CH_2OH

32. Draw the structures of:
   (a) 1-propanol   (c) 3-hexanol
   (b) 2-methyl-2-pentanol   (d) 5-isopropyl-3-octanol

33. In compounds with two or more functional groups the order of precedence in determining parent name is alcohol over alkene over alkyne. Name the following:

   (a) $CH_3CH=CCHCH_3$ (b) $HC\equiv CCH_2CCH_3$
               | | |
             OH CH_3 OH
                                              CH_3

34. Ethers are named as alkoxy derivatives of alkanes. Show the structures of the following:
   (a) 2-methoxybutane   (b) 3-isopropoxyoctane   (c) 2-ethoxy-4-methylpentane

35. Amines are not treated as functional groups but as substituents of the hydrocarbon chains. Names of secondary and tertiary amines derive from naming the alkyl groups attached to the nitrogen. Draw structures for:
   (a) 2-aminobutane   (c) 2-(methylethylamino)-4-bromopentane
   (b) 3-(methylamino)-octane

36. Mercaptans are treated as functional groups like alcohols, with the ending -thiol replacing -ol. Name the following compounds:
   (a) $CH_3CH_2CH_2CHSH$ (b) $H_2NCH_2CH_2CH_2SH$
                 |
               CH_3

37. The IUPAC ending for the aldehyde group $(-\overset{O}{\overset{\|}{C}}H)$ is -al and for the ketone group $(R\overset{O}{\overset{\|}{C}}R)$ is -one. Draw the structures for:
   (a) methanal   (c) 2-pentanone
   (b) cyclohexanone   (d) 2-methylbutanal

ANSWERS

30.

    (a) CH_3CH_2OH (c) $CH_3CH_2CH_2CH_2OH$

    (b) 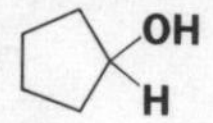   (d) $(CH_3)_3COH$

31.

    (a) 2-propanol   (c) 2-methyl-1-propanol

    (b) cyclohexanol   (d) 2-ethyl-1-butanol

32.

    (a) $CH_3CH_2CH_2OH$ (c) $CH_3CH_2\underset{\overset{|}{OH}}{C}HCH_2CH_2CH_3$

    (b) $CH_3CH_2CH_2\underset{\overset{|}{OH}}{C}(CH_3)_2$

    (d) $CH_3CH_2\underset{\overset{|}{OH}}{C}HCH_2\underset{\overset{|}{CH(CH_3)_2}}{C}HCH_2CH_2CH_3$

33.

    (a) 3-methyl-3-penten-2-ol   (b) 2-methyl-4-pentyn-2-ol

34.

    (a) $CH_3\underset{\overset{|}{OCH_3}}{C}HCH_2CH_3$ (b) $CH_3CH_2\underset{\overset{|}{OCH(CH_3)_2}}{C}H(CH_2)_4CH_3$ (c) $CH_3\underset{\overset{|}{OCH_2CH_3}}{C}HCH_2CH(CH_3)_2$

35.

    (a) $CH_3\underset{\overset{|}{NH_2}}{C}HCH_2CH_3$

    (c) $CH_3\underset{\overset{|}{CH_3NCH_2CH_3}}{C}HCH_2\overset{\overset{Br}{|}}{C}HCH_3$

    (b) $CH_3CH_2\underset{\overset{|}{NHCH_3}}{C}H(CH_2)_4CH_3$

36.

    (a) 2-pentanethiol   (b) 3-amino-1-propanethiol

37.

    (a) $\overset{\overset{O}{\|}}{H}CH$ (c) $CH_3\overset{\overset{O}{\|}}{C}CH_2CH_2CH_3$

    (b) 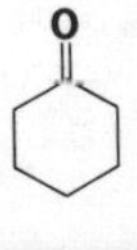   (d) $CH_3CH_2\underset{\overset{|}{CH_3}}{C}H\overset{\overset{O}{\|}}{C}H$

QUESTIONS

38. Give the IUPAC names for:

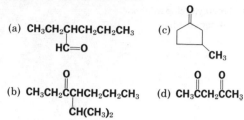

(a) CH₃CH₂CHCH₂CH₂CH₃
     HC=O

(b) CH₃CH₂CCHCH₂CH₂CH₃
     CH(CH₃)₂

(c)

(d) CH₃CCH₂CCH₃

39. The IUPAC ending for a carboxylic acid is -oic acid. Draw the structures for:
(a) methanoic acid   (c) butanoic acid
(b) benzoic acid   (d) 3,5-dimethyloctanoic acid

40. Name each of the following by the IUPAC system:

(a) CH₃CH₂COH

(b) CH₃CHCH₂CHCOH
    Br   Br

(c)
NO₂
COH
NO₂

(d) CH₂=CHCOH

41. Dicarboxylic acids have the characteristic ending -dioic acid. Name the following compounds.

(a) —CHCOH
     CH₂COH
     O

(b) BrCHCOH
    CICH
    CH₂COH
    O

42. The first step in naming an organic ester is to identify and name the acid and alcohol and which it is formed. Do this for each of the following:

(a) CH₃CH₂CH₂COCH₃

(b) CH₃CH₂COCH(CH₃)₂

(c) COCH₂CH₃

(d) (CH₃)₂CHCOCH₂CH₃

ANSWERS

38.

    (a) 2-ethylpentanal   (c) 3-methylcyclopentanone

    (b) 4-isopropyl-3-heptanone   (d) 2,4-pentanedione

39.

    (a)   (c) $CH_3CH_2CH_2\overset{\displaystyle O}{\overset{\|}{C}}OH$

    (b)   (d) $CH_3CH_2CH_2\underset{CH_3}{CH}CH_2\underset{CH_3}{CH}CH_2\overset{\displaystyle O}{\overset{\|}{C}}OH$

40.

    (a) propanoic acid   (c) 2,6-dinitrobenzoic acid

    (b) 2,4-dibromopentanoic acid   (d) propenoic acid

41.

    (a) phenylbutanedioic acid   (b) 2-bromo-3-chloropentanedioic acid

---

42.

    (a) butanoic acid and methyl alcohol   (c) benzoic acid and ethyl alcohol

    (b) propanoic acid and isopropyl alcohol   (d) 2-methylpropanoic acid and ethyl alcohol

QUESTIONS

43. The -oic acid ending of the acid is replaced by -oate in the corresponding ester, and the name is preceded by the name of the alcohol radical. Thus, methyl alcohol and benzoic acid give methyl benzoate. Name each ester in the previous question.

44. Name each of the following:

(a) [structure: phenyl benzoate]

(c) $CH_3CHCH_2CHCOCH_2CH_2CH_3$ with CH_3 and CH_3 substituents, O carbonyl

(b) [structure: cyclopentyl $OCCH_2CH_2CH_3$]

(d) CH_2—OC—phenyl
    CH—OC—phenyl
    CH_2—OC—phenyl
(with O carbonyls)

45. Acid chlorides and anhydrides are named from the acids, with the endings -oyl chloride and -oic anhydride. Name the following compounds:

(a) CH_3CHCCl with O carbonyl and CH_3 substituent

(b) $(CH_3CH_2CH_2CH_2C)_2O$ with O carbonyl

46. Salts and amides are named for the acids. The former employs the name of the metal and the ending -oate. The latter uses the ending -amide. Write the structures of the following:

(a) lithium 2-bromopentanoate   (b) N-ethyl-3-methylpentanamide

47. Acids and acid derivatives containing other functional groups use the names of the acids as parent. Carbonyl groups are indicated by the prefix oxo-, hydroxyl groups by the prefix hydroxy-. Draw structures for the following:

(a) 4-hydroxy-2-pentenoic acid.   (c) 2,6-diaminohexanoic acid
(b) 6-oxohexanoyl chloride   (d) methyl 2-oxopropanoate

48. Name the following compounds by the IUPAC system:

(a) $HOCCH_2CHCH_2COH$ with two O carbonyls and OH group

(c) $CH_3CCH_2CH_2CNH$—cyclohexyl with two O carbonyls

(b) CH_2=$CCOCH_3$ with CH_3 substituent and O carbonyl

(d) phenyl—$CCH_2CH_2CO^-Na^+$ with two O carbonyls

ANSWERS

43.

    (a) methyl butanoate   (c) ethyl benzoate

    (b) isopropyl propanoate   (d) ethyl 2-methylpropanoate

44.

    (a) phenyl benzoate   (c) n-propyl 2,4-dimethylpentanoate

    (b) cyclopentyl butanoate   (d) glyceryl tribenzoate

45.

    (a) 2-methylpropanoyl chloride   (b) pentanoic anhydride

46.

$$\text{(a) } CH_3CH_2CH_2\underset{\underset{Br}{|}}{CH}C\overset{O}{\|}O^-Li^+ \qquad \text{(b) } CH_3CH_2\underset{\underset{CH_3}{|}}{CH}CH_2C\overset{O}{\|}NHCH_2CH_3$$

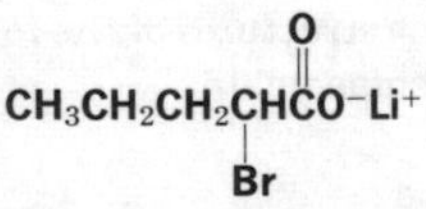

47.

$$\text{(a) } CH_3\underset{\underset{OH}{|}}{CH}CH=CHC\overset{O}{\|}OH \qquad \text{(c) } H_2N(CH_2)_4\underset{\underset{NH_2}{|}}{CH}C\overset{O}{\|}OH$$

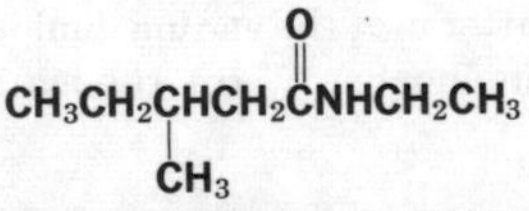

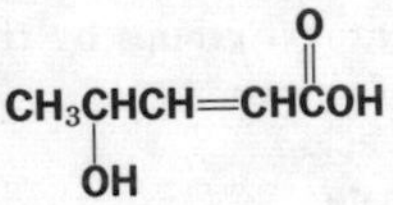

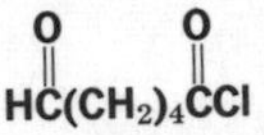

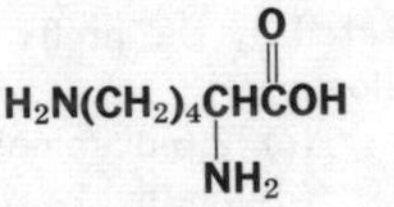

$$\text{(b) } HC\overset{O}{\|}(CH_2)_4C\overset{O}{\|}Cl \qquad \text{(d) } CH_3C\overset{O}{\|}-C\overset{O}{\|}OCH_3$$

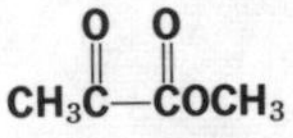

48.

    (a) 3-hydroxypentanedioic acid   (c) N-cyclohexyl-4-oxopentanamide

    (b) methyl 2-methylpropenoate   (d) sodium 4-phenyl-4-oxobutanoate

INDEX